RADIATION AND OPTICS

RADIATION AND OPTICS

An Introduction to the Classical Theory

JOHN M. STONE

Department of Physics
University of California
Berkeley

INTERNATIONAL STUDENT EDITION

McGraw-Hill Book Company, Inc.

New York   San Francisco   Toronto   London

Kōgakusha Company, Ltd.

Tokyo

Radiation and Optics: An Introduction to the Classical Theory

INTERNATIONAL STUDENT EDITION

Exclusive rights by Kōgakusha Co., Ltd. for manufacture and export from Japan. This book cannot be re-exported from the country to which it is consigned by Kōgakusha Co., Ltd. or by McGraw-Hill Book Company, Inc. or any of its subsidiaries.

I

Library of Congress Catalog Card Number 62–21791

TOSHO PRINTING CO., LTD., TOKYO, JAPAN

To the memory of
FRANCIS A. JENKINS

Preface

The purpose of this book is to make available to undergraduates, on their own terms, a substantial part of the classical theory of radiation and optics. The only assumption I have made concerning the reader is that he has completed good elementary courses in physics and calculus. All mathematical and physical ideas above the elementary level are explained in great detail and in such a way as to generate intuitive feeling and good working knowledge. Ultimately, the development leads up to topics of current interest in connection with understanding the behavior of electromagnetic radiation.

The main argument progresses strictly along the lines set down by Lorentz in his theory of electrons. The introduction describes the relation of Lorentz's theory of radiation to earlier and later ones, and the last chapter describes in more detail its relation to the quantum theory. In these days of great pressure on the curriculum, each body of subject matter must be thoroughly justified, and students, understandably anxious to rush on, often question the value of a long study of a classical theory. The reply to this questioning is made several times in the book and is that the Lorentz theory is still useful as a working tool, it provides an excellent foundation for the field of optics, and it is most valuable as background for the quantum theory of radiation and for many branches of physical science. It might even be suggested that the reader follow the introduction immediately with a light scanning of the last chapter, but with the understanding that parts of that chapter necessarily touch on advanced matters and occasionally refer to very advanced literature and, in these respects, are not typical of the rest of the book.

Chapters are followed by problems, very few of which involve mere substitution of numbers. Many contain informative material and are referred to at appropriate places in the text. The statement of a problem and supplementary hints, discussion, and partial answers are such that a student usually has a good basis for judging the correctness and quality of his answer. There is much insistence on the routine drawing of rough graphical illustrations of mathematical formulas.

Many references to the literature are given. Whenever a reference is on a level substantially above that of the present volume, the fact is stated explicitly.

The book contains more material than can be covered with thoroughness in one semester. The following summary of the contents is accompanied by suggestions for omission and compression in a short course. (In my own courses I have customarily made further restriction in defining subject matter for examinations and have issued lists of important topics and formulas.)

The first two chapters contain mathematical preliminaries on vector analysis and on representations of oscillations and waves. Emphasis is on geometric visualization and analytic simplicity. This material can be covered very rapidly and left to be digested as it is used throughout the book.

Chapters 3 and 4 lay the physical foundations of the subject. The Lorentz model of an atom as containing harmonic oscillators is described and justified at considerable length. There are alternative formulations of this model, and I have chosen what seemed to me to be simplest for the purpose. The Maxwell equations as adapted by Lorentz are written, and they are illustrated by a carefully arranged sequence of simple but highly relevant deductions which make connection with elementary knowledge of electricity. Of these deductions only the principle of superposition (Sec. 3-4) and the implications of the Lorentz force (Sec. 3-8) are of general importance for the rest of the book. Conservation of charge (Sec. 3-11) and the wave equation (Sec. 3-15) enter in some later developments. In Chap. 4 Poynting's theorem on energy is built up from simple beginnings and is of prime importance. The troublesome question of units and the reason for choosing the gaussian system are covered in Chap. 3 and are elaborated upon in Appendix A.

Chapter 5 treats in detail, with a wealth of illustration, the fields around a monochromatic dipole oscillator. Much of the rest of the book is based on this chapter, and of special importance are the sections dealing with the fields far away from the oscillator. The derivation of the basic formula is given with full explanation in Appendix B.

Chapters 6 through 10 cover the principles of diffraction and a number of applications. The subject recurs many times in later chapters. Chapter 6 is a qualitative survey intended to give something in the way of physical background for later formalities.

Chapter 7 deals with deductions that can be made on an electromagnetic basis concerning arrays of identical apertures in the Fraunhofer arrangement. Some of the sections on applications could be compressed. The stellar interferometer as involving a double aperture should be included to provide background for a different treatment in Chap. 13, but the long discussion of the use of mirrors could be omitted. The random array (Sec. 7-16) might seem to be merely a curiosity, but it involves in simple context some statistical principles essential to under-standing coherence and other topics that arise later in the book.

Chapter 8 introduces the scalar theory of light and its use in solving problems of diffraction. A full derivation of the Kirchhoff integral is given, but the essential results are pointed out and discussed separately. The chapter is introductory to the two following and contains no problem section.

Chapter 9 covers traditional material on Fraunhofer diffraction and its applications to various problems of resolution. Some aspects of diffraction gratings could be condensed, and the section on the sine con-dition (actually an appendix) could be omitted.

Chapter 10 is on Fresnel diffraction, and the main theme is the relation of geometrical to physical optics and the transition from Fresnel to Fraunhofer diffraction. Some applications are discussed. Interesting mathematical phenomena arise and are related to physical observations. The subject has its fascination, but it is not inconceivable that it be sacrificed to the press of time.

Chapter 11 introduces Fourier integrals, which are indispensable if the subject of radiation is to be developed beyond its most elementary aspects. The essential material is in the first five sections and the last two. The extensive illustrative material drawn from the theory of image formation and making up the rest of the chapter could be omitted in a short course emphasizing physical principles.

Chapter 12 treats radiation from Lorentz atoms (harmonic dipole oscillators with radiation damping). The equation of motion for free oscillation is discussed and solved, and the radiated fields are found for a stationary atom. The fundamental idea of the spectrum is introduced and applied, first to a single emission and then to many random emissions. The latter application is somewhat involved but is very important as background for parts of Chap. 13. (Knowledge of the random array in Sec. 7-16 is very helpful here.) The two sections on broadening of spectrum lines could be compressed to brief descriptions.

Chapter 13, on polychromatic waves, is the climax of the book. It develops, from the standpoints of theory and observation, a complete set of properties characterizing a steady beam of radiation, namely, spectrum, coherence, and polarization. Beautiful applications of Fourier analysis are involved, and several of the sections benefit from very recent advances in radiation theory and physical optics. Each topic is carried far enough to provide working knowledge in simple and effective form. With background already acquired, the chapter is not difficult, and much of its length stems from completeness of explanation. The basic principles of several important optical instruments, including spectro-scopes, the Michelson interferometer, linear polarizers, and quarter-wave plates, enter here.

Chapter 14 is on scattering. An introductory survey brings out the wide scope of the subject, and the rest of the chapter treats some special cases on the basis of the Lorentz theory. The simpler aspects of momentum of radiation are included.

In Chap. 15 the macroscopic Maxwell theory is deduced in a reasonably satisfactory manner from the microscopic theory of Lorentz. A simple theory of the complex refractive index is developed, and the most general type of plane wave in a homogeneous medium is discussed.

Chapter 16 treats many problems of reflection and transmission involving media to which the macroscopic theory is applicable. The method of attack is one that has been developed for handling systems with many boundaries. In a short course attention might be confined to the single interface and the Fabry-Perot interferometer.

Chapter 17 covers double refraction. To unify the subject, optical activity is included as an aspect of double refraction. The types of waves possible in each class of medium and the laws of reflection and refraction at boundaries are drawn from the Maxwell equations. Many applications are described.

Chapter 18 gives the classical theory of most of the magneto-optic and electro-optic effects and describes the Kerr cell.

The nineteenth and last chapter compares the classical and quantum theories. A substantial amount of specific and useful information is given on Planck's law, transition probabilities, lifetimes, and oscillator strengths. The quantized radiation field and results on problems of emission, absorption, and scattering are described and compared with the analogous classical results to bring out the remarkable similarities. The chapter concludes with the spectacular illustrations provided by the laser and the Mössbauer effect.

A note of gratitude is due the many students who have struggled through rough versions of this book as it grew. Their questions and suggestions have been most helpful, and their interest has encouraged me to give somewhat more than minimum coverage. I am forever indebted to Professors Raymond T. Birge, Francis A. Jenkins (1899–1960), and Harvey E. White, who taught me the subject of optics and inspired my love for it. I wish to thank Eleanor Thornhill for expertly typing the manuscript, and my wife for much assistance.

JOHN M. STONE

Contents

Preface vii

Introduction 1

chapter 1   **Vector Analysis** 8
1-1   Vector Algebra 8
1-2   Fields and Their Graphical Representations 11
1-3   Directional Derivatives and Gradient 12
1-4   Line Integrals 14
1-5   Divergence and Gauss' Theorem 14
1-6   Curl and Stokes' Theorem 16
1-7   Time Derivatives 19
1-8   Introduction of Coordinate Systems and the Calculation of Derived
      Fields 19
1-9   A Few Identities 25
1-10   The Inverse Problem of Vector Analysis 25
1-11   Derived Fields of the Second Order 25
      Problems 27

chapter 2   **Sinusoidal Oscillations and Waves**
              and Their Complex Representation 30
2-1   Complex Numbers and Their Representations 30
2-2   Sinusoidal Oscillations in One Dimension 34
2-3   Oscillations in Three Dimensions.   Complex Vectors 36
2-4   Sinusoidal Waves in Scalar Fields 40
2-5   Sinusoidal Waves in Vector Fields 42
2-6   Superposition and Decomposition of Oscillations and Waves . . 44
2-7   Cases in Which the Complex Representation Cannot Be Used . . 46
      Problems 47

chapter 3   **The Microscopic Description of Matter**
              and the Microscopic Maxwell Equations . . . 51
3-1   Microscopic Description of Matter 51
3-2   Microscopic Maxwell Equations 57
3-3   Field about a Spherically Symmetric Static Charge 60

3-4   Principle of Superposition. 61
3-5   Coulomb's Law and the Units of Charge and Current 61
3-6   Field around a Straight Wire Carrying a Steady Current. . . . 62
3-7   Force between Parallel Currents and the Value of c . . . 64
3-8   Measurement of Electric and Magnetic Fields 65
3-9   Field of a Plane-parallel Condenser 67
3-10   Field of a Cylindrical Solenoid 68
3-11   Conservation of Charge 68
3-12   Faraday's Law of Induction 69
3-13   Nonexistence of Magnetic Charge 70
3-14   General Solution of the Maxwell Equations 71
3-15   Wave Equation. 73
       Problems 74

chapter 4   **Energy and Energy Flow**
              in the Electromagnetic Field. **77**
4-1   Work Done in Slowly Charging a Condenser 77
4-2   Work Done in Slowly Energizing a Solenoid 78
4-3   Effects When the Fields Are Built Up Rapidly 79
4-4   General Theorem on Energy 80
4-5   Discussion of the Energy Theorem 82
       Problems 84

chapter 5   **Monochromatic Dipole Radiation** **87**
5-1   Formulas for the Fields of a General Monochromatic
       Dipole Oscillator 87
5-2   Field of a Linear Oscillator 90
5-3   Field for an Elliptical Motion 96
5-4   Wave Zone 96
5-5   Rate of Radiation by a Dipole Oscillator 98
5-6   Fields and Radiation in the Case of Several Oscillators . . . 101
       Problems 105

chapter 6   **Diffraction.   A Preliminary Description** . . . **107**

chapter 7   **Fraunhofer Diffraction by N Identical Apertures**. **115**
7-1   Definition of Fraunhofer Diffraction. 115
7-2   Coordinate System. 117
7-3   General Principles for Identical Apertures 117
7-4   Calculation of the Geometric Difference of Path 119
7-5   General Formulas for the Diffraction Pattern 120
7-6   Abbreviated Notation.   The Term Normal Irradiance . . . 121
7-7   Case $N = 2$.   Young's Experiment 121
7-8   Uniform Linear Array 124
7-9   Reciprocity Theorem and Sensitivity Pattern 128

7-10   Rectangular Array 128
7-11   Crossed Array 130
7-12   Applications of Regular Arrays 130
7-13   Michelson Stellar Interferometer 133
7-14   Radio-frequency Telescopes 137
7-15   Grating Spectroscope 142
7-16   Random Array 146
       Problems 152

chapter 8   **Treatment of Diffraction in the Scalar Approximation.   The Kirchhoff Integral** **156**
8-1   Scalar Theory of Light 157
8-2   Kirchhoff Integral 159
8-3   Application to Diffraction 163
8-4   Comments on the Kirchhoff Method 164
8-5   Reciprocity Theorem 166
8-6   Babinet's Principle 166
8-7   Diffraction by Plane Mirrors 167

chapter 9   **Application of the Kirchhoff Integral to Fraunhofer Diffraction** **168**
9-1   General Formulas 168
9-2   Special Form of Babinet's Principle 171
9-3   Rectangular Aperture 172
9-4   Circular Aperture 175
9-5   Diffraction Gratings with Rectangular Apertures . . . 176
9-6   Resolving Power of Telescope and Microscope 180
9-7   Sine Condition 183
       Problems 184

chapter 10   **Application of the Kirchhoff Integral to Fresnel Diffraction** **188**
10-1   Rectangular Aperture 189
10-2   Limiting Case of a Large Aperture.   Long Slit and Straight Edge . 196
10-3   Transition to the Fraunhofer Case 199
10-4   Circular Aperture 201
10-5   Limiting Case of a Large Aperture 204
10-6   Opaque Disk 205
10-7   Zone Plate 206
10-8   Concluding Remarks on Fresnel Diffraction 207
       Problems 208

chapter 11   **Fourier Analysis and Its Application to Optical Problems** **210**
11-1   Fourier Theorem 210

11-2   Examples of Fourier Transforms 213
11-3   Theorems on Fourier Integrals 216
11-4   Multiple Integrals 219
11-5   Vector Functions 220
11-6   Occurrence of Fourier Integrals in Fraunhofer Diffraction . . . 220
11-7   Snell's Law. Resolving Power of a Prism 221
11-8   Abbe's Theory of the Formation of Images in the Microscope . . 224
11-9   Phase-contrast Method 232
11-10 Rationale of the Fourier Analysis of Linear Systems 236
11-11 Examples 238
       Problems 240

chapter 12 **Radiation from Lorentz Atoms** 243
12-1   The Geissler Tube 243
12-2   Classical Model of the Gaseous Discharge 245
12-3   Equation of Motion and Its Solution 247
12-4   Radiated Fields and Energy 251
12-5   Spectrum of the Radiation 252
12-6   Spectrum in the Case of Many Emissions 255
12-7   Thermal Broadening of Spectrum Lines 260
12-8   Pressure Broadening of Spectrum Lines 264
       Problems 268

chapter 13 **Polychromatic Waves** 271
13-1   Polychromatic Waves and Their Sources 272
13-2   Integrating and Continuous Modes of Detection 274
13-3   Propagation of a Wave from a Small Source through an Optical
       System 277
13-4   Examples of Transmission Functions and Calculation of Diffraction
       Patterns 281
13-5   Spectrographs and the Measurement of Energy Spectra and Power
       Spectra 286
13-6   Incoherence of Independent Sources 291
13-7   Rule for Incoherent Sources 293
13-8   Diffraction with Quasi-monochromatic Sources 294
13-9   Extended Sources 296
13-10 Coherent and Partially Coherent Sources. Lateral Coherence in
       Wave Fields 299
13-11 Longitudinal Coherence in Wave Fields. Michelson Interfer-
       ometer and Its Use as a Spectrograph 302
13-12 Polarization of Polychromatic Waves 309
13-13 Measurement of the Stokes Parameters 313
13-14 Properties and Interpretation of the Stokes Parameters 317
13-15 Techniques for Problems Involving Polarization 320

13-16 Measurement of Spectrum and Coherence by Means of
Beat Frequencies 323
Problems 327

chapter 14 **Scattering** **334**
14-1 Introductory Survey and Definitions 334
14-2 Rayleigh Scattering by a Single Particle 340
14-3 Definitions of Cross Sections 343
14-4 Scattering by a Lorentz Atom and by a Free Electron 344
14-5 Scattering by Gases 347
14-6 Diffraction by Crystals 351
14-7 Forward Scattering. Extinction 355
14-8 Force and Torque Exerted on a Body by Radiation.
Radiation Pressure 357
Problems 359

chapter 15 **The Macroscopic Maxwell Theory** **362**
15-1 Derivation of the First Form of the Macroscopic Equations . . 363
15-2 Classification of Charges and Currents. Second Form of the
Macroscopic Equations 365
15-3 Susceptibilities, Permeabilities, and Conductivity 369
15-4 Monochromatic Plane Waves in Homogeneous Media . . . 371
15-5 Theory of the Complex Refractive Index 376
15-6 Energy Theorem 383
Problems 385

chapter 16 **Reflection and Transmission** **388**
16-1 Collection of Formulas for a Single Medium 388
16-2 Boundary Conditions 389
16-3 Reflection and Transmission at a Single Interface. General
Formulas 390
16-4 Case of Two Transparent Media 397
16-5 Reflection from Metals 401
16-6 Layered Structures. Descriptive Survey 402
16-7 Airy Formula 403
16-8 Fabry-Perot Interferometer 405
16-9 Fabry-Perot Etalon as a Spectrometer 408
16-10 Interference Filters 412
16-11 Single Dielectric Film 412
16-12 Multiple Dielectric Films 415
Problems 417

chapter 17 **Double Refraction** **420**
17-1 Introductory Survey 420
17-2 General Laws for Plane Waves 427
17-3 Nonactive Uniaxial Crystals 428

17-4   Nonactive Biaxial Crystals 430
17-5   Double Refraction at a Boundary 432
17-6   Applications of Double Refraction in Crystals 435
17-7   Optical Activity in Isotropic Media 438
17-8   Optically Active Anisotropic Crystals 441
        Problems 443

chapter 18   **Magneto-optics and Electro-optics** **445**
18-1   Survey of Effects 445
18-2   Zeeman Effect. 448
18-3   Faraday Effect 451
18-4   Cotton-Mouton Effect 453
18-5   Kerr Electro-optic Shutter 455
        Problems 457

chapter 19   **Relation of Quantum to Classical Theory** . . **460**
19-1   Characterization of Radiation Fields 461
19-2   Radiation in Thermal Equilibrium. Cavity and Blackbody . . 462
19-3   Planck's Law and Its Forerunners 465
19-4   Old Quantum Theory of Atoms. 469
19-5   Einstein's Derivation of Planck's Law. Transition Probabilities . 471
19-6   Lifetimes and Oscillator Strengths 473
19-7   Quantum Theory of Atoms and Radiation 477
19-8   Amplification by Stimulated Emission. Maser and Laser . . . 486
19-9   Recoil. Doppler Shift. Mössbauer Effect 489
        Problems 491

Appendix A   Electrical Units 493
Appendix B   Radiation Field of a Dipole Oscillator 508
Appendix C   Table of Fresnel Integrals 522
Appendix D   Calculation of the Spectral Profile of a Line Broadened by
                  Thermal Motions and Collisions 524
Appendix E   Mean Energy of an Oscillator in Cavity Radiation . . . 527

Literature Cited **530**

Index **535**

Introduction

In the history of physics there have occurred certain distinguished times when the gropings for a concise theory to account for a body of accumulated empirical experience have reached a successful conclusion. There have, of course, always been observations not comprehended by *any* theory, and always the postulates with which a theory must begin call for deeper theoretical interpretation. Nevertheless, the theories emerging at these important epochs in the evolution of physics, even though they are later absorbed in more comprehensive ones, have a lasting value and are worthy of study.

The theory to be presented in this book is one which came to final form about 1900 in the hands of H. A. Lorentz (1853–1928). Its original intention was the most ambitious to be entertained seriously up to that time, namely, to account for the whole of the sciences of electricity and optics on the basis of the microscopic structure of individual atoms. Its success was remarkable, and, in spite of the fact that its deficiencies remained to be made up by later quantum theories, it will no doubt always be fundamental in the study of physics. The following highly abbreviated history of the subjects of electricity, magnetism, and optics will serve to orient Lorentz's theory.

Specular reflection of light and the casting of shadows were known to the ancient Greeks and interpreted by them in purely geometrical terms using the idea of rays. Refraction was observed but not reduced to a law. Also known to the Greeks and other ancient peoples were the effects associated with electrification by friction, the interaction of pieces of magnetic iron ore, lightning, and electric eels. The speculations on all these seemingly unrelated phenomena by the ancient and medieval philosophers may be quickly passed over.

By the beginning of the seventeenth century the spirit of experimental observation had achieved so much success, particularly in mechanics and magnetism, that progress in various branches of science came very rapidly. During this century many of the fundamental observations in optics were made. One of the earliest was the deduction of the law of refraction by Snell (or Snellius) in 1621. In 1666 Newton demonstrated the decomposition of white light into monochromatic components, each associated with a definite refractive index in a given medium. The year 1666, then, is the epoch in which the basis of geometrical optics was completed.

Other discoveries of the seventeenth century related to physical optics. They included the phenomena of diffraction, double refraction, polarization in double refraction, and the phenomenon known as "Newton's rings." Especially noteworthy is the first determination of the speed of light, by Römer in 1675, based on observations of a satellite of Jupiter.

The principal proposals of the seventeenth century in the way of a theory of light were a rudimentary wave theory and a corpuscular theory. This wave theory was little more than kinematical and was applied mainly in the well-known construction of Huygens. The corpuscular theory was dynamical and was suggested by Newton. It explained rectilinear propagation and specular reflection in obvious ways. It explained refraction by assuming that the particles were sucked in at the surface of a refracting medium in such a way that the tangential velocity was not changed, but the normal velocity was increased appropriately. Newton and his followers claimed that the wave theory could not account for rectilinear propagation, which, as the theory stood, being without the notions of interference and very short wavelength, was true enough. An important difference between the two theories, and one that was conceivably subject to experimental test, was that the wave theory predicted a velocity in a medium less than that *in vacuo*, while the corpuscular theory predicted the reverse. A direct test did not come until 1850, well after the wave theory was firmly established on other evidence.

Not much happened in the sciences of electricity and magnetism in the seventeenth century. In the eighteenth, on the other hand, not much happened in optics, but important progress was made in the other two sciences. Coulomb's law was established for point charges and for magnetic poles. The electroscope, electrostatic induction, the electrophorus, the Leyden jar, electrostatic generators, and the voltaic battery were discovered. It was demonstrated that the discharge of a Leyden jar, the current due to a battery, and lightning involve transport of electric charge and to this extent are similar in nature.

The theories of the eighteenth century dealt mainly with the nature of the electric and the magnetic "substances." According to one view, an uncharged body contained two fluids, corresponding to the two kinds of charge, which were present in each region of the body in equal amounts.

The process of charging consisted in destroying this balance by removing or adding fluid of one or both kinds. Another view held that there was only one fluid which, in an uncharged body, was present in a certain amount, while in a charged body there was an excess or a deficiency. Both views served their purpose and, in particular, predicted that charge is neither created nor destroyed, a fact for which there was much experimental evidence. Magnetostatics, being so similar in many ways to electrostatics, was also described by one- and two-fluid theories, but with the difference that fluid could be moved about inside a magnetizable body but not taken out of it, for all the experimental evidence indicated that there are no isolated magnetic poles. It was Benjamin Franklin who gave the names "positive" and "negative" to the two kinds of charge, which were known theretofore only as "vitreous" and "resinous," respectively.[1] It is perhaps unfortunate that the electron turned out to be negative.

In the years 1800 to 1802 came the first of the great discoveries which filled the nineteenth century. In these few years Thomas Young, adopting the point of view that light consists of waves, proposed the principle of interference and used it to give the first complete explanation of the colors and other effects associated with Newton's rings. In 1803 he applied the idea in a rather primitive way to the problem of diffraction. In 1808 Malus discovered polarization by reflection, and by 1815 he and Brewster had thoroughly investigated the matter. Since the wave theory at that time contemplated only longitudinal waves, as in sound, it was helpless in the face of polarization and was vigorously attacked by the champions of the corpuscular theory. In 1818 Fresnel presented a comprehensive theory of diffraction in which he combined Huygens' idea of secondary wavelets with Young's idea of interference, the waves still being regarded as longitudinal. The success of this theory was the death of the corpuscular theory. In 1817 Young hit upon the idea of purely transverse waves as a model to explain the phenomena of polarized light, and Fresnel added this idea to his previous ones and developed an even more complete theory of optical phenomena.

To Fresnel, as to all scientists of the nineteenth and earlier centuries, the idea of propagation implied a transmitting medium. In the case of light this medium had been given the name "luminiferous ether" in distinction from "electric ether," the latter being the agent which transmitted electric and magnetic effects. Fresnel suggested that light waves are transverse elastic waves in this ether, unaccompanied by longitudinal waves, which, at a time when transverse elastic waves in solids were not known, was especially brilliant. He stated a simple rule governing the behavior of the oscillations of the three waves—incident,

---

[1] Vitreous electricity is that which remains on glass after it is rubbed with silk; resinous, that which remains on amber after it is rubbed with wool.

reflected, and refracted—at the boundary of a transparent medium and thereby accounted for the relative intensities and polarizations of these waves. It is remarkable that when the theory of elastic waves in solids was developed, beginning in 1821, it was shown that no ordinary elastic solid could be the analogue of the ether, for longitudinal waves always enter in the reflection and refraction of elastic waves. The boundary conditions assumed by Fresnel were not those of elasticity; nevertheless they were correct for treating light. In fact, at this stage Fresnel's theory reached such a satisfactory state that many treatises on light adopt it as a foundation and thereby discuss on the simplest possible basis the topics commonly understood to constitute the subject of physical optics.

In the years following 1821 many efforts were made to conceive a medium, describable in purely mechanical terms, which could serve as an ether. Eventually it became clear that one and the same ether would have to serve for all of electricity, magnetism, and optics; a series of classic experiments showed that these three branches of science are really three aspects of the one grand subject of electromagnetism. In 1819 Oersted discovered the magnetic field around a wire carrying a current, and in 1820 Ampère demonstrated the mutual interaction of two wires carrying currents. Finally, in 1831, Faraday completed the fusion of electricity and magnetism by discovering electromagnetic induction.

Michael Faraday (1791–1867) was the foremost of the nineteenth-century experimentalists, and his written works and his whole life form one of the pinnacles of human history. Limited as this account must be, no adequate idea can be given of the number and magnitude of his contributions to electrical, optical, and chemical science. Only two of these contributions will be singled out for special notice.

Faraday was self-educated and never became conversant with the powerful mathematical methods which were being applied to electrical problems. Actually, this deficiency proved an advantage to the later development of the science, for he devised his own unorthodox line of reasoning, which involved, in the now well-known way, the notion of electric and magnetic fields containing lines of force. The notion of these fields and the manner in which they could be regarded as transmitting the electric and magnetic forces of interaction between ponderable bodies was so fruitful in guiding and understanding his own investigations that it is not surprising to find that later translation into conventional mathematical terms led to an ultimate and completely satisfactory theory.

In 1845 Faraday proved a suspicion, which he and others had long held, that there must be a connection between magnetism and light. After several unsuccessful approaches he succeeded in altering a beam of light with a static magnetic field. This effect, which bears his name, consisted in noting a rotation of the plane of polarization of a beam of light which passed through a rod of glass oriented along the lines of a magnetic field.

This famous experiment was the first to indicate the unity of the sciences of electromagnetism and light.

Of the great mathematical physicists of the nineteenth century, the one who took most careful note of Faraday's experiments and ideas was James Clerk Maxwell (1831–1879). In essence, Maxwell expressed the conceptions of Faraday in proper mathematical terms and added a monumental idea of his own to achieve a complete theory of electromagnetism and light. But to state the matter this bluntly is to grossly oversimplify, for his lines of reasoning were intimately bound up with the rigidly mechanistic thinking about the ether which dominated the physics of the day. The problem of the ether was never solved, and the ether has come to be recognized as an unnecessary idea in discussing the classical theories; but, in a manner difficult to understand after so long a time, it served as a guide to the thinking of the nineteenth century.

Maxwell's final theory appeared in 1861 and 1862 and was presented a second time in 1864 with simplified reasoning. It achieved the goal, long sought after by several scientists, of endowing the electromagnetic field with the property of propagating with a finite velocity. Moreover, the theory itself suggested a type of electrical experiment in which this velocity could be measured. As a matter of fact, such a measurement had suggested itself earlier in another way and was performed by Weber and Kohlrausch in 1856. It was recognized at that time that on the grounds of dimensional reasoning the quantity measured was of the nature of a velocity, and it was also noted that the result agreed with the velocity of light. Maxwell's theory brought these results into harmony if his propagating electromagnetic fields could be identified as light. Since the fields had a transverse character and the theory could be made to yield all the phenomena of wave optics, the identification was inescapable. Direct verification of the theory came in 1886, after Maxwell's death, when Hertz produced and detected the first radio waves and showed that they have properties similar to those of light.

Maxwell's theory treated a ponderable medium as a continuum whose electrical state was represented by charge and current densities, conductivity, and electric and magnetic susceptibilities—all functions which were assumed to vary in continuous ways throughout the body. The conductivity and susceptibilities were characteristic of the medium and were to be determined empirically, although in principle they are related to atomic and molecular processes. Such a theory as Maxwell's, which does not delve into the fine structure of matter, is given the name *macroscopic*. Except for this failure to trace macroscopic effects to their microscopic origins, the Maxwell theory is complete in its accounting for electromagnetic and optical phenomena.

The relating of the gross properties of matter to its atomic structure awaited further knowledge of atoms. This knowledge gradually accumulated through the study of electrolysis, the kinetic theory of gases, and the conduction of electricity through gases, and culminated in the discovery of the electron by J. J. Thomson in 1897. To be sure, there remained a certain amount of conjecture in this discovery, and this was not to be removed for some time; but it was widely accepted that atoms contain negatively charged particles, all having the same charge and mass, values of which were assigned by Thomson through experiment and inference. The atom must also contain positive charge, and associated with this is all but a small fraction of the mass. The distribution of the positive charge and the arrangement of the electrons in or around it remained an open question.

In 1896 Zeeman discovered the effect, known by his name, wherein the lines in an atomic spectrum are split into components by the application of a magnetic field to the source of emission. Lorentz gave an explanation of this effect in 1897 on the basis of a microscopic electromagnetic theory he had developed and which incorporated the idea that atoms contain elastically bound electrons.

The great beauty of Lorentz's theory as it was fully expounded in his book of 1909 [59][1] lay in the vast number of phenomena which could be accounted for on a microscopic basis under only very general assumptions as to the detailed structure of atoms. In particular, the deductions from the theory remain invariant under very diverse assumptions as to the distribution of the positive and negative charges in the atom, and from this fact one infers that the predictions of the theory will not become invalid as evidence dictates more restrictive assumptions. Thus, nothing was fundamentally altered by the discovery of the nucleus by Rutherford in 1911; and to a surprising extent the theory survives the introduction of quantum mechanics. Furthermore, with this invariance taken for granted, a definite and convenient model can be adopted in the chapters following its introduction; we thereby gain the advantages of concrete visualization without loss of generality.

A glaring defect in Lorentz's theory is that it must assume forces of an unexplained nature in its model of an atom. These forces must, first of all, prevent the disruption of the positive and the negative charge under the action of electrostatic forces of repulsion. Second, they are assumed to provide an elastic force, obeying Hooke's law, which binds the centroids of the positive and negative charges to equilibrium positions. This elastic force is the one that enters the theory explicitly, and predictions that depend only on its existence are accurate, while no conclusion can be drawn that would depend on its strength (that is, the "spring constant"). Only the quantum theory of atomic structure (the theory of Schrödinger and Heisenberg), when examined in a certain way, gives the elastic constants involved. Finally, the forces of interaction between atoms—

[1] References at the end of this book are indicated in the text by numbers in brackets.

those which bind atoms into molecules and into crystal lattices, or which disturb the behavior of atoms undergoing collisions—if taken into account at all in the theory, must be introduced *ad hoc* on empirical evidence or from results of quantum theory. In spite of its limitations, the Lorentz theory remains to this day an important tool in thinking about and solving physical problems.

The Lorentz theory is modeled on and greatly resembles the macroscopic Maxwell theory. The resemblance is so strong, in fact, that in this book the Lorentz theory will be referred to as the *microscopic Maxwell theory*. In brief summary, the similarity lies in the fact that the equations forming the bases of the two theories are identical in form, at least if the macroscopic theory is written in one of its several possible forms. The difference lies in the way the symbols in the two theories are to be interpreted.

After the mathematical preliminaries in the first two chapters of the text, the microscopic Maxwell theory will be introduced in Chaps. 3 and 4 and used as the basis of all that follows. In Chap. 15 the macroscopic theory will be derived from the microscopic theory. This order of procedure poses a pedagogical problem for a book addressed to readers who may have had no contact with any of the Maxwell theory but are familiar with those aspects of charge, current, and fields dealt with in elementary physics. For these readers the Maxwell equations will acquire meaning only if they are related to previous knowledge immediately upon their introduction. But, strictly speaking, this previous knowledge is based on physical situations that are properly treated by the macroscopic theory, and hence the discussion should await Chap. 15. In Chap. 3 a way around this difficulty will be found, and close contact with elementary notions will be established. Once a feeling for the microscopic Maxwell equations is gained, the advantage of being able to relate all phenomena to their atomic origins will be obvious.

The brief historical notes in this introduction were selected for purposes of orientation. An excellent and comprehensive history of electricity and optics has been written by Whittaker [99]. Shorter and less mathematical surveys can be found in the appropriate articles of "The Encyclopaedia Britannica," an early edition of which was read by Faraday in his youth.

chapter **1**

Vector Analysis

The Maxwell theory is formulated in terms of scalar and vector fields and uses the techniques of vector analysis. The reader who is not already familiar with vector analysis can quickly acquire a knowledge adequate for the purposes of this book, and the following development of just the necessary topics will perhaps be found sufficient or will at least serve as a guide for further reading. The treatment here places more than usual emphasis on geometrical visualization of the ideas involved in order that the physical ideas implied by the formalism of the Maxwell equations will stand out more clearly.

Two texts which are very suitable for a first study of vector analysis are Weatherburn [95, 96] and Wills [102]. A highly condensed and more advanced treatment, but one which is particularly complete in matters of mathematical rigor, is Phillips [71].

1-1 Vector Algebra The reader is assumed to be familiar with the idea of associating a scalar magnitude with a direction to obtain a vector. He should also be familiar with the idea of the negative of a vector and with addition and subtraction of vectors. We begin then with the further algebraic operations.

When a constant force, represented by the vector **A**, acts on a particle which moves along a straight line through a displacement **B**, the work done is $AB \cos \theta$, where A and B are the (scalar) magnitudes of the two vectors, and θ is the angle between them. One could equally well understand the larger angle θ' shown in Fig. 1-1, since $\cos \theta = \cos \theta'$. This process of deriving a scalar from two vectors occurs so often and is so generally useful in physics that its result is given the name *scalar product* and is denoted by a dot between the vectors: $\mathbf{A} \cdot \mathbf{B} \equiv AB \cos \theta$. Clearly, $\mathbf{A} \cdot \mathbf{B} = \mathbf{B} \cdot \mathbf{A}$. The magnitude of a vector $\mathbf{A}$, which will be denoted sometimes by A and sometimes by $|\mathbf{A}|$, is related to the scalar product of $\mathbf{A}$ with itself by $A^2 \equiv |\mathbf{A}|^2 = \mathbf{A} \cdot \mathbf{A}$. The product $\mathbf{A} \cdot \mathbf{A}$ is sometimes abbreviated $\mathbf{A}^2$.

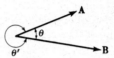

A multiplication has been defined; is there a corresponding division? That is, given $\mathbf{A}$ and $\mathbf{A} \cdot \mathbf{B}$, can $\mathbf{B}$ be found? The answer is no, for all that is known about $\mathbf{B}$ is its *projection* on $\mathbf{A}$.

Fig. 1-1. *Two vectors and the angles between them.*

Graphically, all the vectors indicated as ending on a certain plane perpendicular to $\mathbf{A}$ in Fig. 1-2 have the same scalar product with $\mathbf{A}$.

Another kind of product arises in the following example: If a positively charged particle moves with velocity $\mathbf{A}$ through a magnetic field $\mathbf{B}$, then, apart from a numerical factor depending on the units of the physical quantities, the force on the particle has the magnitude $AB \sin \theta$, where θ is the angle in Fig. 1-1 and is, specifically, the smaller angle. The force has a direction perpendicular to the plane of $\mathbf{A}$ and $\mathbf{B}$ in that sense given by the *right-hand rule,* which states that if the extended fingers of the right hand point in the direction of $\mathbf{A}$ with $\mathbf{B}$ coming out of the palm and with the plane of $\mathbf{A}$ and $\mathbf{B}$ perpendicular to the palm, then the outstretched thumb points in the direction of the force. With Fig. 1-1 representing the given vectors, the force points vertically into the plane of the paper. This process of deriving a third vector from two given ones is generalized by defining the *vector product* of any two vectors, denoted by a cross between them: $\mathbf{A} \times \mathbf{B}$. The resulting vector has magnitude $|\mathbf{A} \times \mathbf{B}| = AB \sin \theta$ and direction perpendicular to the plane of $\mathbf{A}$ and $\mathbf{B}$ in that sense given by the above right-hand rule. Clearly $\mathbf{A} \times \mathbf{B} = -\mathbf{B} \times \mathbf{A}$, so that the order of writing the factors in a vector product is important.

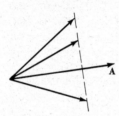

Fig. 1-2. *Three of the possible vectors forming a given scalar product with* $\mathbf{A}$. *The dashed line represents a plane perpendicular to* $\mathbf{A}$.

There is no division corresponding to the vector product, as is seen from Fig. 1-3; all vectors ending on the dashed line parallel to $\mathbf{A}$ have the same vector product with $\mathbf{A}$. However, if $\mathbf{A}$, $\mathbf{A} \cdot \mathbf{B}$, and $\mathbf{A} \times \mathbf{B}$ are given, then $\mathbf{B}$ is uniquely defined (see Prob. 1-1).

Scalar and vector multiplication satisfy the distributive laws:

$$\mathbf{A} \cdot (\mathbf{B} + \mathbf{C}) = \mathbf{A} \cdot \mathbf{B} + \mathbf{A} \cdot \mathbf{C}$$
$$\mathbf{A} \times (\mathbf{B} + \mathbf{C}) = \mathbf{A} \times \mathbf{B} + \mathbf{A} \times \mathbf{C}$$

One can easily construct geometric proofs or refer to Weatherburn [95], pp. 36 and 40.

A *scalar triple product* of three vectors is formed by taking the scalar product of one of the vectors and a vector product of the other two. One can write twelve such products: $\mathbf{A} \cdot \mathbf{B} \times \mathbf{C}$, $\mathbf{A} \times \mathbf{C} \cdot \mathbf{B}$, etc. All have the same magnitude, six being of one sign, and six of the opposite. The rules are: Interchange of dot and cross has no effect; cyclic permutation of the three factors has no effect; interchange of two factors changes the sign. For example,

$$\mathbf{A} \cdot \mathbf{B} \times \mathbf{C} = \mathbf{A} \times \mathbf{B} \cdot \mathbf{C} = \mathbf{C} \cdot \mathbf{A} \times \mathbf{B} = -\mathbf{A} \cdot \mathbf{C} \times \mathbf{B}$$

A geometric proof follows from considering the vectors as forming edges of a parallelepiped—its volume is the magnitude of any of the scalar products.

Fig. 1-3. *Three of the possible vectors ending on a line parallel to* **A.** *All have the same vector product with* **A.**

A *vector triple product* may be formed by first taking the vector product of two vectors, and then the vector product of the result and a third vector: $\mathbf{A} \times (\mathbf{B} \times \mathbf{C})$. The parentheses are important and indicate which product is to be formed first. Twelve such products can be formed with three given vectors, and some of them are equal; for example, $\mathbf{A} \times (\mathbf{B} \times \mathbf{C}) = (\mathbf{C} \times \mathbf{B}) \times \mathbf{A}$.

Vector analysis, like trigonometry, has a wealth of useful identities. Of the few that will be needed, the first to be introduced is

$$\mathbf{A} \times (\mathbf{B} \times \mathbf{C}) = (\mathbf{A} \cdot \mathbf{C})\mathbf{B} - (\mathbf{A} \cdot \mathbf{B})\mathbf{C} \qquad (1\text{-}1)$$

Thus the vector triple product can be expressed as a sum of two vectors lying along the lines of two of the factors. The parentheses on the right are unessential but guard against misreading. A proof of (1-1) can be given directly from the geometrical meaning of the several operations, but an easier proof will be indicated presently.

The identity (1-1) may be thought of as a resolution of the triple product into the sum of two vectors. This idea of resolution admits of several generalizations, of which we shall need two.

Let $\mathbf{F}$ be any vector, and let $\mathbf{a}$, $\mathbf{b}$, and $\mathbf{c}$ be three mutually perpendicular unit vectors. Then

$$\mathbf{F} = (\mathbf{F} \cdot \mathbf{a})\mathbf{a} + (\mathbf{F} \cdot \mathbf{b})\mathbf{b} + (\mathbf{F} \cdot \mathbf{c})\mathbf{c} \qquad (1\text{-}2)$$

The proof by geometrical arguments will be well known to the reader. The scalar $\mathbf{F} \cdot \mathbf{a}$ and the vector $(\mathbf{F} \cdot \mathbf{a})\mathbf{a}$ will be called indiscriminately the *component of* $\mathbf{F}$ *along* $\mathbf{a}$. The identity (1-1) can now be proved by resolving the vectors $\mathbf{A}$, $\mathbf{B}$, and $\mathbf{C}$ according to (1-2) and using the distributive laws. (One can remove an ambiguity in the unit vectors by taking

c to be **a** ⨯ **b**.   One then has the multiplication table

$$\mathbf{a} \cdot \mathbf{a} = \mathbf{b} \cdot \mathbf{b} = \mathbf{c} \cdot \mathbf{c} = 1$$
$$\mathbf{a} \cdot \mathbf{b} = \mathbf{b} \cdot \mathbf{c} = \mathbf{c} \cdot \mathbf{a} = 0 \qquad \mathbf{a} \times \mathbf{a} = \mathbf{b} \times \mathbf{b} = \mathbf{c} \times \mathbf{c} = 0$$
$$\mathbf{a} \times \mathbf{b} = \mathbf{c} \qquad \mathbf{b} \times \mathbf{c} = \mathbf{a} \qquad \mathbf{c} \times \mathbf{a} = \mathbf{b}.)$$

If **F** is any vector, and **a** is a unit vector, then from (1-1),

$$\mathbf{F} = (\mathbf{F} \cdot \mathbf{a})\mathbf{a} - \mathbf{a} \times (\mathbf{a} \times \mathbf{F}) \tag{1-3}$$

This important resolution expresses **F** as the sum of its components along and perpendicular to **a**.

A very useful formula, easily derived from (1-1) and a property of the scalar triple product, is

$$\mathbf{F} \cdot \mathbf{G} = (\mathbf{F} \cdot \mathbf{a})(\mathbf{G} \cdot \mathbf{a}) + (\mathbf{F} \times \mathbf{a}) \cdot (\mathbf{G} \times \mathbf{a}) \tag{1-4}$$

where **F** and **G** are any vectors, and **a** is a unit vector.   [If **F** and **G** are also unit vectors, (1-4) is equivalent to a well-known formula of spherical trigonometry.]

1-2 Fields and Their Graphical Representations If at each point of space a value of some scalar quantity is given, a *scalar field* is defined.   In specific cases it is generally necessary to introduce a coordinate system and specify the field as a scalar function of coordinates. However, the ideas of points in space, of distances between points, and of scalar fields are independent of a coordinate system, and the general properties of the fields can be discussed on the basis of these primitive ideas alone.   The spirit is exactly the same as in ordinary geometry, where the treatment can be according to the methods of Euclid or of Descartes.   We will follow the spirit of the former method as far as possible in order to bring out the main ideas with minimum encumbrance by mathematical formalism.

If at each point of space a vector is defined, we have a *vector field*. Again, the properties of such a field can be discussed on the basis of the primitive definition alone, without the introduction of a coordinate system.

The general discussion of fields is greatly simplified if one can assume that every field has finite magnitude at every point and varies continuously from point to point.   One feels that any physically real field should satisfy these conditions and that the infinite singularities and the discontinuous jumps often occurring in the analysis of physical problems are introduced as abstractions to gain some mathematical advantage. In later work such discontinuities will appear, but each will be treated by a kind of limiting process to be separately discussed in each case. The present treatment of fields, however, will be simplified by the elimination of the possibility of discontinuities.

In a scalar field a useful idea is that of surfaces over which the scalar has a constant value.   Such surfaces are commonly called *level surfaces.* An example of a scalar field is the pressure at each point of the earth's atmosphere, and the curves of intersection of constant-pressure surfaces with the surface of the earth are the isobaric curves on a weather map. If level surfaces are drawn and labeled for equal increments of the scalar, the spacing indicates at a glance the rate of change of the scalar in any direction.

Several schemes are available to represent graphically a vector field. One is to draw at each point of space an arrow, pointing in the direction of the field, with a length proportional to the magnitude of the field vector.   Another is to draw *streamlines*, which form a family of curves,

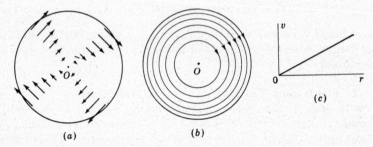

Fig. 1-4.   *Three methods of representing the velocity field in a rigid cylinder rotating about a fixed axis O.*

each of which is tangent at each of its points to the field vector at that point.   To each streamline is attached an arrowhead to indicate the direction of the field along it.   The spacing of the curves is so adjusted that if a small plane area containing some given point P is oriented perpendicularly to the streamlines passing by P, then the number of lines per unit area threading through the surface is proportional to the magnitude of the vector or the "strength" of the field at P.   In a third method, useful if one is particularly interested in the behavior of the field along some line, the components of the vector along three mutually perpendicular directions, one along the line, are plotted as ordinates, with distance along the line as abscissa.   All three representations will be used and are illustrated, for the simple case of the velocity field in a rotating cylinder, by Fig. 1-4.

1-3   Directional Derivatives and Gradient   Let V denote a scalar field, and consider the level surfaces passing through two nearby points P and Q (Fig. 1-5).   Let the surface through P belong to the value V, and that through Q to $V + \delta V$. Draw a unit normal $\mathbf{v}$ at P, and a unit vector $\mathbf{a}$ from P through Q. Denote the angle between the vectors by θ, the normal distance between the surfaces by $\delta\nu$, and the distance between P and Q by δs. The *directional derivative of V in the direction* $\mathbf{a}$ is denoted by dV/ds and is defined by

$$\frac{dV}{ds} \equiv \lim \frac{\delta V}{\delta s}$$

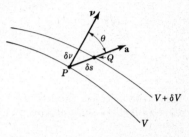

where the limit is taken as Q approaches P along the line of $\mathbf{a}$. A special case is the derivative in the direction $\mathbf{v}$, denoted by $dV/d\nu$. Since $\delta\nu = \delta s \, \mathbf{v} \cdot \mathbf{a}$,

$$\frac{dV}{ds} = \frac{dV}{d\nu} \mathbf{v} \cdot \mathbf{a} \qquad (1\text{-}5)$$

Fig. 1-5. *Level surfaces through neighboring points P and Q, and unit vectors along which directional derivatives are to be taken.*

It is thus clear that if the derivative is known for the direction $\mathbf{v}$, it can be found for any other direction by simple multiplication.

Looking at (1-5), one is led to introduce a vector field called the *gradient* of V, abbreviated grad V, defined by

$$\text{grad } V \equiv \frac{dV}{d\nu} \mathbf{v} \qquad (1\text{-}6)$$

Equation (1-5) can then be written

$$\frac{dV}{ds} = \mathbf{a} \cdot \text{grad } V \qquad (1\text{-}7)$$

The gradient is a vector whose magnitude is $|dV/d\nu|$, which is the largest magnitude the directional derivative can assume. Its direction is normal to the level surface through P in the direction of *increasing V*, which may be in the direction assumed for $\mathbf{v}$ or opposite it, according to the sign of $dV/d\nu$.

As an example of the calculation of the gradient, let r be the distance from a fixed point O to an arbitrary point P, and let V at P be $1/r$ when r is greater than some positive number a. (The latter condition is included to avoid an infinite discontinuity at the origin. For $r < a$, V can vary in some way other than $1/r$ and remain finite.) The level surfaces are spheres about O, and if $\mathbf{v}$ is the normal at P pointing away from O, $dV/d\nu = dV/dr = -1/r^2$, and grad $V = (-1/r^2)\mathbf{v}$ for $r > a$; at every point the gradient is directed toward O, and its magnitude falls off with increasing r according to an inverse-square law.

1-4   Line Integrals   Consider a vector field **F**, and let two points P and Q be joined by some curve.   If the curve, taken in the direction Q to P, is divided into vector elements $d\mathbf{s}$ (of which two typical elements are shown in Fig. 1-6), then the following integral, called the *line integral*, can be written:

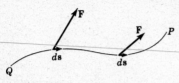

$$\int_{Q}^{P} \mathbf{F} \cdot d\mathbf{s}$$

Fig. 1-6. *Vectors involved in forming the line integral from Q to P.*

In a common application **F** is a force field, and the integral is the work done by the force on a point which moves along the curve from Q to P.

By use of the line integral one can obtain a relation between a scalar field V and its gradient which is analogous to the fundamental proposition of calculus relating the integral to the derivative.   For if **a** is a unit vector in the direction of $d\mathbf{s}$,

$$d\mathbf{s} \cdot \mathrm{grad}\ V = d\mathbf{s}\ \mathbf{a} \cdot \mathrm{grad}\ V = d\mathbf{s}\left(\frac{dV}{ds}\right) = dV$$

and

$$\int_{Q}^{P} d\mathbf{s} \cdot \mathrm{grad}\ V = \int_{Q}^{P} dV = V_P - V_Q$$

1-5   Divergence and Gauss' Theorem   From the last result in the preceding section, a scalar field V can be specified either by its value at every point of space or by its value at one point and the value everywhere of the derived field grad V.   A similar but more complicated situation holds in the case of a vector field **F**.   It can be specified either by the value of **F** at each point of space or by the value of **F** over a sphere of infinite radius and the values everywhere of two derived fields called the *divergence* and *curl* of **F**.   (In all real physical situations fields vanish over a sphere of infinite radius.)   The reason for introducing the derived fields gradient, divergence, curl, and others to be defined later is that the mathematical expression of physical laws involves the derived fields associated with a given problem; the fields themselves are then found by the theorems of vector analysis.   An analogy can be drawn from the mechanics of a particle, in which the equation of motion involves the acceleration, a vector derived from the position of the particle.

The definition of the divergence involves the notion of *normal surface integral*.   To get at this idea, consider the motion of a continuous compressible fluid.   The transport of mass can be specified by giving at each point the value of the vector $\mathbf{F} = \rho\mathbf{v}$, where ρ is the density of the fluid, and **v** is its velocity.   If $d\Sigma$ is an element of an imaginary plane surface, and **n** is a unit normal to $d\Sigma$, the rate at which mass is crossing through

$d\Sigma$ into the region into which $\mathbf{n}$ points is $\mathbf{n} \cdot \mathbf{F} \, d\Sigma$. If $d\Sigma$ is an element of an imaginary closed surface Σ surrounding a region τ, and $\mathbf{n}$ is the normal at $d\Sigma$ pointing out of τ, then the rate at which mass is streaming out of τ is given by the surface integral

$$\int_\Sigma \mathbf{n} \cdot \mathbf{F} \, d\Sigma$$

that is, the integral of the normal component of $\mathbf{F}$ taken over the entire surface Σ. The physical origin of a nonvanishing value is some combination of expansion, compression, creation, and destruction of fluid inside Σ.

The idea of normal surface integral, introduced with special reference to a fluid, can be generalized to a field $\mathbf{F}$ of any nature. The significance of the integral comes from the theory of the field $\mathbf{F}$. For example, if $\mathbf{F}$ is an electric field, it will be seen from the theory of such fields that the integral is proportional to the net charge inside Σ.

A nice geometrical interpretation of the normal surface integral can be given in terms of the mapping of the field by drawing streamlines. The integral is then proportional to the number of lines coming out through Σ minus the number going in. If no lines begin or end, the case in Fig. 1-4, the integral is zero for any closed surface Σ. (In the mapping of fields by streamlines, it is, of course, generally necessary to begin and end lines at various points to maintain the proper spacing. In electric fields, lines begin only on positive charge, and end only on negative.)

The value of the surface integral of $\mathbf{F}$ is a scalar derived from $\mathbf{F}$, but it depends on the choice of Σ and hence is not associated with a definite point and does not define a scalar field. However, the integral can be used to define a scalar associated with individual points in the following way: Let P be any point, and let Σ enclose a small volume $\delta\tau$ which contains P. The *divergence* of $\mathbf{F}$, abbreviated div $\mathbf{F}$, is defined by

$$\text{div } \mathbf{F} \equiv \lim \frac{1}{\delta\tau} \int_\Sigma \mathbf{n} \cdot \mathbf{F} \, d\Sigma \qquad (1\text{-}8)$$

where $\mathbf{n}$ is the outward unit normal at $d\Sigma$, and the limit is to be taken as all the linear dimensions of $\delta\tau$ shrink to zero with P remaining inside $\delta\tau$. That this limit always exists and is independent of the shapes Σ may assume (as long as these shapes are reasonable ones, such as spheres and cubes) will only be asserted here. A proof can be found in Wills [102], chap. III. The divergence constitutes a scalar field derived from $\mathbf{F}$ and may be thought of, to use hydrodynamical terminology, as the outflow in the field $\mathbf{F}$ per unit volume from an infinitesimal region at P. Examples of the calculation of the divergence will be given in a later section.

An important theorem can be derived from (1-8). Consider a finite volume τ bounded by a closed surface Σ. Let τ be divided into infinitesimal volumes (each having all its linear dimensions infinitesimal), and consider two such volumes, $d\tau_1$ and $d\tau_2$, which have a face in common and whose bounding surfaces are Σ_1 and Σ_2. Let $\operatorname{div}_1 \mathbf{F}$ be the value of the divergence at a point in $d\tau_1$, and similarly define $\operatorname{div}_2 \mathbf{F}$. Then

$$\operatorname{div}_1 \mathbf{F}\, d\tau_1 + \operatorname{div}_2 \mathbf{F}\, d\tau_2 = \int_{\Sigma_1} \mathbf{n}_1 \cdot \mathbf{F}\, d\Sigma_1 + \int_{\Sigma_2} \mathbf{n}_2 \cdot \mathbf{F}\, d\Sigma_2$$

where $\mathbf{n}_1$ is an outward normal to Σ_1 at $d\Sigma_1$, and similarly for $\mathbf{n}_2$. Over the common face, $\mathbf{n}_1 \cdot \mathbf{F} = -\mathbf{n}_2 \cdot \mathbf{F}$, and the net contribution to the surface integrals from this face vanishes. The right side of the equation then reduces to a single integral over the surface enclosing the combined volumes $d\tau_1$ and $d\tau_2$. Continuing this argument, one obtains *Gauss' theorem* that the volume integral of the divergence of $\mathbf{F}$ over a volume τ is equal to the surface integral of $\mathbf{F}$ over the surface Σ bounding τ. In symbols,

$$\int_\tau \operatorname{div} \mathbf{F}\, d\tau = \int_\Sigma \mathbf{n} \cdot \mathbf{F}\, d\Sigma \tag{1-9}$$

This theorem allows one to transform a volume integral of the form on the left of (1-9) into a surface integral of the form on the right, and vice versa, a process that will have many applications. It should be emphasized that in all the surface integrals the unit normal was taken to point out of the region enclosed by the surface of integration. This practice will be invariable.

1-6 Curl and Stokes' Theorem There are fields in which the divergence is everywhere zero and yet which have interesting structure. Fields in which all the streamlines form closed curves, as in Fig. 1-4, are examples. In the search for a further property to supplement the divergence in characterizing a field, a natural idea is to consider a surface integral related to the "swirling" of the field. Such an integral is

$$\int_\Sigma \mathbf{n} \times \mathbf{F}\, d\Sigma$$

where Σ is again an imaginary closed surface, and $\mathbf{n}$ is the outward unit normal at $d\Sigma$. The vector $\mathbf{n} \times \mathbf{F}$ is tangential to Σ, and the integral yields a vector. To distinguish this new integral from the one in the preceding section, it may be called a *tangential* surface integral. A derived field called the *curl* of $\mathbf{F}$ is defined, in analogy with (1-8), as

$$\operatorname{curl} \mathbf{F} \equiv \lim \frac{1}{\delta\tau} \int_\Sigma \mathbf{n} \times \mathbf{F}\, d\Sigma \tag{1-10}$$

For a proof of its existence one can refer again to Wills [102], chap. III.

The idea of the curl is more subtle than that of the divergence, and a conceptual device which might help in thinking qualitatively about the curl is the following: Take the surface Σ to be a small sphere of radius a with its center at P. If $\mathbf{r}$ is the radius vector from P to the element $d\Sigma$, $\mathbf{n} = \mathbf{r}/a$. Then

$$\operatorname{curl} \mathbf{F} = \lim \frac{3}{4\pi a^4} \int_\Sigma \mathbf{r} \times \mathbf{F} \, d\Sigma$$

If now $\mathbf{F} \, d\Sigma$ is thought of as a force acting on the element $d\Sigma$, the integral is the torque which would act on Σ and tend to make it rotate about an axis coinciding with the torque vector. This torque, multiplied by the factor outside the integral and taken in the limit of vanishing a, is the curl at P.

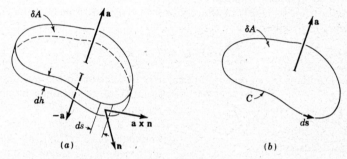

Fig. 1-7. **a.** *Surface of integration for arriving at a component of the curl.* **b.** *Limiting form of the surface.*

In many cases it is easy to calculate the curl directly from (1-10), as will be shown later, but a more generally useful formula is one which gives the component of the curl in any given direction. The curl itself can then be expressed as the sum of its (vector) components in three mutually perpendicular directions.

Let $\mathbf{a}$ be a unit vector, and take the volume $\delta\tau$ in (1-10) to be a thin plane disk perpendicular to $\mathbf{a}$ (Fig. 1-7a). Let each of the two plane surfaces have area δA and let the thickness of the disk be dh. The unit normal for one of the plane surfaces, call it the top, is $\mathbf{a}$, and for the bottom is $-\mathbf{a}$. At an element of the edge, of dimensions ds by dh, let the unit normal be $\mathbf{n}$. Consider now the component $(\mathbf{a} \cdot \operatorname{curl} \mathbf{F})\mathbf{a}$. If T, B, and E stand for top, bottom, and edge, respectively,

$(\mathbf{a} \cdot \operatorname{curl} \mathbf{F})\mathbf{a}$

$$= \lim \frac{1}{\delta A \, dh} \left(\int_T \mathbf{a} \cdot \mathbf{a} \times \mathbf{F} \, d\Sigma - \int_B \mathbf{a} \cdot \mathbf{a} \times \mathbf{F} \, d\Sigma + \int_E \mathbf{a} \cdot \mathbf{n} \times \mathbf{F} \, d\Sigma \right) \mathbf{a}$$

The triple products in the first two integrals are zero, since they contain a repeated factor. In the third, interchange the dot and cross, replace

$d\Sigma$ by $dh\ ds$, and write $\mathbf{a} \times \mathbf{n}\ ds$ as $d\mathbf{s}$. Then the final formula is

$$(\mathbf{a} \cdot \text{curl } \mathbf{F})\mathbf{a} = \lim \frac{1}{\delta A} \left(\int_C \mathbf{F} \cdot d\mathbf{s} \right) \mathbf{a} \tag{1-11}$$

where the integral on the right is a line integral around the contour C, the bounding contour of, say, the top of $\delta\tau$. Here dh has canceled out, and the result is unaffected by dh going to zero, leaving only the plane area δA with bounding contour C, as in Fig. 1-7b. Note that the direction of integration and the direction of $\mathbf{a}$ are related by a right-hand rule such that if the fingers of the right hand curl around C in the direction of $d\mathbf{s}$, the outstretched thumb points in the direction of $\mathbf{a}$. The right side of (1-11) gives the component of curl $\mathbf{F}$ along $\mathbf{a}$. Its evaluation will be illustrated in a later section.

Application to (1-10) of the arguments that led from (1-8) to Gauss' theorem (1-9) gives

$$\int_\tau \text{curl } \mathbf{F}\ d\tau = \int_\Sigma \mathbf{n} \times \mathbf{F}\ d\Sigma \tag{1-12}$$

This formula is not of much practical use. Of the utmost importance is a formula to be obtained by similar reasoning from (1-11).

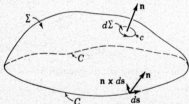

Let Σ be an *open* surface with boundary C, as in Fig. 1-8. Choose a direction of travel around C, indicated by the vector element $d\mathbf{s}$. Draw a unit normal at each point of Σ such that all the normals point from the same side of Σ. The rule for choosing the side is that for a normal at a point at the edge of Σ the vector $\mathbf{n} \times d\mathbf{s}$ points to the interior of Σ, as shown in

Fig. 1-8. *Open surface with the unit normal* $\mathbf{n}$ *at any point related to the direction of passing around the boundary.*

Fig. 1-8. Let $d\Sigma$ be an element with bounding curve c to which a direction is associated in relation to $\mathbf{n}$ by the right-hand rule. Then, from (1-11),

$$\mathbf{n} \cdot \text{curl } \mathbf{F}\ d\Sigma = \int_c \mathbf{F} \cdot d\mathbf{s}$$

If $d\Sigma_1$ and $d\Sigma_2$ are two elements with an edge in common, and equations like the last are written and added, then the line integrals reduce, through cancellation along the common edge, to a single integral around the contour bounding the combined elements. Extending this argument to all the elements into which Σ is imagined to be divided gives *Stokes' theorem:*

$$\int_\Sigma \mathbf{n} \cdot \text{curl } \mathbf{F}\ d\Sigma = \int_C \mathbf{F} \cdot d\mathbf{s} \tag{1-13}$$

Formula (1-13) states that the line integral of **F** around a contour C is equal to the normal surface integral of curl **F** over any open surface bounded by C, where the direction of integration around C and the directions of **n** are related by the rule stated earlier. This important theorem allows one to transform a surface integral of the type on the left of (1-13) into a line integral of the form on the right, and vice versa.

1-7 Time Derivatives In general, fields vary with time, and all the considerations up to this point hold for the whole of space at any instant. Variation with time gives rise to the idea of fields obtained by taking time derivatives, and such fields often appear explicitly in physical laws. With regard to scalar fields, no comment is necessary except that the derivative is written with a ∂ to indicate a partial derivative in the sense that the position in space is held fixed. The only distinguishing feature of the derivative of a vector field is that in the defining relation

$$\frac{\partial \mathbf{F}(P,t)}{\partial t} = \lim \frac{\mathbf{F}(P,\, t + \delta t) - \mathbf{F}(P,t)}{\delta t}$$

vector subtraction is involved in the numerator, so that a change in direction as well as magnitude contributes to the derivative.

1-8 Introduction of Coordinate Systems and the Calculation of Derived Fields The three coordinate systems to be used are the

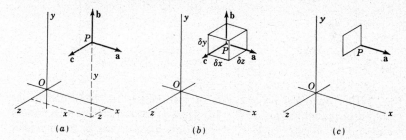

Fig. 1-9. *Cartesian system of coordinates.* **a.** *Definition of the coordinates and unit vectors at P.* **b.** *Appropriate volume to use in finding the divergence or curl.* **c.** *Appropriate area to use in finding the x-component of the curl.*

cartesian, the *spherical polar,* and the *cylindrical polar.* Their construction is shown as (*a*) of Figs. 1-9 to 1-11. Each identifies an arbitrary point P by a triplet of numbers and associates with P a set of three unit vectors **a**, **b**, and **c** pointing in the directions in which the several coordinates increase. In each system it should be carefully noted how **a**, **b**, and **c** are related to the three coordinate variables and that $\mathbf{a} \times \mathbf{b} = \mathbf{c}$.

These systems are called *right-hand* systems, and certain formulas to be given below will yield the right sign only if a right-hand system is used. In a cartesian system the resolution (1-2) is abbreviated to read

$$\mathbf{F} = F_x\mathbf{a} + F_y\mathbf{b} + F_z\mathbf{c}$$

in the spherical polar, $\mathbf{F} = F_r\mathbf{a} + F_\theta\mathbf{b} + F_\phi\mathbf{c}$; and in the cylindrical polar, $\mathbf{F} = F_r\mathbf{a} + F_\theta\mathbf{b} + F_z\mathbf{c}$.

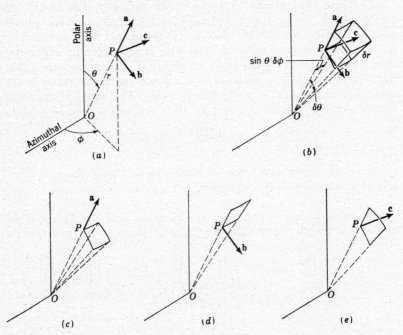

Fig. 1-10. *Spherical polar system of coordinates.* **a.** *Definition of the coordinates and unit vectors at P.* **b.** *Appropriate volume to use in finding the divergence or curl.* **c** *to* **e.** *Appropriate areas to use in finding components of the curl.*

Formulas for the scalar and vector products in coordinate representation are obtained by applying the distributive laws to the resolutions of the vectors and using the multiplication table for the unit vectors. In cartesian representation,

$$\mathbf{F} \cdot \mathbf{G} = F_x G_x + F_y G_y + F_z G_z \tag{1-14}$$

$$\mathbf{F} \times \mathbf{G} = (F_y G_z - F_z G_y)\mathbf{a} + (F_z G_x - F_x G_z)\mathbf{b} + (F_x G_y - F_y G_x)\mathbf{c}$$

$$= \begin{vmatrix} \mathbf{a} & \mathbf{b} & \mathbf{c} \\ F_x & F_y & F_z \\ G_x & G_y & G_z \end{vmatrix} \tag{1-15}$$

The determinant is an aid to memory. The corresponding formulas in the other representations are obtained by replacing x, y, and z by r, θ, and ϕ or r, θ, and z, respectively.

We turn now to the calculation of the divergence and curl of a vector field when the field is specified with reference to a coordinate system. There are two ways to attack this problem. In the first, one makes direct application of the definitions (1-8) and (1-10) or (1-11) to each individual

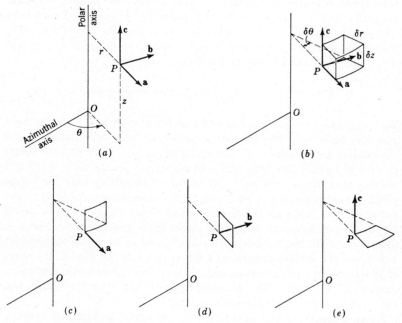

Fig. 1-11. *Cylindrical polar system of coordinates.* **a.** *Definition of the coordinates and unit vectors at* P. **b.** *Appropriate volume to use in finding the divergence or curl.* **c** *to* **e.** *Appropriate areas to use in finding components of the curl.*

problem. In the second, one evaluates these defining limits for an arbitrary field and obtains working formulas for divergence and curl involving partial differentiation. In almost all cases in this book in which the divergence or curl of a specific field will have to be found (mostly in the problems), the geometry is simple enough that the two methods involve about the same amount of labor, and unless the reader is very secure in his feeling for the two derived fields, it is recommended that the first method be used many times in order that he remain close to the original geometric definitions. This method will be illustrated in the next paragraphs by a few examples. In Appendix B some complicated calculations are carried out, and there the formulas involving partial differentiation have a distinct advantage. Those that will be needed will be derived from the primary definitions later in this section.

Consider the following simple field, conjured up at random and referred to spherical polar coordinates: $\mathbf{F} = (1/r^3)\mathbf{a}$. To find its divergence by (1-8), take the volume $\delta\tau$ to be that shown in Fig. 1-10b. Since $\mathbf{F}$ has only a radial component, contributions to the surface integral come only from the faces perpendicular to $\mathbf{a}$. To the lowest order of approximation, the area of the face at r is $r^2 \sin \theta\, \delta\theta\, \delta\phi$, and at $r + \delta r$ is $(r + \delta r)^2 \sin \theta\, \delta\theta\, \delta\phi$. The outward normal at the former is $-\mathbf{a}$, and at the latter is $\mathbf{a}$. The magnitude of F_r at the former is $1/r^3$, and at the latter is $1/(r + \delta r)^3$. The value of the surface integral is then

$$\int_\Sigma \mathbf{n} \cdot \mathbf{F}\, d\Sigma \approx \left(\frac{1}{r + \delta r} - \frac{1}{r} \right) \sin \theta\, \delta\theta\, \delta\phi \approx -\frac{1}{r^2} \sin \theta\, \delta r\, \delta\theta\, \delta\phi$$

To lowest order, $\delta\tau \approx r^2 \sin \theta\, \delta r\, \delta\theta\, \delta\phi$, and hence div $\mathbf{F} = -1/r^4$. Note that by considering the relative areas of the faces (varying as r^2) and the relative magnitudes of F_r, one could see at the outset that the divergence will be different from zero and negative. In the same way, it is obvious that div $(1/r^2)\mathbf{a} = 0$. With regard to writing only the lowest order of approximation at each step in the calculation, this is what one naturally does when all the dimensions of $\delta\tau$ are imagined to be infinitesimal, which amounts to passing to the limit first instead of last. A more correct but more tedious procedure would be to obtain the product $1/\delta\tau$ times the surface integral as a power series in the dimensions of $\delta\tau$, of which only the term independent of these dimensions would remain on passing to the limit. The procedure carried out above is simple and adequate and gives the divergence exactly.

As an example of the calculation of the curl, consider the velocity field $\mathbf{v}$ in a rigid cylinder rotating about its axis, illustrated in Fig. 1-4. It is appropriate to use cylindrical coordinates with the z axis coincident with the axis of rotation. The field has only a θ component, and if ω is the angular velocity, $v_\theta = \omega r$. To apply (1-10), take for $\delta\tau$ the volume in Fig. 1-11b. Contributions to the surface integral come only from the pair of faces perpendicular to $\mathbf{a}$ and from the pair perpendicular to $\mathbf{c}$, and for the latter pair the contributions are equal in magnitude and opposite in sign (because of the independence of z and the opposite directions of the outward normals). The surface integral is therefore

$$(-\mathbf{a}) \times \omega r \mathbf{b}\, r\, \delta\theta\, \delta z + \mathbf{a} \times \omega(r + \delta r)\mathbf{b}\, (r + \delta r)\, \delta\theta\, \delta z \approx 2\omega r\, \delta r\, \delta\theta\, \delta z\, \mathbf{c}$$

Since $\delta\tau \approx r\, \delta r\, \delta\theta\, \delta z$, curl $\mathbf{v} = 2\omega\mathbf{c}$.

To obtain the same result by using (1-11) to find the components of the curl, one uses the three contours shown in Fig. 1-11c to e. The θ component is zero, since **v** is perpendicular to the contour at all points, and hence the line integral is zero. The r component is zero, since the line integral receives contributions only from the top and bottom, and they are equal in magnitude and opposite in sign. Already much has been determined about the curl at a glance. Just as easily, one sees that there will be a z component and it will be positive. The quantitative calculation of this component is as follows: Contributions to the line integral come only from the sides of the contour at r and $r + \delta r$, and the net result is

$$\omega(r + \delta r)(r + \delta r)\, \delta\theta - \omega r\, r\, \delta\theta \approx 2\omega r\, \delta r\, \delta\theta$$

The area enclosed by the contour is $\delta A \approx r\, \delta r\, \delta\theta$; hence

$$(\mathbf{c} \cdot \text{curl } \mathbf{v})\mathbf{c} = 2\omega\mathbf{c}$$

It can be verified quickly by the arguments just used that the first field, whose divergence was found, has no curl, and the field for which the

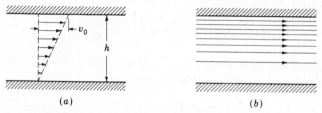

$$(a) \qquad\qquad\qquad\qquad (b)$$

Fig. 1-12. *Two representations of the velocity field in the nonturbulent shearing motion of a fluid. In* (**b**) *the streamlines are properly spaced. The curl points vertically into the plane of the figure.*

curl was found has no divergence. Less special fields have both divergence and curl.

One more example will be cited to show that a nonvanishing curl does not imply that the streamlines must be curved in some way. Consider two plane parallel plates at fixed separation h. One plate is fixed, and the other moves with velocity v_0. Between the plates is a viscous fluid showing no turbulence. The velocity field then has the linear dependence indicated in Fig. 1-12. It is left to the reader to see qualitatively that there is a curl directed into the plane of the figure and to show from (1-10) and again from (1-11) that its magnitude is v_0/h. Cartesian coordinates are appropriate.

For a note on the advantage of (1-11) over (1-10) as a working formula, see Prob. 1-10.

Formulas for obtaining the gradient, divergence, and curl by means of partial differentiation will now be deduced from the original definitions for the one case of cartesian coordinates.

From (1-7) and (1-2), if $V(x,y,z)$ defines a scalar field,

$$\operatorname{grad} V = \frac{\partial V}{\partial x} \mathbf{a} + \frac{\partial V}{\partial y} \mathbf{b} + \frac{\partial V}{\partial z} \mathbf{c} \tag{1-16}$$

While the derivatives are directional derivatives, formerly written with d's, they are in this case also partial derivatives in the ordinary sense and are appropriately indicated by ∂'s.

If $\mathbf{F}(x,y,z)$ is a vector field, we calculate the divergence by taking for the $\delta\tau$ in (1-8) the volume in Fig. 1-9b. The contribution to the surface integral from the faces perpendicular to $\mathbf{a}$ is

$$[\mathbf{a} \cdot \mathbf{F}(x + \delta x, y, z) + (-\mathbf{a}) \cdot \mathbf{F}(x,y,z)] \, \delta y \, \delta z$$
$$= [F_x(x + \delta x, y, z) - F_x(x,y,z)] \, \delta y \, \delta z \approx \frac{\partial F_x}{\partial x} \delta x \, \delta y \, \delta z$$

Adding the corresponding contributions for the other two pairs of faces and dividing by $\delta\tau = \delta x \, \delta y \, \delta z$,

$$\operatorname{div} \mathbf{F} = \frac{\partial F_x}{\partial x} + \frac{\partial F_y}{\partial y} + \frac{\partial F_z}{\partial z} \tag{1-17}$$

For the curl, the same volume $\delta\tau$ is used in (1-10). The contribution to the integral from the faces perpendicular to $\mathbf{a}$ is

$$[\mathbf{a} \times \mathbf{F}(x + \delta x, y, z) + (-\mathbf{a}) \times \mathbf{F}(x,y,z)] \, \delta y \, \delta z$$
$$\approx \mathbf{a} \times \left(\frac{\partial F_x}{\partial x} \mathbf{a} + \frac{\partial F_y}{\partial x} \mathbf{b} + \frac{\partial F_z}{\partial x} \mathbf{c} \right) \delta x \, \delta y \, \delta z$$
$$= \left(\frac{\partial F_y}{\partial x} \mathbf{c} - \frac{\partial F_z}{\partial x} \mathbf{b} \right) \delta x \, \delta y \, \delta z$$

Adding the contributions from the other four faces and dividing by $\delta\tau$ gives

$$\operatorname{curl} \mathbf{F} = \left(\frac{\partial F_z}{\partial y} - \frac{\partial F_y}{\partial z} \right) \mathbf{a} + \left(\frac{\partial F_x}{\partial z} - \frac{\partial F_z}{\partial x} \right) \mathbf{b} + \left(\frac{\partial F_y}{\partial x} - \frac{\partial F_x}{\partial y} \right) \mathbf{c}$$
$$= \begin{vmatrix} \mathbf{a} & \mathbf{b} & \mathbf{c} \\ \dfrac{\partial}{\partial x} & \dfrac{\partial}{\partial y} & \dfrac{\partial}{\partial z} \\ F_x & F_y & F_z \end{vmatrix} \tag{1-18}$$

One can use the same methods to find the analogous expressions for spherical and cylindrical coordinates. The calculations are longer than the above and involve the complication that the unit vectors change direction on moving from one point to another. The results are given in any standard text but will not be needed here.

1-9   A Few Identities   If V is a scalar field and $\mathbf{F}$ and $\mathbf{G}$ are vector fields, three identities that will be found useful are:

$$\operatorname{div}(V\mathbf{F}) = V \operatorname{div}\mathbf{F} + \mathbf{F}\cdot\operatorname{grad}V \tag{1-19}$$

$$\operatorname{curl}(V\mathbf{F}) = V \operatorname{curl}\mathbf{F} - \mathbf{F}\times\operatorname{grad}V \tag{1-20}$$

$$\operatorname{div}(\mathbf{F}\times\mathbf{G}) = \mathbf{G}\cdot\operatorname{curl}\mathbf{F} - \mathbf{F}\cdot\operatorname{curl}\mathbf{G} \tag{1-21}$$

These relations are usually proved in cartesian representation, using formulas from the end of the last section

1-10   The Inverse Problem of Vector Analysis   All the discussion up to this point has dealt with the direct problems of finding the derived fields gradient, divergence, curl, and time derivatives associated with given fields. The inverse problem, of prime importance in physical theories involving fields, is to find the fields of interest when information is given only about certain of their derived fields.

To cope with this inverse problem, vector analysis gives a large number of theorems which provide, on the one hand, criteria as to when sufficient information for a unique solution is at hand, and on the other, methods in very general terms for finding the solutions.   Applying these methods to specific cases usually involves the techniques of advanced mathematical analysis—ordinary and partial differential equations, integral equations, etc., all taken in connection with boundary values.   But every theory also contains simple yet important problems for which solutions can be found by elementary and illuminating arguments, and the whole of this book will be based on such simple cases arising in the Maxwell theory of electromagnetism.   The one exception is the radiation field of a dipole oscillator, the derivation of which, given in Appendix B, is moderately difficult but can be discussed in quite simple terms.   In that appendix the most important and interesting of the general theorems for solving the Maxwell equations will be derived preliminary to solving the dipole problem.   These theorems, taken independently of their proofs, are very simply stated and have simple and beautiful interpretations, and hence are quite appropriately included in Chap. 3 as part of the discussion of the Maxwell equations.   On the other hand, a number of problems worked out in that chapter show how much can be done with just the theorems of Gauss and Stokes.

1-11   Derived Fields of the Second Order   The Maxwell equations and all but one of the formulas to be deduced from them involve only the gradient, divergence, curl, and time derivative, and hence are subject to simple geometrical interpretation.   However, the processes of deducing formulas from the Maxwell equations often involve the introduction of derived fields of the second order—div curl, curl curl, second time derivatives, etc.—and the use of certain identities which they satisfy.

Conceptually, these repeated operations introduce no essentially new ideas, but the geometrical relations between a given field and its second-order derived fields are so involved that attempts to visualize are generally fruitless, and their use becomes rather formal.

With regard to time derivatives, the only comment necessary is that in those operations involving a time derivative and one of the operations div, grad, or curl, the result is independent of whether the time differentiation is performed first or last. Thus, for example,

$$\frac{\partial}{\partial t} \operatorname{div} \mathbf{F} = \operatorname{div} \frac{\partial \mathbf{F}}{\partial t}$$

which follows from noting that in the integrand of (1-8) time enters as a parameter (a fact not indicated explicitly in the formula), and by the well-known rule for differentiating a definite integral with respect to a parameter in the integrand, the differentiation and integration may be performed in either order.

A second-order field associated with a scalar field V is div grad V, which occurs so frequently that it is usually abbreviated $\nabla^2 V$ (read "del-squared V"), and this notation will be used in the rest of the book.[1] This field will be used in connection with cartesian and spherical polar coordinate systems. For the former, it is easily seen from (1-16) and (1-17) that

$$\nabla^2 V = \frac{\partial^2 V}{\partial x^2} + \frac{\partial^2 V}{\partial y^2} + \frac{\partial^2 V}{\partial z^2} \tag{1-22}$$

For the latter, one can find in texts various ways of showing that

$$\nabla^2 V = \frac{1}{r^2} \frac{\partial}{\partial r}\left(r^2 \frac{\partial V}{\partial r}\right) + \frac{1}{r^2 \sin \theta} \frac{\partial}{\partial \theta}\left(\sin \theta \frac{\partial V}{\partial \theta}\right) + \frac{1}{r^2 \sin^2 \theta} \frac{\partial^2 V}{\partial \phi^2} \tag{1-23}$$

Another field associated with V is curl grad V. It satisfies

$$\operatorname{curl\ grad} V \equiv 0 \tag{1-24}$$

which is easily seen from (1-11) with $\mathbf{F}$ replaced by grad V; for according to the relation at the end of Sec. 1-4, the line integral of grad V around any closed contour is zero, and hence any component of curl grad V is zero.

A second-order scalar field associated with a vector field $\mathbf{F}$ is div curl $\mathbf{F}$. It is always zero:

$$\operatorname{div\ curl} \mathbf{F} \equiv 0 \tag{1-25}$$

---

[1] In most texts on vector analysis a "vector operator" ∇ (read "del") is introduced and used in an alternative notation for all the operations grad, div, etc. In this book the symbol ∇ will be used only in the form ∇^2, standing for div grad. It is also common to denote div grad simply by Δ. A name often given to the field $\nabla^2 V$ is *laplacian* of V.

A proof comes from (1-8) with **F** replaced by curl **F**; any closed surface Σ can be regarded as two open surfaces joined at a common boundary C, and (1-25) then follows from a simple application of Stokes' theorem.

Two vector fields associated with a given field **F** are grad div **F** and curl curl **F**. An important deduction (the wave equation) can be drawn from the Maxwell equations by defining a third field, grad div **F** − curl curl **F**, which for the moment will be denoted by **G**. Expressions for the two fields defining **G**, and hence also for **G** itself, can be found in any coordinate representation. For our purposes it is sufficient to consider only the cartesian representation, and one easily shows that **G** takes the form of the right side of (1-22) with V replaced by **F**. [G_x is then the right side of (1-22) with V replaced by F_x, and similarly for G_y and G_z.] On this evidence it seems appropriate to denote **G** by $\nabla^2\mathbf{F}$, and this notation will be adopted.[1] We thus have

$$\text{curl curl } \mathbf{F} = \text{grad div } \mathbf{F} - \nabla^2\mathbf{F} \tag{1-26}$$

where $\nabla^2\mathbf{F}$ is a vector field whose cartesian representation is

$$\nabla^2\mathbf{F} = \frac{\partial^2\mathbf{F}}{\partial x^2} + \frac{\partial^2\mathbf{F}}{\partial y^2} + \frac{\partial^2\mathbf{F}}{\partial z^2} \tag{1-27}$$

[It might be remarked that in spherical polar representation, $\nabla^2\mathbf{F}$ is given by replacing V by **F** in the right side of (1-23). Expressions for the components of $\nabla^2\mathbf{F}$ in terms of the components of **F** are then very complicated because the unit vectors depend on the coordinates. Analogous statements hold for other curvilinear coordinate systems.]

All the necessary topics in vector analysis have now been covered. The numerous applications in later chapters will aid materially in fixing the ideas in the reader's mind.

Problems

1-1. Given $\mathbf{A} \cdot \mathbf{B} = a$ and $\mathbf{A} \times \mathbf{B} = \mathbf{C}$, where a, **A**, and **C** are known, write general expressions for the magnitude of **B** and the angle between **B** and **A** and explain how the direction of **B** is determined.

1-2. If **A** is a fixed vector, and **r** is the radius vector from an origin O to an arbitrary point of space, the equation $\mathbf{r} \cdot \mathbf{A} = c$, with c a constant, defines a plane. What is

---

[1] In connection with this second use of ∇^2, it might be asked if there is an inconsistency with the preceding footnote, which states that ∇^2 will always stand for div grad. Actually, there is none, for it is possible to extend the idea of gradient to define the gradient of a vector field, the result being a new kind of field called a tensor field of second rank. Moreover, one can define the divergence of a tensor field, the result being a vector field. It then turns out that **G** (or $\nabla^2\mathbf{F}$) is in fact div grad **F**. These points need not be pursued.

the perpendicular distance from O to the plane, and what is the direction of the normal to the plane?

1-3. Let **A** and **r** have the same significance as in Prob. 1-2. The equation $\mathbf{A} \times \mathbf{r} = \mathbf{C}$, with **C** a constant vector, defines a straight line. What is the direction of the line, and what is its distance from O?

1-4. Let **k** be a unit vector, and **r** be the radius vector from the origin to an arbitrary point of space. Let the smaller of the two angles between **k** and **r** be θ. Denote by **A** the vector $\mathbf{r} \times \mathbf{k}/r^2$. Describe the vector **A** by giving its magnitude and the relations of its direction to those of **r** and **k**. Draw a figure to illustrate the relations of the directions at a given point.

1-5. Repeat Prob. 1-4 for the vector **B** defined as $\mathbf{r} \times (\mathbf{r} \times \mathbf{k})/r^3$. In addition, describe the relation of **B** to **A**.

1-6. With **r** and **k** as in Prob. 1-4, give the magnitudes and directions of the three terms in (1-1) if $\mathbf{A} = \mathbf{B} = \mathbf{r}$ and $\mathbf{C} = \mathbf{k}$. Draw a figure and show that this relation is satisfied.

1-7. Using the vectors **A** and **B** from Probs. 1-4 and 1-5, describe the vector $\mathbf{C} = \mathbf{B} \times \mathbf{A}$ by giving its magnitude and its direction with respect to **r**, **k**, **A**, and **B**. What are the values of $\mathbf{A} \cdot \mathbf{k}$, $\mathbf{A} \cdot \mathbf{r}$, $\mathbf{B} \cdot \mathbf{k}$, $\mathbf{B} \cdot \mathbf{r}$, $\mathbf{C} \cdot \mathbf{k}$, $\mathbf{C} \cdot \mathbf{r}$, $\mathbf{A} \cdot \mathbf{B}$, $\mathbf{A} \cdot \mathbf{C}$, and $\mathbf{B} \cdot \mathbf{C}$?

1-8. Calculate the normal surface integral of the vector **C** of Prob. 1-7 over a sphere of radius r with center at the origin. (Use spherical polar coordinates with **k** along the polar axis.)

1-9. Find the divergence of the field **F** whose components in a spherical polar coordinate system are $F_r = r \cos \theta$, $F_\theta = F_\phi = 0$. Make direct application of definition (1-8) with the $\delta\tau$ shown in Fig. 1-10b.

1-10. Find the r, θ, and ϕ components of the curl of the field of Prob. 1-9. Make direct application of (1-11), using for δA the three areas shown in Fig. 1-10c to e. [To find the curl by use of (1-10) applied to the volume in Fig. 1-10b is more difficult, since changes in the directions of the unit vectors on crossing the volume must be considered. This complication in the direct use of (1-10) generally arises in problems referred to curvilinear coordinates.]

1-11. Show that if curl $\mathbf{F} = 0$ everywhere, then **F** can be written as the gradient of a scalar. (The solution of this simple problem is given in every book on vector analysis. There is another proposition which states that if div $\mathbf{F} = 0$ everywhere, then **F** can be written as the curl of another vector field. A proof of this statement is much more difficult; one can be found in Phillips [71], p. 104.)

1-12. In a later chapter, Green's theorem will be used. For those who do not already know it, let the simple steps in obtaining it serve as exercises. The arguments are given in full in any text on vector analysis. Start with Gauss' theorem (1-9), and replace **F** by $V\mathbf{G}$. Use the identity (1-19). Replace **G** by grad U, and hence obtain the *first form of Green's theorem:*

$$\int_\tau [V \, \nabla^2 U + (\text{grad } V) \cdot (\text{grad } U)] \, d\tau = \int_\Sigma V \mathbf{n} \cdot \text{grad } U \, d\Sigma$$

where V and U are any scalar fields.

1-13. From the result of Prob. 1-12 prove the *second form of Green's theorem:*

$$\int_\tau (V \, \nabla^2 U - U \, \nabla^2 V) \, d\tau = \int_\Sigma \mathbf{n} \cdot (V \text{ grad } U - U \text{ grad } V) \, d\Sigma$$

(These theorems were first given as part of George Green's famous "Nottingham essay" of 1828. For an idea of the stir this paper caused, see S. P. Thompson, "Life of Lord Kelvin," Macmillan & Co., Ltd., London, 1910, vol. I, pp. 113–119.)

1-14. Use the first form of Green's theorem (Prob. 1-12) to show that if div **F** and curl **F** vanish everywhere, and if **F** vanishes at infinity, then **F** = 0 everywhere. (*Hints:* Use the theorem in Prob. 1-11 to write **F** = grad U. Taking $V = U$ in Green's theorem, show that grad U must vanish. For a complete solution, see Wills [102], p. 106.)   An important consequence of the theorem of this problem is the following uniqueness theorem: If div **F** and curl **F** have prescribed values, and **F** vanishes at infinity, then **F** is uniquely determined.   If two fields satisfied the given conditions, their difference would satisfy the conditions of the theorem at the beginning of this problem and could not be different from zero.

chapter **2**

Sinusoidal Oscillations and Waves and Their Complex Representation

Sinusoidal oscillations and waves play an important role in treating problems in electromagnetic radiation, as well as problems in many other branches of physics. We shall now examine these sinusoidal functions and develop mathematical techniques for dealing with them. A great saving in writing and thought results from the use of a representation employing complex numbers and complex vectors, and much of this chapter will be devoted to gaining facility with this important tool.

The reader should be familiar with complex numbers; the first section summarizes some of their properties.

2-1 Complex Numbers and Their Representations A complex number is an association of two real numbers x and y and an *imaginary unit* i in the form $x + iy$. In the algebraic operations addition, subtraction, multiplication, and division as defined for these numbers, they are treated as ordinary binomials, except that the imaginary unit has the property $i^2 = -1$. Thus

$$(x_1 + iy_1) \pm (x_2 + iy_2) = (x_1 \pm x_2) + i(y_1 \pm y_2) \tag{2-1}$$

$$(x_1 + iy_1)(x_2 + iy_2) = (x_1 x_2 - y_1 y_2) + i(x_1 y_2 + y_1 x_2) \tag{2-2}$$

$$\frac{x_1 + iy_1}{x_2 + iy_2} = \frac{x_1 + iy_1}{x_2 + iy_2} \frac{x_2 - iy_2}{x_2 - iy_2} = \frac{(x_1 x_2 + y_1 y_2) + i(y_1 x_2 - x_1 y_2)}{x_2^2 + y_2^2} \tag{2-3}$$

Equation (2-3) holds only if $x_2^2 + y_2^2 \neq 0$.

Associated with the complex number $x + iy$ are its *negative,*

$$-(x + iy) = -x + i(-y) \tag{2-4}$$

its *reciprocal,*

$$(x + iy)^{-1} = \frac{x - iy}{x^2 + y^2} \tag{2-5}$$

and its *complex conjugate,*

$$(x + iy)^* = x - iy \tag{2-6}$$

The last will be of special importance and appears already in (2-3) and (2-5).

The real number x and the complex number $x + i0$ are equivalent. The complex number $0 + iy$ is said to be *pure imaginary* and is represented as simply iy. In this way mixed operations involving real, pure imaginary, and complex numbers are defined through (2-1) to (2-3). The numbers 0, $i0$, and $0 + i0$ all have the same effect in an algebraic expression (division by any of them being excluded), and the last two may be written simply as 0. In the complex number $x + iy$, x is called the *real part*, and y the *imaginary part*.

If z stands for any complex number, its real part may be denoted by Re (z), and its imaginary part by Im (z). Thus

$$z = \text{Re } (z) + i \text{ Im } (z)$$

Its complex conjugate will be denoted by z^*.

$$\text{Re } (z) = \tfrac{1}{2}(z + z^*) \qquad \text{Im } (z) = \frac{1}{2i} (z - z^*) \tag{2-7}$$

There are two schemes for representing a complex number graphically, Both make use of a euclidean plane referred to cartesian axes labeled "real" and "imaginary." In the first, a complex number is represented by a *point* whose coordinates are the real and imaginary parts of the number. In the second, the number is represented by *any* of the *vectors* which can be drawn in the plane so as to have components in the directions of the real and imaginary axes equal to the real and imaginary parts of the number, respectively. In the second representation, which will be used almost exclusively, two vectors having the same direction and length represent the same complex number; no point of the plane has the special significance of an origin, and the real and imaginary axes serve only to define two directions at right angles. These points are illustrated in Fig. 2-1a, which shows two of the possible vectors representing a number z which happens to have positive real and imaginary parts. By convention, the axes will always be taken horizontally and vertically in the arrangement shown.

Addition of complex numbers according to the definition (2-1) can be represented graphically by addition of vectors. It is convenient and permissible to draw the vectors representing the summands end to end, as in Fig. 2-1b, and they can be drawn in any order. This graphical addition will be a powerful device in later work.

The vector representing $-z$ has the same length as that representing z, but opposite direction. The vectors representing z and z^* are related as in Fig. 2-1c.

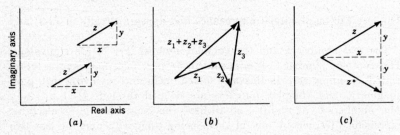

Fig. 2-1. *Vectorial representation of complex numbers.* **a.** *Two vectors representing the same complex number $z = x + iy$.* **b.** *Graphical addition of complex numbers.* **c.** *Relation between a complex number and its conjugate.*

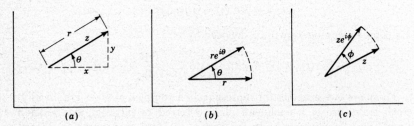

Fig. 2-2. **a.** *Graphical definition of the magnitude and angle of a complex number.* **b** *and* **c.** *Interpretation of the exponential as a rotator.*

The vectorial representation suggests specifying a complex number by the length r of the vector and the angle θ the vector forms with the positive real axis, as illustrated in Fig. 2-2a. The angle is taken to *increase* in the *counterclockwise* direction. The number z can then be written in the two ways

$$z = x + iy = r(\cos \theta + i \sin \theta) \qquad (2\text{-}8)$$

The second form is called the *polar form* of z; r is called the *magnitude* of z, and θ is called the *angle* of z. The magnitude will sometimes be denoted $|z|$, and alternative names for it are *absolute value* or *modulus*. The polar form of z^* is $r(\cos \theta - i \sin \theta)$.

Multiplication and division are particularly simple in polar form. Given $z_1 = r_1(\cos\theta_1 + i\sin\theta_1)$ and $z_2 = r_2(\cos\theta_2 + i\sin\theta_2)$,

$$z_1 z_2 = r_1 r_2 [\cos(\theta_1 + \theta_2) + i\sin(\theta_1 + \theta_2)]$$
$$\frac{z_1}{z_2} = \frac{r_1}{r_2}[\cos(\theta_1 - \theta_2) + i\sin(\theta_1 - \theta_2)] \tag{2-9}$$

A complex number can be written in an *exponential form*, which is the most useful of all for our purposes. Recall Euler's formula[1]

$$e^{i\theta} = \cos\theta + i\sin\theta \tag{2-10}$$

where θ is in *radians*. Thus $e^{i\theta}$ is a complex number whose angle is θ and whose modulus is unity (such numbers are called *unimodular*). The exponential form of the number z in (2-8) is·

$$z = re^{i\theta} \tag{2-11}$$
and
$$z^* = re^{-i\theta} \tag{2-12}$$

Formulas (2-9) become

$$z_1 z_2 = r_1 r_2 e^{i(\theta_1 + \theta_2)} \qquad \frac{z_1}{z_2} = \frac{r_1}{r_2} e^{i(\theta_1 - \theta_2)} \tag{2-13}$$

The exponential $e^{i\theta}$ can be interpreted graphically as a rotator, for if the real number r is represented vectorially as in Fig. 2-2b, the number $re^{i\theta}$ is represented by a vector obtained by rotating r through θ radians, in the *counterclockwise* direction if θ is *positive*. Similarly, if z is any complex number, the vector representing $ze^{i\phi}$ is obtained by rotating that representing z through ϕ radians as in Fig. 2-2c. The numbers i, $i^2 = -1$, $i^3 = -i$, and $i^4 = 1$ correspond to rotations through $\pi/2$, π or $-\pi$, $3\pi/2$ or $-\pi/2$, and 2π or 0, respectively. (The formula $e^{i\pi} = -1$ is perhaps the most striking one in elementary mathematics.)

Finally, a few useful facts and formulas should be written. If a complex number is given as an algebraic expression, however complicated, its complex conjugate is obtained by replacing i by $-i$ wherever it appears in the expression. The modulus can be calculated by

$$|z| = (zz^*)^{1/2} \tag{2-14}$$

Especially important for later use are the formulas

$$|z_1 z_2| = |z_1|\,|z_2| \qquad \left|\frac{z_1}{z_2}\right| = \frac{|z_1|}{|z_2|} \tag{2-15}$$

which are immediate consequences of (2-14) and can be extended to any number of factors. Another important relation is

$$|z_1 + z_2 + \cdots| \leq |z_1| + |z_2| + \cdots \tag{2-16}$$

---

[1] This formula can be proved in various ways. The most common proof uses the Taylor series for $\cos x$, $\sin x$, and e^x, and can be worked out by the reader if he has not already seen it.

where the sums can contain any number of terms; the interpretation is that the modulus of the sum is at most equal to the sum of the moduli, the truth of which is seen at a glance from Fig. 2-1b.

Always,

$$|e^{i\theta}| = 1 \qquad (2\text{-}17)$$

When θ is a sufficiently small fraction of a radian, $\cos \theta \approx 1$, $\sin \theta \approx \theta$, and Euler's formula becomes

$$e^{i\theta} \approx 1 + i\theta \qquad \theta \ll 1 \qquad (2\text{-}18)$$

Oftentimes θ will be sufficiently small that $e^{i\theta} \approx 1$ will be an adequate approximation. From (2-10) one obtains Euler's formulas for $\cos \theta$ and $\sin \theta$:

$$\cos \theta = \tfrac{1}{2}(e^{i\theta} + e^{-i\theta}) \qquad \sin \theta = \frac{1}{2i}(e^{i\theta} - e^{-i\theta}) \qquad (2\text{-}19)$$

2-2 Sinusoidal Oscillations in One Dimension The ideas involved in sinusoidal oscillations are brought out most clearly by considering the specific case of an oscillating particle. Simple extensions

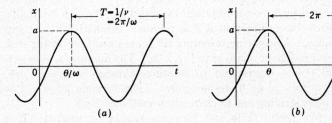

Fig. 2-3. a. *Sinusoidal motion along an x axis as a function of time with characteristic features labeled.* **b.** *Same motion as a function of ωt.*

will then bring in the notions of sinusoidal oscillations and waves in scalar and vector fields.

Taking first the simple case of one dimension, consider a particle undergoing sinusoidal ("simple harmonic") motion along an x axis between the limits $x = a$ and $x = -a$. As a function of time, the motion is represented by the curve in Fig. 2-3a, and a convenient formula expressing this curve is

$$x = a \cos (\omega t - \theta) \qquad (2\text{-}20)$$

The three parameters a, ω, and θ, which are constants completely fixing the motion, receive the following names and interpretations:

a The *amplitude* and the largest displacement of the particle from the center of the oscillation. It is a positive number.

ω The *angular frequency*, to be given in radians per second, such that if t increases by 1 sec, the argument $\omega t - \theta$ of the cosine increases by ω radians. Associated with ω is the frequency $\nu = \omega/2\pi$, which has the significance that the particle executes ν cycles of oscillation in 1 sec. Another parameter associated with ω is the *period* $T = 2\pi/\omega = 1/\nu$, which is the time between successive maxima of x. In (2-20), ωt could be replaced by $2\pi\nu t$ or $2\pi t/T$. The advantage of using ω is clear, and whenever there is no danger of confusion with ν, it will be called simply the *frequency*.

θ The *phase angle*, which serves to fix the position of the curve in Fig. 2-3a along the time axis. It is to be given in radians and can have any value, positive or negative, but since θ can be increased or decreased by any integral multiple of 2π without affecting (2-20), it is convenient always to reduce θ to the range $0 \leqq \theta < 2\pi$. In this case θ/ω is the time of occurrence of the first maximum of x after $t = 0$ (or at $t = 0$ if $\theta = 0$).

It will be convenient at times to refer to the x in (2-20) as the *instantaneous amplitude* of the particle, and to refer to $(\omega t - \theta)$ as the *instantaneous phase*. If x is plotted as a function of ωt as in Fig. 2-3b, one obtains a curve which is very simply related to the parameters a and θ.

The motion can be given a most concise and most useful expression if it is noted that (2-20) is the real part of

$$x_c = ae^{-i(\omega t - \theta)} = ae^{i\theta}e^{-i\omega t} = a_c e^{-i\omega t} \qquad (2\text{-}21)$$

We call x_c the *instantaneous complex amplitude* and a_c $(= ae^{i\theta})$ the *complex amplitude*, and we say that (2-21) is the *complex representation* of the oscillation. The two parameters a and θ are combined in the complex amplitude, and any oscillation of given frequency can be specified by assigning a value to a_c.

The minus sign prefixing $i\omega t$ in (2-21) is purely a matter of convention. A plus sign could be used equally well (in which case a_c would be $ae^{-i\theta}$), and it might seem more natural. In connection with waves it will appear that there is some advantage in writing the time factor as $e^{-i\omega t}$, and there is great advantage in using the same time factor always, whether a wave is involved or only an oscillation. To be inconsistent in the time factor is to run the risk of misinterpreting phase relations, with serious consequences. It must be pointed out that many authors on optics and other wave phenomena prefer $e^{+i\omega t}$, and one must be careful to interpret their formulas accordingly. The choice $e^{-i\omega t}$ is almost universal in works on quantum mechanics, which is a strong argument in favor of the choice in this book. On the other hand, in electrical engineering the choice $e^{+i\omega t}$ is firmly established, and to change it would mean changing such a familiar expression as the inductive reactance $i\omega L$ to $-i\omega L$.   That one must be consistent and unambiguous in this matter of sign, as in all conventions involving sign, cannot be overemphasized.

A useful graphical representation of an oscillation in one dimension is obtained by drawing vectors in the complex plane.   The motion is completely specified by just the one fixed vector representing the complex amplitude a_c, together with the frequency.   An animated representation, which gives a nice mental image but is not otherwise useful, is the vector representing the instantaneous complex amplitude x_c.   It is a vector of the same length as a_c rotating in the clockwise direction at ω radians sec^{-1}.   Its projection on the real axis is the instantaneous real amplitude.

2-3 Oscillations in Three Dimensions. Complex Vectors   In three dimensions the most general sinusoidal motion with frequency ω is such that the cartesian coordinates of the oscillating particle are

$$x = a_1 \cos(\omega t - \theta_1) \quad y = a_2 \cos(\omega t - \theta_2) \quad z = a_3 \cos(\omega t - \theta_3) \quad (2\text{-}22)$$

where the three amplitudes and three phase angles may be chosen arbitrarily.   It will be shown later that the motion is always confined to a plane and describes an ellipse with center at the origin.

While the three component oscillations (2-22) completely specify the motion, there are other representations which are preferable in most circumstances.   Let the position of the particle be given by the radius vector **r** extending from the origin to the particle.   If **a**, **b**, and **c** are the unit vectors belonging to the coordinate system,

$$\mathbf{r} = a_1 \cos(\omega t - \theta_1)\, \mathbf{a} + a_2 \cos(\omega t - \theta_2)\, \mathbf{b} + a_3 \cos(\omega t - \theta_3)\, \mathbf{c} \quad (2\text{-}23)$$

A complex representation is introduced by taking **r** to be the real part of a complex vector.

Now the definition of a complex vector is based on that of a complex number.   The complex vector $\mathbf{A} + i\mathbf{B}$, with **A** and **B** real vectors, is defined such that in any operation of vector algebra it behaves like an ordinary sum of two vectors, one multiplied by a scalar, except that i has the usual property $i^2 = -1$.   Thus

$$(\mathbf{A}_1 + i\mathbf{B}_1) \pm (\mathbf{A}_2 + i\mathbf{B}_2) = (\mathbf{A}_1 \pm \mathbf{A}_2) + i(\mathbf{B}_1 \pm \mathbf{B}_2)$$
$$(\mathbf{A}_1 + i\mathbf{B}_1) \cdot (\mathbf{A}_2 + i\mathbf{B}_2) = (\mathbf{A}_1 \cdot \mathbf{A}_2 - \mathbf{B}_1 \cdot \mathbf{B}_2) + i(\mathbf{A}_1 \cdot \mathbf{B}_2 + \mathbf{B}_1 \cdot \mathbf{A}_2)$$

A third law is obtained by replacing the dots in the second by crosses. The scalar product results in a complex number, and the vector product results in a complex vector.   Multiplication of a complex vector by a complex number is a straightforward extension of the same ideas.   A complex vector can be resolved along three real orthogonal unit vectors

a, **b**, and **c**, and the resolution can be written in the two ways:

$$\mathbf{A} + i\mathbf{B} = (A_1\mathbf{a} + A_2\mathbf{b} + A_3\mathbf{c}) + i(B_1\mathbf{a} + B_2\mathbf{b} + B_3\mathbf{c})$$
$$= (A_1 + iB_1)\mathbf{a} + (A_2 + iB_2)\mathbf{b} + (A_3 + iB_3)\mathbf{c}$$

In the second form of the expansion, one can think of the quantities $A_1 + iB_1$, etc., as the "complex components" along the unit vectors.

The radius vector **r** given by (2-23) can now be regarded as the real part of

$$\mathbf{r}_c = (a_1 e^{i\theta_1}\mathbf{a} + a_2 e^{i\theta_2}\mathbf{b} + a_3 e^{i\theta_3}\mathbf{c})e^{-i\omega t} \tag{2-24}$$

Both (2-23) and (2-24) relate to a set of unit vectors, but **r** and $\mathbf{r}_c$ have significances independently of this relation, and the fact is brought out by writing (2-24) in the form

$$\mathbf{r}_c = (\mathbf{A} + i\mathbf{B})e^{-i\omega t} \tag{2-25}$$

where

$$\mathbf{A} = a_1 \cos\theta_1\, \mathbf{a} + a_2 \cos\theta_2\, \mathbf{b} + a_3 \cos\theta_3\, \mathbf{c}$$
$$\mathbf{B} = a_1 \sin\theta_1\, \mathbf{a} + a_2 \sin\theta_2\, \mathbf{b} + a_3 \sin\theta_3\, \mathbf{c} \tag{2-26}$$

We call $\mathbf{A} + i\mathbf{B}$ the *complex vector amplitude* of the oscillation. To any set of a's and θ's corresponds à pair of vectors **A** and **B**, and conversely. It follows that *the most general sinusoidal oscillation in three dimensions* can be defined independently of a coordinate system by saying that it *is represented by the vector* **r** *which is the real part of* (2-25) *with* **A** *and* **B** *arbitrary real vectors.*

From (2-25) one easily deduces the nature of the path described by the oscillating particle. The real part can be written

$$\mathbf{r} = \mathbf{A} \cos\omega t + \mathbf{B} \sin\omega t \tag{2-27}$$

Hence the motion described by the end point of **r** always lies in the plane defined by the vectors **A** and **B**. That the motion is an ellipse is most easily seen in the following way: Let ξ and η be cartesian coordinates in the plane of the motion. The coordinates of the end point of **r** are then

$$\xi = A_\xi \cos\omega t + B_\xi \sin\omega t$$
$$\eta = A_\eta \cos\omega t + B_\eta \sin\omega t$$

The parameter t can be eliminated by solving these equations for $\cos\omega t$ and $\sin\omega t$, squaring each, and adding. It is not necessary actually to carry out this calculation, since it is obvious that the result would be a quadratic equation in ξ and η with no linear terms, whence the motion is a conic section with center at the origin. Since ξ and η are always finite, this section must be an ellipse.

The relation of **A** and **B** to the ellipse is very simple and provides a powerful means of visualizing oscillations and waves. From (2-27), special values of **r** are: $\mathbf{r} = \mathbf{A}$ when $\omega t = 0$; $\mathbf{r} = \mathbf{B}$ when $\omega t = \pi/2$.

Now $d\mathbf{r}/dt$ is the velocity of the particle and is a vector tangent to the path at the point $\mathbf{r}$.   From (2-27),

$$\frac{d\mathbf{r}}{dt} = -\omega\mathbf{A}\sin\omega t + \omega\mathbf{B}\cos\omega t$$

Special values of $d\mathbf{r}/dt$ are: $\omega\mathbf{B}$ when $\omega t = 0$; $-\omega\mathbf{A}$ when $\omega t = \pi/2$. Hence when $\mathbf{r} = \mathbf{A}$, the motion is in the direction of $\mathbf{B}$; when $\mathbf{r} = \mathbf{B}$, it is in the direction of $-\mathbf{A}$.   The relation of the path to the vectors $\mathbf{A}$ and $\mathbf{B}$ is therefore the one shown in Fig. 2-4*a*.   Note the construction of the circumscribing parallelogram, which is touched at the mid-points of two sides by $\mathbf{A}$ and $\mathbf{B}$ and has sides parallel in pairs to $\mathbf{A}$ and $\mathbf{B}$.   Note also the direction of motion, namely, from the end point of $\mathbf{A}$ to the end point of $\mathbf{B}$ along the *shorter* of the two arcs.   Finally, bear in mind that $\mathbf{A}$ is the real part of the complex vector amplitude, and $\mathbf{B}$ is the imaginary part.

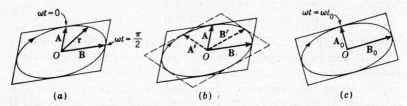

Fig. 2-4.   *Relation of the ellipse representing a sinusoidal vector oscillation to the real and imaginary parts of the complex vector amplitude.*

Two vectors related to an ellipse as in Fig. 2-4*a* (that is, through the parallelogram construction) are called *conjugate radii*.   Any two given vectors radiating from the same point are conjugate radii of one and only one ellipse, but for a given ellipse a pair of conjugate radii can be defined in an infinite number of ways, as illustrated in Fig. 2-4*b*.   It must be pointed out, however, that the ellipse alone does not completely specify a sinusoidal motion; it is necessary to give the position of $\mathbf{r}$ at some specified time and to give the direction of motion; it follows that then $\mathbf{A}$ and $\mathbf{B}$ in the representation (2-25) are uniquely determined if $\mathbf{A}$ is the position of $\mathbf{r}$ at $t = 0$.

Nevertheless, any alternative pair of conjugate radii, such as $\mathbf{A}'$ and $\mathbf{B}'$ in Fig. 2-4*b*, can be used in a complex representation of the motion. For let $\mathbf{A}'$ be the value of $\mathbf{r}$ when t has some fixed value t', so that by (2-27),

$$\mathbf{A}' = \mathbf{A}\cos\omega t' + \mathbf{B}\sin\omega t' \tag{2-28}$$

The radius conjugate to $\mathbf{A}'$ is $\mathbf{B}'$, obtained as the value of $\mathbf{r}$ at $\omega t = \omega t' + \pi/2$:

$$\mathbf{B}' = -\mathbf{A}\sin\omega t' + \mathbf{B}\cos\omega t' \tag{2-29}$$

(One easily shows by the previous argument that $\mathbf{A}'$ and $\mathbf{B}'$ are indeed conjugate radii.) Solving the last two equations for $\mathbf{A}$ and $\mathbf{B}$ in terms of $\mathbf{A}'$ and $\mathbf{B}'$ and substituting in (2-27) gives

$$\mathbf{r} = \mathbf{A}' \cos \omega(t - t') + \mathbf{B}' \sin \omega(t - t')$$

which is the real part of the complex representation

$$\mathbf{r}_c = (\mathbf{A}' + i\mathbf{B}')e^{-i\omega(t-t')} \tag{2-30}$$

By taking different values of t' and finding the corresponding vectors $\mathbf{A}'$ and $\mathbf{B}'$, one can get the complex representation of the motion referred to any pair of conjugate radii, $\mathbf{r}$ always having the position $\mathbf{A}'$ at $t = t'$.

Comparing (2-25) and (2-30), one can note explicitly the relation

$$\mathbf{A}' + i\mathbf{B}' = (\mathbf{A} + i\mathbf{B})e^{-i\omega t'} \tag{2-31}$$

Hence the complex vectors formed by any two pairs of conjugate radii differ only by a unimodular scalar factor.

A particularly important pair of conjugate radii are the *principal radii* $\mathbf{A}_0$ and $\mathbf{B}_0$, which lie along the axes of symmetry of the ellipse and are defined by a circumscribing rectangle, as in Fig. 2-4c. They satisfy $\mathbf{A}_0 \cdot \mathbf{B}_0 = 0$, so that if, corresponding to (2-28) and (2-29),

$$\begin{aligned}
\mathbf{A}_0 &= \mathbf{A} \cos \omega t_0 + \mathbf{B} \sin \omega t_0 \\
\mathbf{B}_0 &= -\mathbf{A} \sin \omega t_0 + \mathbf{B} \cos \omega t_0
\end{aligned} \tag{2-32}$$

we have

$$\mathbf{A}_0 \cdot \mathbf{B}_0 = (B^2 - A^2) \cos \omega t_0 \sin \omega t_0 + \mathbf{A} \cdot \mathbf{B}(\cos^2 \omega t_0 - \sin^2 \omega t_0) = 0$$

or

$$\tan 2\omega t_0 = \frac{2\mathbf{A} \cdot \mathbf{B}}{A^2 - B^2} \tag{2-33}$$

We thus have the following rule for finding principal radii: Express the oscillation in the form (2-25); take for the angle ωt_0 any of the four values in the range $0 \leqq \omega t_0 < 2\pi$ given by (2-33); substitute in (2-32) to obtain a pair of principal radii $\mathbf{A}_0$ and $\mathbf{B}_0$; the complex representation of the oscillation in terms of these principal radii is then

$$r_c = (\mathbf{A}_0 + i\mathbf{B}_0)e^{-i\omega(t-t_0)} \tag{2-34}$$

Note that this rule yields any one of four possible pairs of principal radii, of which only one is shown in Fig. 2-4c.

The complex representation (2-25) or (2-30) will be the most useful, but occasionally a calculation will yield an oscillation referred to cartesian coordinates in the plane of the motion in a form such as

$$x = a_1 \cos (\omega t - \theta_1) \qquad y = a_2 \cos (\omega t - \theta_2) \tag{2-35}$$

and while the complex representation could be written, it is sometimes convenient to be able to construct the ellipse directly from (2-35).

Clearly, the ellipse is circumscribed by the rectangle of dimensions $2a_1$ by $2a_2$ shown in Fig. 2-5. The positions of the points of contact and the corresponding values of ωt are found at once from (2-35) and are indicated in the figure. A simple way to deduce the direction of motion around the ellipse is the following: At $\omega t = \theta_1$ we have

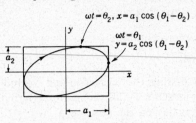

$$x = a_1, \ y = a_2 \cos (\theta_1 - \theta_2)$$

and

$$dy/dt = \omega a_2 \sin (\theta_2 - \theta_1)$$

Fig. 2-5. *Construction of the ellipse representing a vector oscillation whose cartesian components are given.*

The point will be moving down, the case shown in Fig. 2-5, if $\sin (\theta_2 - \theta_1)$ is negative; otherwise it will be moving up. It is safest to go through this complete line of reasoning each time a problem is worked, since a rule such as the one relating to the sign of $\sin (\theta_2 - \theta_1)$ depends on several conventions of notation which may, on occasion, be changed or not correctly remembered. The problems will illustrate this point.

2-4 Sinusoidal Waves in Scalar Fields In a scalar field let the value of the scalar at point P and time t be denoted $V(P,t)$. If the dependence on time is sinusoidal at every point,

$$V(P,t) = A(P) \cos [\omega t - \phi(P)] \qquad (2\text{-}36)$$

If the amplitude $A(P)$ and the phase angle $\phi(P)$ vary continuously from point to point, we say that (2-36) represents a *sinusoidal scalar wave.*[1] An alternative name which will be used often is *monochromatic* wave, a term borrowed from spectroscopy for reasons to be brought out in later chapters.

In general, waves arise as solutions of the fundamental equations of a physical theory. This aspect of waves will be the central topic of this book, but in the present chapter certain mathematical descriptions of waves of types to appear again later will be discussed independently of a physical theory.

The simplest type of monochromatic wave in a scalar field is a *plane, propagating wave having constant amplitude and constant velocity of*

---

[1] In order to include some types of waves that will be of interest to us, it will be necessary to relax the condition of continuity to allow A and ϕ to jump discontinuously on crossing certain surfaces. The main point is that, in general, if A and ϕ are assigned at each point without any restriction whatever, one does not get anything that could properly be called a wave.

propagation. A formula to represent such a wave is

$$V = a \cos (\omega t - \mathbf{k} \cdot \mathbf{r} - \theta) \tag{2-37}$$

where a is the constant amplitude, θ is a phase angle (independent of position and time), $\mathbf{k}$ is a constant vector called the *wave vector*, and $\mathbf{r}$ is the vector from some fixed point O to an arbitrary point P.

At a particular instant, the level surfaces of V are defined by $\mathbf{k} \cdot \mathbf{r} = constant$. These surfaces are planes perpendicular to $\mathbf{k}$; hence the wave is said to be plane. At $t = t_0$, consider the variation of V along a line parallel to $\mathbf{k}$ (therefore perpendicular to the level surfaces). Take, for example, the line through O, and let distances from O along this line be denoted by s, with s increasing in the direction of $\mathbf{k}$. Then for points

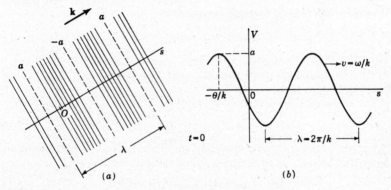

Fig. 2-6.   **a.** *Level surfaces in a plane, sinusoidal scalar wave.* **b.** *Amplitude along a line perpendicular to the level surfaces.*

on the line, $\mathbf{k} \cdot \mathbf{r} = ks$, and $V = a \cos (\omega t_0 - ks - \theta)$. Thus V varies sinusoidally with s when t is fixed. The constant k (the magnitude of $\mathbf{k}$) is called the *wave number* and is related to the distance between the planes of successive maxima of V, this distance being, by definition, the *wavelength* λ. For if s_0 is the position of one maximum, the next is at $s_0 + \lambda$, and we must have $k(s_0 + \lambda) = ks_0 + 2\pi$, or

$$k = \frac{2\pi}{\lambda} \tag{2-38}$$

A graphical representation of the wave at a given instant can now be given. For simplicity, and to bring out the significance of θ, take $t = 0$. Figure 2-6a shows a set of level surfaces spaced to indicate the variation of V. The dashed lines indicate planes of maxima and minima at which V equals a and $-a$, respectively. Figure 2-6b shows the variation of V along the s axis. The significance of θ is that it fixes the positions of the maxima relative to the origin, and the particular relation shown in

Fig. 2-6*b* is predicated on the assumption that $0 \leqq \theta < 2\pi$; this condition can always be met.

As t increases, the level surfaces move in the direction of **k** with the velocity

$$v = \frac{\omega}{k} \tag{2-39}$$

To see this, suppose a point moves along the s axis in such a way that it is always on some given maximum of V. Then its abscissa s satisfies $\omega t - ks - \theta = 2\pi m$, with m some integer, and $v \equiv ds/dt = \omega/k$.

The wave (2-37) is a special case of (2-36) in which

$$A(P) = a \qquad \phi(P) = \mathbf{k} \cdot \mathbf{r} + \theta$$

If space is referred to cartesian coordinates,

$$\phi(x,y,z) = k_x x + k_y y + k_z z + \theta$$

Thus the plane wave can be thought of as a monochromatic wave in which the amplitude A is constant and the phase angle ϕ is a linear function of x, y, and z.

The complex representation of (2-36) is

$$V_c(P,t) = A(P)\, e^{-i[\omega t - \phi(P)]} = A_c(P)\, e^{-i\omega t} \tag{2-40}$$

For given ω, the wave is completely specified by the complex amplitude $A_c = A e^{i\phi}$ at each point of space. For the plane wave,

$$A_c = ae^{i(\mathbf{k}\cdot\mathbf{r} + \theta)} = ae^{i(k_x x + k_y y + k_z z + \theta)} \tag{2-41}$$

If the plane wave propagates in a direction parallel to the x axis, its complex representation can be written

$$V_c = ae^{i(\pm kx - \omega t + \theta)}$$

where k is the magnitude of **k** (and not the x component), and the ambiguous sign is positive for propagation in the positive x direction. Here one sees an advantage, rather slight, to be sure, in writing the time factor as $e^{-i\omega t}$. A greater advantage is that frequently in later work the time factor will be left understood and not written; the remaining exponential $e^{i\mathbf{k}\cdot\mathbf{r}}$ in the general plane wave is shorter than it would be if a minus sign had to be written in the exponent.

2-5 Sinusoidal Waves in Vector Fields A vector field $\mathbf{F}(P,t)$ is sinusoidal if each component in a coordinate representation is a sinusoidal function of time with the same frequency, so that

$$\mathbf{F}(P,t) = C_1(P) \cos{[\omega t - \phi_1(P)]}\, \mathbf{a} + C_2(P) \cos{[\omega t - \phi_2(P)]}\, \mathbf{b}$$
$$+ C_3(P) \cos{[\omega t - \phi_3(P)]}\, \mathbf{c} \tag{2-42}$$

If the C's and ϕ's are continuous functions of position (except that in some cases they may jump discontinuously on crossing certain surfaces), we say that (2-42) represents a *sinusoidal vector wave*.

It is possible to deal with such a wave by treating each component as a scalar wave, but then one has difficulty in picturing the field in most cases. It is advantageous to pass at once to a complex representation independent of a coordinate system. The argument is based on the methods of Sec. 2-3, for (2-42) is of the same form as (2-23). By the steps which led to (2-25), the vector wave can be written in the complex form

$$\mathbf{F}_c(P,t) = [\mathbf{A}(P) + i\,\mathbf{B}(P)]e^{-i\omega t} \tag{2-43}$$

Thus the original definition of a sinusoidal vector wave can be replaced by the statement that such a wave is the real part of (2-43) in which $\mathbf{A}(P)$ and $\mathbf{B}(P)$ are real vector fields independent of the time and otherwise arbitrary except for satisfying appropriate conditions of continuity.

This second definition provides the means of visualizing the wave. At point P and time t draw an arrow from P representing the real vector $\mathbf{F}(P,t)$. With P fixed and t increasing, the end point of the arrow describes an ellipse of which $\mathbf{A}(P)$ and $\mathbf{B}(P)$ are conjugate radii; all the ideas in Sec. 2-3 apply. To visualize the whole wave, it is only necessary to visualize the variation of $\mathbf{A}$ and $\mathbf{B}$, since the ellipse at each point is so simply related to them. In particular,

$$\mathbf{F}(P,0) = \mathbf{A}(P) \qquad \mathbf{F}(P, \pi/2\omega) = \mathbf{B}(P)$$

As the simplest example, consider a *plane, propagating vector wave of constant amplitude and constant velocity of propagation*. It is defined in analogy with the scalar case by the requirement that in a cartesian representation the scalar components in (2-42) are plane scalar waves with the same wave vector $\mathbf{k}$. Thus C_1 is now independent of P, and ϕ_1 is now $\mathbf{k} \cdot \mathbf{r} + \theta_1$, where θ_1 is independent of P; similarly for the other two components. In a complex representation independent of a coordinate system,

$$\mathbf{F}_c = (\mathbf{A} + i\mathbf{B})e^{i(\mathbf{k}\cdot\mathbf{r}-\omega t)} \tag{2-44}$$

and the wave is completely specified by the frequency together with the three *constant* vectors $\mathbf{k}$, $\mathbf{A}$, and $\mathbf{B}$. (The six parameters $C_1, \cdots, \theta_3$ are incorporated in the vectors $\mathbf{A}$ and $\mathbf{B}$, which require six parameters in their definitions.)

According to (2-43), the complex vector amplitude of the wave (2-44) at the point P whose position vector is $\mathbf{r}$ is not $\mathbf{A} + i\mathbf{B}$, but rather it is

$$\mathbf{A}(P) + i\,\mathbf{B}(P) = (\mathbf{A} + i\mathbf{B})e^{i\mathbf{k}\cdot\mathbf{r}} \tag{2-45}$$

By the argument in connection with (2-31), $\mathbf{A}(P)$ and $\mathbf{B}(P)$ always constitute a pair of conjugate radii of one and the same ellipse. It follows that the oscillation of the vector at any point of space is represented by the same ellipse, and it is in this sense that the wave has constant amplitude.

At a particular instant the field **F** is constant (in magnitude and direction) over any plane defined by $\mathbf{k} \cdot \mathbf{r} = constant$, and such a plane is the analogue of a level surface in the plane scalar wave. At a particular point of space the representative ellipse is traced by a moving point whose direction of motion is such that it passes from the end point of **A** to the end point of **B** along the shorter of the two arcs connecting them and makes one revolution in the period $T = 2\pi/\omega$. On the other hand, if t is held constant, and one moves along a straight line in the direction of **k**, the representative point moves around the ellipse in the opposite direction and makes one revolution in the distance equal to the wavelength $\lambda = 2\pi/k$. By the same argument as was used in the case of a scalar wave, the surfaces of constant field move in the direction of **k** with velocity $v = \omega/k$.

In the electromagnetic theory, plane vector waves of the sort just discussed emerge as solutions of the Maxwell equations, and in most cases they are such that **A** and **B** are perpendicular to **k**. Such waves are said to be *transverse*, and associated with them is the notion of *polarization*. Let the elliptical motion representing the oscillation of the field vector at any fixed point be viewed in the direction *opposite* to **k** (that is, looking *against* the direction of propagation). If the motion appears to proceed in the *clockwise* sense as time increases, the wave is said to have *right-hand* polarization. If the motion is *counterclockwise*, the wave is *left-hand*. In general the polarization is *elliptical*. A special case occurs when **A** and **B** are collinear; then the polarization is said to be *linear;* handedness does not enter, and one speaks of the *plane of oscillation* of the wave, the plane containing **A**, **B**, and **k**. In another special case, **A** and **B** have equal magnitudes and are perpendicular to each other; the ellipse is then a circle, and one speaks of *circular polarization*, either right-hand or left-hand.

2-6 Superposition and Decomposition of Oscillations and Waves

The electromagnetic theory contains a "principal of superposition," which gives a physical significance to the process of adding together two or more oscillations or waves to obtain a resultant. The purely mathematical aspects of this addition will now be discussed.

Suppose one is given two oscillations in three dimensions, both having the same frequency and taking place about the same fixed point. Let them be represented by

$$\mathbf{r}_{c1} = (\mathbf{A}_1 + i\mathbf{B}_1)e^{-i\omega t} \qquad \mathbf{r}_{c2} = (\mathbf{A}_2 + i\mathbf{B}_2)e^{-i\omega t}$$

The resultant is

$$\mathbf{r}_c = \mathbf{r}_{c1} + \mathbf{r}_{c2} = (\mathbf{A} + i\mathbf{B})e^{-i\omega t}$$

where $\quad\quad\quad\mathbf{A} = \mathbf{A}_1 + \mathbf{A}_2 \quad\quad \mathbf{B} = \mathbf{B}_1 + \mathbf{B}_2$

Thus the resultant is again a sinusoidal oscillation and has the same frequency as the given ones. This superposition is illustrated in Fig. 2-7a, in which the ellipses need not be thought of as lying in the same plane. The process can obviously be extended to the addition of any number of oscillations of the same frequency. (To anticipate one of the physical applications, if two electrons in a classical model of an atom oscillate with the motions represented by $\mathbf{r}_{c1}$ and $\mathbf{r}_{c2}$, the radiated electric and magnetic fields at distant points are the same as for a single electron executing the resultant motion.)

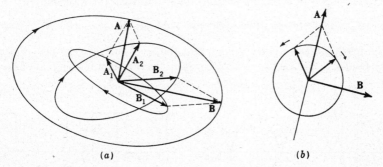

(a)   (b)

Fig. 2-7. a. *Addition of two vector oscillations to obtain the resultant.* **b.** *Relation between a linear oscillation and two oppositely rotating circular oscillations.*

The inverse of the process of superposition is the decomposition of a given oscillation into two or more component oscillations of the same frequency such that the given oscillation is the resultant of the components. Thus, Fig. 2-7a could be thought of, alternatively, as a decomposition. In applications the decomposition is usually into oscillations of types that are especially easy to handle in the particular problem. For example, if one is given the linear oscillation

$$\mathbf{r}_c = \mathbf{A}e^{-i\omega t}$$

it may be appropriate to resolve it into two circular oscillations in the same plane with opposite directions of rotation. Choosing a vector $\mathbf{B}$ satisfying $|\mathbf{B}| = |\mathbf{A}|$ and $\mathbf{A} \cdot \mathbf{B} = 0$, one writes

$$\mathbf{r}_c = \tfrac{1}{2}[(\mathbf{A} + i\mathbf{B}) + (\mathbf{A} - i\mathbf{B})]e^{-i\omega t}$$

This decomposition is illustrated in Fig. 2-7b. Any elliptical oscillation can be decomposed into linear oscillations along any three mutually perpendicular directions. Formula (2-25) can be regarded as a decomposition into linear oscillations along **A** and **B**, these oscillations being out of phase by one-quarter period, or $\pi/2$ radians. Problem 2-20 and the solution given describe an especially important type of resolution.

Addition of two sinusoidal scalar waves of the same frequency is very simple when the waves are expressed in the complex form (2-40). One only need add the complex amplitudes at each point. To illustrate, consider two plane, propagating waves of the same frequency, wave number, and amplitude, one propagating in the positive x direction, and the other in the negative:

$$V_{c1} = ae^{i(kx-\omega t+\theta_1)} \qquad V_{c2} = ae^{i(-kx-\omega t+\theta_2)}$$

With $\alpha = \frac{1}{2}(\theta_1 - \theta_2)$ and $\beta = \frac{1}{2}(\theta_1 + \theta_2)$, the resultant wave is

$$V_c = a[e^{i(kx+\alpha)} + e^{-i(kx+\alpha)}]e^{-i(\omega t-\beta)} = 2a \cos (kx + \alpha) e^{-i(\omega t-\beta)} \quad (2\text{-}46)$$

The resultant wave is sinusoidal, and the level surfaces are planes perpendicular to the x axis. At any instant t_0, the scalar V (the real part of

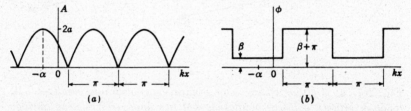

Fig. 2-8. *Amplitude and phase functions for a pure standing scalar wave.*

V_c) is a sinusoidal function of x with amplitude $2a \cos (\omega t_0 - \beta)$. As t varies, the planes over which $V = 0$ (called the *nodal planes*) do not move; there is no propagation, and the wave is called a *pure standing wave*. It is left to the reader to visualize further the behavior of V in space and time. The last expression in (2-46) is not of the form (2-40). While it is not particularly significant to reduce it to this form, it can be reduced by taking $A(x)$ (which must always be positive) to be the "rectified" function $2a|\cos (kx + \alpha)|$ (plotted in Fig. 2-8a), and $\phi(x)$ to be the discontinuous function (shown in Fig. 2-8b) taking only the values β and $\beta + \pi$ ($e^{i\varphi}$ takes values $e^{i\beta}$ and $-e^{i\beta}$).

To add vector waves, add the vector oscillations taking place at each point, making use of the ideas described in connection with oscillating particles. Examples will be given in the problems.

2-7 Cases in Which the Complex Representation Cannot Be Used The process of superposing oscillations and waves was greatly facilitated by the complex representation. The physically significant quantities are always the real parts, and the complex method could be used because the real part of the sum of two complex numbers or vectors is equal to the sum of the real parts.

Now when questions of energy are taken up, it will be seen that physical significance attaches to certain products, such as scalar and vector products of a vector field with itself or another field. It is of the utmost importance to note that in these cases the correct physical result is not attained by substituting complex representations for the factors and taking the real part of the product, for one does not thereby obtain the product of the real parts.

As an example, consider a particle of mass m oscillating along the x axis according to $x = a \cos \omega t$. The kinetic energy is

$$\tfrac{1}{2}m(dx/dt)^2 = \tfrac{1}{2}ma^2\omega^2 \sin^2 \omega t$$

The complex representation is $x_c = ae^{-i\omega t}$, and the kinetic energy is *not* $\tfrac{1}{2}m \operatorname{Re}[(dx_c/dt)^2]$, which fact one should verify in detail.

We conclude this section with a strong word of warning: The use of a complex representation in ways that do not give physically correct results is a pit which contains many victims.

Problems

2-1. Find the absolute value of

$$\frac{x + iy}{(u + iv)^2}\,(e^{i\phi} + e^{i\theta})e^{i\psi}$$

That is, find an expression in simplest form not involving i. Make use of (2-14) and (2-15). First do the problem algebraically throughout, and then do it by treating the sum of the exponentials graphically, applying trigonometry to the vector diagram. In the algebraic solution, follow two courses, one using (2-10) in summing the exponentials, and one not using this formula but eventually using (2-19). Bring all the solutions to that form which contains a factor $|\cos \tfrac{1}{2}(\phi - \theta)|$.

2-2. Draw a vector diagram to represent the complex numbers $e^{i\theta}$, $e^{i(\theta+\phi)}$, and $e^{i(\theta+2\phi)}$, with the vectors placed end to end as in Fig. 2-1b. Draw the vector representing the sum, and call the latter z. Apply trigonometry to the figure, and use appropriate identities, if necessary, to show that $z = (\sin 3\psi/\sin \psi)e^{i(\theta+\phi)}$, where $\psi = \phi/2$. (It is suggested that one look into several alternative procedures. For example, try drawing the given vectors in various orders, and think of various ways of drawing auxiliary lines to facilitate applying trigonometry. One way, not the first to come to mind, gives $\sin 3\psi/\sin \psi$ without the use of identities.) Make a rough plot of $\sin 3\psi/\sin \psi$ against ψ, indicating the values of the abscissas at zeros, maxima, and minima, and of the ordinates at maxima and minima. (This plotting becomes easy if one first expands $\sin 3\psi$ in powers of $\sin \psi$ by a standard identity.) Plot, to the same scale of ψ, the curve of $|z|^2$. (This problem is typical of those arising in connection with the diffraction of light.)

2-3. Find the sum z in Prob. 2-2 by purely algebraic means. (The formula for the sum of a geometric progression will be useful in one method of solving this problem.)

2-4. The time average of a function $f(t)$ over the interval T beginning at t_0 will be denoted by $\langle f(t) \rangle$. It is defined by

$$\langle f(t) \rangle \equiv \frac{1}{T} \int_{t_0}^{t_0+T} f(t) \, dt$$

Referring to (2-20) and (2-21), find the averages of x, x^2, Re $(x_c{}^2)$, and $|x_c|^2$ in the limit as T becomes infinite, and again when T is one period. Note the different results for x^2 and Re $(x_c{}^2)$. Which is significant in a physical problem?

2-5. Show that (1-1) is true when **A**, **B**, and **C** are arbitrary complex vectors.

2-6. Show that if in the oscillation (2-25) the vectors **A** and **B** are collinear, the maximum real displacement is $r_{\max} = \sqrt{A^2 + B^2}$. At what times are the extreme displacements reached?

2-7. Let two vector oscillations in complex form be

$$\mathbf{F}_c = (\mathbf{A} + i\mathbf{B})e^{-i\omega t} \qquad \mathbf{G}_c = (\mathbf{C} + i\mathbf{D})e^{-i\omega t}$$

Let **F** and **G** be the real parts. Calculate $\mathbf{F} \times \mathbf{G}$ and the real part of $\mathbf{F}_c \times \mathbf{G}_c$. Bring the results to as nearly the same form as possible and note the difference. Which expression would be significant in a physical problem?

2-8. Make a rough drawing of the ellipse in the xy plane and indicate the direction of motion for the oscillation

$$x = a_1 \cos\left(\omega t + \frac{\pi}{3}\right) \qquad y = a_2 \cos\left(\omega t - \frac{\pi}{4}\right)$$

Work directly from the given expressions, using the general reasoning given under (2-35) [that is, do not reduce them to the standard form (2-35) by adding 2π to the second phase constant in order that the special rule obtained under (2-35) be applicable].

2-9. Repeat Prob. 2-8 for

$$x = a_1 \cos\left(\omega t + \frac{4\pi}{3}\right) \qquad y = a_2 \sin\left(\omega t - \frac{3\pi}{4}\right)$$

2-10. Repeat Prob. 2-8 for

$$x = a_1 \cos\left(\omega t + \frac{\pi}{4}\right) \qquad y = a_2 \cos\left(\omega t - \frac{3\pi}{4}\right)$$

2-11. Draw the ellipse and indicate the direction of rotation for

$$x = \cos \omega t + 2 \sin \omega t \qquad y = 2 \cos \omega t + \sin \omega t$$

[Reduce to a form similar to (2-35).] Repeat when y is replaced by $2 \cos \omega t - \sin \omega t$.

2-12. Let **a** and **b** be perpendicular unit vectors. Let two vector oscillations in complex form be

$$\mathbf{F}_c = (\mathbf{A} + i\mathbf{B})e^{-i\omega t} \qquad \mathbf{G}_c = (\mathbf{C} + i\mathbf{D})e^{-i\omega t}$$

where $\mathbf{A} = \mathbf{a}$, $\mathbf{B} = \mathbf{b}$, $\mathbf{C} = -\mathbf{a} + \mathbf{b}$, and $\mathbf{D} = \mathbf{a} + \mathbf{b}$. Draw a figure in the manner of Fig. 2-7a to show the paths of the real vectors **F**, **G**, and **F** + **G**. Show in light construction lines the vector additions and the appropriate parallelograms (see

Fig. 2-4*a*). Show the directions of rotation. (Once the parallelograms are drawn, good ellipses can be drawn freehand.)

2-13. Repeat Prob. 2-12 for $\mathbf{A} = 4\mathbf{a}$, $\mathbf{B} = 2\mathbf{b}$, $\mathbf{C} = -\mathbf{a}$, and $\mathbf{D} = 2\mathbf{b}$.

2-14. Repeat Prob. 2-13 with $\mathbf{D} = -2\mathbf{b}$.

2-15. Repeat Prob. 2-14 with $\mathbf{C} = \mathbf{a}$ (see Prob. 2-21).

2-16. Show that if $\mathbf{A}$, $\mathbf{B}$ and $\mathbf{A}'$, $\mathbf{B}'$ are two pairs of conjugate radii of an ellipse, then $A^2 + B^2 = A'^2 + B'^2$. Show also that $\mathbf{A} \times \mathbf{B} = \mathbf{A}' \times \mathbf{B}'$. From the latter draw the conclusion that the area of the ellipse is $\pi|\mathbf{A} \times \mathbf{B}|$, where $\mathbf{A}$ and $\mathbf{B}$ are any conjugate radii.

2-17. Let $\mathbf{a}$ and $\mathbf{b}$ be perpendicular unit vectors. Given the oscillation $\mathbf{r}_c = (2\mathbf{a} + 3\mathbf{b} + i3\mathbf{a})e^{-i\omega t}$, find a pair of principal radii and the time at which $\mathbf{r}$ coincides with each. Illustrate the problem using the ideas in Fig. 2-4*a* and *c*, but draw only one ellipse.

2-18. Given the elliptical oscillation $(\mathbf{A}_0 + i\mathbf{B}_0)e^{-i\omega t}$, where $\mathbf{A}_0$ and $\mathbf{B}_0$ are principal radii, find the unique resolution into two oppositely directed circular oscillations in the plane of the given one. Illustrate the relations involved. This problem can be solved by mere inspection.

2-19. As an extension of Prob. 2-18, discuss how an arbitrary elliptical oscillation can be resolved into a linear oscillation along the z axis and two opposite circular oscillations in the xy plane. (This resolution enters in one method of treating the Zeeman effect.)

2-20. Any elliptical oscillation can be resolved into two elliptical oscillations in the plane of the given one and having the following properties: (1) The ratios of major to minor diameters are the same but otherwise arbitrary; (2) the major axes of the two components are at right angles; and (3) the directions of rotation are opposite. Find general formulas for the component oscillations. (This type of resolution will be seen to have many applications in optical problems.)

(*Solution:* Let the given oscillation be $\mathbf{r}_c = \mathbf{r}_0 e^{-i\omega t}$, where $\mathbf{r}_0$ is the complex amplitude. Let $\mathbf{a}$ and $\mathbf{b}$ be perpendicular unit vectors along which the principal axes of the component oscillations are to lie. Define vectors $\mathbf{e}_1 = \alpha\mathbf{a} + i\beta\mathbf{b}$, $\mathbf{e}_2 = \beta\mathbf{a} - i\alpha\mathbf{b}$, where $\alpha^2 + \beta^2 = 1$ and α/β is the desired ratio of principal diameters. These two vectors are analogous to orthogonal unit vectors inasmuch as they satisfy $\mathbf{e}_1 \cdot \mathbf{e}_1^* = \mathbf{e}_2 \cdot \mathbf{e}_2^* = 1$ and $\mathbf{e}_1 \cdot \mathbf{e}_2^* = 0$. Then $\mathbf{r}_0$ can be written $\mathbf{r}_0 = r_{01}\mathbf{e}_1 + r_{02}\mathbf{e}_2$ if $r_{01} = \mathbf{r}_0 \cdot \mathbf{e}_1^*$ and $r_{02} = \mathbf{r}_0 \cdot \mathbf{e}_2^*$. The component oscillations are then $r_{01}\mathbf{e}_1 e^{-i\omega t}$ and $r_{02}\mathbf{e}_2 e^{-i\omega t}$.)

2-21. Letting $\mathbf{a}$ and $\mathbf{b}$ be perpendicular unit vectors, apply the results of Prob. 2-20 to resolve the linear oscillation $r_c = 5\mathbf{a}e^{-i\omega t}$ into components with ratio 2:1 of major to minor diameter, having principal axes along $\mathbf{a}$ and $\mathbf{b}$. The answer is the pair of oscillations in Prob. 2-15.

2-22. Use the results of Prob. 2-20 to resolve the oscillation $\mathbf{r}_c = (4\mathbf{a} + i2\mathbf{b})e^{-i\omega t}$ into two circular oscillations. Here $\mathbf{a}$ and $\mathbf{b}$ are orthogonal unit vectors. Illustrate the solution.

2-23. In Fig. 2-6*a* imagine a line drawn through O at an angle θ to the s axis. Let this line be the axis of a variable u, and find V as a function of u. If the figure analogous to Fig. 2-6*b* were drawn, it would define a wavelength λ_u. Relate λ_u to λ.

2-24. Think of k_x in (2-41) as being 2π divided by a wavelength, say λ_x. What is the significance of this wavelength? What is its relation to the ordinary wavelength λ?

2-25. If in the wave (2-44) $\mathbf{A}$ and $\mathbf{B}$ are not collinear, and $\mathbf{k}$ is in the direction of $\mathbf{A} \times \mathbf{B}$, is the wave right-hand or left-hand?

2-26. Consider the following two waves traveling in opposite directions:

$$\mathbf{F}_{c1} = (\mathbf{a} + i\mathbf{b})e^{i(kz - \omega t)} \qquad \mathbf{F}_{c2} = (\mathbf{a} + i\mathbf{b})e^{i(-kz - \omega t)}$$

where **a** and **b** are unit vectors in the x and y directions, respectively.   Describe the polarizations of the given waves, and discuss fully the real field $\mathbf{F}_1 + \mathbf{F}_2$ as a function of space and time.

2-27. Repeat Prob. 2-26 when the amplitude of $\mathbf{F}_{c2}$ is changed to $\mathbf{a} - i\mathbf{b}$.

2-28. Repeat Prob. 2-26 for the following two waves traveling at right angles to each other:

$$\mathbf{F}_{c1} = \mathbf{a}e^{i(ky-\omega t)} \qquad \mathbf{F}_{c2} = \mathbf{b}e^{i(kx-\omega t)}$$

In the xy plane draw an array of ellipses to show how the oscillation varies from point to point.   For each ellipse (except when it reduces to a line) show the real and imaginary parts of the complex vector amplitude when the resultant wave is written in the form (2-43).   As a suitable array, draw ellipses at the 25 points $x = m\lambda/8$, $y = n\lambda/8$, with m and n taking the values 0, 1, 2, 3, and 4 independently.   The drawing will cover a square of side $\lambda/2$ with enough detail that one can see the trend of the pattern.   (This resultant field is invoked to explain one of O. Wiener's celebrated experiments on the wave field in front of a mirror reflecting linearly polarized light incident at 45°.)

chapter 3

The Microscopic Description of Matter and the Microscopic Maxwell Equations

In this chapter the presentation of the Lorentz theory of matter and radiation will begin. A general description of the fundamental assumptions of the theory concerning the microscopic structure of matter and the interactions of its various parts will be followed by the presentation of the Maxwell equations, on which most of the theory is based. Then from these equations will be deduced, by very simple methods, a number of solutions which represent well-known elementary propositions in electricity. The solutions will show the necessity of each term appearing in the equations and thereby give the equations a certain plausibility.

Let it be understood at once that the atomic model to be introduced is a classical one. It was developed about 1900 and is still useful, since many of the results to be drawn from it are the same as those coming from the more complicated quantum model. Further comments on these points appear at the end of Sec. 3-1, and Chap. 19 contains a detailed comparison of the classical and quantum theories.

3-1 Microscopic Description of Matter According to the description adopted by the Lorentz theory, matter is composed of three entities: mass, positive electric charge, and negative electric charge. The distributions of the two kinds of charge at a given instant are assumed to be specified by the values at each point of space of two scalar fields: the density of positive charge ρ_+ and the density of negative charge ρ_-. By definition, ρ_+ is the positive charge per unit volume at any point and is always a positive number; ρ_- is the negative charge per unit volume at any point and will also be written as a positive number. Thus $\rho_+ - \rho_-$ is the net charge per unit volume, denoted by ρ and given the name *charge density*.[1] Each of these densities is assumed to be finite and to vary continuously from point to point.

The kinematics of the charges is described by two vector fields, the current densities of positive and negative charge, the definitions being that if, at a given point and instant, the positive charge is moving with velocity $\mathbf{v}_+$, and the negative charge with velocity $\mathbf{v}_-$, the current densities are $\mathbf{j}_+ = \rho_+\mathbf{v}_+$ and $\mathbf{j}_- = \rho_-\mathbf{v}_-$. These definitions imply the following ideas: Consider the positive charge. Let $\delta\Sigma$ be a small element of an imaginary plane surface having a unit normal $\mathbf{n}$ (in either of the two possible directions). Then if $\mathbf{j}_+$ is evaluated at $\delta\Sigma$, $\mathbf{j}_+ \cdot \mathbf{n} \, \delta\Sigma$ is the rate at which positive charge flows across $\delta\Sigma$ into the region into which $\mathbf{n}$ points; $\mathbf{j}_+ \cdot \mathbf{n}$ is the rate per unit area; and $\mathbf{j}_+$ itself can be described as the flow of positive charge per unit area per unit time through an imaginary surface oriented perpendicularly to the vector $\mathbf{j}_+$, the flow being in the direction of $\mathbf{j}_+$. Analogous ideas apply to $\mathbf{j}_-$, and by the conventions being adopted, $\mathbf{j}_-$ points in the direction in which the negative charge is moving. The net current density is $\mathbf{j}_+ - \mathbf{j}_-$, which will be denoted by $\mathbf{j}$ and called simply the *current density;* its significance is that through a surface oriented perpendicularly to $\mathbf{j}$, a net charge j flows per unit area per unit time in the direction of $\mathbf{j}$. (The lightface letter j denotes the magnitude of the vector $\mathbf{j}$.)

The terms charge density and current density imply that charge may be divided into infinitesimal elements, and each element may be labeled and its motion followed. It is characteristic of classical physics to see no difficulty in such an idea, which, in essence, asserts that observations can be made on an indefinitely fine scale and in such a way as to cause indefinitely small disturbance on the system under study. Recognition that there are limits on smallness in these two respects is fundamental in quantum mechanics. In the Lorentz theory the classical attitude is adopted, and it is remarkable how good and widely applicable the results are.

From a purely kinematical point of view, the positive and negative charges are taken to be independent and capable of moving through each

---

[1] The reader will, of course, interpret these formal introductory definitions and statements in terms of what he already knows about charge. However, it is not strictly necessary to do so, since the development to follow will ultimately relate the notion of charge and the unit in which it is measured to the primitive notion of force, just as though none of this connection were previously known.

other. The further description of matter specifies the types of distributions of densities that can occur and the physical interactions between charges.

Matter is assumed to consist of atoms, sometimes well separated in space and sometimes assembled into molecules and into more or less dense media with the properties of a gas or a liquid or a solid. For the moment, consider an isolated atom. It is pictured as a small region of space in which there are equal amounts of positive and negative charge, at least in the case of a neutral atom, to which most of the discussion will be confined. Now in the early days of the Lorentz theory it could not be foreseen how far the theory could be pushed, and many attempts were made to assign definite distributions of charge within an atom with the goal of finding one which would account for all the properties of atoms and matter in bulk. The discovery of the nucleus narrowed the search considerably. However, the inherent limitations of the Lorentz theory are now known, and it turns out that all the results within these limitations can be deduced on the basis of any of a large number of atomic models, to which the laws of classical mechanics and electricity are to be applied. The most satisfactory procedure would be to choose that model which resembles, as closely as a classical model can, the one given by the present quantum theory. One can go quite far in this direction, but the model becomes too abstract and nebulous for an introductory account. Let us therefore adopt a very simple and specific model, and let us endow it with just those properties sufficient for treating, on the simplest basis, electromagnetic phenomena at the very high frequencies involved in light waves. This model will now be described, and at the end of the section it will be compared with other models.

The positive charge is assumed to be confined to a very small spherical region, which for definiteness may be given a radius of order 10^{-13} cm (the size of actual nuclei). The negative charge consists of some integral number, say Z, of equal parts, each of total charge $-e$, where e is a positive number equal to about 1.6×10^{-19} coulomb or 4.8×10^{-10} esu (the charge of the electron). Each of these parts of the negative charge will be called, as usual, an electron; each electron retains its separate identity at all times (an idea which has to be abandoned in the quantum theory).[1] Furthermore, the charge of each electron will be assumed to occupy a small sphere the same size as that of the nucleus. The details of the distributions ρ_+ in a nucleus and ρ_- in an electron can be arbitrary and will

---

[1] The symbol Z is the one ordinarily used to represent the atomic number of an atom; this number distinguishes one chemical element from another. In the model being described, the number Z is introduced only for the sake of a definite picture and has no further significance, since the Lorentz theory is unable to distinguish different kinds of atoms by predicting different chemical properties for different Z, or, in fact, any chemical properties at all.

be chosen to make the mathematical analysis as simple as possible by avoiding all problems of discontinuity. The image to carry in mind is a distribution which is constant throughout the small sphere, except that in a thin layer at the surface it falls smoothly to zero. These considerations will enter in Appendix B. The electrons and the nucleus are pictured as being capable of passing through each other. In the quiet or "unexcited" state of the atom, all the charges are assumed at rest with respect to each other, and all occupying, together with the nucleus, the same small volume of some 10^{-13} cm diam, so that the sum of the densities of the positive and all the negative charges is zero at every point. The case in mind is that of a neutral atom in which the total charge is zero. The total positive charge in the nucleus must be Ze. In this unexcited state the electrons are said to be in their *equilibrium positions*.

The various motions which the parts of the atom can undergo are determined by the dynamical properties assigned to the model, these properties relating to masses and internal and external forces. Each electron has a mass m equal to about 9.1×10^{-28} g. The positive charge has a mass M which is about 2000 times the combined mass of the electrons. A process of excitation consists in an external influence causing one or more electrons to depart from the equilibrium position. Suppose an exciting influence has acted for a short time, at the end of which several electrons are away from the equilibrium position and are moving with some set of velocities. The subsequent motion is determined by Newton's law applied with forces now to be discussed.

Each electron and the nucleus (the latter supposed rigidly attached to the unexcited electrons) will be acted upon by ordinary electric forces of attraction and repulsion due to the other particles in the atom, these forces being given by Coulomb's law. With these forces alone, the motion can be found, but it gives rise to radiation of a character in distinct disagreement with experience. The Lorentz theory now makes the fundamental assumption that the internal forces in an atom involve additional forces of a nonelectrical nature. The term "nonelectrical" is introduced here to imply that the origin of these forces is not to be explained by the theory. These additional forces combine with the coulomb forces to produce net forces with the following characteristics: Each electron experiences at every instant a force whose direction is toward the center of equilibrium (the center of the nucleus) and whose magnitude is proportional to the distance from the center of the electron to the center of equilibrium. The constant of proportionality may be assigned arbitrarily and may be different for each electron. Such a force, being reminiscent of Hooke's law, can be referred to as *elastic*. It is an immediate consequence of the nature of these forces that each excited electron executes a motion which is independent of the presence and motions of other excited electrons, so that the motion of each electron becomes a separate (and simple) mechanical problem. It also follows that if at the end of a process of excitation some electrons have not been excited and are at rest in the position of equilibrium, they will remain there. The force on the nucleus is simply the vector sum of the reactions to all the forces on the electrons, and in most problems this force is of such a nature that, because of its great mass, the nucleus remains essentially at rest. To the elastic force acting on each particle must be added a small correction called the *radiation reaction*. The latter will be discussed in a later chapter, and it will be seen that when it is included, the motion of each electron is still a separate problem and still simple.

The remaining forces acting on an atom arise from external causes, and since there is nothing else in space but atoms, these external forces must arise from the presence of other atoms. Again there is a division into electrical and nonelectrical forces, but here they do not combine into a single kind of net force as do the internal forces. The nonelectrical forces are assumed to be of short range, so that two atoms interact through them only when the distance between their centers is of order 10^{-8} cm or less, this figure representing the sizes ascribed to actual atoms.[1] When one atom moves past another and comes within this small distance (so that the short-range forces come into play), the atoms are said to experience a *collision*. By introducing the idea of collisions and assigning them certain properties *ad hoc*, as occasion demands, the Lorentz theory is able to speak of certain naturally occurring phenomena which are relevant to but do not properly come out of the theory; the process of excitation by collision constitutes an example. Again, the binding of atoms into molecules and liquids and solids is attributed to these short-range forces.[2]

The purely electrical interactions between atoms can take place over great distances; for example, excited atoms in a star may interact with an observer's eye and lead to the sensation of light. This long-range interaction is the most interesting aspect of the Lorentz theory and the one with which we will be most concerned. Our procedure is to make use of the Maxwell theory of the electromagnetic field and its interaction with matter. The detailed presentation of the Lorentz theory and its

---

[1] The sizes of atoms were originally inferred from the kinetic theory of gases, particularly an equation of state, such as the Van der Waals equation. Independently they were inferred from the spacings in crystal lattices, assuming neighboring atoms to be just touching. More recently, the sizes are given by quantum theory, which, in distinction to the Lorentz theory, can assign to an atom of a given element a definite structure and range of interaction.

[2] In connection with the unexplained nonelectrical forces, particularly the ones leading to the elastic binding of electrons in atoms, it might be remarked that they constitute an example of the prophetic insight by which leading physicists have made important advances well before their steps could be justified as following from a more comprehensive theory.

applications will begin with the study of the Maxwell theory in the rest of this chapter and the next.

It is appropriate to add to this section some concluding words on the philosophy behind the model adopted. The most usual model used to exploit Lorentz's ideas differs from ours in that it provides the possibility of circulating currents in an atom even in the unexcited state, and some such provision is essential if a medium is to show magnetic properties in a static or slowly varying magnetic field. The idea of these circulating currents was introduced very early by Ampère and are often referred to as *amperian loops.* (Such loops entered as the stationary orbits of electrons postulated by the old quantum theory of Bohr.) In the unexcited state of this more elaborate model, the charges are to be regarded as being in "equilibrium positions" even though they are in some kind of circulating motion, and in an excited state there is an oscillation about the equilibrium positions against elastic restoring forces. The charges can be pictured as particles or as being distributed continuously in a quite arbitrary way, and the predictions of the Lorentz theory are always the same. It is by taking the distribution to be continuous that one achieves a strong resemblance to modern quantum ideas.

Now for the purposes of this book some simplifications are possible. We will limit the scope to the phenomena occurring at frequencies from those of very short radio waves to those of X rays. It turns out that, under excitation by waves of these frequencies, the magnetic properties of atoms and matter in bulk play a negligible role for reasons best left for later discussion (particularly in Chap. 15). If a model is set up to incorporate circulating currents, the latter ride along as excess baggage at the high frequencies and might as well be eliminated. Only the elastic binding of the charges to equilibrium positions need be retained, and there is a distinct advantage to thinking in terms of particles rather than in terms of some arbitrary continuous distribution. The model we have adopted now appears as the simplest and most concrete that can be imagined, yet one that gives all the useful results that can come from the Lorentz theory at very high frequencies. The reader may wish to compare the treatment based on our simplified model with a more advanced one (still classical) using a model of great generality and incorporating magnetic effects. An excellent reference, written from a modern point of view but on a much higher level than the present volume, is Rosenfeld [78].

The characterization of some of the forces in the Lorentz theory as being "nonelectrical" has to be understood in the proper sense if it is not to be misleading. In the next section the classical forces exerted by electric and magnetic fields on charges and currents will be introduced and will be called electrical forces. It is impossible to build a theory of structure and interactions of atoms using just these forces and the classical laws of mechanics and electricity, or rather it is possible to build a theory, but it gives definitely wrong predictions. It was Lorentz's idea to assume additional forces of just the right nature to give qualitatively correct predictions and, by empirical adjustment of a few constants, to give even many quantitatively correct ones. The quantum theory, in one way of interpreting it, justifies the assumption of these additional forces and shows them to be of electrical origin, but the Lorentz theory is unable to arrive at this unifying view and must regard some of its forces as being of an *ad hoc* character. It is appropriate to distinguish sharply these unexplained forces, and it has been decided, perhaps unwisely, to call them nonelectrical.

3-2 Microscopic Maxwell Equations The Maxwell theory asserts that charges and currents give rise to electric and magnetic fields and these fields in turn exert forces on the charges and influence their motions. This interplay is governed by a set of equations which, firstly, relate the fields to the charges and currents, secondly, relate the fields to the forces they exert on charges, and, thirdly, specify the law of motion of charges and their associated masses under the influence of all forces acting, including nonelectrical as well as electrical forces. The law of motion is just that of Newton (force equals mass times acceleration) and need not be discussed further. The remaining equations constitute the set called Maxwell's equations.

The problems which can be solved by the Maxwell theory take many different forms and in general require elaborate mathematics. However, many problems in radiation and optics, even quite complicated ones, have the simplifying feature of separating into parts, each of which can be treated by itself. This point will become increasingly clear as examples occur later on, but the simplest of all examples can be described now to give the general idea.

An isolated atom, which will be called the *source*, has one of its electrons excited in some way into motion about its equilibrium position. This motion, as will be brought out in Chap. 5, gives rise to an electromagnetic wave traveling outward in all directions. At some large distance from the source is a second isolated atom, which will be called the *receiver*. The wave passes over the receiver and gives rise to forces on its electrons which set the latter into motion; this motion results in a secondary electromagnetic wave radiating from the receiver. In principle, the secondary wave falls on the source and influences its motion and the wave it emits, but actually, and this is the simplification, the secondary wave, when it arrives at the source, is weak enough in its action on the electrons to cause a negligible effect on the wave emitted by the source. Thus this problem separates into a "source problem" in which the motion of the charges is given and the radiated field is to be found, and a "receiver problem" (which, in a case such as the one being discussed, will be called more appropriately a scattering problem) in which an incident wave is given and a secondary (or scattered) wave is to be found.

The scattering problem will be deferred to later chapters. In the meantime the Maxwell equations will be introduced with specific reference to "pure source problems," that is, problems in which the distribution and motion of all the charges in space are completely specified and the corresponding fields are to be found.

The quantities that specify the charges and their motions are the densities ρ_+, ρ_-, j_+, and j_-. Now the quantities that appear in the Maxwell equations and determine the fields are the net densities

$$\rho = \rho_+ - \rho_-$$

and $j = j_+ - j_-$, so that the contributions to the fields arising from the charges and currents in any small volume are determined by these net densities in that volume, and not by the way in which they may be composed of positive and negative parts. The charges and currents give rise to an electric and a magnetic field, which will be denoted by **e** and **b**, respectively. The relations from which **e** and **b** can be found for given distributions of ρ and j are the following, the first four of the microscopic Maxwell equations:

$$\text{div } \mathbf{e} = 4\pi\rho \tag{3-1}$$

$$\text{curl } \mathbf{e} = -\frac{1}{c}\frac{\partial \mathbf{b}}{\partial t} \tag{3-2}$$

$$\text{div } \mathbf{b} = 0 \tag{3-3}$$

$$\text{curl } \mathbf{b} = \frac{1}{c}\frac{\partial \mathbf{e}}{\partial t} + \frac{4\pi}{c}\mathbf{j} \tag{3-4}$$

The first thing to be observed is that these equations, which hold at each point of space and each instant of time, give information about the derived fields, divergence, curl, and time derivative, from which the fields themselves are to be found by the methods o vector analysis. The second point is that constants appear, including a c whose value is not yet specified. These constants have to do with the units that will be adopted. It will be shown how these units and the value of c are defined by the equations themselves.

Now the new quantities **e** and **b**, and, in fact, ρ and j as well, have to be given significance in terms of some tangible physical idea already familiar. This idea will be force, and it enters the theory through the fifth equation:

$$\mathbf{f} = \rho\mathbf{e} + \frac{\mathbf{j} \times \mathbf{b}}{c} \tag{3-5}$$

Here **f** is a *force density* with the following significance: Consider a small volume of space $\delta\tau$ in which the charge density is ρ and the current density is j. If at $\delta\tau$ the fields have values **e** and **b**, the theory asserts that the net force on the matter in $\delta\tau$ arising from the action of the electric and magnetic fields is $\delta\mathbf{F} = \rho\,\delta\tau\,\mathbf{e} + \mathbf{j}\,\delta\tau \times \mathbf{b}/c$. Writing $\delta\mathbf{F}$ as $\mathbf{f}\,\delta\tau$ then defines $\mathbf{f}$ as the net force per unit volume in $\delta\tau$.

In Eqs. (3-1) to (3-5), ρ and $\mathbf{j}$ originate in some distribution of electrons and nuclei, so that the fields are to be found from the complete microscopic description of matter; hence the term *microscopic* equations.[1] Now it has been remarked that electrons and nuclei may overlap in various ways, each maintaining a separate identity at all times. In the case of overlap, (3-5) is not all that the theory has to say about forces, for the net force alone does not give the force acting on each of the overlapping particles. The complete statement is that the density of the force acting on a nucleus of charge and current densities ρ_+ and $\mathbf{j}_+$ is

$$\mathbf{f}_+ = \rho_+\mathbf{e} + \frac{\mathbf{j}_+ \times \mathbf{b}}{c} \tag{3-6}$$

and on an electron of charge and current densities ρ_- and $\mathbf{j}_-$,

$$\mathbf{f}_- = -\rho_-\mathbf{e} - \frac{\mathbf{j}_- \times \mathbf{b}}{c} \tag{3-7}$$

Adding expressions (3-6) and (3-7) for all the overlapping particles and using the definitions of ρ and $\mathbf{j}$ gives (3-5) as a corollary to the complete statement.

In the following sections some simple solutions and deductions will be drawn from the Maxwell equations, and in the course of this work the physical interpretations of $\mathbf{e}$, $\mathbf{b}$, ρ, and $\mathbf{j}$ in terms of force will come out. There remains the question of units. Some of them can be specified now, and the rest will be defined later. The units to be adopted for mass, length, and time are the cgs units. Newton's equation of motion then defines the unit of force as the dyne and the unit of $\mathbf{f}$ as the dyne per cubic centimeter. The electrical units to be adopted, together with the centimeter, gram, and second, will form a set called the *gaussian* system. This system is the one most commonly used in treatises on radiation and quantum mechanics. It is well known that there are many different systems of units in use, and that the diversity is very troublesome. In subjects such as optics, in which attention is primarily on formulas rather than numerical results, and in which, moreover, the important results involve mostly ratios (independent of the system of units) rather than absolute values, the mks system, with its more numerous symbols, does not find general favor. This is so in spite of the desirability of avoiding the complications in electrical units by universally adopting one

---

[1] The equations are often referred to as the equations for the *vacuum*. This terminology will not be used in this book, where by vacuum will be meant a region free of all matter and, in particular, of charge and current.

system which incorporates the "practical" units of charge, current, and potential. In advanced fields of physics the mks system is so far from universal that there is no choice but to be at ease with the whole subject of units, and to this end Appendix A, which is intended to be read after this chapter, may be of help.

3-3 Field about a Spherically Symmetric Static Charge In this and several of the following sections, some large-scale electrical problems, familiar from elementary physics, will be examined in the light of the Maxwell equations. As pointed out in the Introduction, to take up these problems now is to get ahead of the story, for any large-scale distribution of charge or current involves a complicated microscopic structure, the discussion of which must be developed gradually. In elementary physics these problems are successfully handled by merely ignoring the microscopic structure and conceiving perfectly smooth and uniform charge and current distributions. In a certain sense this procedure is valid and will be justified on the basis of the Lorentz theory in Chap. 15. In the meantime, these problems can be discussed by imagining large-scale distributions of ρ and $\mathbf{j}$ which are uniform even over large volumes and applying Eqs. (3-1) to (3-4) to them.

Consider a spherical region of arbitrary radius a containing a static charge whose density ρ is constant throughout. Outside the region, $\rho = 0$. Equations (3-1) to (3-4) reduce to

$$\text{div } \mathbf{e} = 4\pi\rho \qquad \text{div } \mathbf{b} = 0$$
$$\text{curl } \mathbf{e} = 0 \qquad \text{curl } \mathbf{b} = 0$$

By the statement in Prob. 1-14, $\mathbf{b} = 0$, the well-known result that a static charge gives rise to no magnetic field. Let the center of the sphere be the origin of a spherical polar coordinate system. Surround the charged region by an imaginary, concentric spherical surface of radius $r > a$ and apply Gauss' theorem to the field $\mathbf{e}$. By the spherical symmetry of the problem, $\mathbf{e}$ can have only a radial component e_r. Gauss' theorem then gives

$$4\pi r^2 e_r = 4\pi \int_\tau \rho \, d\tau = 4\pi Q$$

where the left-hand expression is the value of the surface integral, τ is the region inside the spherical surface, and Q is the total charge involved in the problem. The tentative solution for the field outside the charge is then $e_r = Q/r^2$, $e_\theta = e_\phi = 0$. It remains to verify that the two Maxwell equations involving $\mathbf{e}$ are satisfied at every point outside the charge (see Prob. 3-1). One can go on to find the field inside the charge distribution (Prob. 3-2). The interior field calculated in this way would show marked differences from an actual field arising from a distribution of charged particles if the observation were on a microscopic scale, but would be in agreement if the observation were coarse in a sense to be discussed in Chap. 15. The exterior field, on the other hand, is the same whether calculated on the assumptions of this section or on a strictly microscopic basis, as long as one avoids points very near the surface of the charge distribution.

3-4 Principle of Superposition Consider any distributions of charge and current ρ_1 and j_1, and let the fields due to them be e_1 and b_1; for a second pair of distributions ρ_2 and j_2, let the fields be e_2 and b_2; finally consider the combined distributions $\rho = \rho_1 + \rho_2$ and $j = j_1 + j_2$, with fields e and b. The principle of superposition states that

$$e = e_1 + e_2$$

and $b = b_1 + b_2$. The proof is as follows: From (3-1) we have

$$\text{div } e_1 = 4\pi\rho_1$$

and div $e_2 = 4\pi\rho_2$. Now taking the divergence is a linear operation, as is easily seen from (1-8), so that div e_1 + div e_2 = div $(e_1 + e_2)$. It follows that div $e = 4\pi\rho$. The same argument applies to (3-2) to (3-4) because of the linearity of the curl and the time derivative. Thus e and b are solutions corresponding to the distributions ρ and j.

The principle of superposition is of the utmost importance in optical problems in that it allows one to calculate the fields due to a complicated motion of many charged particles by finding the fields due to each particle alone and adding the results. In most cases the problem of the individual particle will be comparatively simple.

3-5 Coulomb's Law and the Units of Charge and Current An electric field e exists inside the spherical charge considered in Sec. 3-3, and it is easily found. Then the element of charge in a small volume $\delta\tau$ experiences a force $\rho e \, \delta\tau$, and the effect of all these forces by themselves would be a disruption of the charge. Supposing the body to remain intact implies additional stabilizing forces of some sort to just balance the electrostatic forces. The charge in $\delta\tau$ may be acted upon by an electrostatic field e which is the sum of the internal field e_i arising from the charges in the sphere itself and an external field e_e arising from neighboring charges; the electrostatic force on $\delta\tau$ is $\rho e \, \delta\tau = \rho e_i \, \delta\tau + \rho e_e \, \delta\tau$. The first term on the right is balanced by the stabilizing force, and hence the net force is just that due to the external field.

Let the sphere already discussed be in the external field of a second, identical sphere. Let the distance between centers be $d > 2a$. At any point in either sphere the external field of the other is known, and the calculation of the net force on each sphere is a straightforward problem of integration. However, consider the very simple case in which d is much larger than $2a$. Then with negligible error one can take the external field over either of the spheres to be constant and equal to its value at the center, which is Q/d^2 in magnitude. The net force on each sphere has magnitude Q^2/d^2 and has a direction away from its neighbor. This result is Coulomb's law for identical point charges, and it is seen to hold with negligible error for charges of finite sizes if the separation is very large compared to their dimensions. (A detailed calculation yields the stronger statement in Prob. 3-4.)

Coulomb's law is used to define the unit of charge in the gaussian system: If two identical point charges are at a separation of 1 cm, and each experiences a force of 1 dyne, the charge on each is 1 unit. This unit is given the name *electrostatic unit of charge*, abbreviated *esu of charge*, or the alternative name *statcoulomb*. The unit of ρ is the *statcoulomb per cubic centimeter*. The unit of current is that current which transports charge at the rate of 1 statcoulomb sec^{-1} and is called the *esu of current*, or *statampere*. The unit of j is the *statampere per square centimeter*.

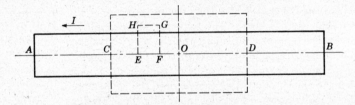

Fig. 3-1. *Long, narrow, rectangular loop carrying current I.*

3-6 Field around a Straight Wire Carrying a Steady Current

Only with some difficulty and a little intuition can the magnetic field around a wire carrying a current be found by elementary arguments such as those used in Sec. 3-3. The reason is that such arguments rely heavily on symmetry introduced into the problem for the purpose of simplification, and in the case of a current one is limited in this respect by the fact that the current must flow in a closed path.[1] The most favorable case is a long, narrow rectangle of thin wire, as indicated by the solid lines in Fig. 3-1. Let the cross section of the wire be circular with radius a, and imagine that a current flows and has density j which is constant over any cross section and is parallel to the axis. The charge density in the wire will be assumed zero everywhere, which is equivalent to assuming that the wire has no resistance, and no battery or other device is needed to make the current flow once it is started.

[1] The case, commonly discussed, of an infinitely long straight wire with charge drawn from the infinite reservoir at one end and allowed to accumulate at the other contains special problems concerning the behavior of the field at infinity and is best avoided.

The Maxwell equations become

$$\text{div } \mathbf{e} = 0 \qquad \text{div } \mathbf{b} = 0$$

$$\text{curl } \mathbf{e} = 0 \qquad \text{curl } \mathbf{b} = \frac{4\pi}{c}\,\mathbf{j}$$

It follows that there is no electric field. The magnetic field is found by the following arguments:

Figure 3-1 has a twofold axis of symmetry perpendicular to the plane of the figure through the center O, which is to say that if the figure is rotated 180° about this axis, the configuration of current is unchanged, and the configuration of the associated field must be unchanged. One conclusion about the field that can be drawn rigorously is that at each point of the axis of symmetry the direction of the field must be along it. Intuition now adds that if the points C and D in the figure are such that the lengths AC and DB are large compared with the width of the rectangle, the field inside the cylindrical surface represented by the larger dashed rectangle in the figure is determined primarily by the nearby long sides of the loop, and the contributions from the ends at A and B can be neglected. It follows that to good approximation the field inside the cylinder is independent of z, where z is a coordinate in the direction B to A. Then, from the symmetry, $b_z = 0$ along the line CD. Consider the line integral of $\mathbf{b}$ around the rectangle $EFGH$ shown in the figure. Since the component of $\mathbf{j}$ perpendicular to the plane of this rectangle is everywhere zero, the same is true of the component of curl $\mathbf{b}$, and by Stokes' theorem the line integral is zero. Now the contribution to the integral from the side EF is zero, and, because of the independence of z, those from FG and HE must be equal in magnitude but opposite in sign if they are not zero. It follows that b_z is zero along HG, and since the points E and F and the length FG can be chosen arbitrarily, and the rectangle can be rotated about the line EF without altering these conclusions, it follows that $b_z = 0$ throughout the cylinder, even inside the wires; the streamlines in this region are in planes perpendicular to the axis of z.

Consider points in the cylinder very near the wire forming one side of the loop. The field at any of these points consists of a strong contribution from the nearby wire and a comparatively negligible one from the distant parallel wire. Considering only the strong component, we have a problem with cylindrical symmetry about the axis of the wire in which it is known that the component of the field parallel to the wire is zero. Draw a cylindrical surface coaxial with the wire with circular top and bottom perpendicular to the axis of the wire. Let its radius be greater than a but much smaller than the width of the wire loop. From div $\mathbf{b} = 0$, it follows by Gauss' theorem that the surface integral over the cylinder is zero. There is no contribution to the integral from the top or bottom, and it follows that the radial component of $\mathbf{b}$, which must be constant over the cylindrical sides, is zero. Set up cylindrical coordinates with the z axis coincident with the axis of the wire and with the current flowing in the positive z direction. Draw a circle $r = constant > a$, $z = constant$, and consider the line integral in the direction of increasing θ. Because of the cylindrical symmetry, b_θ is a function of r only, and the value of the integral is $2\pi r b_\theta$. By Stokes' theorem and the Maxwell equations, the integral is also equal to

$$\frac{4\pi}{c} \int j_z \, d\Sigma = \frac{4\pi}{c} I$$

the integral being over the plane bounded by the circle, and I being the total current in the wire. Thus the field near the wire is $b_\theta = 2I/cr$, $b_r = b_z = 0$. The streamlines are circles with directions related to the direction of the current by the usual right-hand rule. This solution is only the strong contribution to the field near one of the wires, but its validity in representing the total field around the wire improves and extends over larger radii if the dimensions of the loop are made larger. In the limit of infinite dimensions, with the side in question remaining in finite space, it becomes exact for all finite radii and finite z. The field inside the wire can be found by further application of the arguments in this paragraph.[1]

3-7 Force between Parallel Currents and the Value of c Given the magnetic field around a single long, straight wire, the field due to two parallel wires can be obtained by superposition. The force on a unit length of either wire due to the magnetic field acting on the current can then be calculated by integrating (3-5), in which only the term with **b** is involved. By arguments similar to those given in Sec. 3-5, the net force on one wire is due entirely to the contribution to **b** from the other wire. Take the wires to have the same radius a and to carry equal currents I flowing in the same direction. Take the separation of the wires to be $d \gg a$. The external field in one of the wires is then practically constant and equal in magnitude to $2I/cd$ and has direction perpendicular to the wire. The magnitude of the force per unit length is $2I^2/c^2d$, and it is easily seen that the direction of the force is toward the other wire.

Having the unit of current, one can make an experiment in which the force between parallel currents of given equal magnitudes and given separation is measured, whence c can be found from the above formula.

---

[1] If the wire had had resistance, the conclusions about the magnetic field would have been unaltered, since, as will be seen in Sec. 3-14, the field depends only on the current. However, a battery would have been necessary, and the charge density in the wire and the battery would have been different from zero and would have given rise to an electric field. A discussion of these points would digress too far from the main subject.

It would not be the best way to determine c, but in principle it would give the right value, which, for our purposes, can be rounded off to

$$c = 3 \times 10^{10} \text{ cm sec}^{-1}$$

This number turns out to agree with the measured velocity of light. Also, it will be shown that the c in the Maxwell equations is the velocity of the electromagnetic waves which the equations predict. It was this set of facts that first led to identifying light with electromagnetic waves.

3-8 Measurement of Electric and Magnetic Fields In (3-5) the value of c is now known and units have been defined for all quantities except **e** and **b**. We wish to see how **e** and **b** could be measured and their units defined. For this purpose we consider using a charged *test particle*. Such a particle, by definition, consists of a distribution of charge, each of whose elements is in some way held rigidly fixed with respect to the others regardless of what electrical forces act on it. The part of these electrical forces due to the charges and currents in the particle itself is balanced by stabilizing forces, as discussed in Secs. 3-5 and 3-7. The rest of the electrical force on the particle is due to fields arising from charges and currents not belonging to the particle, and these are just the fields to be measured by introducing the test particle. In order that the system under study be undisturbed by the presence of the particle, it is assumed that the latter is of infinitesimal size and has infinitesimal charge dq (ideas admissible in classical physics). Moreover, it is assumed that the particle can be controlled to such a degree that it can be held fixed at any point or given a definite velocity at any point, and in all cases the force due to the fields under study can be measured at any instant. If the particle moves with velocity **v** without rotation, it gives rise to a current density $\mathbf{j} = \rho\mathbf{v}$ at each point, and (3-5) can be integrated to give the total force on the particle as

$$d\mathbf{F} = dq\left(\mathbf{e} + \frac{\mathbf{v} \times \mathbf{b}}{c}\right) \tag{3-8}$$

Before application of (3-8) to the measurement of fields, some extensions of the formula itself should be discussed. Consider an electron or a nucleus which forms part of a physical system (not a test particle). If it is not near other charges, the external fields $\mathbf{e}_e$ and $\mathbf{b}_e$ arising from other charges are essentially constant over it, and the net force $\mathbf{F}$ is again obtained by integrating (3-5) to give

$$\mathbf{F} = q\left(\mathbf{e}_e + \frac{\mathbf{v} \times \mathbf{b}_e}{c}\right) \tag{3-8a}$$

where q is the total charge of the particle (for example, $-e$ for an electron) and **v** is the velocity of the particle. Formula (3-8a) will be very important in later work, and several comments should be made to ensure complete understanding.

1. The fields e_e and b_e are the fields arising from all charges and currents except those in the particle itself.

2. Because of the finiteness of the charge on the particle, its influence on neighboring charges cannot always be neglected, but it is supposed that e_e and b_e have been calculated with this influence taken into account.

3. If the particle is part of or is in collision with an atom, additional forces of a nonelectrical nature enter, and special rules apply to them, as already discussed.

4. Formula (3-8a) applies to a particle moving without rotation, so that v is the same at all its points. It also applies to a rotating particle if v is the velocity of the centroid of the charge. Rotation gives rise to a torque (which depends on b_e and not on e_e), but this point will not be pursued, since rotating particles will be excluded on the grounds that the Lorentz theory does not say sufficiently interesting things about them to warrant the complication.

5. If the motion of the particle involves acceleration, there is a small force of radiation reaction to be added to (3-8a). This matter will be discussed later (Sec. 12-3).

6. If v is very small compared with c, which is the nonrelativistic limit and the only case to be considered, the second term on the right of (3-8a) is small compared with the first in those frequent cases in which the electric and magnetic fields are of the same order of magnitude, and often the effects of this small term can be neglected.

Returning to the measurement of e and b, let an infinitesimal test charge be at rest at a point in the fields. The force on the particle is then $dF = e\, dq$, and $e = dF/dq$. Knowing dq and measuring dF gives e, and the unit of e is the dyne per statcoulomb. Alternative names for this unit are *esu of electric field* or *statvolt per centimeter*. (The statvolt is the esu of potential difference and is defined in terms of work by saying that between two points there is a difference of potential of 1 statvolt if the work done by the electric field per statcoulomb in transporting an infinitesimal charge from one point to the other is 1 erg. For an infinitesimal path in the direction of e, the work per statcoulomb per centimeter is e; clearly e can be expressed in statvolts per centimeter.)

Refer space to a cartesian coordinate system, and let the test particle move in the y direction with velocity v and no acceleration. Subtract the force due to the electric field (now known); the x component of the remaining force is $dF_x = dq\, vb_z/c$, or $b_z = (c/v)\, dF_x/dq$. Similarly, take the velocity in the z direction; b_x is found from the y component of the force, etc. The unit of b is the *gauss*.

None of the many practical procedures for measuring fields will be discussed here; all of them depend on the principles contained in the idealized discussion just given but involve apparatus of finite size and hence limited spatial resolution; the readings given by the various instruments can be traced back ultimately to forces on static and moving charges. In the framework of the Lorentz theory, the idea of measuring fields by indefinitely small test charges is pushed to the extent of speaking of measuring fields with microscopic precision even inside electrons and nuclei, and it is in this sense that e and b have meaning at all points of space.

3-9 Field of a Plane-Parallel Condenser   In Chap. 4 reference will be made to a condenser and a solenoid of simple geometries. The most essential features of the fields involved will now be deduced from the Maxwell equations.

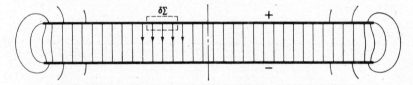

Fig. 3-2. *Electric field in a plane-parallel condenser.*

Let two thin, circular metal plates of identical radii r_0 be parallel to each other with axes coincident, and let the separation be $d \ll r_0$. Let the plates have charges of equal magnitudes and opposite signs. Because of the cylindrical symmetry, the electric field at points on the axis has no component perpendicular to the axis. From (3-1) and arguments given in Sec. 1-5, the streamlines of the field can begin only on positive charge, that is, at the positive plate, and end only on negative charge, at the negative plate. In order to make use of the simple arguments used in preceding sections, it is necessary to start with the qualitative knowledge that at distances r from the axis that are less than r_0 by two or three times d, the field is independent of r (the fringing at the edges having become negligible), and the field is appreciable only between the plates. It follows that throughout this central region the streamlines are the same as at the center, that is, straight and parallel to the axis, and they point from the positive to the negative plate. In this region the field is of uniform strength, the magnitude of which will now be calculated.

Draw an imaginary closed cylindrical surface with top and bottom surfaces, of area $\delta\Sigma$, parallel to and on opposite sides of one of the plates, say the positive one, as indicated by the dashed outline in Fig. 3-2. Suppose the surface density of charge on the plate at the location of the cylindrical surface is σ statcoulomb cm^{-2}. Apply Gauss' theorem to the surface; the surface integral receives a contribution only from the inner plane face of amount $e\ \delta\Sigma$. By (3-1) the volume integral is 4π times the total charge enclosed, that is, $4\pi\sigma\ \delta\Sigma$. Hence $e = 4\pi\sigma$, and since e is constant in the central region, σ is constant over each plate except near the edge.

3-10 Field of a Cylindrical Solenoid Consider a tightly wound, one-layer solenoid of circular cylindrical form with radius r_0 and length $l \gg r_0$. In order to eliminate the presence of an electric field and to make the magnetic field as simple as possible, let the wire have no resistance. Then the return path from one end to the other can be eliminated by supposing the solenoid to be a stack of circular closed loops of wire, all with equal currents. The currents, once set up, will continue indefinitely. Finally, one can think of the solenoid as a cylindrical current

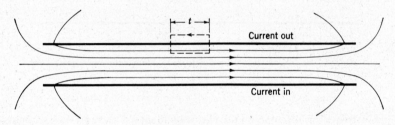

Fig. 3-3. *Magnetic field in a circular-cylindrical solenoid.*

sheet with uniform surface current density J statamp cm^{-1}, where $J = NI$, N being the number of turns per centimeter, and I the current in each turn.

Concerning the magnetic field, one concludes at once from (3-3) that the streamlines form closed loops. From the cylindrical symmetry, one streamline coincides with the axis of the solenoid (and closes on itself at infinity, where, however, the field has fallen to zero). Qualitatively, it is known that, except near the ends, the field is parallel to the axis inside the solenoid and negligible outside. Draw a rectangular loop in a plane through the axis, as shown dashed in Fig. 3-3. Apply Stokes' theorem; the line integral, taken in the sense indicated in the figure, receives a contribution only from the inner of the two sides parallel to the axis; its value is bt. By (3-4) (with the time derivative set equal to zero), the surface integral is $4\pi Jt/c$. Hence $b = 4\pi J/c$, and since the rectangle can extend any distance into the region surrounded by the solenoid, the field is uniform in this region except near the ends.

3-11 Conservation of Charge A deduction from the Maxwell equations is that charge is neither created nor destroyed. For, taking the divergence of both sides of (3-4) and using (1-25) and (3-1),

$$\text{div } \mathbf{j} = -\frac{\partial \rho}{\partial t} \qquad (3\text{-}9)$$

That this formula asserts that charge is conserved is most easily seen by multiplying both sides by $d\tau$ and integrating over a volume τ enclosed by an arbitrary surface Σ. Apply Gauss' theorem to the volume integral on the left side, interchange the order of differentiation and integration on the right, and write the integral of ρ as the total charge Q in the volume:

$$\int_{\Sigma} \mathbf{n} \cdot \mathbf{j} \, d\Sigma = -\frac{dQ}{dt} \qquad (3\text{-}10)$$

(The derivative is not partial because Q, unlike ρ, is a function of t only.) The left side of (3-10) gives the rate at which charge is flowing out through Σ, and this rate is just equal to the rate at which the total charge inside Σ is diminishing. If Σ is taken to be outside all the charge and current in space, then the left side of (3-10) is zero, and the total charge in space is constant.

Note that, in obtaining (3-9), the term in $\partial\mathbf{e}/\partial t$ in (3-4) played an essential role. This term was Maxwell's great contribution to the science. The evidence originally available to him, much of it coming from the experiments of Faraday, received mathematical expression in a set of equations (3-1) to (3-4), but without $\partial\mathbf{e}/\partial t$. His arguments in adding this term are not what one would prefer nowadays, since they contain much reference to an ether, but in essence the term was added in order that the theory imply conservation of charge. One aspect of Maxwell's argument persists in that $(1/4\pi)\,\partial\mathbf{e}/\partial t$ is often called the "displacement current." Without going into the origin of the word "displacement," the idea of calling it a current (more properly, a current density) might be thought natural when the Maxwell equations are written in the conventional way with the time derivatives on the right, as in (3-2) and (3-4). Then the two terms on the right of (3-4) can be regarded as $4\pi/c$ times a "total" current of which a part is $\mathbf{j}$ and the rest is the displacement current. This total current has zero divergence, and hence its streamlines form closed loops, while those of $\mathbf{j}$ need not (for example, conduction current may flow into a condenser plate and end there). This divergenceless character of the "total" current is another, but less transparent, way of expressing the law of conservation of charge. The attitude adopted in this book is that $\partial\mathbf{e}/\partial t$ is a field derived from $\mathbf{e}$ and is not to be thought of in any other way.

3-12 Faraday's Law of Induction Consider an arbitrary distribution of charge and current varying with time in any way. In principle the Maxwell equations could be solved for the resulting **e** and **b** as functions of time and position. Concerning the solution, the following perfectly general deduction can be drawn from (3-2): Let C be a closed curve bounding any open surface Σ. Assign a direction to C and normals to Σ in the usual way for applying Stokes' theorem. Considering the field **e**, Stokes' theorem, combined with (3-2), gives

$$\int_C \mathbf{e} \cdot d\mathbf{s} = -\frac{1}{c}\frac{d}{dt}\int_\Sigma \mathbf{n} \cdot \mathbf{b}\, d\Sigma = -\frac{1}{c}\frac{d\Phi}{dt} \qquad (3\text{-}11)$$

This formula is Faraday's law of induction, for the line integral receives the physical interpretation that if a fine wire were fitted to C but had a small gap left open, so that no current could flow, the voltage measured across the gap would be the value of the line integral. This voltage is equal to the right-hand side of the formula, which is $1/c$ times the negative of the rate of change of the magnetic flux Φ through the loop. [The flux at any instant depends only on C and not on the shape of the surface Σ, as is easily seen from (3-3) with the aid of Gauss' theorem.]

It would seem trivial to remark that in the surface integral of **b**, which defines Φ, one must take the actual value of **b** at each element $d\Sigma$. However, the remark takes on significance when one observes the approximation made in applying Faraday's law to problems of self- and mutual induction in low-frequency alternating-current curcuits. Consider a transformer with an open secondary. Let the current in the primary be sinusoidal with some low frequency. In finding the flux through the secondary, one takes the magnetic field at any given instant to be that which would be present if the primary current were constant at the value it has at that instant. The approximation involved is that a change in the current during a short interval causes a corresponding change in the magnetic field which does not occur instantly at all points of space, but rather propagates outward from the location of the current with a velocity which depends upon the media involved but is of the order of the velocity of light. The approximation is valid if the dimensions of the transformer are small compared with the distance light travels in a small fraction of the period of the alternating current. At the time of Faraday's original observations the technical means of producing rapidly varying currents and measuring correspondingly rapid events were not available, and the finite velocity of propagation of fields went unnoticed.

3-13 Nonexistence of Magnetic Charge In the preceding sections all the Maxwell equations (3-1) to (3-5), and even the individual terms on the right of (3-4), were used in obtaining elementary results. The assertion that the equations as they stand are adequate to account for *all* classical electromagnetic phenomena has stood the test of time. Only one more remark about the elementary implications of the equations is in order.

A certain asymmetry is apparent in Eqs. (3-1) to (3-4). The electric densities ρ and $\mathbf{j}$ appear in (3-1) and (3-4), but in the corresponding places in (3-2) and (3-3), where one might look for densities of magnetic charge and current, there is nothing. There is no experimental evidence of magnetic charge, and the Maxwell equations were written in such a way as to take this fact into account.[1]

3-14 General Solution of the Maxwell Equations When the densities ρ and $\mathbf{j}$ of all the charge and current in space are known as functions of time and position, the electric and magnetic fields can be found by direct processes of calculation with the aid of theorems to be discussed in this section. The proofs are given in Appendix B.

Consider first the case of static distributions of charge and current. The fields show no variation in time, and the Maxwell equations reduce to

$$\operatorname{div} \mathbf{e} = 4\pi\rho \qquad \operatorname{div} \mathbf{b} = 0$$

$$\operatorname{curl} \mathbf{e} = 0 \qquad \operatorname{curl} \mathbf{b} = \frac{4\pi}{c}\,\mathbf{j}$$

The general problem with given *static* charges and currents thus consists of two separate problems, one for $\mathbf{e}$, depending only on ρ, and one for $\mathbf{b}$, depending only on $\mathbf{j}$.

If the discussion is confined to realizable situations, all the charge and current will lie in finite space, and on physical grounds the fields must vanish at infinity.[2] In this case a solution for the electric field (and by Prob. 1-14, the only solution) is obtained in the following way: Define a scalar field ϕ, called the *scalar potential*, by

$$\phi(P) = \int \frac{\rho(P')}{r}\,d\tau \tag{3-12}$$

where P is an arbitrary point in the field, P' is the location of the volume element $d\tau$, r is the distance between P and P', and the integral extends over all space. Then

$$\mathbf{e} = -\operatorname{grad} \phi \tag{3-13}$$

---

[1] If one has in mind magnetic "poles" and cites them as examples of magnetic charge, it should be remarked that they are concepts that are suggested by the configurations of certain magnetic fields (for example, around a bar magnet) and receive precise mathematical expression in the macroscopic Maxwell theory, but they are not properly magnetic charges, and all fields originate ultimately from electric charge and current.

[2] For example, in the next chapter it will be seen that if the fields did not vanish at infinity, an infinite amount of work would have been required to set up the distribution of charge and current.

The solution for **b** (and, again, the only solution) is obtained by defining a vector field **A**, called the *vector potential*, by

$$\mathbf{A}(P) = \int \frac{\mathbf{j}(P')}{cr} \, d\tau \qquad (3\text{-}14)$$

Then
$$\mathbf{b} = \text{curl } \mathbf{A} \qquad (3\text{-}15)$$

Applications of these results to the examples already solved in preceding sections is called for in the problems.

Consider now the general Maxwell equations (3-1) to (3-4) with ρ and **j** given functions of space and time. The problem does not separate as in the static case, but a general solution remarkably similar to the static solution can be written. Define the scalar potential ϕ and vector potential **A** at point P and time t by

$$\phi(P,t) = \int \frac{\rho(P',t')}{r} \, d\tau \qquad (3\text{-}16)$$

$$\mathbf{A}(P,t) = \int \frac{\mathbf{j}(P',t')}{cr} \, d\tau \qquad (3\text{-}17)$$

where
$$t' = t - \frac{r}{c} \qquad (3\text{-}18)$$

and the range of integration and the significance of r are as in (3-12) and (3-14). Then, as is shown in Appendix B, the fields **e** and **b** are given by

$$\mathbf{e} = -\text{ grad } \phi - \frac{1}{c}\frac{\partial \mathbf{A}}{\partial t} \qquad (3\text{-}19)$$

$$\mathbf{b} = \text{curl } \mathbf{A} \qquad (3\text{-}20)$$

The interpretation of (3-16) to (3-20) is as follows: By comparison of (3-16) and (3-17) with (3-12) and (3-14), the potentials ϕ and **A** at point P and time t are exactly what they would be for a static distribution if the densities of charge and current at each point P' had the values the actual time-varying densities have, not at time t, but at the earlier time $t' = t - r/c$. The difference $t - t' = r/c$ is the time a point moving on a straight line with velocity c would take to go from P' to P. Hence a characteristic feature of (3-16) and (3-17) is that a change in ρ and **j** in the element of volume $d\tau$ at time t' does not produce a corresponding change in ϕ and **A** at P until the later time $t = t' + r/c$; also the fields **e** and **b** at P do not react to changes taking place in $d\tau$ at time t' until the later time t. A *retardation* is involved whereby the effects on the potentials and fields resulting from a change in the charge and current densities at P' do not occur instantly at all points of space, but propagate outward from P' with velocity c. This appearance of a retardation has led to calling $\phi(P,t)$ and $\mathbf{A}(P,t)$ *retarded potentials*, and

$t' = t - r/c$ the *retarded time* at P' corresponding to the time t at P (even though t' is earlier than t). A lively way to think of the relation of t' to t is to imagine a sphere with center at P and with a radius which decreases from infinity at the rate c cm $\sec^{-1}$ in such a way as to become zero at time t. The retarded time t' at P' is then the time at which the sphere sweeps over P'.

Formulas (3-12) to (3-15) are corollaries to the general theorem stated by (3-16) to (3-20), for in the static case time plays no role, or, equivalently, the densities ρ and j at the retarded time t' are the same as at the time of observation t.

It is hard to find simple examples to illustrate the use of retarded potentials in calculating fields. One is given in Prob. 3-16. In Appendix B the method is used to find the fields for an oscillating electron. At the end of that appendix some easy illustrative problems are given.

3-15 Wave Equation The retarded potentials give the clearest and most immediately convincing statement of the fact that electromagnetic fields propagate with velocity c. Moreover, they relate the fields to the charges and currents from which they originate. There is, however, another way to bring out this feature of propagation and the relation of fields to charges and currents, namely, through the wave equation.

The wave equation for electromagnetic fields is derived from the Maxwell equations in the following way: Take the curl of both sides of (3-2), expand the left side by (1-26), and substitute from (3-1) and (3-4):

$$\nabla^2 e - \frac{1}{c^2}\frac{\partial^2 e}{\partial t^2} = 4\pi \operatorname{grad} \rho + \frac{4\pi}{c^2}\frac{\partial j}{\partial t} \tag{3-21}$$

In the same way, take the curl of (3-4), expand the left side, and substitute from (3-2) and (3-3):

$$\nabla^2 b - \frac{1}{c^2}\frac{\partial^2 b}{\partial t^2} = -\frac{4\pi}{c}\operatorname{curl} j \tag{3-22}$$

In a region in which $\rho = 0$ and $j = 0$, both e and b satisfy

$$\nabla^2 g - \frac{1}{c^2}\frac{\partial^2 g}{\partial t^2} = 0 \tag{3-23}$$

where g stands for either e or b. Equations (3-21) and (3-22) are called *inhomogeneous wave equations,* and (3-23) is called the *homogeneous wave equation.*

Drawing all the implications from a wave equation is a matter of considerable mathematical difficulty. In this section only the simplest solution of the homogeneous equations (3-23) will be considered in order to show that the equation does, indeed, involve propagation with velocity c.

Write the components of (3-23) in a cartesian representation, using (1-27). Then it is seen by substitution that one solution is

$$g_x = f(z - ct) \qquad g_y = g_z = 0$$

where f stands for an arbitrary function. Suppose an observer moves along the z axis in such a way that he always sees the same value of g_x. His motion is described by $z - ct = constant$, and hence his velocity is c.

The wave equation will appear again in Chap. 8, where it will serve as a guide in obtaining a scalar model of a light wave. It will also appear in Appendix B.

Problems

3-1. Show by direct application of (1-8) and (1-10) or (1-11) that the electric field found in Sec. 3-3 satisfies the Maxwell equations at all points outside the charge.

3-2. By the type of argument used in Sec. 3-3, find the electric field inside the spherical charge, and show that it satisfies the Maxwell equations at each point. Make a rough plot of the magnitude of the field as a function of r for r extending from zero to some distance outside the charge.

3-3. Find the field inside and outside a uniformly charged sphere by evaluating (3-12) and applying (3-13). The problem of finding the gradient of ϕ outside the sphere will be just the example worked out in Sec. 1-3 except for signs. Apply the same method to find **e** inside the charge.

3-4. Consider two spheres of arbitrary radii and containing arbitrary charges Q_1 and Q_2. Let the distance between centers be d. Let the distribution of charge in each sphere be spherically symmetric, but not necessarily uniform. Show that as long as the spheres do not overlap, the force between them is Q_1Q_2/d^2. Qualitatively, why does this result not apply to charged metal spheres except as a good approximation when their radii are very small compared with d? (*Hint:* The simplest procedure is to find the potential energy of interaction V by integrating $\rho\phi$ over the volume of one of the spheres, where ϕ is the scalar potential of the other sphere alone. Then the magnitude of the force is the magnitude of the derivative of V with respect to d. One should carefully consider why this method is valid.)

3-5. In the spirit of Prob. 3-1, check the solution found in Sec. 3-6.

3-6. Extend the calculation of Sec. 3-6 to find the field inside the wire. Check that the Maxwell equations are satisfied.

3-7. Use (3-14) and (3-15) to find the contribution to the magnetic field from one of the two long sides of the wire loop in Fig. 3-1. Consider only points whose distance r from the wire is large compared with the radius of the wire but small compared with the length of the side, and which are not near one end of the wire. Calculate **A** and take its curl by direct application of (1-11). [*Hints:* Introduce cylindrical coordinates with the polar axis along the wire and with point O of Fig. 3-1 in the plane $z = 0$. Find **A** in the plane $z = 0$, and infer from the formula that **A** is essentially independent of z over a reasonably small range about zero. Let the length of the rectangle be L. The integral can be written as twice the integral over the half of the wire from $z = 0$ to $z = L/2$. Substitution of the upper limit gives a large contribution to **A** (approaching infinity with L), but one which will turn out to give a vanishing contribution to curl **A**. For a very long wire one can ignore this large contribution by the argument that a constant vector can be added to **A** without affecting its curl.]

3-8. Two neighboring wires carrying currents can be said to have an energy of interaction W, the volume integral of $\mathbf{j} \cdot \mathbf{A}/c$ taken over one of the wires, where $\mathbf{j}$ is the current density in that wire, and **A** is the vector potential due to the other wire. Consider the two long parallel sides of the rectangular loop in Fig. 3-1. Take the separation to be d, and calculate the interaction integral for a unit length of one of the wires near $z = 0$, taking **A** for the other wire from the results of Prob. 3-7 (omitting the large and unessential part of **A** mentioned in that problem). Differentiate with respect to d to find the force per unit length, and compare with Sec. 3-7.

3-9. Find the scalar potential in the central region of the condenser of Sec. 3-9. It is sufficient to calculate the values along the axis of symmetry assuming the surface density of charge on each plate to be constant clear to the edge. Find **e** at points on the axis from ϕ and show that the result is essentially independent of r_0 when $r_0 \gg d$.

3-10. Show that the field **b** found in the central region of the solenoid in Sec. 3-10 can be found from a vector potential **A** whose streamlines are circles concentric with the axis and lying in planes perpendicular to it (that is, show that a solution can be found if the streamlines are assumed to have this character). Plot the magnitude of **A** as a function of radius.

3-11. Use formula (3-10) to prove that in a wire carrying a steady current, the same current flows through any cross section.

3-12. Find the analogue of Faraday's law of induction (3-11) in which the roles of **e** and **b** are interchanged.

3-13. Suppose the outer surfaces of the plates of the condenser in Sec. 3-9 are connected by wires to a generator which charges the condenser at the steady rate I statamp. Show that there is a magnetic field between the plates and, using the symmetry of the condenser and the result of Prob. 3-12, find this field at points not too near the edges of the plates. (Treat the charge density as though it were perfectly uniform over the whole of each plate.) Compare the result with the field inside a cylindrical conductor carrying a conduction current of uniform density (see Prob. 3-6).

3-14. Consider a region in which there are fields but no charge or current. Under what assumptions which can always be made on physical grounds do (3-2) and (3-4) imply (3-1) and (3-3) in this region?

3-15. Consider a very thin conducting sheet covering the whole xy plane. Let $\rho = 0$ throughout the sheet, and let $\mathbf{j} = \mathbf{g}e^{-i\omega t}$, where $\mathbf{g}$ is a constant real vector in the x direction (so that at all points of the sheet $\mathbf{j}$ is the same at a given instant). Let d be the thickness of the sheet, and let $\mathbf{G} = d\mathbf{g}$. If d goes to zero, and $\mathbf{g}$ to infinity, in such a way as to keep **G** constant, one is left with a surface current $\mathbf{J} = \mathbf{G}e^{-i\omega t}$ statamp cm^{-1}. Show that the Maxwell equations are satisfied by the following fields: When $z > 0$,

$$\mathsf{e}_x = -Be^{i(kz-\omega t)} \qquad \mathsf{b}_y = -Be^{i(kz-\omega t)}$$

where $B = 2\pi G/c$; when $z < 0$,

$$\mathsf{e}_x = -Be^{i(-kz-\omega t)} \qquad \mathsf{b}_y = Be^{i(-kz-\omega t)}$$

and for all z, $\mathsf{e}_y = \mathsf{e}_z = \mathsf{b}_x = \mathsf{b}_z = 0$. What must be the value of k, and what are the natures of these fields? In checking the equations, make direct application of (1-8) and (1-11). Since all operations are linear, one can work with the complex representation throughout.

3-16. The fields in Prob. 3-15 can be found from the given distribution of current by the method of retarded potentials (Sec. 3-14), but some mathematical difficulties enter. The calculation will now be outlined to point out these subtleties, and the reader can fill in the gaps. In the first place, $\phi = 0$ everywhere, and **A** clearly depends only on z and t and need be calculated only on the z axis. The simplest way to evaluate the integral is to introduce polar coordinates r and θ in the xy plane. Then

$$\mathbf{A}(z,t) = \frac{2\pi\mathbf{G}}{c} e^{-i\omega t} \int_0^\infty \frac{e^{ik\xi}}{\xi} r \, dr$$

where $\xi = (r^2 + z^2)^{1/2}$, the positive root being taken. Since $r \, dr = \xi \, d\xi$, the integral becomes

$$\int_a^\infty e^{ik\xi} \, d\xi$$

where $a = |z|$; that is, $a = z$ for $z > 0$, and $a = -z$ for $z < 0$. The difficulty which now appears is that this integral does not have a definite value, as is seen by taking the upper limit to be R and letting R go to infinity. This behavior is merely an accident associated with the polar coordinates; if the integration had been performed in cartesian coordinates, or in almost any other way, the uncertainty would not have occurred. (No uncertainty whatever would arise if the current sheet were bounded by some finite curve, but then the exact solution for all points of space would be enormously more difficult.) The value of **A** which gives the desired plane waves is that obtained from the lower limit only:

$$\mathbf{A}(z,t) = \frac{i2\pi\mathbf{G}}{\omega} e^{i(\pm kz - \omega t)}$$

where the ambiguous sign in the exponent is positive for $z > 0$ and negative for $z < 0$. The calculation of **e** and **b** is now straightforward.

3-17. Suppose that at time $t = 0$ the following fields exist in a region free of matter:

$$e_x = A e^{ikz} \qquad b_y = A e^{ikz} \qquad e_y = e_z = b_x = b_z = 0$$

where A is a constant. Show that such fields cannot be static, and find the fields as functions of time as well as position on the assumption that the time appears in **e** as a factor $f(t)$ multiplying the value at $t = 0$ and enters **b** as the same factor. [That is, find $f(t)$ such that $f(0) = 1$ and the Maxwell equations are satisfied.] Interpret the resulting fields, and show that they satisfy the homogeneous wave equation.

chapter 4

Energy and Energy Flow
in the Electromagnetic Field

Mechanics begins with the notion of force acting on a body and from it derives the notions of work and kinetic and potential energy. The idea of energy is then extended until it appears in all branches of physics; since the sum total of energy of all kinds in the universe is believed to be constant, energy is the common coin of exchange in physics, and one aspect of any physical process is a transferring of energy from one place and form to others. The role of these ideas in the electromagnetic theory will be the topic of this chapter. The procedure will be to lead up to the central propositions through consideration of some simple situations, and then to obtain a general theorem from the Maxwell equations.

4-1 Work Done in Slowly Charging a Condenser Consider again the plane-parallel condenser discussed in Sec. 3-9. Imagine that it is charged in an infinite number of steps, in each of which an infinitesimal positive charge dq is removed from the center of the lower plate, transported along the axis of symmetry, and deposited at the center of the upper plate. After each transfer enough time is allowed for the charges on the two plates to distribute themselves and give the electric field the static configuration. At each stage of the process the agent making the transfer must do work in the amount $dW = eh\,dq$, where e is the magnitude of the field existing at that stage, and h is the separation of the plates. In order to bring out in the clearest way the principal idea of this section, imagine that the field does not show any fringing at the edges of the plates, so that the density of surface charge on either plate is perfectly uniform with magnitude $\sigma = q/A$, q being the total charge, and A the area of the plate; the field is perfectly uniform between the plates, with magnitude $e = 4\pi\sigma$, and zero outside. Transporting charge dq increases the field by the amount $de = (4\pi/A)\,dq$. The total work done in charging to a final charge q_0 and final field $e_0 = (4\pi/A)q_0$ is then

$$W = \frac{Ah}{4\pi} \int_0^{e_0} e\,de = Ah\,\frac{e_0^2}{8\pi} \tag{4-1}$$

Now the work W was calculated by writing the work dW in transferring dq as force times distance in the usual way and summing for all the transfers. The result, the last form in (4-1), suggests that there might be another way of thinking of this work and of calculating it. For Ah is the volume between the plates and is therefore a property of the geometry of the condenser, while $e_0^2/8\pi$ is a property of the field. If, then, one thinks of $e_0^2/8\pi$ as a density of energy at each point of the field (the same at all points between the plates and zero outside in the present idealized example), W is the integral of this energy density over all space.

The result just obtained is perfectly general, as will be proved in Sec. 4-4, so that the work done in slowly establishing an electrostatic field of any configuration can be calculated in the following two alternative ways:

1. Calculate the work done in transferring charge, an infinitesimal amount at a time, against the force due to the electrostatic field which gradually builds up; or

2. Find the final electrostatic field, regard the work done as having produced a distribution of energy in the field with density $u = e^2/8\pi$, and integrate u over all space.

The first method deals only with the tangible idea of force and the work done against a force. The second method introduces the less tangible idea of energy being stored in the electrostatic field. Aside from the fact that the second method is sometimes easier to apply, the introduction of the notion of energy in a field is an important addition to the method of treating the items of ultimate physical interest (namely, the forces and energies of interaction between charges and currents) through the intermediary of fields.

4-2 Work Done in Slowly Energizing a Solenoid Consider the solenoid discussed in Sec. 3-10. Let it have radius a and length l and consist of a stack of circular loops of resistanceless wire with n loops per centimeter. Let each loop have a gap in which is placed an idealized generator of such small dimensions that its presence will not distort the magnetic field in the solenoid. These generators will be supposed as identical and as slowly building up a current I in each loop from the initial value zero to the final value I_0. In doing so, they will have to perform work because of electromagnetic induction. To simplify the calculation, imagine again that there is no fringing, so that the field at any instant is $\mathsf{b} = 4\pi nI/c$ at all points inside the solenoid and zero outside. The voltage across each generator is given by Faraday's law of induction as $V = (\pi a^2/c)\, d\mathsf{b}/dt$. The rate at which all the generators do work is $dW/dt = nlIV$. Then

$$W = \frac{a^2 l}{4} \int_0^{b_0} \mathsf{b}\, d\mathsf{b} = \pi a^2 l \frac{\mathsf{b}_0{}^2}{8\pi} \qquad (4\text{-}2)$$

The result is exactly analogous to the electrostatic case. The work W, calculated as the work done by the generators in carrying charge across the gaps which they fill, has come out to be the volume of the solenoid times $\mathsf{b}_0{}^2/8\pi$; the latter can be regarded as a density of energy in the magnetostatic field. Again, this example is a special (and idealized) case of a general theorem which states that the work done in slowly establishing a magnetostatic field of any configuration can be calculated in the following two ways:

1. Calculate the work done in transporting charge against the electric field resulting from electromagnetic induction; or

2. Find the final magnetostatic field, regard the work done as having produced a distribution of energy in the field with density $u = \mathsf{b}^2/8\pi$, and integrate u over all space.

4-3 Effects When the Fields Are Built Up Rapidly When fields are made to vary rapidly, new effects enter which will now be surveyed qualitatively before a precise formulation is given in the next section. If the charging of the condenser discussed in Sec. 4-1 had taken place rapidly, so that the final charge q_0 had been transferred in a finite time, then contemplation of the Maxwell equations (3-1) to (3-4) indicates that the calculation in Sec. 4-1 would not be correct. For one thing, a finite current would be involved, which would give rise to a magnetic field. For another, both $\partial\mathsf{e}/\partial t$ and $\partial\mathsf{b}/\partial t$ would be different from zero. Hence all the terms in the Maxwell equations would come into play, and the solution of the problem would become complicated and would involve radiation.

At the end of a rapid charging process, after the charges have ceased to move, the field between and immediately around the plates is just the usual static electric field, but in addition there is an electromagnetic wave radiating outward from the region of the condenser with the velocity of light. The wave involves both electric and magnetic fields and is confined to a spherical shell of thickness ct_0, where t_0 is the duration of the charging process. The bearing of this fact on considerations of energy is the following: At any instant during the rapid charging process the charge on either plate is, say, q in magnitude, but this charge has not settled into static equilibrium; hence the electric field is not the static field corresponding to q. The work done against the electric field in transporting the next increment dq of charge is not the dW used in Sec. 4-1, and the total work is not the last expression in (4-1), but has some other value, say W'. That is, the actual work W' of charging is not equal to the volume integral of the energy density in the final static field in and around the condenser. If, however, one were to imagine that, at some instant after the completion of the charging, $\mathbf{e}$ and $\mathbf{b}$ at every point in the radiated wave were measured, and if the energy density $u = (\mathbf{e}^2 + \mathbf{b}^2)/8\pi$ were integrated over all space (including the static field in the condenser) and the result were called U, then one would find that $W' = U$. The difference between this result and (4-1) is that $W' - W$ is just the energy contained in the radiated wave. When the charging is carried out very slowly, this difference is a very small fraction of W, and the results of Sec. 4-1 are essentially correct. Even the simplest illustrative example from which one could draw a quantitative verification of these statements would involve a long calculation, but a proof in perfectly general terms is very easy and will be given in the next section.

4-4   General Theorem on Energy   The discussions in the preceding sections of this chapter have introduced basic ideas by dealing with macroscopic situations and have implicitly invoked the argument that there is validity in ignoring the microscopic structure of charge and current through substitution of smoothed-out densities. The justification of this procedure when dealing with questions of energy in macroscopic problems will be discussed in Chap. 15. In the present section we shall adopt a strictly microscopic point of view, and the results will be perfectly valid for any problem comprehended by the Lorentz theory.

As described in Chap. 3, matter consists of electrons and nuclei with densities ρ_+, ρ_-, $\mathbf{j}_+ = \rho_+\mathbf{v}_+$, and $\mathbf{j}_- = \rho_-\mathbf{v}_-$. The forces which act on them are the Lorentz forces, with densities at each point of space

$$\mathbf{f}_+ = \rho_+\mathbf{e} + \frac{1}{c}\mathbf{j}_+ \times \mathbf{b} \qquad \mathbf{f}_- = -\rho_-\mathbf{e} - \frac{1}{c}\mathbf{j}_- \times \mathbf{b} \qquad (4\text{-}3)$$

and nonelectrical forces. Nonelectrical forces are essential entities in the Lorentz model of an atom; in addition, they are occasionally invoked by hypothesis to bring about some particular motion of charges (for example, the forces which transported the charges in Sec. 4-1 were tacitly nonelectrical). In this section nonelectrical forces will be treated in general terms.[1]

Let τ be any region of space containing charges. The rate at which the Lorentz forces acting inside τ do work is

$$\int_\tau (\mathbf{f}_+ \cdot \mathbf{v}_+ + \mathbf{f}_- \cdot \mathbf{v}_-) \, d\tau = \int_\tau (\rho_+\mathbf{v}_+ - \rho_-\mathbf{v}_-) \cdot \mathbf{e} \, d\tau = \int_\tau \mathbf{j} \cdot \mathbf{e} \, d\tau$$

The second form is obtained by substituting (4-3) and noting that the terms involving $\mathbf{b}$ contain triple products with repeated factors and hence vanish. If the particles in τ are enumerated by an index j, and if the velocity of the jth particle is $\mathbf{v}_j$, and the nonelectrical force acting on it is $\mathbf{F}_j$, the rate at which all forces acting in τ do work, that is, the power generated by them, is

$$P = \sum_j \mathbf{F}_j \cdot \mathbf{v}_j + \int_\tau \mathbf{j} \cdot \mathbf{e} \, d\tau \tag{4-4}$$

Equation (4-4) might be called the "local" form of the energy theorem in the sense that it involves the forces acting on each individual charge. The integral on the right will now be given an alternative form which involves only the fields in the volume τ. From (3-4),

$$\mathbf{j} \cdot \mathbf{e} = -\frac{1}{4\pi} \mathbf{e} \cdot \frac{\partial \mathbf{e}}{\partial t} + \frac{c}{4\pi} \mathbf{e} \cdot \text{curl } \mathbf{b}$$

The expression $\mathbf{e} \cdot \text{curl } \mathbf{b}$ brings to mind the identity (1-21); to exploit it, one writes, from (3-2),

$$0 = -\frac{1}{4\pi} \mathbf{b} \cdot \frac{\partial \mathbf{b}}{\partial t} - \frac{c}{4\pi} \mathbf{b} \cdot \text{curl } \mathbf{e}$$

Adding the last two equations,

$$\mathbf{j} \cdot \mathbf{e} = -\frac{\partial}{\partial t}\left(\frac{\mathbf{e}^2 + \mathbf{b}^2}{8\pi}\right) - \text{div}\left(\frac{c}{4\pi} \mathbf{e} \times \mathbf{b}\right) \tag{4-5}$$

Introduce the notation

$$u = \frac{1}{8\pi}(\mathbf{e}^2 + \mathbf{b}^2) \qquad U = \int_\tau u \, d\tau \tag{4-6}$$

$$\mathbf{S} = \frac{c}{4\pi} \mathbf{e} \times \mathbf{b} \tag{4-7}$$

---

[1] The distinction between electrical and nonelectrical forces in the Lorentz theory was discussed at the end of Sec. 3-1. Specifically, the electrical forces are just those given by (4-3).

Then (4-5) takes the form

$$\mathbf{j} \cdot \mathbf{e} = -\frac{\partial u}{\partial t} - \operatorname{div} \mathbf{S} \tag{4-8}$$

and, with the use of Gauss' theorem, (4-4) becomes

$$P = \sum_j \mathbf{F}_j \cdot \mathbf{v}_j - \frac{dU}{dt} - \int_\Sigma \mathbf{n} \cdot \mathbf{S} \, d\Sigma \tag{4-9}$$

where Σ is the surface bounding τ, and $\mathbf{n}$ is the outward normal to Σ.

Equation (4-9) is a form of the energy theorem equivalent to (4-4). An interpretation of the last two terms on the right is suggested by the discussions in Secs. 4-1 to 4-3. The quantity u can be regarded as a density of energy in the electromagnetic field. In general, it is a function of time and position. Then U is the total field energy in τ and is a function of time only. The surface integral must represent a flow of field energy through Σ, and $\mathbf{S}$ must be the flux density of field energy. If this integral is positive, there must be a net loss of energy from the region τ through radiation.

The vector $\mathbf{S}$ is called the *Poynting vector* after J. H. Poynting, who discovered formula (4-9) in 1884. [It is common to refer to (4-9) as Poynting's theorem.] In more explicit terms, the interpretation of $\mathbf{S}$ is that at any point in a field at which $\mathbf{S}$ is different from zero, one can say that electromagnetic energy is flowing in the direction of $\mathbf{S}$ such that through a small plane surface perpendicular to $\mathbf{S}$ the rate of flow of energy is $|\mathbf{S}|$ erg sec^{-1} cm^{-2}. However, it must be emphasized that the quantities u and $\mathbf{S}$ merely give an alternative (but very useful) view of the transfer of energy by electrical processes. One must be very careful in thinking of $\mathbf{S}$ as representing a flow of energy, as will be brought out strikingly in the next section.

4-5 · Discussion of the Energy Theorem Application of (4-9) to specific cases involving radiation by electromagnetic waves originating in moving charges must await the next and following chapters. However, a number of remarks about the energy theorem can be made now.

If the electrical and nonelectrical forces on each particle do not balance at all times, the particles acquire varying amounts of kinetic energy. It follows from (4-4) that P represents the rate of increase of total kinetic energy in the region τ.

Let us reexamine the condenser discussed in Sec. 4-1. If the agent which transports the infinitesimal charges exerts a (nonelectrical) force just sufficient to overcome the force due to the electric field, the net force on the charge is at all times essentially zero, and in (4-9) $P = 0$. Let Σ be a very large sphere with the condenser at the center. Then over Σ the electric fringing field is essentially zero, and the magnetic field due to the infinitesimal, slowly moving charges is also negligible. Hence the surface integral is zero. The remaining two terms can be integrated with respect to time over the interval of the charging process. The integral of the sum (in which j now enumerates the elements of charge transferred) gives the work done by the moving agent, while the integral of $(dU/dt) \, dt = dU$ gives the total increase in field energy. This result is more general than that obtained in Sec. 4-1, since it applies to the establishment of a static field of any configuration as long as the charging is done slowly.

If the charging is done rapidly, then, granting that there will be a radiated wave as described in Sec. 4-3, one can verify the statement made in that section that the total work of charging is equal to the total field energy at the completion of the process by considering (4-9) at a time before the radiated fields have reached the large sphere Σ. (One can assume that the large charging current results from a large number of elementary charges being transported simultaneously, each with very small velocity; hence $P = 0$ at all times.) Eventually, the wave will pass through Σ and be received by any absorbers in the path or disappear in the infinite void.

A simple static situation in which the Poynting vector is not zero is that of a wire having resistance and carrying a current. Let the wire have radius a, and consider a long straight section. Imagine that the current density $\mathbf{j}$ is uniform and constant throughout the wire. There is an electric field inside the wire given by $\mathbf{j} = \sigma \mathbf{e}$, where σ is the conductivity. If one draws a rectangle in a plane through the axis such that two sides are parallel to the axis with one inside the wire and the other outside, then application of Stokes' theorem to (3-2), in which $\partial \mathbf{b}/\partial t = 0$, shows that the electric field outside the wire is the same as inside. The magnetic field at the surface has magnitude $b = 2I/ca$ and is in such a direction that the Poynting vector is directed radially toward the axis. The fields $\mathbf{e}$ and $\mathbf{b}$ are perpendicular, and $S = (c/4\pi)(I/\sigma A)(2I/ca)$, where A is the cross-sectional area of the wire. Let the surface integral in (4-9) be evaluated over a cylinder of length l coinciding with the surface of the wire. There is no contribution from the ends, and the result is $I^2(l/\sigma A) = I^2 R$, where R is the resistance of the length l of wire. Thus the power $I^2 R$, which one usually thinks of as arising from work done by the electric field on the carriers of the current, can be thought of, alternatively, as coming from the energy in surrounding fields. The field continually acquires energy from the battery or generator, since at these devices the Poynting vector is directed outward. One can qualitatively visualize the streamlines of $\mathbf{S}$ as beginning at the battery and ending at various points of the wire.

If a charged condenser is placed in a uniform magnetic field between the poles of a permanent magnet in such a way that, between the plates,

e and **b** are perpendicular, one has the apparently paradoxical result of a nonvanishing Poynting vector and a flow of energy in an otherwise perfectly static situation. The resolution of the paradox comes from considering (4-9). Here P and the first two terms on the right are zero, and hence the surface integral is zero for any closed surface Σ, which means that any energy that flows in through Σ must flow out again, and there can be no net gain to show up as a physical effect. Another way of seeing this result is from the fact that (4-8) gives div $\mathbf{S} = 0$; the streamlines of $\mathbf{S}$ must form closed loops, which they do by passing between the plates as more or less straight and parallel lines and then curving around through the fringing field to join on themselves outside the plates. There is no harm in thinking of this flow of energy, since it can never be detected physically. This example brings out the important fact that *the Poynting vector must always be considered in connection with a surface integral over a closed surface.* It is only the net result of this integral that receives a physical interpretation. As another simple illustration of this point, consider a sheet of black paper placed before a light source. It will be shown later that the theory gives the expected result that in the region through which the light passes, the Poynting vector is in the direction of the rays. However, on the back side of the paper is a dark shadow, indicating absence of fields and zero Poynting vector. The energy absorbed by the paper would now be calculated by surrounding it with a closed surface, which, however, may be taken to fit tightly over the front and back surfaces. The contribution to the surface integral would come only from the front surface. From this particular example, which is typical of most applications to problems of radiation, one easily falls into the habit of assigning physical significance to the integral of $\mathbf{S}$ over an open surface, thereby obtaining results that are sometimes paradoxical.

Problems

4-1. Consider a condenser consisting of two concentric spherical shells of radii r_1 and r_2. Calculate the work done by the moving agent in slowly charging the condenser to final charge q_0. Show that the result is equal to the integral of the energy density in the final static field. (If the charging were rapid, the radiation mentioned in Sec. 4-3 would consist of waves confined to the region between the conducting spheres. The conductors are not resistanceless, and the energy of the waves would eventually convert into heat.)

4-2. Consider two thin, coaxial cylindrical shells of radii r_1 and r_2 and length l. The ends of the region between the shells are closed by thin conducting sheets. In a gap in the inner cylinder is a generating device which causes current I to flow along the inner cylinder and back along the outer one. Assume that the currents in the sheets have cylindrical symmetry and that the presence of the generator has no effect on the shape of the magnetic field. Calculate the work done by the generator in slowly building up the current to value I_0, and compare it with the integral of the final density of magnetic field energy.

4-3. Consider a condenser which is being charged at a uniform rate, as described in Prob. 3-13. Using the fields found in that problem, calculate u and $\mathbf{S}$, and show that the energy theorem in the form (4-8) is satisfied in the region over which the fields have been found.

4-4. Consider the linearly polarized, plane electromagnetic wave

$$\mathsf{e}_x = Ae^{i(kz-\omega t)} \qquad \mathsf{b}_y = Ae^{i(kz-\omega t)}$$

all other components being zero, where $k = \omega/c$. Find the energy density u, and Poynting vector $\mathbf{S}$. (Beware of using the complex representation!) Describe the behavior of u as a function of space and time. Show how the field energy moves along with the wave. Show that $\mathbf{S}$ just accounts for the motion of the energy. For simplicity, assume A real.

4-5. Find the time average of $\mathbf{S}$ for the wave of Prob. 4-4 (see Prob. 2-4) when the averaging is done over an infinite time, and again over one period.

4-6. On the wave of Prob. 4-4 is superposed the wave

$$\mathsf{e}_x = Be^{i(kz-\omega t+\phi)} \qquad \mathsf{b}_y = Be^{i(kz-\omega t+\phi)}$$

all other components being zero. Find u, $\mathbf{S}$, and $\langle\mathbf{S}\rangle$ for the resultant wave, and show that in general none is equal to the sum of the corresponding quantities for the separate waves. Assume B real.

4-7. Repeat Prob. 4-6 with the additional wave replaced by

$$\mathsf{e}_y = Be^{i(kz-\omega t+\phi)} \qquad \mathsf{b}_x = -Be^{i(kz-\omega t+\phi)}$$

all other components being zero. Show that in this case u, $\mathbf{S}$, and $\langle\mathbf{S}\rangle$ for the resultant wave are the sums of the corresponding quantities for the individual waves. What is the nature of the resultant electric wave? How are the resultant electric and magnetic waves related?

4-8. On the wave of Prob. 4-4 is superposed the following wave traveling in the opposite direction:

$$\mathsf{e}_x = Ae^{i(-kz-\omega t)} \qquad \mathsf{b}_y = -Ae^{i(-kz-\omega t)}$$

Describe the resultant fields as functions of space and time. Find u and $\mathbf{S}$. Discuss how the energy is sometimes all in the electric field, and sometimes all in the magnetic. Show how $\mathbf{S}$ accounts for this transfer. Find all the fixed planes perpendicular to the z axis such that no energy flows across any of them.

4-9. In the situation described in Prob. 3-15, find the power supplied per square centimeter by the agent maintaining the current in the sheet under the assumption that no kinetic energy is associated with the moving charges. Show that this power is carried away by the radiation. Show that even if there were kinetic energy, the energy supplied in one period would be equal to the energy carried away by the waves in the same time.

4-10. Consider the plane electromagnetic wave

$$\mathsf{e} = (\mathbf{A} + i\mathbf{B})e^{i(\mathbf{k}\cdot\mathbf{r}-\omega t)} \qquad \mathsf{b} = \frac{\mathbf{k}}{k} \times (\mathbf{A} + i\mathbf{B})e^{i(\mathbf{k}\cdot\mathbf{r}-\omega t)}$$

where $\mathbf{k}$ is the wave vector ($\mathbf{k}/k$ being a unit vector), and $\mathbf{A}$ and $\mathbf{B}$ are arbitrary vectors perpendicular to $\mathbf{k}$. Show that the Maxwell equations are satisfied with an appropriate value of k in terms of ω. (It is suggested that one verify and remember the convenient formulas

$$\text{div } (\mathbf{C}e^{i\mathbf{k}\cdot\mathbf{r}}) = i\mathbf{k}\cdot\mathbf{C}e^{i\mathbf{k}\cdot\mathbf{r}} \qquad \text{curl } (\mathbf{C}e^{i\mathbf{k}\cdot\mathbf{r}}) = i\mathbf{k}\times\mathbf{C}e^{i\mathbf{k}\cdot\mathbf{r}}$$

if **C** is a constant vector, real or complex. The verification can be done most easily in a cartesian representation.) Draw a pair of ellipses to represent the oscillations of the real parts of **e** and **b** at an arbitrary point, and draw vectors to represent **e** and **b** at an arbitrary time. (The points to illustrate are the relative sizes and orientations of the ellipses and the relative phase of the oscillations—the angle between **e** and **b**.) Show that the time average of the Poynting vector, taken over an infinite time or over one period, can be written

$$\langle\mathbf{S}\rangle = \frac{c}{8\pi k}(A^2 + B^2)\mathbf{k}$$

or

$$\langle\mathbf{S}\rangle = \frac{c}{8\pi}\text{ Re }(\mathbf{e}\times\mathbf{b}^*)$$

where **e** and **b** stand for the *complex* representations.

4-11. The last formula in Prob. 4-10 is an example of a general proposition worth looking at explicitly. Let two real oscillating vectors **F** and **G** have the complex representations

$$\mathbf{F}_c = (\mathbf{A} + i\mathbf{B})e^{-i\omega t} \qquad \mathbf{G}_c = (\mathbf{C} + i\mathbf{D})e^{-i\omega t}$$

where the real vectors **A**, **B**, **C**, and **D** satisfy no special condition. Show that $\langle\mathbf{F}\times\mathbf{G}\rangle = \frac{1}{2}\text{ Re }(\mathbf{F}_c\times\mathbf{G}_c^*)$. (The same theorem holds for scalar rather than vector multiplication and when **F** or **G** or both are replaced by oscillating scalars.)

4-12. Show that if a plane transverse wave (as in Prob. 4-10) of given polarization and amplitude (that is, given complex amplitude) is resolved into two component waves such that at any fixed point of space the oscillations of the electric fields in the components are related as in Prob. 2-20, the time average of the Poynting vector for the given wave is the sum of those for the components. (*Hints:* Note that the first formula for $\langle\mathbf{S}\rangle$ given in Prob. 4-10 shows that one need know only the electric fields in the several waves and need not write out the associated magnetic fields. Note also that, if $\mathbf{A} + i\mathbf{B}$ is denoted $\mathbf{e}_0$, $A^2 + B^2 = |\mathbf{e}_0|^2 \equiv \mathbf{e}_0\cdot\mathbf{e}_0^*$, which will suggest an efficient way of using the multiplication table for the vectors $\mathbf{e}_1$ and $\mathbf{e}_2$ in Prob. 2-20.) In contrast, show that if two plane waves of arbitrary polarizations but of the same direction of propagation and the same frequency are superposed, $\langle\mathbf{S}\rangle$ is, in general, not additive in this way. (If the two component waves in Prob. 2-20 are said to have *complementary polarizations*, the result of the present problem is to show that complementary polarizations never show. effects of interference. This law was verified experimentally by Arago and Fresnel for linear polarizations in 1819.)

4-13. Let two plane waves of the type in Prob. 4-10 travel in the same direction and have arbitrary polarizations and *different* frequencies. Write the general expression for the instantaneous Poynting vector, and show that its average over a long time is the sum of the averages for the separate waves. (Contrast this with Prob. 4-12.)

chapter 5

Monochromatic Dipole Radiation

The radiation field most fundamental to the Lorentz theory is that of an atom in which an electron undergoes a monochromatic sinusoidal oscillation. The derivation of this field from the Maxwell equations is the long calculation given in Appendix B. In this chapter the final formulas will be written and given a detailed interpretation in readiness for later applications. The geometry and kinematics of the field are matters of the greatest beauty, and while at first they may appear rather complicated, they will ultimately come to seem very simple. It is important to become thoroughly conversant with this field, for in many problems in radiation and optics it constitutes the essential result of the Maxwell equations, and very little further recourse to these equations is needed.

5-1 Formulas for the Fields of a General Monochromatic Dipole Oscillator Consider an atom whose nucleus is at rest and of which one electron undergoes a monochromatic oscillation, in general elliptical. Let **s** be the vector from the center of the nucleus to the center of the electron.

As usual, the formulas and calculations to be given are shortened by use of complex representation, and in order to be economical of symbols, some conventions of notation will be introduced. In the first place, the subscript c used in Chap. 2 to distinguish the complex from the real representation will be omitted; it will be clear from the context or an explicit statement which is meant. When in a formula or group of formulas a complex number or vector X appears together with its real

and imaginary parts, the notation $X = X' + iX''$ will sometimes be used as an alternative to $X = \text{Re}(X) + i\,\text{Im}(X)$.

With these conventions the complex representation of the motion of the electron is written

$$\mathbf{s} = \mathbf{s}_0 e^{-i\omega t} = (\mathbf{s}_0' + i\mathbf{s}_0'')e^{-i\omega t} \tag{5-1}$$

where $\mathbf{s}$ is now the complex representation of the vector from the center of the nucleus to the center of the electron, and $\mathbf{s}_0 = \mathbf{s}_0' + i\mathbf{s}_0''$ is the complex vector amplitude.

Fig. 5-1. *Atom at the origin of a spherical polar coordinate system. An electron undergoes an elliptical oscillation in any plane passing through the origin.*

In this chapter the motion is postulated without consideration of the forces necessary to maintain it; such considerations will be taken up later. The electron has charge $-e$, and the vector $-e\mathbf{s}$ is called the *dipole moment* of the electron, sometimes denoted by $\mathbf{p}$. For some of the later work the atom will be taken at the origin of a spherical polar coordinate system, as in Fig. 5-1.

Before writing the expressions for the fields due to the motion (5-1), recall the field which holds when the electron is static at the distance s_0 (real) from the nucleus. There is no magnetic field, and if s_0 is in the direction of the polar axis, it is well known that the electric field at the point P in Fig. 5-1 has components

$$\mathbf{e}_r = -\frac{2es_0 \cos\theta}{r^3} \qquad \mathbf{e}_\theta = -\frac{es_0 \sin\theta}{r^3} \qquad \mathbf{e}_\phi = 0 \tag{5-2}$$

These expressions are easily seen to be the components of the vector relation (independent of the coordinate system)

$$\mathbf{e} = -e\left[\frac{2}{r^3}(\mathbf{s}_0 \cdot \hat{\mathbf{r}})\hat{\mathbf{r}} + \frac{1}{r^3}\hat{\mathbf{r}} \times (\hat{\mathbf{r}} \times \mathbf{s}_0)\right] \tag{5-3}$$

where $\hat{\mathbf{r}}$ is a unit vector from the nucleus toward P. The right side of (5-3) gives $\mathbf{e}$ in a resolution along and perpendicular to the radius vector to P. A plot of the streamlines of $\mathbf{e}$ in one of the planes $\phi = constant$ is shown in Fig. 5-2.

Formulas (5-2) and (5-3) are approximations good only for distances r large compared with the displacement s_0. This condition will be called the *dipole condition*. At points P such that r is of the same order as s_0, the streamlines have the familiar configuration for two point charges seen from P as well separated, and they are not given with sufficient accuracy by (5-2)

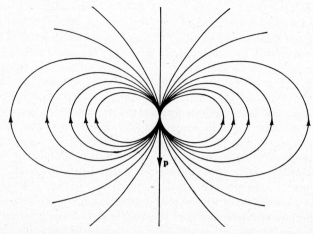

Fig. 5-2. *Streamlines of the field of a static dipole. The (negative) electron is displaced upward a distance too small to show on the figure.*

When the electron moves according to (5-1), the electric field is more complicated than (5-3), and there is a magnetic field. The formulas are

$$\mathbf{e} = -ek^3 \left\{ \left[\frac{2}{(kr)^3} - \frac{2i}{(kr)^2} \right] (\mathbf{s}_0 \cdot \hat{\mathbf{r}})\hat{\mathbf{r}} \right.$$

$$\left. + \left[\frac{1}{(kr)^3} - \frac{i}{(kr)^2} - \frac{1}{kr} \right] \hat{\mathbf{r}} \times (\hat{\mathbf{r}} \times \mathbf{s}_0) \right\} e^{i(kr-\omega t)} \quad (5\text{-}4)$$

$$\mathbf{b} = -ek^3 \left[\frac{i}{(kr)^2} + \frac{1}{kr} \right] \hat{\mathbf{r}} \times \mathbf{s}_0 e^{i(kr-\omega t)} \quad (5\text{-}5)$$

where
$$k = \frac{\omega}{c} \quad (5\text{-}6)$$

The real fields associated with the real motion of the electron are the real parts of (5-4) and (5-5).

Before entering into the interpretation of (5-4) and (5-5), it must be pointed out that again the formulas are approximations good under the *two* conditions

$$r \gg s_{\max} \quad (5\text{-}7)$$

where $s_{\max}$ is the largest (real) displacement of the electron from the nucleus [whence (5-7) is just the dipole condition], and

$$s_{\max} \ll \frac{c}{\omega} \quad (5\text{-}8)$$

The significance of condition (5-8) is as follows: Let the motion (5-1) be referred to a pair of principal radii s'_{00} and s''_{00} in the manner of (2-34). If s'_{00} is the larger of the two, then $s_{max} = |s'_{00}|$. The maximum velocity of the electron is $\omega|s'_{00}| = \omega s_{max}$, and (5-8) requires that the maximum velocity be small compared with the velocity of light. It will be seen that this condition is well satisfied when s_{max} is of the order of the radius of an atom (about 10^{-8} cm) and the frequency is that of visible light.

Points to notice at once about (5-4) and (5-5) are: Firstly, **e** and **b** appear as $e^{-i\omega t}$ multiplied by complex vector amplitudes which depend in complicated ways on the position of point P, so that qualitatively one can say that the fields oscillate sinusoidally at each point and constitute some sort of monochromatic wave; secondly, **e** appears as the sum of two complex vectors, one having both real and imaginary parts along $\hat{r}$, and the other having its parts perpendicular to $\hat{r}$, while **b** appears as a single complex vector with both parts perpendicular to $\hat{r}$; thirdly, the appearance of k in the exponentials and the definition (5-6) leads one to expect that the fields will involve a wavelength $\lambda = 2\pi/k$, but because of the complicated dependence of the amplitudes on the position of P, it is not at once obvious what significance this wavelength will have; and fourthly, if ω, and hence k, approaches zero, the fields becoming static, (5-4) approaches (5-3), and **b** approaches zero.

5-2   Field of a Linear Oscillator   To bring out the nature of the fields represented by (5-4) and (5-5), it is best to consider first the special case of a linear oscillation of the electron. For simplicity, let s_0 be real (so that the electron is at its maximum displacement at $t = 0$), and let it lie along the polar axis of the coordinate system (in the direction $\theta = 0$). The components of (5-4) and (5-5) are

$$e_r = -es_0k^3 \cos\theta \left[\frac{2}{(kr)^3} - \frac{2i}{(kr)^2} \right] e^{i(kr-\omega t)}$$

$$e_\theta = -es_0k^3 \sin\theta \left[\frac{1}{(kr)^3} - \frac{i}{(kr)^2} - \frac{1}{kr} \right] e^{i(kr-\omega t)} \qquad (5\text{-}9)$$

$$e_\phi = 0 \qquad b_r = 0 \qquad b_\theta = 0$$

$$b_\phi = es_0k^3 \sin\theta \left[\frac{i}{(kr)^2} + \frac{1}{kr} \right] e^{i(kr-\omega t)}$$

The streamlines of the real field **b** are circles concentric with and in planes perpendicular to the polar axis. The streamlines of **e** are in planes passing through the polar axis and show no dependence on the angle ϕ. The electric field shows the more interesting behavior, and maps of the streamlines at various instants, together with the first solution of the dipole problem, were given by H. Hertz in 1889 (see Hertz [39]). Figure 5-3 is adapted from Hertz's drawings and shows the

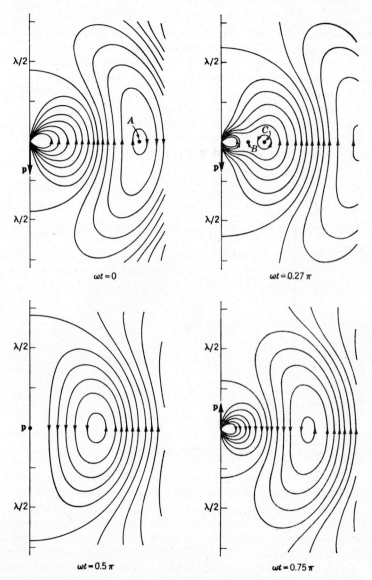

Fig. 5-3. *Streamlines of the electric field about a linear dipole oscillator of moment* $p = p_0 \cos \omega t$. *The displacement of the electron giving rise to* p *is too small to show on the figure.*

field at $\omega t = 0$, 0.27π, 0.5π, and 0.75π. The same figures, with the directions of all the streamlines reversed, give the appearance at $\omega t = \pi$, 1.27π, 1.5π, and 1.75π (altogether, a full cycle in steps of one-eight cycle except that the second and sixth steps are slightly delayed in order to show the genesis of the closed loops, which does not quite occur at $\omega t = 0.25\pi$ and 1.25π).

The qualitative features of Fig. 5-3 are as follows: Very near the atom the field appears as in Fig. 5-2. In fact, it will be shown presently that, at any instant, the field in this region is essentially the same as that for a static dipole whose moment is equal to the value of the oscillating

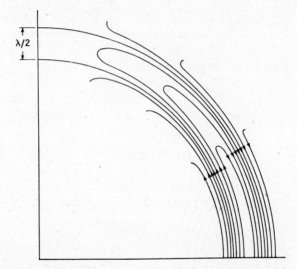

Fig. 5-4. *Set of closed streamlines of the electric field of a linear oscillator after propagating to a large distance from the atom.*

moment. For this reason the innermost region is called the *static zone*. The strength of the field in the static zone is maximum at $t = 0$, when the moment **p** is maximum, and decreases to zero during the first quarter cycle. However, this decrease does not result entirely in streamlines contracting and disappearing at the origin, but rather there is a necking down and pinching off into closed loops which then propagate outward. If a few sets of closed loops are followed well beyond the region covered by Fig. 5-3, they appear as in Fig. 5-4, and from the spacing of the lines it is clear that the radial component of **e** is rapidly becoming negligible compared with the θ component—the electric vector is approaching the condition of being purely transverse to the radial direction. Moreover, the distance between successive maxima of the θ component becomes essentially constant at the value $\lambda = 2\pi/k$ as the wave moves outward.

The region at large distances from the atom, where the field is transverse and a definite wavelength has appeared, is called the *wave zone*. The region between the static and wave zones, where the radial component is appreciable compared with the θ component, where there is no definite wavelength, and where the closed loops originate—altogether a very complicated region—is called the *intermediate zone*.

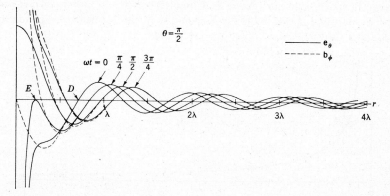

Fig. 5-5. *Transverse components of the electric and magnetic fields as functions of radius along the direction $\theta = \pi/2$ at four times one-eighth cycle apart.*

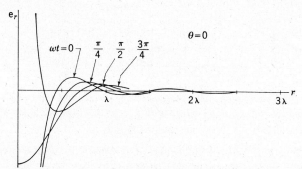

Fig. 5-6. *Radial component of the electric field as a function of radius along the direction $\theta = 0$ at four times one-eighth cycle apart.*

Another representation of the fields which illustrates the features described above in another way is obtained by plotting the real parts of the components (5-9) against r along a radial line from the atom. Figure 5-5 shows e_θ and b_ϕ, plotted for the times indicated, along a line with $\theta = \pi/2$. For any other value of θ the ordinates need only be multiplied by $\sin \theta$. Figure 5-6 shows e_r along the polar axis. For other directions the ordinates are to be multiplied by $\cos \theta$. Both figures show clearly the outward propagation during the first half-cycle. Curves for the second half-cycle are obtained by inverting the ordinates of those shown. The figures also show that the radial component of **e** has become negligible and a definite wavelength has appeared at about 2λ from the atom, which is then the approximate boundary between the intermediate and wave zones. Note also that **e** and **b** have equal magnitudes in the wave zone (a special and convenient feature of the gaussian units). To relate the curves of Fig. 5-5 to Fig. 5-3, point D in the former corresponds to point A in the latter. Slightly later than $\omega t = 0.25\pi$ the maximum

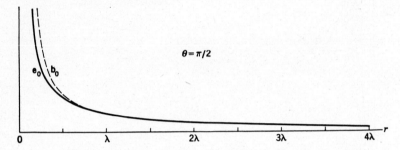

Fig. 5-7. *Amplitudes of the oscillations of the real electric and magnetic fields as functions of radius along a line with $\theta = \pi/2$.*

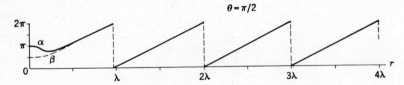

Fig. 5-8. *Phase angles of the oscillations of the electric and magnetic fields as functions of radius along a line with $\theta = \pi/2$. The angle for the electric field is α, and that for the magnetic field is β.*

marked E in Fig. 5-5 will have risen above the axis to give two zeros in e_θ corresponding to points marked B and C in Fig. 5-3.

To relate the complicated curves of Fig. 5-5 to a simpler and more unified picture, still another representation can be given. At each point along a radial line with $\theta = \pi/2$, the real parts of e_θ and b_ϕ oscillate sinusoidally with amplitudes e_0 and b_0 and phase angles α and β, respectively, all four being functions of r obtained as the magnitudes and angles of the complex numbers multiplying $e^{-i\omega t}$ in (5-9). Plots of these quantities are shown in Figs. 5-7 and 5-8, the scale of ordinates in Fig. 5-7 being the same as in Fig. 5-5. In Fig. 5-9 complex numbers having the magnitudes and angles shown in Figs. 5-7 and 5-8 are plotted with respect to a fixed point as origin of a polar coordinate system in the complex plane. If one thinks of an r axis projecting vertically out of the plane of the figure from the origin of the complex plane, the spirals become three-dimensional curves as indicated for e by the inset in Fig. 5-9. Viewing these spirals from the side, along the directions labeled a, b, c, and d, one sees the curves of Fig. 5-5.

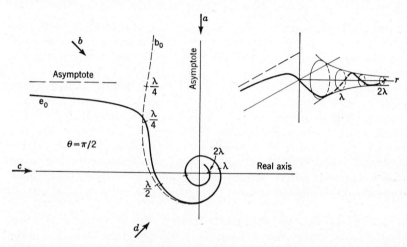

Fig. 5-9. *Complex amplitudes of the electric and magnetic fields along the direction $\theta = \pi/2$. Values of r are indicated along the curves. Inset shows (for the electric field) how the spirals can be thought of as three-dimensional curves which can be viewed along the directions a, b, c, and d to see the curves of Fig. 5-5.*

To prove the statements made about the static zone, consider points so near the atom that

$$kr \ll 1 \tag{5-10}$$

or $r \ll \lambda/2\pi$. Then in (5-9) all terms involving $1/(kr)^2$ and $1/kr$ are negligible compared with those involving $1/(kr)^3$. Moreover, $e^{ikr} \approx 1$. Hence Eqs. (5-9) reduce to (5-2) with s_0 replaced by $s_0e^{-i\omega t}$, and the real electric field at any time t is essentially that of a static dipole of moment $-es_0 \cos \omega t$. If one arbitrarily takes the outer limit of the static zone to be at $kr \approx 0.1$, then $r \approx \lambda/60$, so that the static zone extends out only a very short distance compared with λ and is actually too small to be seen in Fig. 5-3.

On the other hand, the wave zone covers the region in which

$$kr \gg 1 \tag{5-11}$$

and only the terms in (5-9) involving $1/kr$ are appreciable. The components of the field become

$$e_\theta = \frac{es_0 k^2 \sin \theta}{r} e^{i(kr-\omega t)}$$

$$b_\phi = e_\theta \tag{5-12}$$

$$e_r = e_\phi = b_r = b_\theta = 0$$

If the inner boundary of the wave zone is taken to be at $kr \approx 10$, then $r \approx 2\lambda$, as already concluded. For later applications the wave zone will be the most important part of the field, and further comment about it will be made in Sec. 5-4.

If the wavelength is between 4000 and 7000 A,[1] the radiation constitutes visible light. Condition (5-8), which can be rewritten $s_{max} \ll \lambda/2\pi$, is certainly well satisfied for visible light if s_{max} is no larger than the radius of an actual atom, which is of the order of 1 A. It begins to fail at a wavelength of about 50 A unless the amplitude of motion is further restricted. However, 50 A is the long limit of the X-ray region, in which quantum effects become marked and the classical theory is of correspondingly limited use.

5-3 Field for an Elliptical Motion In the general elliptical motion (5-1), giving rise to fields (5-4) and (5-5), the static and wave zones are not essentially more complicated than those for linear oscillation. Under condition (5-10) the magnetic field is negligible compared with the electric, and the latter reduces to (5-3) multiplied by $e^{-i\omega t}$; the field in the static zone at any instant is that of a static dipole whose moment is the same as the oscillating moment. Under condition (5-11) the fields in the wave zone become

$$\mathbf{e} = \frac{ek^2}{r} \hat{\mathbf{r}} \times (\hat{\mathbf{r}} \times \mathbf{s}_0) e^{i(kr-\omega t)}$$

$$\mathbf{b} = -\frac{ek^2}{r} \hat{\mathbf{r}} \times \mathbf{s}_0 e^{i(kr-\omega t)} \tag{5-13}$$

It will be seen presently that the fields in the wave zone are easily visualized.

In the intermediate zone the fields are very complicated and not easily visualized. In particular, **e** and **b** are not everywhere perpendicular, in contrast to the linear case (see Prob. 5-4).

5-4 Wave Zone The fields (5-13) can be given a simple geometrical interpretation. At a point P distant r from the atom in the direction of

---

[1] The symbol A stands for the *angstrom unit*, which is 10^{-8} cm. Other units for specifying wavelengths are the micron (10^{-4} cm, symbol: μ), the millimicron (10^{-7} cm, symbol: mμ), and the X unit (10^{-11} cm, symbol: XU).

the unit vector $\hat{\mathbf{r}}$, the real vectors **e** and **b** oscillate sinusoidally in a plane perpendicular to $\hat{\mathbf{r}}$, the oscillations being representable by ellipses.

The complex vector amplitude of **e** is

$$\frac{ek^2}{r}\,\hat{\mathbf{r}} \times [\hat{\mathbf{r}} \times (\mathbf{s}_0' + i\mathbf{s}_0'')]e^{ikr} = \frac{ek^2}{r}\,(\mathbf{A} + i\mathbf{B})e^{ikr}$$

Now $\mathbf{A} = \hat{\mathbf{r}} \times (\hat{\mathbf{r}} \times \mathbf{s}_0')$ is the negative of the component of $\mathbf{s}_0'$ perpendicular to $\hat{\mathbf{r}}$ [see (1-3)], and **B** is similarly related to $\mathbf{s}_0''$. Moreover, apart from the numerical factor ek^2/r, **A** and **B** are conjugate radii of the ellipse described by the real vector **e**. [With regard to the factor e^{ikr}, see

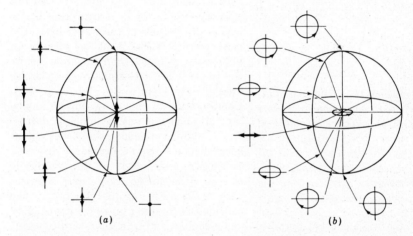

Fig. 5-10. *Paths described by the electric vector at a large fixed distance and different directions from an atom in whtch an electron executes* (**a**) *linear and* (**b**) *circular oscillation. The scale of the electronic oscillation is greatly exaggerated.*

the discussion of (2-31).] The result is that the ellipse representing **e** has the same shape and orientation as the projection onto a plane perpendicular to $\hat{\mathbf{r}}$ of the ellipse described by the electron, but differs in size by the factor ek^2/r and, in particular, shrinks in proportion to $1/r$ as P recedes from the atom. The direction of motion of **e** around its ellipse is the same as the direction of the projected motion of the electron. The relation of the ellipse representing **e** to the motion of the electron for fixed r and different directions of $\hat{\mathbf{r}}$ is illustrated in Fig. 5-10 for linear and circular motions of the electron. The phase of the oscillation of **e** (that is, the instantaneous position of **e** in its elliptical motion) can be thought of as falling farther and farther behind that of the electron as r increases; it falls behind by one additional cycle as r increases by one wavelength (and kr increases by 2π radians). The velocity of expansion of a spherical surface over which the phase remains constant comes from the condition $kr - \omega t = constant$ and hence, by (5-6), is c.

It is easily seen from (5-13) that the real vector **b** and the ellipse it describes are obtained by rotating the real vector **e** and its ellipse through 90° about $\hat{\mathbf{r}}$ in that sense which makes **e** × **b**, and hence the Poynting vector, point in the direction of $\hat{\mathbf{r}}$, the direction of propagation of the wave. This relation is illustrated in Fig. 5-11.

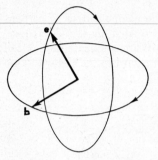

At large distances from the atom, the spherical wave fronts become nearly plane over a small area. However, the significant measure of the departure from planeness is in fractions of the wavelength, and in the case of visible light one must be an impressive distance from an atom before the fraction becomes small over a circular area of only 1 cm radius (see Prob. 5-3). Consideration of this point will be important in connection with Fraunhofer diffraction. Another phenomenon occurring at large distances is the fractional decrease, between r and $r + \Delta r$, in the amplitude of **e** or **b** becoming smaller as r increases with Δr fixed (see again Prob. 5-3). The conclusion is that in a given volume of space

Fig. 5-11. *Relations of the electric and magnetic vectors in an elliptically polarized wave. In the example shown the Poynting vector and the direction of propagation are toward the reader, and the polarization is right-hand.*

the wave emitted by an atom is essentially a plane wave with constant amplitude, in general elliptically polarized, if the atom is far enough away.

5-5   Rate of Radiation by a Dipole Oscillator   The instantaneous Poynting vector at a point in the wave zone is $c/4\pi$ times the vector product of the real parts of **e** and **b** obtained from (5-13). However, one ultimately wants the time average of the Poynting vector, and it is most easily calculated by the formula

$$\langle \mathbf{S} \rangle = \frac{c}{8\pi} \, \text{Re} \, (\mathbf{e} \times \mathbf{b}^*) \qquad (5\text{-}14)$$

where **e** and **b** are the complex vectors (5-13) (see Probs. 4-10 and 4-11). Thus

$$\langle \mathbf{S} \rangle = - \frac{ce^2 k^4}{8\pi r^2} \, \text{Re} \, \{[\hat{\mathbf{r}} \times (\hat{\mathbf{r}} \times \mathbf{s}_0)] \times (\hat{\mathbf{r}} \times \mathbf{s}_0^*)\}$$

By (1-1) and the statement in Prob. 2-5,

$$\langle \mathbf{S} \rangle = \frac{ce^2 k^4}{8\pi r^2} \, [(\hat{\mathbf{r}} \times \mathbf{s}_0) \cdot (\hat{\mathbf{r}} \times \mathbf{s}_0^*)]\hat{\mathbf{r}} \qquad (5\text{-}15)$$

(It is now evident that the right side is already real.)   Write

$$s_0 = s_0' + is_0''$$

Then

$$\langle S \rangle = \frac{ce^2k^4}{8\pi r^2} [(\hat{r} \times s_0')^2 + (\hat{r} \times s_0'')^2]\hat{r}$$

If $(\hat{r}, s_0')$ denotes the angle between $\hat{r}$ and s_0', and similarly for $(\hat{r}, s_0'')$, the final formula is

$$\langle S \rangle = \frac{ce^2k^4}{8\pi r^2} [s_0'^2 \sin^2 (\hat{r}, s_0') + s_0''^2 \sin^2 (\hat{r}, s_0'')]\hat{r} \tag{5-16}$$

Note that $\langle S \rangle$ points radially outward from the atom (but only in the wave zone) and falls off with distance according to the inverse-square law.   It varies as k^4, as $1/\lambda^4$, or, by (5-6), as ω^4; for a given amplitude of oscillation of the electron, the rate of radiation goes up rapidly as the frequency increases.

To illustrate the dependence of $\langle S \rangle$ on the direction of $\hat{r}$, consider first a linear oscillator with s_0 real.   Then (5-16) holds with $s_0' = s_0$ and $s_0'' = 0$. The magnitude $\langle S \rangle$ varies as $\sin^2 (\hat{r}, s_0)$, and if for each direction of $\hat{r}$ and for any constant value of r a point is marked at distance $\langle S \rangle$ from the atom, one obtains Fig. 5-12, called a *polar plot* of the *radiation pattern*.

The complete pattern is a toroid obtained by rotating the figure eight about s_0 as axis.[1]

In the case of elliptical motion of the electron, formula (5-16) states that the total radiation pattern is given by a summation of two patterns, each like Fig. 5-12, one having s_0' as axis of symmetry and dimensions proportional to $s_0'^2$, and the other being similarly related to s_0''.   It is advantageous, particularly in thinking qualitatively about the total pattern, to make use of principal radii according to

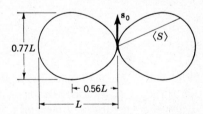

Fig. 5-12. *Radiation pattern of a linear dipole oscillator. Length L is proportional to the square of the amplitude* s_0. *The characteristic dimensions of the oval will be useful in the problems.*

the following idea: Recall that when the motion is written in the form (5-1), s_0' and s_0'' constitute a pair of conjugate radii of the ellipse described by the electron, the electron being at the end of s_0' at $t = 0$. The motion can equally well be written

$$s = (s_{00}' + is_{00}'')e^{-i\omega(t-t_0)} \tag{5-17}$$

[1] It can be shown that the ovals in Figs. 5-2 and 5-12 happen to have the same shape.

where s'_{00} and s''_{00} are a pair of principle radii [at right angles to each other—see discussion of (2-34)], the electron being at the end of s'_{00} at $t = t_0$. Substituting the factor multiplying $e^{-i\omega t}$ in (5-17) for s_0 in (5-13), one ultimately obtains $\langle S \rangle$ as the formula (5-16) with s'_0 and s''_0 replaced by s'_{00} and s''_{00}, respectively.[1] The construction of the total radiation pattern with the use of principal radii is illustrated for the three planes of symmetry by Fig. 5-13.

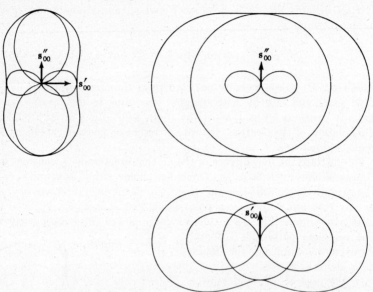

Fig. 5-13. *Radiation patterns in three mutually perpendicular planes for an elliptical dipole oscillator referred to principal radii s'_{00} and s''_{00}. The outer curves are traces of the total pattern obtained by summation of the two component patterns.*

The total rate of radiation from the atom is obtained by multiplying the magnitude of (5-16) by an element of surface on a sphere of radius r, centered at the atom, and integrating over the sphere. Each of the two terms may be treated separately, and in a spherical polar coordinate system with s'_0 along the polar axis, the integration of the first term is

$$\frac{ce^2 k^4 s_0'^2}{4} \int_0^\pi \sin^3 \theta \, d\theta = \frac{ce^2 k^4 s_0'^2}{3}$$

The same procedure can be applied to the second term, and the total rate of radiation, the power (which will always be understood to be the time

[1] It is now evident that in (5-16), s'_0 and s''_0 could stand for *any* pair of conjugate radii associated with the elliptical motion of the electron.

average), is

$$P = \frac{ce^2k^4}{3}(s_0'^2 + s_0''^2) \tag{5-18}$$

Here s_0' and s_0'' could be replaced by any pair of conjugate radii associated with the elliptical motion (see Prob. 2-16).

5-6 Fields and Radiation in the Case of Several Oscillators
The considerations in the preceding sections of this chapter have dealt with a single electron undergoing a monochromatic oscillation, in general elliptical. Many applications will involve several electrons in the same or different atoms, with each electron undergoing a monochromatic oscillation at the same frequency ω. The problem will be to find the total electric and magnetic fields, the total radiation pattern, and the total power radiated. The total fields can be found by the principle of superposition, whereby the fields at a given point of space are the resultants of the fields due to the oscillators taken separately. The time average of the Poynting vector is then found from the total fields by (5-14), and since the operation of taking a product is involved, the result is not the sum of the Poynting vectors for the several oscillators taken separately except in very special cases, each of which must be proved individually as a theorem. Similarly, the total power radiated is not the sum of the powers radiated by the several oscillators acting separately except in special cases. These points will now be illustrated by a few simple examples.

Consider two oscillating electrons, either in the same atom or in two atoms separated by only a very small fraction of a wavelength and hence essentially at the same point as far as the radiated fields are concerned. Let the motions of the electrons be

$$\mathbf{s}_1 = \mathbf{s}_{01}e^{-i\omega t} \qquad \mathbf{s}_2 = \mathbf{s}_{02}e^{-i\omega t}$$

where $\mathbf{s}_{01}$ and $\mathbf{s}_{02}$ are the vector amplitudes, in general complex. The fields in the wave zone are given by (5-13) with $\mathbf{s}_0 = \mathbf{s}_{01} + \mathbf{s}_{02}$. The time average of the Poynting vector is given by (5-16) with $\mathbf{s}_0' = \mathbf{s}_{01}' + \mathbf{s}_{02}'$ and $\mathbf{s}_0'' = \mathbf{s}_{01}'' + \mathbf{s}_{02}''$. The result will be the sum of the vectors $\langle \mathbf{S} \rangle$ for the separate oscillators only in such special cases as $\mathbf{s}_{02}' = \mathbf{s}_{01}'' = 0$. The total power is given by (5-18) with $\mathbf{s}_0'^2 = (\mathbf{s}_{01}' + \mathbf{s}_{02}')^2$ and

$$\mathbf{s}_0''^2 = (\mathbf{s}_{01}'' + \mathbf{s}_{02}'')^2$$

The powers of the separate oscillators will be additive if and only if $\mathbf{s}_{01}' \cdot \mathbf{s}_{02}' + \mathbf{s}_{01}'' \cdot \mathbf{s}_{02}'' = 0$.

The ideas in the preceding paragraph can be extended to any number of monochromatic oscillators of the same frequency at or within a small fraction of a wavelength of the same point. They are equivalent, as far as the resultant electric and magnetic fields are concerned, to a single oscillator in which an electron undergoes an oscillation with a vector amplitude equal to the sum of the amplitudes of the separate oscillations.

The argument can be reversed to allow a given oscillator to be regarded as equivalent to any number of oscillators of the same frequency at the same point. Each component oscillator is to consist of an electron oscillating with some vector amplitude such that the sum of all the amplitudes equals the given one—just the idea of decomposition discussed in Sec. 2-6. Thus the oscillator with amplitude (5-1) is equivalent to two linear oscillators with amplitudes $s_0'e^{-i\omega t}$ and $is_0''e^{-i\omega t}$. (These two linear oscillations, out of phase by $\pi/2$ radians, present one of the few examples in which the time average of the Poynting vector for the resultant motion is the sum of those for the components.) A particularly important resolution is that of an oscillation such as (5-1) into an equivalent set of three linear oscillations along three given mutually perpendicular directions. Some features of this resolution will be brought out by the problems.

As a second example, consider two atoms, one at the origin of a spherical polar coordinate system, and the other on the polar axis at distance $q\lambda$ from the origin, where q is a positive number which may be large compared with unity. Let an electron in the atom at the origin oscillate linearly according to $s_1 = s_0 e^{-i\omega t}$, where s_0 is real and lies along the polar axis. Let an electron in the other atom oscillate according to

$$s_2 = s_0 e^{-i(\omega t - \alpha)}$$

where α is an arbitrary phase angle. (The amplitude s_0 is the same for both motions.)

Draw a sphere with center at the origin and radius very large compared with the larger of λ and $q\lambda$ (so that even if q is less than unity, the sphere is in the wave zone). If Q is any point on this sphere, then, from the geometry of Fig. 5-14a, $r_2 \approx r_1 - q\lambda \cos \theta$.

The fields at Q are obtained by writing (5-12) for each atom and adding. With negligible error, the angle θ and the factor $1/r$ can be taken as the same for both atoms. In the exponentials, however, the difference $q\lambda \cos \theta$ between r_1 and r_2 cannot be neglected, for it appears multiplied by k to give $2\pi q \cos \theta$, which may be a large angle. The result of the superposition is then

$$e_\theta = b_\phi = \frac{e s_0 k^2 \sin \theta}{r} \left(1 + e^{i(\alpha + 2\pi q \cos \theta)}\right) e^{i(kr - \omega t)}$$

all other components being zero. The time average of the magnitude of the Poynting vector is (see Probs. 4-10 and 4-11)

$$\langle S \rangle = \frac{c e^2 s_0^2 k^4}{4\pi r^2} \sin^2 \theta \left[1 + \cos (\alpha + 2\pi q \cos \theta)\right] \tag{5-19}$$

The first term on the right is just twice the $\langle S \rangle$ for one of the atoms alone, and it is seen that the second term, called the *interference term*, makes the total pattern markedly different from the sum of the two separate patterns. Figure 5-14b gives $\langle S \rangle$ as a function of θ in a cartesian plot (hence a representation of the radiation pattern alternative to a polar plot) for $\alpha = 0$ and $q = 3.5$. The dashed curves are respectively two and four times the $\langle S \rangle$ for one of the atoms alone. As q increases, the spacing of the maxima decreases, since the number of times the solid curve touches the upper dashed curve is $2n + 1$ if n is the largest integer less than or equal to q. As α varies, the positions of all the maxima move

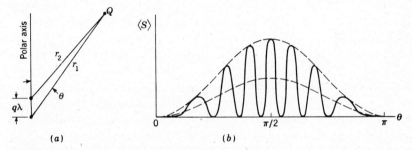

Fig. 5-14.   **a.** *Geometrical relations between two atoms at separation $q\lambda$ and a field point Q at a large distance.* **b.** *Radiation pattern for two identical linear oscillators arranged as in* (**a**) *and oscillating along the polar axis. The oscillators are in phase, and $q = 3.5$. The dashed curves are, respectively, twice and four times the pattern for one of the oscillators alone.*

to one side; in particular, when $\alpha = \pi$, a maximum replaces a zero, and vice versa. When $\alpha = 0$, there is a maximum at $\theta = \pi/2$ for any value of q.

If the atoms are many wavelengths apart, the oscillations in Fig. 5-14b come very close together but are not reduced in amplitude. If the radiation field is explored with a detector that does not have sufficient spatial resolution, the readings give averages over several cycles of oscillation in the true pattern and indicate essentially the lower dashed curve, so that on this scale of observation the total pattern appears to be the sum of the patterns of the separate atoms. This point should be carefully noted, since it will arise many times in more complicated forms.

The total power radiated is obtained by multiplying (5-19) by $2\pi r^2 \sin \theta \, d\theta$ and integrating from 0 to π. With $2\pi q \cos \theta$ as a new variable of integration, the result is easily shown to be

$$P = 2P_1 \left[1 + 3 \cos \alpha \left(\frac{\sin y}{y^3} - \frac{\cos y}{y^2} \right) \right] \qquad (5\text{-}20)$$

where P_1 is the power radiated by one of the atoms alone, and $y = 2\pi q$.
Figure 5-15 shows P as a function of q for $\alpha = 0$, $\pi/2$, and π. The
oscillations in these curves indicate that the atoms interact appreciably
only when they are less than about two wavelengths apart (one atom in
the intermediate or static zone of the other).

It is worthwhile to relate the features of Fig. 5-15 to other points of
view. When q is essentially zero, the two oscillators are equivalent to a
single one whose dipole moment is the sum of the individual moments.
When $\alpha = 0$, this resultant moment is $2es_0$, and since P is proportional
to the square of the moment, the total rate of radiation is four times that
of a single atom. The same result comes from Fig. 5-14b, since now the

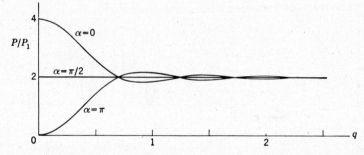

Fig. 5-15. *Total rate of radiation by two identical linear and collinear*
oscillators as a function of separation for various relative phases. The
separation is q wavelengths, and the oscillators are in phase when $\alpha = 0$ and
of opposite phase when $\alpha = \pi$. The total rate is denoted by P, while P_1 is
the rate for a single oscillator.

total pattern is identical with the upper dashed curve, which is four
times as high as the pattern for a single atom. When $\alpha = \pi$, the total
dipole moment is zero, and the total radiation pattern is zero in all
directions. When $\alpha = \pi/2$, the total dipole moment is $\sqrt{2}\, es_0$, and the
radiation pattern is the lower dashed curve in Fig. 5-14b. Both $\langle S \rangle$ and
P are additive in this last case. When q is large, $\langle S \rangle$ is not additive for
any value of α (except under the condition of coarse observation mentioned earlier), but P is additive for all values, since P is the area under a
curve such as that of Fig. 5-14b except that the dashed curves are proportional to $\sin^3 \theta$ instead of $\sin^2 \theta$ and the maxima are very numerous.
This area is seen at a glance to be one-half the area under the envelope,
and hence twice the power radiated by a single atom, in agreement with
Fig. 5-15.

This second example, while it involves oscillations of a quite special
character, has brought out some fundamental ideas which will be prominent in chapters to come, beginning with the next. To sum up the whole

section, the one infallible rule is: First superpose the fields due to all the oscillators involved, and *then* calculate the Poynting vector and the total rate of radiation. Only in special cases can the powers radiated by the separate oscillators be added to obtain the correct total power, and only in even more special cases can the separate Poynting vectors be added to obtain the correct total pattern.

Problems

5-1. A sphere of radius R is made to pulsate, so that R is a function of time. The sphere has a fixed total charge, and the density ρ is at every instant uniform throughout the volume. Show that there is no radiation. (*Hints:* The simplest argument involves the property of the electric and magnetic fields that can be inferred at once from the symmetry of the problem. A longer proof involves actually finding the fields. To do so, begin with the conjecture—suggested by the symmetry and to be verified by a final check of the Maxwell equations—that there is no magnetic field. The electric field throughout space can then be found by the methods of Sec. 3-3. To check that the solution satisfies the Maxwell equations it is necessary to find div **e**, curl **e**, $\partial\mathbf{e}/\partial t$, and **j** everywhere in space. It has already been assumed that **b** = 0. Finally, discuss the Poynting vector.)

5-2. Let **a**, **b**, and $\mathbf{c} = \mathbf{a} \times \mathbf{b}$ be mutually perpendicular unit vectors. Let an electron oscillate with the motion $\mathbf{s} = (\sqrt{2}\,\mathbf{a} + i\mathbf{b})e^{-i\omega t}$. Describe the polarization of the electric wave in the wave zone in the directions of **c**, **a** + **c**, **a**, **a** − **c**, −**c**, **b** + **c**, **b**, and **b** − **c**. Draw ellipses to the same scale to illustrate each case, all at the same distance from the atom.

5-3. At what distance from a radiating atom does a wave front become plane within 1 per cent of a wavelength over a circular area 1 cm in radius if $\lambda = 5000$ A (blue-green light)? Denote the answer by r_0; then what is Δr such that the amplitude at $r_0 + \Delta r$ is 1 per cent less than it is at r_0? Give the answers in kilometers.

5-4. In (5-4) and (5-5) write $\mathbf{s}_0 = \mathbf{s}_0' + i\mathbf{s}_0''$. Write the real parts **e**′ and **b**′ of the fields and show that $\mathbf{e}' \cdot \mathbf{b}' = -(e^2 k/r^5)\hat{\mathbf{r}} \cdot \mathbf{s}_0' \times \mathbf{s}_0''$. Interpret the result in the light of Prob. 2-16. Discuss all conditions under which the fields are orthogonal. (Under some conditions orthogonality will hold only at certain points of space.) Note that because of the factor $1/r^5$ the fields rapidly become orthogonal in any case as one moves away from the atom.

5-5. An electron in an atom executes a linear oscillation of amplitude 1 A and emits a wave with $\lambda = 5000$ A. What is the frequency in cycles per second? What is the total rate of radiation in ergs per second? What is the rate if the oscillation is circular with radius 1 A? What is the rate in the linear case if $\lambda = 2500$ A? If a photographic plate requires 10^{-4} erg cm^{-2} to render half the grains developable (the case of 5000 grains per square millimeter and a quantum efficiency of 10^{-3}), how long must the plate be exposed at a distance of 1 m from the atom in a direction perpendicular to the line of motion in the linear case with $\lambda = 5000$ A in order that half the grains be developable?

5-6. Draw radiation patterns similar to Fig. 5-13 for a circular oscillation of an electron. (One can draw ovals similar to Fig. 5-12 freehand with sufficient accuracy if the characteristic proportions indicated in that figure are laid out. The addition can be done graphically in enough directions to fix the total pattern. The result for this problem can be partially checked by noting whether or not the proper symmetry emerges.)

5-7. Let **a** and **b** be perpendicular unit vectors, and let an electron in an atom oscillate with an elliptical motion whose complex amplitude is $s_0' + is_0'' = 2\mathbf{a} + 3\mathbf{b} + i3\mathbf{a}$. In the plane of **a** and **b** draw radiation patterns for the separate linear oscillations with amplitudes s_0' and s_0'' (see remarks on drawing these patterns in Prob. 5-6). Add graphically to obtain the total pattern. Refer the elliptical motion to a pair of principal radii (use the result of Prob. 2-17), and again draw the patterns for the two linear oscillations and add. The total pattern should be the same by the two methods.

5-8. Resolve the elliptical oscillation of Prob. 5-7 into linear oscillations along **a** and **b**. Draw radiation patterns in the plane of **a** and **b** for these linear oscillations taken separately, and add to show that the sum is not the correct total pattern found in Prob. 5-7.

5-9. For each of the three resolutions into linear oscillations involved in Probs. 5-7 and 5-8, calculate the power radiated by the separate linear oscillations and add. The result should be the same for all three resolutions.

5-10. A general oscillator with amplitude $s_0' + is_0''$ is at the origin of a cartesian coordinate system. Resolve the motion into linear oscillations along the coordinate axes, and show that the total power radiated is the sum of the powers for the separate component oscillators. Show that at points on the coordinate axes, but not at all points, the total value of $\langle S \rangle$ is the sum of the values for the separate component oscillators.

5-11. Let **a** and **b** be perpendicular unit vectors. Resolve the linear oscillator with vector amplitude $s_0 = \mathbf{a}$ into opposite circular motions in the plane of **a** and **b**. Show that the total power radiated is the sum of the powers for the separate component oscillators. Show that in the two directions perpendicular to the plane of **a** and **b** the total $\langle S \rangle$ is the sum of the values for the component oscillators. This additivity holds along some other directions, but show that it does not hold along **a** or **b**.

5-12. From (5-13) find the instantaneous Poynting vector in the wave zone when $s_0 = s_0' + is_0''$. Take the time average, and compare it with (5-16). Integrate the normal component of the instantaneous Poynting vector over a sphere of radius r to find the instantaneous power flowing through the sphere, and take the time average; compare it with (5-18).

chapter 6

Diffraction.
A Preliminary Description

If light from a small source, essentially a point, illuminates a white screen from a distance of a meter or so, and an opaque obstacle, such as a coin or a sheet of black paper with a hole, is interposed midway between the source and the screen, a coarse observation of the white screen shows a perfectly dark shadow with a sharp edge and a region outside the shadow of the same brightness as if there were no obstacle. The edge of the shadow is defined by the intersection with the observing screen of a cone whose vertex is at the source and whose generators touch the edge of the obstacle. Careful observation on a fine scale, as first reported by Grimaldi in 1665, shows that the edge of the shadow is not perfectly sharp—the brightness falls only gradually to zero on passing into the shadow, and just outside the geometrically defined boundary the illuminated region shows deviations from the brightness observed with the obstacle removed. The effect is most striking if the light is nearly monochromatic, in which case the region just outside the geometrically defined shadow shows a distinct set of bright and dim bands, generally paralleling the boundary. These bands are referred to as *fringes;* Fig. 6-1 illustrates this phenomenon. The conclusion is that light does not propagate exactly according to the simple notions of geometrical ray optics, but rather the direction of propagation is affected slightly by the presence of an obstacle. This deviation from the predictions of geometrical optics is called *diffraction.*

In the course of the development of the general theory of the propagation of waves, whether sound waves, elastic waves, waves on water, electromagnetic waves, or any other, it was recognized that diffraction always arises when a wave is partially obstructed in some way, so that diffraction is a general characteristic of wave motion. In fact, the wave theory can be said to have been established by the failure to find any mode of propagation of light other than waves which would account for diffraction. Moreover, the theory showed that the angular deviation from rectilinear propagation is proportional to the wavelength, and hence

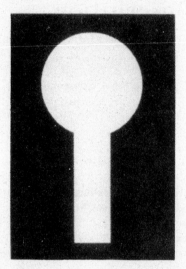 

Fig. 6-1. *Right: Diffraction pattern formed with a very small and nearly monochromatic source. Left: Corresponding shadow predicted by geometrical optics.*

diffraction effects are of small scale in the case of light with its very short wavelength, and of very gross scale in the case of sound or radio waves, where the comparison of scale is always with the minimum length readily perceived with the unaided human eye. If the wavelength is imagined to go to zero, diffraction disappears; the laws of geometrical optics emerge from those of wave optics in the limit of vanishing wavelength. More will be said on this point later.

There are two ways to approach an understanding of diffraction. One is to express mathematically the propagation of waves by means of a wave equation and to seek a solution for the amplitude in the wave field which behaves properly at the boundaries of the material media in space. This treatment as a "boundary-value problem" is in general exceedingly difficult, and the underlying physical processes in the media are buried in the statement of the boundary conditions. Nevertheless, in later chapters very satisfactory solutions for diffraction by apertures in opaque screens will be obtained with ease through this approach by making some simplifying approximations. The other approach, which will be discussed in a preliminary way in the rest of this chapter and applied in the next, is best suited to gaining a qualitative appreciation of the physical cause of the diffraction of light. It involves considering the microscopic details of the interaction of the wave field and the material media on which it impinges.

A clue to the origin of diffraction is gained by performing one of the simplest of all experiments. In a sheet of black paper cut a hole a few centimeters across with cleanly cut edges. Place a small bare lamp bulb across a darkened room and view it through the hole, held at arm's length. The edge of the hole is seen to be outlined by a fine line of light. If the line from the eye to the lamp passes near one side of the hole, that side becomes particularly bright. When the screen is moved to just hide the lamp, the edge nearest the line from eye to lamp continues to show a brightly luminous segment, and as the screen is moved farther in the same direction (the eye moving farther into the shadow), this segment gradually dims. If the paper screen is replaced by the sharp edge of a razor blade to eliminate possibility of a reflecting or fuzzy edge, the effects are observed to be the same. The conclusion is that the light from the lamp falls on the diffracting obstacle and sets some of the charged particles it contains into oscillation so that they radiate. These moving charges are confined to a thin layer over the surface of the illuminated side of the obstacle, giving rise to a certain amount of reflection back toward the lamp, and to a narrow band surrounding the aperture on the dark side of the screen. It is the radiation from the moving charges in this narrow band that is observed as the luminous edge in the above experiment.

One cannot go very far on the basis of the Lorentz theory in explaining all the complicated processes undergone by the charged particles in the diffracting screen when light is incident. For example, most of the energy of the light falling on black paper is converted into heat, and in such a complicated material a microscopic analysis of this conversion, and hence the origin of the opacity and low reflectance of the screen, cannot be made very satisfactory, even with the best available atomic theories. The case of metal screens is more favorable, and if one assumes infinite conductivity (in which case no energy is absorbed by the screen, it being a perfect reflector) and treats the material as a continuum, ignoring the microscopic structure, it is possible to solve the Maxwell equations exactly in cases of simple geometry (for example, a semi-infinite screen with a straight edge) and find the current in the screen which gives rise to the reflected and diffracted radiation. However, without entering into all the details of what happens in the screen, it is possible to give a partial and somewhat phenomenological description from which much information concerning diffraction patterns can be drawn.

In setting up a more specific situation for analysis, the first item to consider is the light source. From here to the end of Chap. 10 the source will be idealized in two respects—it will be taken to be a point and to be perfectly monochromatic. One can carry in mind a single atom in which an electron oscillates sinusoidally, as discussed in Chap. 5. The idealization can be appreciated with the following considerations: The actual sources used in observing and applying the phenomenon of diffraction consist of many charged particles undergoing various motions and radiating energy. In order to have sufficient intensity, the source must contain many elementary charges and have a nonvanishing size, the effects of which must eventually be considered. Moreover, the source cannot emit perfectly monochromatic light, since by definition such light comes only from an oscillator in which the motion is perfectly sinusoidal (with constant amplitude and unvarying phase angle) for all time—from $t = -\infty$ to $t = +\infty$. Any departure from this rigorous condition gives rise to nonmonochromatic light, the discussion of which will be deferred to Chaps. 12 and 13. Nevertheless, when the discussion of extended sources emitting nonmonochromatic light is completed, it will be seen that there are situations, easily realized physically, in which observed diffraction patterns depart by negligible amounts from those calculated on the assumption of a monochromatic point source. Hence the results to be obtained in the next few chapters are in fact close to real experience. Moreover, the treatment of monochromatic point sources plays an essential role in the theory of nonmonochromatic extended sources as they will be treated by Fourier analysis in Chap. 13

As to what occurs in the diffracting screen, a description adequate for some important calculations in the next chapter can be inferred by again considering some experimentally observed facts. Let the screen be illuminated by light from a small discharge tube combined with a filter which isolates a single line in the atomic spectrum. This light can be regarded for present purposes as a very good approximation to perfectly monochromatic light. (The justification and limitations of this statement are considered in Chaps. 12 and 13.) The light reflected and diffracted by the screen is observed to be of the same spectral character as that of the source. The conclusion is that in the idealized case of a perfectly monochromatic source, each of the electrons that are set into motion in the screen can be regarded as oscillating with sinusoidal motion of the same frequency as the source.

Each moving electron, whether in the screen or the source, is therefore assumed to execute an oscillation about a fixed nucleus of the type represented by (5-1) (all with the same frequency) and to give rise to a radiated wave represented by (5-4) and (5-5). According to the principle of superposition, the total electric and magnetic fields at any point of space are then obtained as the sums of all the dipole fields due to the oscillators in the source and in the screen. Nonoscillating electrons contribute nothing to the fields.

Consider an opaque screen of large extent having no aperture. Behind the screen there is no light, which means that its oscillators must have amplitudes and phases such that the resultant of their dipole fields completely cancels the incident wave at all points behind the screen. Moreover, these oscillations must be confined to a layer of thickness t at the illuminated surface such that a sheet of thickness t is just opaque. In a highly absorbing material, t may be only a few wavelengths, while the screen will ordinarily be much thicker, and it is therefore conceived that, except in this thin layer, the net fields (and hence the motions of the electrons) are zero inside the material of the screen.

As to the mechanism that determines the amplitudes and phases of the oscillations in the screen, only the following qualitative ideas need be noted. A given electron in an atom will be set into motion by virtue of the force due to an external electric field in which the atom finds itself. This field consists of the primary incident field plus all the secondary fields from the other oscillators in the screen and is different from zero only in the thin layer at the illuminated surface. (The force due to the magnetic field is smaller by a factor v/c and can be neglected.) An important question for the problem of diffraction is that of the effective range of interaction of a given oscillator on its neighbors, and an answer can be inferred by again considering the experimental facts.

From the screen just considered, let an area be removed to leave an aperture. This process can be thought of as removing the oscillators originally covering the aperture, and hence removing their influence on the electrons remaining in the screen. One can then look for evidence of changes in the behavior of the oscillators in the remaining parts of the screen, and since the only effect observed is the development of a luminous edge around the aperture, it is reasonable to conclude that any influence of the oscillators that were removed could not have extended more than a very short distance beyond the edge.

With this much background one can now see three equivalent ways of thinking of the phenomenon of diffraction from a microscopic point of view. Let a monochromatic point source be located in front of a diffracting screen containing an aperture. Some distance behind the aperture let there be an observing screen on which light falls to form a diffraction pattern. The first and most direct view of the effect of the diffracting screen is that it contains oscillators whose amplitudes and phases are determined by the combined action of the primary wave from the source and the secondary waves (but ultimately just of the primary wave, without which there would be no secondary oscillators in the screen), and the secondary waves superpose on the primary wave to produce the resultant amplitude at each point of the observing screen. The contribution of the secondary waves is obtained by a summation of waves coming from oscillators distributed all over the diffracting screen.

The second point of view corresponds most closely with what is actually seen from various points of the observing screen. According to it, the oscillators in the screen are divided into two classes. Class I consists of those oscillators that are very near the edge of the aperture and contribute to the luminous edge described earlier. Class II consists of all remaining oscillators. The resultant wave from the members of class II has the simple effect of exactly canceling the primary wave at all points of the observing screen which lie in the geometrically defined shadow, and it has no effect (that is, the amplitude of this resultant wave is zero) at any points from which the source can be seen through the aperture. Thus the oscillators of class II would combine with the primary source to give rise to just the pattern on the observing screen with a perfectly sharp boundary predicted by geometrical optics. On this partial resultant is then superposed the rather complicated wave originating in the members of class I; the final resultant wave then leads to a pattern showing the fringes and other details characteristic of observed diffraction patterns. It is required of any detailed theory of diffraction to reconcile these two views, and the extent to which the reconciliation has been brought out by existing theories will be described in later chapters.

The third point of view, which corresponds most closely with the method that is almost always used in actually calculating diffraction patterns, comes about in the following way: Construct from a sheet of opaque material a cap that just fits the aperture of the diffracting screen. When the aperture is open, let the amplitude of, say, the electric field at a point P of the observing screen be $\mathbf{A}$, in general a complex vector (the time factor $e^{-i\omega t}$ can be omitted). When the cap covers the aperture, the amplitude at P is reduced to zero, which means that oscillators have been set into motion in the cap in just such a way that by themselves they produce at P an amplitude $-\mathbf{A}$. Enumerate the oscillating electrons in the cap by an index j, and suppose the jth oscillator has complex amplitude $\mathbf{s}_{0j}$. Imagine now that the source is removed and all the oscillators in the original diffracting screen are brought to rest, but the oscillators in the cap are still maintained, except that the amplitude $\mathbf{s}_{0j}$ is changed to $-\mathbf{s}_{0j}$. One then has a set of *fictitious oscillators* distributed over the aperture which, *by themselves*, give the amplitude $\mathbf{A}$ at P and hence produce the same pattern of illumination over the observing screen as did the source and the original diffracting screen with its aperture. This third point of view places in a physical context the essential idea of the well-known principle of Huygens, and this principle, in the form given it by Kirchhoff (fully developed in Chaps. 8 to 10), is the usual basis for calculating diffraction patterns.

In the above description nothing was said about the details of the oscillators near the edge of the aperture (the oscillators of class I) except in a broad phenomenological way. The question remains as to how much of this detail must be ascertained if a diffraction pattern is to be accurately calculated. The answer depends on the size of the aperture and where one wishes to find the diffraction pattern.

In the simplest case—the one to which the following chapters will be almost exclusively devoted and which covers most of the important applications of diffraction—the aperture is large enough that practically all its area consists of points lying a large number of wavelengths (say more than 10) from the edge, and the observing screen is many wavelengths from the diffracting screen. In this case the details of the oscillators at the edge of the aperture are unimportant, as evidence the experimental fact that the diffraction pattern is not perceptibly altered by changing the material of the diffracting screen from one opaque substance to another or making the edge of the aperture sharp or rounded. To understand this fact in a qualitative way, consider the third view in more detail. When the cap is placed over the aperture, not only will oscillators be set into motion over the cap, but those in the original screen belonging to class I will be somewhat altered. The set of fictitious oscillators must then consist not only of those in the cap, but also some additional ones bordering its edge, to compensate the changes in class I. If the cap is large, these additional oscillators constitute a small fraction of the total number, and, since none of them is especially close to the observing point, they can be neglected.

Less simple cases are of two kinds. In one, the observing screen is not near the aperture, but the latter is a very small pinhole or a very narrow slit. In the .other, the aperture may be large, but the fields are examined very near its edge. For these problems many experimental data have been gathered, mostly by microwave techniques, and they have been represented by various empirical formulas, but very few cases have been covered by good theory, and such theory is always very difficult. In all these problems the detailed behavior of the oscillators near the edge are of dominant importance, and hence the nature of the material of the screen and the roundness or sharpness of the edge are important. The nature of the diffracting edges continues to have effect on the pattern as one passes to a large aperture and a distant observing screen, but the effect becomes very small and can be observed without elaborate technique only in the very faint light arriving at points far inside the geometrical shadow. An example will be described in Sec. 10-6.

The complete calculation of a diffraction pattern by methods that can be considered within the scope of this book will necessarily involve some rather radical simplifications. The results, when compared with experiment, will generally turn out to be very good, but they will be obtained by mathematical devices—the scalar model and the Kirchhoff integral—which are only weakly related to fundamental physical ideas concerning light. There is, however, a class of diffraction problems for which it is possible to calculate quantitatively some important properties of the patterns by arguments based strictly on the Lorentz theory. This class is the subject of the next chapter, and one of the main results will be the theory of the grating spectrograph. The important subject of the spectra emitted by various sources of radiation will be treated extensively beginning in Chap. 12, and it will be satisfying to have the discussion of experimental measurements of spectra based squarely on the one theory which is adopted as fundamental in this book and to have available as a concrete example the diffraction grating. (Other types of spectrographs, notably the various interferometers, will also be treated on an electromagnetic basis, but they will not have been taken up at the time the idea of a spectrum first enters.)

This chapter has given a qualitative description of the physical origin of diffraction. The description is obviously oversimplified, as it must be if it is to be based on the Lorentz theory, but it corresponds reasonably well with observation of diffraction, and it will be found useful as background for the next few chapters.

chapter **7**

Fraunhofer Diffraction by N Identical Apertures

The first problem in diffraction to be considered is that of any number N of identical apertures of any size and shape arranged in some way in a plane, opaque screen. The apertures are assumed to be similarly oriented so that if, for example, they are of elliptical shape, all the long axes are parallel. In addition, it will be assumed that the boundaries of two apertures never come closer together than a fairly large number of wavelengths, so that the behavior of the oscillators around the edge of one is unaffected by the presence of the other. (This condition is violated in some important cases and will be reconsidered later.) If the primary source of radiation and the observing screen are so placed with respect to the array of apertures as to give rise to what is known as the Fraunhofer type of diffraction, then some very general conclusions about the diffraction pattern can be drawn; these conclusions will be of great importance in many applications.

7-1 Definition of Fraunhofer Diffraction A monochromatic point source S is on one side of the diffracting screen, and an observing point P is on the other side. These points are taken to be at great distances from the apertures, the distances being precisely specified in the following way: Let C be a circle drawn on the diffracting screen so as to enclose all the apertures. With C as base construct cones with vertices at S and P. Draw a sphere about S as center such that it

touches a point of C; do the same with P as center.   The result is shown
in Fig. 7-1, in which A and B represent diametrically opposite points of
the circle C, and Σ_1 and Σ_2 are traces of the two spheres.   The conditions to be satisfied are that those parts of the spherical surfaces included

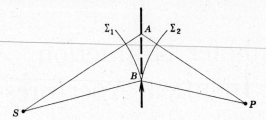

Fig. 7-1.   *Construction for defining Fraunhofer diffraction.*

in the cones depart from planes by not more than a small fraction of a
wavelength, say one-twentieth.   These conditions define what is called
the *Fraunhofer case*.   On an observing screen whose points are sufficiently
far away to satisfy the above condi-
tion, the distribution of light is called a
Fraunhofer diffraction pattern.   If either
S or P or both are too close to the
screen to yield the Fraunhofer case,
one has the *Fresnel case*, which will be
the subject of a later chapter.

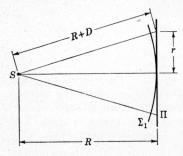

Fig. 7-2. *Construction for finding the order of magnitude of R
implied by the condition for
Fraunhofer diffraction.*

To see what distances are implied
by the definition of Fraunhofer diffraction, consider Fig. 7-2, in which the
sphere Σ_1 is compared with the plane
Π over a circle of radius r, this being
the radius of the circle C in the definition.   In all cases to be considered, r
will be many wavelengths long, and
since D must be a small fraction of a wavelength, it is clear that R must
be much greater than D.   Then the pythagorean relation

$$(R + D)^2 = R^2 + r^2$$

becomes approximately

$$R \approx \frac{r^2}{2D}$$

If λ is the wavelength of some color of visible light and $D \leqq \lambda/10$ and r
is of the order of 1 cm, R must be at least of the order of 1 km, so that
very great distances indeed can be involved.   Achieving Fraunhofer
diffraction in less space by means of lenses and other devices will be

discussed later, but in order not to obscure the arguments, these accessories will be omitted for the time being. An important consequence of the large distances is that from S or P all the apertures are seen to lie in essentially the same direction, since the distance from the apertures to S or P is very large compared with the diameter of the circumscribing circle C.

7-2 Coordinate System To specify the positions of the apertures, choose a point O in the screen near the apertures (that is, such that it can be included in a circle C having properties as in the last section) and set up a cartesian coordinate system with O as origin. In each aperture choose a point labeled Q together with a subscript to distinguish the aperture. All these points are to be in corresponding positions, as illustrated in Fig. 7-3. The position of each aperture is then specified by the coordinates of its representative point Q.

To specify the position of the source S and observing point P with respect to the diffracting screen, the coordinate system shown in Fig. 7-4 will be used. In this system reference planes parallel to the diffracting screen are passed through S and P, and in each a pair of cartesian axes

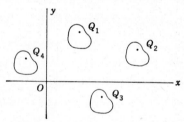

Fig. 7-3. *Identical apertures in a diffracting screen referred to cartesian coordinates.*

are drawn such that the line O_1O_2 is perpendicular to the screen through its origin O. The three x axes are parallel, as are the y axes. Note carefully the definitions of the four angles $\theta_1, \ldots, \phi_2$. Note particularly that the two lines defining θ_1 lie in a plane passing through the x axis in the diffracting screen, and similarly for the three other angles. The angles are measured positively in the directions indicated.

7-3 General Principles for Identical Apertures The problem of N identical apertures can be broken into two separate parts. It will be seen that the flux density of the energy passing by P in unit time is that which passes when just one aperture is open multiplied by a factor which depends only on the number and relative positions of the apertures, that is, on the positions of the points Q. The present chapter deals with the latter factor. The calculation of the diffraction pattern of a single aperture of given size and shape is the subject of Chap. 9, and in the present discussion only a few of the properties of such a pattern need be noted.

Suppose that all but one of the apertures are covered. On an observing screen covering the X_2Y_2 plane in Fig. 7-4, a diffraction pattern appears

about which the following facts, to be verified in Chap. 9, can be stated:
The intensity of the pattern varies in a more or less complicated way
from point to point, but the region over which it is appreciable is much
larger than the size of the aperture. The reason is that the angular
spread of the diffracted light, measured in radians, is of the order of the
wavelength divided by a representative linear dimension of the aperture
(for example, the diameter in the case of a circle), and even though this
angle is small when the aperture is large compared with λ, it results in a
large pattern on the very distant observing screen. Suppose now that
the aperture just considered is covered and another is opened. A pattern
of the same size having the same relative distribution of intensity is

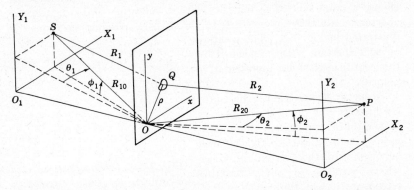

Fig. 7-4. *Complete coordinate system for a problem in Fraunhofer diffraction.*

formed, but is shifted with respect to the first. The length of the shift
is the distance between the points in the X_2Y_2 plane defined by the lines
from S through the points Q associated with the two apertures. Under
the conditions of Fraunhofer diffraction this shift is very small compared
with the size of the pattern, and hence the intensity at a given point P
is practically independent of which aperture is open.

With regard to the electric (or magnetic) field at P when one aperture
is open, one can now conclude that only its phase, and not its amplitude
or polarization, depends on which particular aperture is open. The
argument can be based on any of the three points of view described in
Chap. 6, but it is simplest to invoke the third, according to which the
field at P can be thought of as originating in a set of fictitious oscillators
covering the aperture. These oscillators execute motions determined
by the nature of the primary incident wave, and since the latter is essentially a plane wave over the array of apertures, the only difference in this
wave at corresponding points in any two apertures (such as the points Q)
is a difference of phase when the wave is not normally incident on the

screen. The fictitious oscillators at a pair of corresponding positions in the two apertures then execute the same sinusoidal motion except for this difference of phase. The difference of phase between waves arriving at P from two different apertures receives one contribution from the difference between the oscillators in the apertures and a second contribution from the different distances from the apertures to P.

To express the ideas of the last paragraph in workable form, the phase of the wave arriving at P from an aperture whose point Q is at location (x,y) in the screen will be compared with that of the wave which would arrive from an aperture whose point Q is located at the origin O (where there may or may not actually be an aperture). Suppose the reference wave from O has an electric field at P whose complex amplitude is $\mathbf{A} + i\mathbf{B}$. From Fig. 7-4, the difference between the distances from the two apertures to S is $\Delta_1 = R_1 - R_{10}$, and the difference between the distances to P is $\Delta_2 = R_2 - R_{20}$. The complex amplitude of the wave at P from the aperture at (x,y) is then, simply,

$$(\mathbf{A} + i\mathbf{B})e^{ik(\Delta_1 + \Delta_2)} \tag{7-1}$$

The quantity in the exponent can be written $2\pi(\Delta_1 + \Delta_2)/\lambda$. It is customary to refer to $\Delta_1 + \Delta_2$ as the *geometric difference of path* for the two apertures. Dividing by λ expresses this difference as a number of wavelengths, and multiplying by 2π expresses it in radians. The whole expression $k(\Delta_1 + \Delta_2)$ is called the *difference of phase* between the two waves arriving at P.

7-4 Calculation of the Geometric Difference of Path Expressions for Δ_1 and Δ_2 in terms of the coordinates in Fig. 7-4 are obtained in the following way: By the law of Pythagoras, the square of the length L from O to O_1 can be written in two ways:

$$L^2 = R_1{}^2 - (x - X_1)^2 - (y - Y_1)^2 = R_{10}{}^2 - X_1{}^2 - Y_1{}^2$$

Hence

$$\Delta_1 = R_1 - R_{10} = \frac{\rho^2}{R_1 + R_{10}} - \frac{2}{R_1 + R_{10}}(xX_1 + yY_1)$$

where $\rho^2 = x^2 + y^2$, and ρ is the distance from O to (x,y). The term involving ρ^2 can be neglected, since it is easily deduced from the calculations in Sec. 7-1 that this term is always a small fraction of a wavelength and therefore contributes a negligible amount to the difference of phase. Then, since $R_1 + R_{10} \approx 2R_{10}$, it is sufficient to write

$$\Delta_1 = -\frac{1}{R_{10}}(xX_1 + yY_1)$$

Neglecting the term involving ρ^2 in the exact expression for Δ amounts to treating the spherical wave front arriving at the apertures as though it were plane.   Now

$$\frac{X_1}{R_{10}} = \sin \theta_1 \qquad \frac{Y_1}{R_{10}} = \sin \phi_1$$

so the final expression is

$$\Delta_1 = -x \sin \theta_1 - y \sin \phi_1 \qquad\qquad (7\text{-}2)$$

In the same way,

$$\Delta_2 = -x \sin \theta_2 - y \sin \phi_2 \qquad\qquad (7\text{-}3)$$

Note that the approximate expressions (7-2) and (7-3) are good for all values of $\theta_1, \ldots, \phi_2$ between $-\pi/2$ and $\pi/2$.

7-5   General Formulas for the Diffraction Pattern   The total amplitude of the electric field at P is now obtained by substituting in (7-1) the appropriate values of Δ_1 and Δ_2 for each aperture, as given by (7-2) and (7-3), and summing.   If the jth aperture is at (x_j, y_j), the result is

$$\mathbf{e}_P = (\mathbf{A} + i\mathbf{B})e^{-i\omega t} \sum_{j=1}^{N} e^{-ik[x_j(\sin \theta_1 + \sin \theta_2) + y_j(\sin \phi_1 + \sin \phi_2)]} \qquad (7\text{-}4)$$

The magnetic field is equal in magnitude and at right angles to the electric field (since both fields are ultimately sums of dipole fields, each of which has these properties, and all of which arrive at P from essentially the same direction).   It can be written

$$\mathbf{b}_P = \frac{\mathbf{k}}{k} \times \mathbf{e}_P \qquad\qquad (7\text{-}5)$$

where $\mathbf{k}$ is the wave vector (pointing away from the apertures).   Substituting (7-4) and (7-5) in (5-14) and recalling that $\mathbf{A}$ and $\mathbf{B}$ must be perpendicular to $\mathbf{k}$, the time average of the Poynting vector at P is

$$\langle \mathbf{S}_P \rangle = \langle \mathbf{S}_P \rangle_1 \left| \sum_{j=1}^{N} e^{-ik[x_j(\sin \theta_1 + \sin \theta_2) + y_j(\sin \phi_1 + \sin \phi_2)]} \right|^2 \qquad (7\text{-}6)$$

where

$$\langle \mathbf{S}_P \rangle_1 = \frac{c}{8\pi k} (A^2 + B^2)\mathbf{k} \qquad\qquad (7\text{-}7)$$

The last expression is just the time average of the Poynting vector at P when only one aperture is open.

7-6   Abbreviated Notation.   The Term Normal Irradiance Formula (7-6) is the fundamental result for N identical apertures, and it will be convenient to represent it by the abbreviated notation

$$I = I_1 |F|^2 \tag{7-8}$$

where I and I_1 stand for the magnitudes of the vectors on the left of (7-6) and (7-7), and

$$F = \sum_{j=1}^{N} e^{-ik[x_j(\sin\theta_1 + \sin\theta_2) + y_j(\sin\phi_1 + \sin\phi_2)]} \tag{7-9}$$

The symbol I stands for the magnitude of the time average of the Poynting vector of the resultant wave arriving at P when all the apertures are open.   Its physical significance is such that if a detector of radiation has a small, plane sensitive surface, and if this surface passes through the point P and is oriented to be normal to the direction of propagation of the wave, then I is the time average of the rate at which energy falls on the detector divided by the area of the detector.   It is appropriate to introduce a concise name for this important idea, and it will be called the *normal irradiance* of the wave.[1]   The quantity I_1 is then the normal irradiance of the wave arriving at P when just one aperture is open.

Formula (7-8) is the quantitative form of the opening statements of Sec. 7-3, since the effect on the diffraction pattern of the particular arrangement of the apertures is contained entirely in the factor $|F|^2$. The work of the rest of this chapter will consist largely in evaluating $|F|^2$ for various arrays and examining the resulting patterns.

The choice of the x and y axes in the diffracting screen fixes the whole system of Fig. 7-4.   The final diffraction pattern is independent of this choice, and one is free to choose these axes with respect to the array of apertures so as to make the calculation of $|F|^2$ and the interpretation of the result as simple as possible.   The only condition that must be observed is the one already mentioned, namely, that the origin O must not be so far from the apertures that the approximations leading to (7-2) and (7-3) cease to be valid.

7-7   Case $N = 2$.   Young's Experiment Consider two identical apertures separated by a distance d.   Take the representative point Q_1 for the first to be at the origin O of the xy plane in Fig. 7-4, so that $x_1 = y_1 = 0$.   Take the point Q_2 for the second to be at $x_2 = d$, $y_2 = 0$. Thus the coordinate system is related to the apertures as in Fig. 7-5a.

---

[1] Many authors use the term *intensity*, but the disadvantage is that this word has been given so many meanings that it becomes definite only through careful attention to the particular context.   In the term "normal irradiance," the word "normal" will often be left understood.

Define δ by

$$\delta = \frac{kd}{2\pi}(\sin\theta_1 + \sin\theta_2) = \frac{d}{\lambda}(\sin\theta_1 + \sin\theta_2) \qquad (7\text{-}10)$$

Then $F = 1 + e^{-i2\pi\delta} = (e^{i\pi\delta} + e^{-i\pi\delta})e^{-i\pi\delta} = 2\cos\pi\delta\, e^{-i\pi\delta}$

and $|F|^2 = 4\cos^2\pi\delta \qquad\qquad\qquad\qquad\qquad\qquad (7\text{-}11)$

The two terms giving F can also be added by applying trigonometry to the vector diagram in the complex plane as illustrated in Fig. 7-5b.

[While it is definitely appropriate to pass the x axis through a pair of corresponding points in the two apertures, the choice of the origin O on this axis is not so uniquely suggested. One should consider choices other than the one made above. For example, take O midway between the two points Q, and show that then $F = 2\cos\pi\delta$. More generally, one easily sees that for any array of apertures, a translation of the x and y

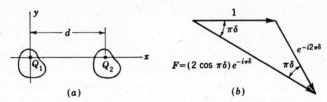

Fig. 7-5.   **a.** *Two apertures related to cartesian coordinates.*   **b.** *Vector summation giving F.*

axes changes F, as given by (7-9), by a unimodular factor, but does not change $|F|^2$.]

The interpretation of formulas (7-10) and (7-11) is as follows: Let the source S have some fixed position defined by the angles θ_1 and ϕ_1. The position of the observing point P is specified by the angles θ_2 and ϕ_2, and with each position of P is associated a value of δ. The significance of δ is that it is the geometric difference of path measured in wavelengths. That is, the paths SQ_1P and SQ_2P differ by δ wavelengths (see end of Sec. 7-3). If this difference is zero or an integer, positive or negative, the two waves arriving at P are in phase and reinforce to give a maximum in the pattern. At points P such that δ is half an odd integer, the waves cancel, and no radiation appears. This behavior is seen again by considering the values of δ which give $|F|^2$ its maximum value (4) and those which give the minimum value (0).

The type of diffraction pattern produced by two apertures is illustrated most simply by the special case of normal incidence on the diffracting screen, so that S is at O_1 in Fig. 7-4 and $\theta_1 = \phi_1 = 0$. Let the observing screen be the X_2Y_2 plane, and suppose the apertures are circles. The single-aperture pattern I_1 then appears as in Fig. 7-6a. Its center is at the origin O_2 of the observing plane, and while its details are unimportant for the present, some feeling for its size is given by the fact that the dark ring surrounding the bright central region has an angular diameter as seen from the aperture equal to about λ/D radians, where D is the diameter of the aperture. Usual values are 10^{-2} or less, so that only small values of θ_2 and ϕ_2 are of interest. If L is the distance between the diffracting and observing screens, the linear diameter of the dark ring is about $\lambda L/D$. To illustrate the effects of opening several apertures, attention will be confined to just the bright central region of the single-aperture pattern. This part is shown enlarged and less heavily exposed in Fig. 7-6b.

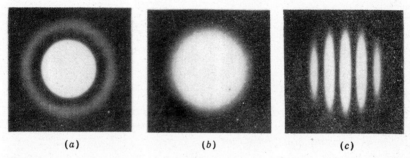

(a)   (b)   (c)

Fig. 7-6. **a.** *Single-aperture pattern for a circular aperture.* **b.** *Central bright region of the pattern of* (**a**) *enlarged and less heavily exposed.* **c.** *Pattern for two circular apertures.*

When both apertures are open, the pattern appears as in Fig. 7-6c. The fringes, which are perpendicular to the X_2 axis, are the result of the factor $|F|^2$. When the angles θ_2 and ϕ_2 are small, $\delta \approx \theta_2 d/\lambda$, and from Fig. 7-4 it is seen that $\delta \approx X_2 d/\lambda L$. When δ increases by unity, θ_2 increases by λ/d, and X_2 increases by $\lambda L/d$, the latter then being the linear distance between successive maxima of the fringes. It is customary to identify each fringe by the integral value of δ associated with it and to call this value the *order* of the fringe. The zeroth order coincides with the Y_2 axis and is flanked by orders $+1$ and -1, etc. All these relations are illustrated to a greatly distorted scale by Fig. 7-7. (In particular, d is shown much too large with respect to the size of the pattern.) Here the solid curve plotted along the X_2 axis is $I = 4I_1 \cos^2 \pi\delta$, and the dashed envelope is the function $4I_1$.

The original observation of the diffraction pattern formed by a double aperture was made by Thomas Young at the beginning of the nineteenth century. His source was a pinhole illuminated by white sunlight, and his diffracting apertures were two other pinholes. The fringes, being formed in white light, were less distinct than they would have been with nearly monochromatic light, but the results gave the first clear evidence of interference between two separate beams of light when these beams originate in the same source. The discussion in this section constitutes only a partial explanation of Young's experiment with white light, since it is limited to strictly monochromatic light. The additional theory required will be given in Chap. 13.

Even the photographs in Fig. 7-6 must eventually be considered in the light of the theory of Chap. 13. While they were made with nearly monochromatic light from a very small source and could be shown to agree within experimental error with the calculations of this section, it

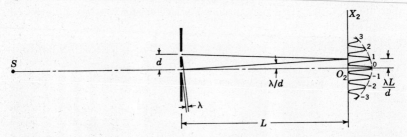

Fig. 7-7. *Geometrical relation of the fringes to the two apertures producing them. The individual fringes are identified by their order numbers. Relative proportions are grossly distorted.*

remains to show why this agreement should hold when the light is not strictly monochromatic and the source is not strictly a point.

7-8 Uniform Linear Array Let N identical apertures be equally spaced along the x axis of Fig. 7-4. Let the locations of their representative points Q on this axis be $x_1 = 0$, $x_2 = d$, $x_3 = 2d$, . . . ,

$$x_N = (N - 1)d$$

Introducing again the δ defined by (7-10),

$$F = \sum_{j=1}^{N} e^{-i(j-1)2\pi\delta} \tag{7-12}$$

This series is a geometric progression, and one can apply the general formula

$$1 + a + a^2 + \cdots + a^{N-1} = \frac{1 - a^N}{1 - a}$$

to obtain

$$F = \frac{1 - e^{-iN2\pi\delta}}{1 - e^{-i2\pi\delta}} = \frac{e^{iN\pi\delta} - e^{-iN\pi\delta}}{e^{i\pi\delta} - e^{-i\pi\delta}} \frac{e^{-iN\pi\delta}}{e^{-i\pi\delta}} = \frac{\sin N\pi\delta}{\sin \pi\delta} e^{-i(N-1)\pi\delta} \tag{7-13}$$

Finally,

$$|F|^2 = \frac{\sin^2 N\pi\delta}{\sin^2 \pi\delta} \tag{7-14}$$

For $N = 2$, this result is equivalent to (7-11).

An alternative evaluation of F is to perform the summation in (7-12) as a graphical addition of vectors in the complex plane, as illustrated in Fig. 7-8. Here all the vectors being added are of unit length, and C is the center of a circle of radius ρ which passes through the end points of all the vectors. The value of ρ is found from one of the small isosceles triangles to be

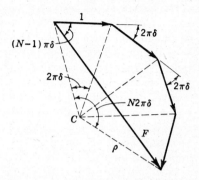

$$\rho = \frac{1}{2 \sin \pi \delta}$$

The resultant F then has magnitude

$$|F| = |2\rho \sin N\pi\delta| = \left| \frac{\sin N\pi\delta}{\sin \pi\delta} \right|$$

and F itself is obtained by removing the vertical bars and multiplying by $e^{-i(N-1)\pi\delta}$.

Fig. 7-8. *Typical vector diagram for finding F in the case of a linear array of N apertures. In general, the polygon of unit vectors may describe several revolutions.*

A plot of $|F|^2$ as a function of δ is most easily drawn by first plotting the factor $1/\sin^2 \pi\delta$ and then multiplying each ordinate by $\sin^2 N\pi\delta$. The plot is periodic in δ with period unity, and the significant range is

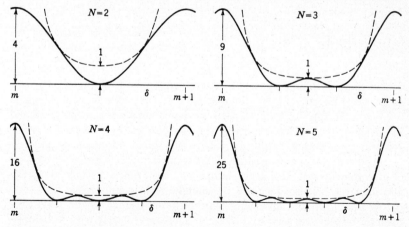

Fig. 7-9. *$|F|^2$ for a linear array as a function of δ for several values of N. The curves are periodic in δ with period unity; only one period is shown.*

between those values of δ for which $\theta_2 = \pm\pi/2$. Figure 7-9 shows the result for several small values of N. Here the dashed curves represent the factor $1/\sin^2 \pi\delta$, and m is any integer. When δ is an integer, the numerator and denominator of $|F|^2$ are both zero, and one shows that the value of the indeterminate form is N^2.

The curves of $|F|^2$ are characterized as having a *principal maximum* at each integral value of δ. The integer is called the *order* of the principal maximum to which it belongs. Between two principal maxima fall $N - 1$ zeros at intervals of $1/N$ in δ (the zeros of the numerator of $|F|^2$) and $N - 2$ *secondary maxima*. The solid curve touches the dashed one whenever the numerator of (7-14) is equal to unity, but the secondary maxima do not lie exactly at these points, except when N is odd and $\delta = m + \frac{1}{2}$, the ordinate of this maximum always being unity. As N increases, the widths of the principal maxima become smaller and smaller as a fraction of the spacing between these maxima, a point of utmost importance for applications.

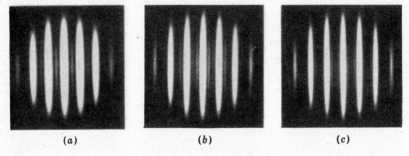

(a)   (b)   (c)

Fig. 7-10. *Fraunhofer patterns for linear arrays of three, four, and five circular apertures.*

The final diffraction pattern is obtained by multiplying $|F|^2$ by the single-aperture pattern I_1. Photographs of the cases $N = 3$, 4, and 5 with circular apertures and normal incidence are shown in Fig. 7-10 and can be compared with the cases $N = 1$ and 2 in Fig. 7-6. A photographic reproduction cannot faithfully render the great range of irradiances involved. If a visual experiment is performed in which one after another of the apertures in the array is opened, the fringes become narrower and brighter. This effect can be thought of in these terms: The total power falling on the observing plane is proportional to the total area open to the incident wave and therefore increases linearly with N. Interference causes this power to be concentrated in fringes whose widths vary as $1/N$. The power density, i.e., the irradiance, at a principal maximum therefore increases as N^2.

In the case of very large N only those secondary maxima which lie in a small range of δ on each side of a principal maximum have ordinates comparable to that of the principal maximum itself. If one considers the region about $\delta = m$ and lets $\delta' = \delta - m$, then (7-14) can be approximated by

$$|F|^2 \approx \frac{\sin^2 N\pi\delta'}{(\pi\delta')^2} \qquad N \gg 1, |\delta'| \ll 1 \qquad (7\text{-}15)$$

Figure 7-11 shows a plot of this function. The dashed curve is the factor $1/(\pi\delta')^2$. Each secondary maximum now has a height which is a definite fraction of the height of the principal maximum independently of the value of N; in particular, to the largest ones correspond the fraction 0.047.

The function $|F|^2$ is defined for all positions of the source S and observing point P, although it has significance only for those positions far enough from the apertures to yield the Fraunhofer case. For certain applications of linear arrays, it is important to have in mind the loci of points P satisfying $|F|^2 = constant$ when S, and hence θ_1 and ϕ_1, are

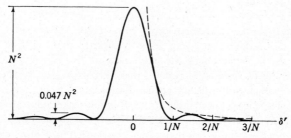

Fig. 7-11. *Profile of $|F|^2$ in the immediate vicinity of a principal maximum for a linear array with large N.*

fixed. The locus passing through any given position of P has a definite value of δ associated with it, and hence the locus is the surface defined by $\theta_2 = constant$. From Fig. 7-4, such a surface is seen to be a cone whose vertex is at O, whose axis is the x axis (the axis along which the apertures are arranged), and whose generators form the angle $\pi/2 - \theta_2$ with the positive x axis. On an observing screen $|F|^2$ is constant along any locus which is the intersection of one of these cones and the screen. For example, if the screen is the X_2Y_2 plane in Fig. 7-4, the intersection is a branch of a hyperbola whose vertex is on the X_2 axis and whose asymptotes pass through the origin O_2 and form angles $\pm(\pi/2 - \theta_2)$ with the positive X_2 axis. Thus the fringes in Figs. 7-6 and 7-10 are actually arcs of hyperbolas, only the center one being straight, but such small ranges of values of θ_2 and ϕ_2 are involved in these photographs that the curvatures are not evident. Again, if the observing screen is a hemisphere with center at O, the loci are semicircles whose planes are perpendicular to the x axis. The cone defining the zero-order principal maximum of $|F|^2$ always contains as one of its generators the extension of the line from S through O, and this line can be said to define the *forward direction* from the apertures. On any observing screen there will be a point P_0 lying in the forward direction. The single-aperture pattern is then distributed around P_0 in a manner determined by the size and shape of the aperture and the angle of incidence; this pattern is crossed by the fringes defined by the factor $|F|^2$. The zero-order fringe always passes through P_0.

It is also important for some applications to consider the behavior of $|F|^2$ at a fixed observing point when the source is moved. The value of $|F|^2$ remains constant if S moves on a cone $\theta_1 = constant$. When S moves to other cones, the irradiance at P passes through a principal maximum whenever θ_1 is such as to give δ an integral value. However, the irradiance at P contains that due to a single aperture as a factor and hence can be different from zero only if P_0 (which moves when S moves) is not too far from P.

7-9 Reciprocity Theorem and Sensitivity Pattern From the discussion of the last two paragraphs it appears that there is a certain symmetry in the behavior of the irradiance at P when P is moved and when S is moved. This symmetry is precisely expressed by the *reciprocity theorem*, which states that the irradiance at P when a given source is at S is the same as the irradiance at S when the same source is at P. The proof consists in showing that in (7-8) the factors I_1 and $|F|^2$ separately are unaffected by interchanging the source and observing point. The proof for I_1 will be given in the next chapter. That for $|F|^2$ is simply that in (7-9) the subscripts 1 and 2 can be interchanged without affecting $|F|^2$. (The argument thus applies to any array and not just to a linear one.)

The reciprocity theorem allows one to think of the variation in irradiance at P as S is moved in terms of a *sensitivity pattern* in the space in which the source lies. Suppose S is to move over some surface Σ, such as the X_1Y_1 plane. Let the intensity of the source at S be measured in terms of some unit, and let a source of unit intensity be placed at P. The latter produces a diffraction pattern on Σ. Let the irradiance at its various points be denoted by $\mathcal{S}$. Then the irradiance at P due to the given source at S is the intensity of that source multiplied by the *sensitivity* $\mathcal{S}$.

7-10 Rectangular Array Consider a rectangular array of NM apertures arranged in N columns and M rows, as shown in Fig. 7-12. The position of the aperture in column j (counting to the right) and row l (counting up) has coordinates

$$x_{jl} = (j - 1)d_x \qquad y_{jl} = (l - 1)d_y$$

Substitute these coordinates in (7-9); the single sum over j in that formula now becomes a double sum over j and l. Let

$$\delta_x = \frac{kd_x}{2\pi}(\sin\theta_1 + \sin\theta_2) \qquad \delta_y = \frac{kd_y}{2\pi}(\sin\phi_1 + \sin\phi_2)$$

Then
$$F = \sum_{j=1}^{N}\sum_{l=1}^{M} e^{-i2\pi[(j-1)\delta_x + (l-1)\delta_y]}$$

$$= \sum_{j=1}^{N} e^{-i2\pi(j-1)\delta_x} \sum_{l=1}^{M} e^{-i2\pi(l-1)\delta_y}$$

(One easily satisfies oneself that the double sum factors into two single sums in the above manner. For example, write out all the terms when $N = M = 2$ to see this property in less compressed form.) The single sums are evaluated as for the linear array, and the final result is

$$|F|^2 = \frac{\sin^2 N\pi\delta_x}{\sin^2 \pi\delta_x}\frac{\sin^2 M\pi\delta_y}{\sin^2 \pi\delta_y} \quad (7\text{-}16)$$

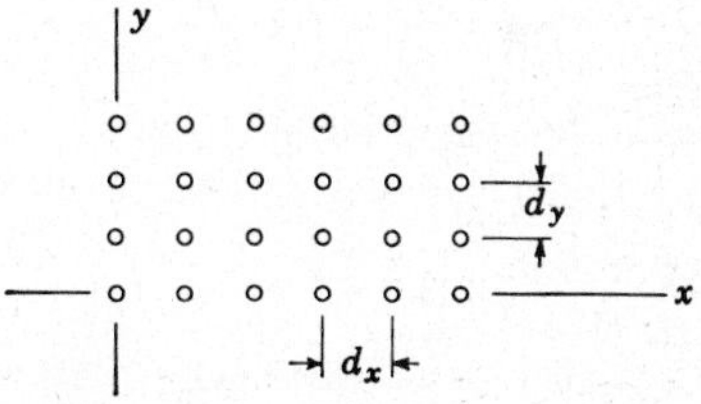

Fig. 7-12. *Rectangular array of apertures referred to cartesian coordinates.*

The diffraction pattern, as far as it is determined by $|F|^2$, is dominated by principal maxima which are now spots rather than bands and which are located at those points of the observing screen defined by giving integral values to both δ_x and δ_y. The resulting value of $|F|^2$ is N^2M^2. On the X_2Y_2 plane these points are the intersections of two families of hyperbolas, one defined by $\theta_2 = constant$, and the other by $\phi_2 = constant$. With normal incidence, the single-aperture pattern limits the observed spots to the region around O_2, where the families of hyperbolas form essentially two sets of equally spaced straight lines, one parallel to the X_2 axis with spacing proportional to $1/d_y$ and the other parallel to the Y_2 axis with spacing proportional to $1/d_x$. The spacing of the spots is therefore geometrically similar to the spacing in the array of points in Fig. 7-12 if that array is turned through 90°. The photograph in Fig. 7-13a shows this pattern when the individual apertures are circles and $d_x = d_y$. Between the principal maxima occur secondary maxima, which are also spots, and which have various brightnesses. If N and M are large, approximations analogous to those in (7-15) can be made in (7-16) to obtain a formula valid in the immediate vicinity of any principal maximum; it will be shown in Chap. 9 that this local pattern has the same appearance as that for a single rectangular aperture whose edges coincide with the outermost rows and columns in Fig. 7-12. For the time being, ignore these secondary maxima, and think of the whole pattern as consisting merely of a rectangular array of bright spots.

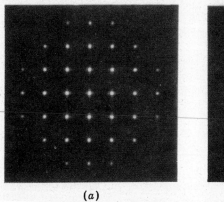
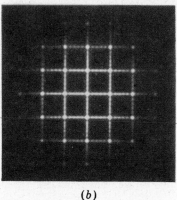

(a)   (b)

Fig. 7-13. a. *Fraunhofer pattern for the rectangular array of Fig. 7-12 with 10 rows and 10 columns and the same spacing in the two directions.* **b.** *Pattern for the crossed array of Fig. 7-14 with 11 holes horizontally and vertically.*

7-11 Crossed Array An array not only interesting in itself but which has been applied in radio astronomy consists of two uniform linear arrays at right angles, as illustrated in Fig. 7-14. If the two arms contain the same odd number N of circular apertures (the total number then being $2N - 1$ since the center aperture is common to both arms),

and if the spacing is the same in the two directions, the pattern appears as in Fig. 7-13*b*. The main features are (1) a square grid of fine fringes and (2) bright spots where the fringes cross. In addition there is a complicated set of secondary maxima and minima, but we shall ignore them. It will be left as one of the problems to calculate $|F|^2$ for this array and to show that when N is large, $|F|^2$ is approximately constant and equal to N^2 along the center lines of the fringes, except that it rises to $4N^2$ at the intersections. A second problem will deal with a related array, and these two problems will be followed by a brief description of an application. Some necessary background for this description will be given in Sec. 7-14.

Fig. 7-14. *Crossed array of apertures.*

7-12 Applications of Regular Arrays The basis of applications of regular arrays is the fact that for a given array and observing screen, the positions of the principal maxima depend on the position of the source and on the wavelength. According as the application is either to find the position of a source emitting a known wavelength or to determine the wavelength emitted by a source of known position, one speaks of either an *interference telescope* or a *spectroscope*.

(The diffraction pattern also depends on the spacings involved in the array; the latter can be determined from observation with a source of known position and wavelength. The main applications of this idea are to the three-dimensional arrays involved in crystal structures and will be discussed later under the heading of scattering, a topic closely related to diffraction.)

In principle, the most straightforward observation would be to measure the values of θ_2 for the principal maxima of various orders (supposing the case of a linear array along the x axis of Fig. 7-4), to set (7-10) equal to the appropriate integers, and finally to infer θ_1 or λ, according to the problem. The difficulty is that measuring the values of θ_2 requires locating a reference frame with respect to the array, and only rarely can this be done with the accuracy that would take full advantage of the sharpness of the fringes. As a result, most applications giving high accuracy compare the positions of two sources or compare two wavelengths. In order to understand these applications, it is necessary to state some facts about the formation of diffraction patterns with two or more independent sources acting simultaneously. The justification of these statements will be an important result to come from the work in Chaps. 12 and 13.

As already mentioned, an actual source can never be a true point and can never be perfectly monochromatic, but there are cases in which the theory based on the idealization of a true monochromatic point source predicts diffraction patterns which agree with observation. Imagine now that there are two real sources completely independent of each other and so small and so nearly monochromatic that with either one alone the idealized theory can be employed to predict with negligible error the irradiance in the diffraction pattern that results. When both sources operate simultaneously, whether they be at essentially the same point or at different points, and whether they emit the same wavelength or two different wavelengths, the rule is that at any point in the diffraction pattern *the irradiance is the sum of the irradiances at that point when each source operates alone.* This rule, which extends to any number of sources, each of which is essentially a point monochromatic source, is called the *rule for incoherent sources* and will be used through Chap. 10 without further inquiry. However, it can be pointed out in advance that it is proved by starting with the universally applicable rule of adding instantaneous amplitudes (no matter how complicated they may be as functions of the time), calculating the instantaneous Poynting vector, and taking a time average. With independent sources this time average will come out as a sum of terms, one for each source, in accordance with the above rule. The rule can be augmented slightly to cover an extended source.   Here one divides the area of the source into small elements and treats all of them as incoherent point sources.

Another preliminary matter to be discussed is the practical means of achieving the conditions of Fraunhofer diffraction in reasonable space. These means take various forms, but all involve a single idea which can be brought out by an example using lenses.   Consider a point mono-chromatic source S in the focal plane of a positive lens, as in Fig. 7-15. According to the notion of rays, the ray SA in the object space becomes the ray BC in the image space and appears to have come from a point source at an infinite distance.   However, in connection with diffraction it is more to the point to think in terms of a set of wave fronts spaced

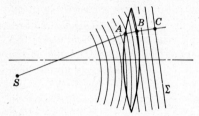

Fig. 7-15.   *Manner in which a positive lens converts spherical wave fronts from a source in its focal plane into plane wave fronts.*

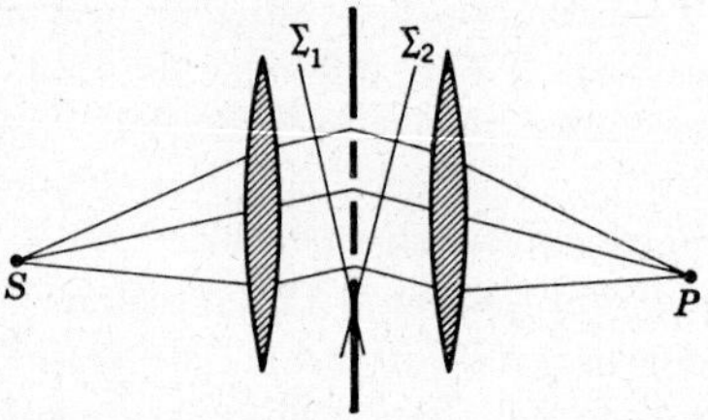

Fig. 7-16.   *Use of lenses in achieving the conditions of Fraunhofer diffraction in a small space.*

one wavelength apart.   The function of the lens is to convert the spherical wave fronts leaving the source in the object space into plane wave fronts in the image space.   The most important feature of Fig. 7-15 is that along any ray from S to the plane Σ one counts the same number of wavelengths, allowing for the fact that the wavelength in the glass is less than that in air.   The length of a ray such as $SABC$ can be expressed in two ways.   One is to give the total length in centimeters, called the *geometrical length,* and the other is to give the number of wavelengths counted along the ray, called the *optical length* of the ray.[1]   Unlike the geometrical length, the optical lengths of all rays connecting the source and the plane wave front Σ in Fig. 7-15 (or connecting any two wave fronts) are equal.

The complete arrangement for Fraunhofer diffraction with a plane diffracting screen containing several identical apertures and with nearby source and observing point is shown in Fig. 7-16.   The difference of phase

[1] It is more common to define the optical length of a path which passes through several homogeneous media as the sum of the products of the geometrical length in each medium and the refractive index of that medium.   Dividing the optical length defined in this way by the wavelength *in vacuo* gives the optical length in the sense to be used in this book, the latter being more readily extended to the electric transmission lines appearing in some applications to be discussed.

of waves arriving at P from two different apertures is in this case just $2\pi/\lambda$ multiplied by the difference of geometrical lengths of those parts of the paths from S to P via the two apertures which are cut off by the reference planes Σ_1 and Σ_2. This difference of geometrical length can be calculated just as before by use of Fig. 7-4 if the S and P of that figure are the images of the actual source and observing point formed by the lenses. The results are (7-2) and (7-3), which are exact relations if the image points are at infinity. Moreover, the diffraction pattern formed on a screen passing through P in Fig. 7-16 is found by the same arguments as when no lenses are used. For the angles $\theta_1, \ldots, \phi_2$, which determine the directions of rays arriving at any aperture from S and leaving to arrive at P, associate a value of the function F with each position of P through (7-9); if I_1 is the irradiance at P due to a single aperture, the total irradiance is again given by (7-8).[1] The only complication the lenses have added is the trivial problem of relating the positions of S and P to their images, and hence to the angles $\theta_1, \ldots, \phi_2$, through the ordinary laws of geometrical optics. The simplest view is that the diffraction pattern which would be formed on a distant screen if the second lens were removed is imaged by the lens on a nearby screen to produce the same pattern on a reduced scale and with increased brightness. However, it is necessary to resort to the more fundamental view in terms of optical lengths of rays in less simple cases than that represented by Fig. 7-16, as the next two sections will show.

7-13 Michelson Stellar Interferometer The first application to be discussed involves two apertures adapted to the astronomical problem of measuring the small angles between double stars or the small angular diameters of large nearby stars. The idea was suggested by Fizeau in 1868 and realized in an instrument of great versatility by Michelson in 1920. Since that time, Michelson's arrangement has become largely a matter of historical interest, but it is worth examining, since it involves an interesting application of the principles of the formation of diffraction patterns. The idea of the double aperture has been adapted to radio astronomy, but there the instrumental arrangement is much simpler in concept than Michelson's. This point will become clear in the next section.

Consider the two stars indicated by S_1 and S_2 in Fig. 7-17. Let the stars be regarded as point sources, and let their angular separation be α.

---

[1] The argument involves the same approximation as in the case of no lenses, namely, that all the waves arriving at P travel in essentially the same direction and have the same amplitude and polarization. If the focal length of the second lens is too short, this condition is violated, and the problem is no longer simple, in spite of the identical natures of the apertures themselves. Also, if the focal length of the first lens is too short, the amplitude and polarization of the incident wave are not the same at all the apertures.

A diffraction pattern is formed with a diffracting screen having two apertures at separation d in front of a lens of focal length L. Suppose for the moment that the stars are of equal intensity and emit monochromatic light of wavelength λ. Each star gives rise to a pattern of fringes with a "cosine-squared" distribution, as shown to a greatly exaggerated scale in the figure. The dashed envelope represents the shape of the single-aperture pattern. The two zero-order maxima are at P_1 and P_2, and the first-order maximum in the pattern due to S_1 is at P_1'. The angle β is given by $d \sin \beta = \lambda$ or, for small angles, by $\beta = \lambda/d$. The linear distance from P_1 to P_1' is $\beta L = \lambda L/d$, and in order that the fringes be not too fine for observation, L must be sufficiently large in comparison with d. The important point to notice is that this separation is inversely proportional to d/L, which is essentially the angle with

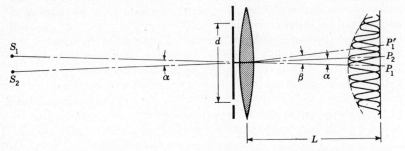

Fig. 7-17. *Using a double aperture as a stellar interferometer. The angle α and the vertical scale of the pattern at the right are greatly enlarged.*

which the interfering beams from the apertures converge at the observing plane. For practical work at visible wavelengths this angle can be no more than about 3° (see Prob. 7-11).

If d is adjusted to make P_2 lie midway between P_1 and P_1', then the sum of the irradiances in the separate patterns gives a total pattern showing no fringes. When this condition is established by observation by gradually increasing d from a small initial value until the fringes first disappear, one has $\alpha = \beta/2 = \lambda/2d$ as the angular separation of the stars in radians.

The question as to how much one gains by adding the apertures rather than using the unobstructed lens as a telescope in the usual way does not have a unique answer. The reason comes from the following considerations: The simple theory of the telescope, to be given later, states that two stars can be "resolved" and the angle between them measured if the angle in radians is not less than $1.22\lambda/D$, where D is the diameter of the objective lens. However, even under the best conditions the turbulence of the atmosphere limits the validity of this formula to diameters no larger than about 10 in.; further increase of D produces a brighter image of a star but not a smaller one, and there is no increase in resolution.   On the other hand, the visibility of the fringes produced by the two apertures (i.e., the contrast of light fringes to dark) turns out to be fairly insensitive to this turbulence regardless of the value of d, but the limitation of the angle of convergence to a maximum of 3° means that with most astronomical telescopes d cannot be made as large as the diameter of the objective.   As a result of all these factors, it turns out that by use of a double aperture in the simple arrangement of Fig. 7-11, it is possible to make a substantial gain in the accuracy with which small angles can be measured over what could be done with a bare telescope limited only by

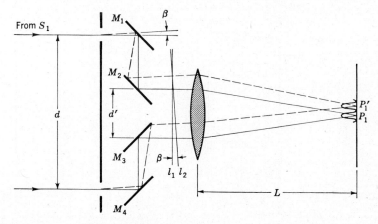

Fig. 7-18. *Michelson's arrangement of the stellar interferometer with the construction for finding the separation of the fringes for one of the two stars.*

turbulence.   Nevertheless, great interest centers on angles that require values of d much larger than can be used in the simple arrangement.

Michelson's arrangement for making use of large separations in conjunction with a lens of reasonable focal length is shown in Fig. 7-18. Behind a screen with two apertures are four plane mirrors $M_1, \ldots, M_4$ accurately adjusted to be parallel in pairs and at 45° to the axis of the lens.   Moreover, the distance between the planes of M_1 and M_2 is exactly equal to that between M_3 and M_4.   Two beams from a star which pass through the apertures at separation d enter the lens at the smaller separation d'.   The angle between two stars is measured by increasing d (and moving M_1 and M_4 symmetrically) until fringes in the focal plane of the lens disappear.   It will now be shown that the angle is then given by the formula applying to Fig. 7-17 using the d of Fig. 7-18, but that the separation of the fringes is fixed at the value corresponding to a pair of apertures at the smaller separation d'.   (In practice no screen is used, and M_1 and M_4 serve as "apertures." However, discussion is facilitated by divorcing the apertures from the mirrors.)

The spacing of the fringes is found from the construction in Fig. 7-18. Two rays from a single star (assumed again to be monochromatic) are normally incident on the screen and pass through the centers of the apertures. Undeviated rays continue as the solid lines and arrive at the zero-order maximum P_1, while two rays deflected through such an angle β as to arrive at the first-order maximum P_1' are shown dashed. The optical length of the lower dashed path must be greater by unity than that of the upper. Let l_1 and l_2 be reference lines perpendicular to the solid and dashed paths, respectively, and intersecting on the upper

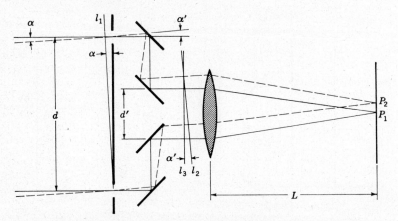

Fig. 7-19. *Michelson's stellar interferometer with the construction for finding the separation of the two zero-order fringes.*

dashed path. One easily sees that the optical lengths of the dashed paths between the apertures and l_1 are equal and that those between l_2 and P_1' are equal. Then β must be given by $\beta = \lambda/d'$, and the distance between P_1 and P_1' is $\beta L = \lambda L/d'$.

To find the separation of the zero-order maxima at P_1 and P_2 when there are two stars, consider the construction in Fig. 7-19. Let rays from one star fall normally on the screen and continue to P_1 as the solid lines. Let rays from the other star, shown dashed, arrive at angle α and be deflected to α' such as to arrive at P_2. Let lines l_1 and l_2 be perpendicular to the dashed paths on the left and right of the diffracting screen, respectively, and let l_3 be perpendicular to the solid paths. The condition that P_2 lie at zero order is $\alpha d = \alpha' d'$, and the distance between P_1 and P_2 is $\alpha' L = \alpha L d/d'$. When d is adjusted for first disappearance of the fringes, P_2 is midway between P_1 and P_1', or $\alpha L d/d' = \lambda L/2d'$, whence $\alpha = \lambda/2d$, the same formula as applies to Fig. 7-17.

In measuring the angular diameter of an individual star, one deals with a source that extends over a circular disk. For a disk of uniform brightness, a calculation which will not be given here shows that as d is increased, a separation is reached for which the fringes disappear, and the angular diameter α is then given by $\alpha = 1.22\lambda/d$. (This result will be derived elegantly in Sec. 13-9.) A correction of rather uncertain magnitude must be made for the fact that the stellar disk is brighter at the center than at the edge (a phenomenon for which observational data exist only for the sun). To measure the larger diameters of stars, which are some hundredths of a second of arc, d must be 3 m or more. The largest instrument that has been built is at Mt. Wilson Observatory; it allows d to be as great as 15 m (50 ft).

There are a number of technical difficulties inherent in the use of a stellar interferometer. Images of stars are faint, and one cannot afford to use a filter which passes quasi-monochromatic light. In white light the fringes, except for the zero order, are strongly tinged with color owing to the dependence of the spacing on wavelength, and considerable judgment must be exercised in deciding when the fringes can be said to have disappeared and for what effective wavelength. In measuring the angle between double stars, there is the complication that the two stars are rarely of the same brightness or the same color, so that the fringes never disappear even approximately, but only pass through a minimum in contrast. Moreover, with white light only the fringes of low order are visible at all, and one must arrange to have the zero-order maximum fall near the center of the single-aperture pattern, which itself is very small if the apertures are large enough to admit sufficient light. For a description of an interesting device for making the final adjustment bringing the small single-aperture patterns into coincidence and the zero-order maximum to the center of them, see Michelson and Pease [65].

7-14 Radio-frequency Telescopes The discovery, made by Jansky in 1932, that radiation at radio frequencies arrives at the surface of the earth from extraterrestrial sources has opened the important field of radio astronomy. The wavelengths involved in this field are limited to the range for which the earth's atmosphere is transparent—from 1 cm to 10 m. The first aim of the observations is to measure the irradiance of the incident radiation as a function of the direction of arrival and frequency. The equipment consists of a highly directional antenna feeding into a radio receiver tuned to be sensitive to a single but adjustable frequency (at least in idealization—in practice a narrow band of frequencies). Auxiliary equipment provides for calibration and for discrimination against interference of terrestrial origin. The discussion in this section will deal with the problem of obtaining an antenna system with a highly directional pattern of sensitivity, and it will be seen that there is a complete analogy with the corresponding problem at visible frequencies.

Those antenna systems used in radio astronomy to which the theory of Fraunhofer diffraction by N identical apertures can be applied consist of a number of identical antenna units, each at the end of a length of cable. The units are distributed over the ground in some array, and the free ends of the cables are connected to the input resistance of the receiver in such a way that across this resistance appears a voltage which is the sum of the voltages appearing when each antenna unit is connected by itself. The individual antennas are analogous to the single apertures of the optical case, the point at which the signal is fed into the receiver is analogous to the observing point P, and the cables are analogous to the optical paths from the apertures to the observing point. The length of a cable can be specified as a number of wavelengths of the voltage waves that travel along it at the given frequency. The length so specified is called the electrical length of the cable and is analogous to the optical length of a light ray.

Concerning an individual antenna, only a few general points need be noted, just as in the case of the single aperture. The structure of the antenna may be any one of the large variety known to radio engineers, the choice in any case being determined by the frequency and directional characteristics desired. However, the properties to be described below are common to all. Let the discussion be limited by the assumption that the receiver is sensitive only to sinusoidal voltages of a single frequency applied at the input. Conclusions based on this idealization hold with negligible error in actual cases in which the receiver is sensitive to a very narrow band of frequencies.

If the antenna is driven by a sinusoidal voltage at the receiver frequency, it will radiate a wave which at a distant point is transverse and, being monochromatic, has a definite polarization, in general elliptical. The polarization is determined by the construction of the antenna and depends on the direction, but in many cases it is the same or nearly the same in all directions for which the radiated wave has appreciable amplitude and is usually arranged to be linear or circular. The relation of the receptive to the radiative characteristics of the antenna is expressed by a reciprocity law. As far as it relates to polarization, this law states the following: Let the polarization (the shape and orientation of the representative ellipse and its handedness) of the wave radiated by the antenna at the receiver frequency and in a given direction be denoted symbolically by $\mathcal{P}$. Now let a monochromatic plane wave at the receiver frequency be incident on the antenna from the same direction and have arbitrary polarization. By use of the resolution described in Prob. 2-20, decompose this wave into two components, one of which has the polarization $\mathcal{P}$ and the other having what can be called the orthogonal polarization and denoted by $\mathcal{P}'$. (For example, if $\mathcal{P}$ is linear in one direction, $\mathcal{P}'$ is linear at right angles; if $\mathcal{P}$ is right-hand circular, $\mathcal{P}'$ is left-hand circular.)   Then the receiver responds only to the component with polarization $\mathcal{P}$ and is completely insensitive to the presence of the other component.   Thus when a wave from an astronomical source of radio noise falls on the antenna, only the irradiance of that spectral component with the receiver frequency and only that part of it with polarization $\mathcal{P}$ is detected.   A complete measurement of the flux density of power in the incident wave involves repeating the observation with the receiver tuned to different frequencies and again with the antenna modified to be sensitive to the polarization $\mathcal{P}'$ (in which case it is insensitive to polarization $\mathcal{P}$).   The total irradiance is then given by an integration with respect to frequency and a summation over the two polarizations (see statement of Prob. 4-12).

It remains to define a sensitivity for the apparatus.   The idea behind the sensitivity $\mathcal{S}$ defined in Sec. 7-9 does not carry over to the radio case without substantial elaboration.   Moreover, in the case of an astronomical source whose distance is unknown, one is constrained to refer only to the irradiance of the wave arriving at the antenna and the direction of arrival.   Here the simplest concept for specifying sensitivity is that of the *effective area* of the antenna, cable, and receiver combined. It is defined in the following way: If a monochromatic plane wave of *unit* irradiance arrives from a given direction and has the frequency and polarization to which the receiver and antenna are sensitive, a certain amount of power will enter the receiver and be measured.   Imagine now that one has a sheet of material that is perfectly black, so that it completely absorbs any radio-frequency energy falling on it.   Let its area $\mathcal{C}$ be so adjusted that when the sheet is oriented perpendicularly to the direction of arrival of the incident wave, it absorbs just the amount of power that entered the receiver.   Then $\mathcal{C}$ is called the effective area for that direction.   If the incident wave has unknown irradiance I but the same polarization and frequency, and if the input power at the receiver is P, then $I = P/\mathcal{C}$.

For given antenna and frequency, the effective area depends only on direction into space, and except for those rare cases when it can be predicted theoretically, it must be measured by experimental calibration, a difficult technical task.   Usually the effective area has no obvious relation to any geometrical area in the antenna structure.   For example, a simple linear dipole has an effective area but no geometrical area.   An important exception is a paraboloidal reflector with a dipole at its focus, as represented in cross section by Fig. 7-20a.   If the diameter D of the paraboloid is many wavelengths, the effective area, shown as a polar plot in Fig. 7-20b, can be calculated with good accuracy.   With proper design of the pickup and proper connection to the receiver, the effective area along the axis is practically the geometric area, and the angle α from the axis to the first zero is $1.22\lambda/D$ in radians. This highly directional character has a useful consequence to be mentioned. If the dipole pickup at the focus is linear, the polarization to which the antenna is sensitive is practically linear in the central lobe but becomes progressively more elliptical in the small side lobes.

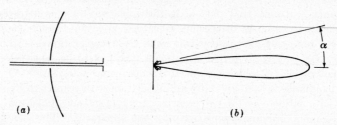

(a)   **(b)**

Fig. 7-20.   a. *Cross-sectional view of a dipole antenna with paraboloidal reflector.*   **b.** *Polar plot of the effective area of the arrangement shown in* (**a**).

Assume a horizontal array of identical antennas; suppose for definiteness that the individual antennas are of the paraboloidal type with all their axes parallel.   Let the position of a paraboloid be specified by the position of its focal point, denoted by Q, referred to x and y axes in the ground plane.   Let the cables to the receiver be of equal length.   When a plane monochromatic wave falls on the array, the sinusoidal voltages at the receiver due to the individual antennas are of equal amplitude but in general differ in phase.   No difference is introduced by the cables. (In the optical analogue the observing point is fixed in the direction normal to the plane of the array of apertures.)   The difference of phase resulting from oblique incidence of the wave is calculated by use of the left half of Fig. 7-4.   The final expression for the difference of phase between an antenna at (x,y) and one at O is (7-2) multiplied by k.   If the voltage due to an antenna at O has complex amplitude V_1, the total voltage due to the array is

$$V = V_1 \sum_{j=1}^{N} e^{-ik(x_j \sin\,\theta_1 + y_j \sin\,\phi_1)} = V_1 F$$

If R is the input resistance of the receiver, the average power entering the latter is $P = |V|^2/2R$, and

$$P = P_1|F|^2$$

where $P_1 = |V_1|^2/2R$, the power due to one of the antennas alone. Finally, if the incident wave has the polarization characteristic of the antenna and has unit irradiance, P_1 is equal to the effective area α_1 of a single antenna, and the effective area of the whole array is

$$\alpha = \alpha_1 |F|^2$$

As a specific case, consider a large number N of antennas arranged along the x axis, taken in the east-west direction, with uniform spacing d, as shown in Fig. 7-21. Since $y_j = 0$, the principal maxima of $|F|^2$ are given by $d \sin \theta_1 = m\lambda$, where m is the order. The zeroth order lies along a great circle in the celestial sphere coincident with the local meridian, and the other orders are on small circles (small in the sense of spherical geometry) defined by the intersections of the cones $\theta_1 = con$-$stant$ with the celestial sphere. The angular widths of the maxima are

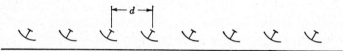

Fig. 7-21. *Uniform linear array of paraboloidal antennas. The antennas are to be imagined as connected to a receiver by equal lengths of cable.*

made small by using large N. As the earth rotates, a celestial source sweeps through the principal maxima, and as each one is crossed, a signal is given by the receiver. To tell which order is being observed and hence partially locate the source in the sky, the maximum in the pattern of each individual antenna is directed toward one of the principal maxima to enhance it over its neighbors. Even then the interpretation of the record is often a complicated process.

If an extended source such as the sun, having local areas of intense emission distributed over a general background, sweeps over a principal maximum, one obtains a stripwise scan of the source. To complete the mapping of the source, one can obtain a stripwise scan at right angles to the first by making use of a north-south array and the north-south component of the motion of celestial bodies observed when one is not at the equator. However, it would be advantageous to have an array whose effective area forms a pattern concentrated in fine pencils. A square array would suffice, but it has the disadvantage that the angular resolution goes up linearly with the number of antennas in a row, while the cost goes up as the square. An arrangement giving essentially the pattern of a square array but at a cost proportional to the resolution is the *Mills cross*, to be described in connection with two of the problems.

The idea of the stellar interferometer has been used extensively in radio astronomy. Obtaining large separations (in some cases hundreds of meters) merely involves long cables and none of the complication of the four mirrors used at optical frequencies. The reader who wishes to pursue this and other topics in radio astronomy can refer to Pawsey and Bracewell [70] (see also Sec. 13-16).

7-15 Grating Spectroscope If in a Fraunhofer arrangement, referred to the coordinate system of Fig. 7-4, a linear array of N apertures at uniform spacing d lies along the x axis, the source is on the X_1 axis, and the observing point P is on the X_2 axis, the condition that P be at the principal maximum of order m when the wavelength of the light is λ is that the δ given by (7-10) be equal to m, or

$$d(\sin \theta_1 + \sin \theta_2) = m\lambda \qquad m = 0, \pm 1, \pm 2, \ldots \qquad (7\text{-}17)$$

With a given position of the source, and hence a given value of θ_1, the position of P is determined by the value of θ_2 satisfying (7-17), and the fact that this position depends on λ is the basis of using the linear array as a spectroscope. One says that the positions of the principal maxima show *dispersion* with respect to wavelength (or wave number or frequency), and Eq. (7-17) relating the positions to the wavelength is called a *dispersion relation*. When a regular linear array is used as a spectroscope, it is customary to refer to it as a *diffraction grating*.

The significant values of θ_2 lie between $+\pi/2$ and $-\pi/2$ ($\sin \theta_2$ lying between $+1$ and -1), and for given λ and m there is at most one such value. On the other hand, for given λ there may be several values of m which give admissible values of θ_2, and $m = 0$ always gives an admissible value. The zero-order maximum is unique in that it lies at the same position (given by $\theta_2 = -\theta_1$) for any value of λ, and hence shows no dispersion.

So far the discussion has been referring tacitly to the diffraction pattern only insofar as it depends on the function $|F|^2$. The actual irradiance at the observing point is given by (7-8) and depends on the irradiance in the single-aperture pattern. If the apertures are of simple shape, such as rectangles or circles, it will be shown in Chap. 9 that if the dimension parallel to the x axis is large compared with λ, the single-aperture pattern as observed along the X_2 axis is concentrated about the zero-order maximum of $|F|^2$. However, if this dimension is comparable with λ, the single-aperture pattern shows appreciable irradiance for all admissible values of θ_2. The point to note for the present is that the single-aperture pattern depends on wavelength. The general character of the pattern formed by the grating can then be indicated as a function of $d(\sin \theta_1 + \sin \theta_2)$ by Fig. 7-22, which is based on the supposition that the source emits just two wavelengths λ_1 and λ_2. The small secondary maxima have been omitted. The dashed curves represent possible shapes of the single-aperture patterns, and when maxima for the two frequencies fall together, as at the zeroth order, the rule for incoherent sources is applied.

Figure 7-22 indicates a difficulty arising in the use of a grating as a tool for measuring unknown wavelengths.   This difficulty is known as *overlapping of orders* and arises from the fact that associated with a given value of θ_2 is a definite value of the product $m\lambda$, and to find the wavelength giving rise to an observed maximum, one must determine m in some independent way.   The following two methods will cover all cases: Suppose it is known from the character of the source that no wavelength less than 2000 A can be involved, and a maximum is observed which

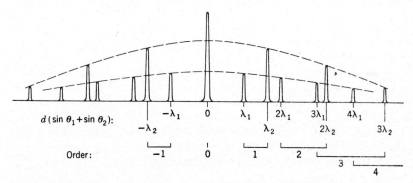

Fig. 7-22. *Diffraction pattern formed by a grating when the source emits just two wavelengths λ_1 and λ_2. Secondary maxima adjacent to the principal maxima are not shown.*

could be either 5000 A in the first order or 2500 A in the second.   A sheet of ordinary soft glass placed over the source would absorb 2500 A completely and eliminate the ambiguity.   On the other hand, if one is observing in high order, so as to use the consequent higher resolution to be discussed below, and observes what could be 5000 A in order 1000 or 5000 × 1000/1001 A in order 1001, the two cannot be discriminated by crude filtering, and one resorts to a preliminary measurement at low order with just sufficient accuracy to determine which case is involved.   In some instruments involving a grating operating at high order, a second grating (or sometimes a prism) is incorporated to give a simultaneous observation for a preliminary determination of λ with just sufficient accuracy to eliminate the uncertainty about the order.

The accuracy with which a wavelength can be measured once the order is known is determined by the width of the fringe and the distance it moves for a given small change in wavelength.   Figure 7-23a shows as a solid curve a fringe of given order formed with wavelength λ, and as a dashed curve a fringe of the same order for $\lambda + \delta\lambda$.   The value of $\delta\lambda$ has been assumed just such that the principal maximum of one curve falls over the first zero of the other.   Lord Rayleigh proposed that the shift of a fringe determined by this condition be taken as a measure, known as the·*Rayleigh criterion*, of the minimum shift that could be detected reliably, and the corresponding $\delta\lambda$ be regarded as the smallest change in wavelength which could be detected reliably in the given order. Now the principal maxima for given λ are uniformly spaced on the axis of $\sin\theta_2$ at intervals of λ/d, and the value of $\delta(\sin\theta_2)$ indicated in Fig. 7-23a is λ/Nd. On the other hand, by differentiating (7-17), we see that

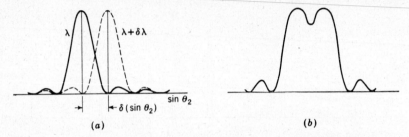

(a)   (b)

Fig. 7-23.   a. *Rayleigh criterion for the minimum difference of wavelength resolvable by a grating.*   **b.** *Observed profile for two lines of equal intensity which are just resolved according to the Rayleigh criterion.*

$\delta(\sin\theta_2) = m\,\delta\lambda/d$.   Hence if $\delta\lambda$ has the value given by the Rayleigh criterion, and if one defines the *chromatic resolving power* to be

$$\mathcal{R} = \frac{\lambda}{\delta\lambda} \tag{7-18}$$

then $\mathcal{R} = mN$

which is just the product of the order and the number of apertures. [Note that because of the relation $\lambda = c/\nu = 2\pi c/\omega$, the alternative definitions of chromatic resolving power,

$$\mathcal{R} = \frac{\nu}{\delta\nu} = \frac{\omega}{\delta\omega} \tag{7-18a}$$

are practically equivalent to (7-18) when $\mathcal{R}$ is large.]

The chromatic resolving power is a dimensionless quantity from which one can find the minimum resolvable difference of wavelength at any given wavelength. The appropriateness of using the term "resolving" power is seen if one considers a source emitting the two wavelengths λ and $\lambda + \delta\lambda$ simultaneously and with equal intensity. Adding the two patterns in Fig. 7-23a, one obtains a pattern with a small dip at the center, as shown in Fig. 7-23b, and one says that the two wavelengths are *resolved*. If $\delta\lambda$ is reduced only slightly, this dip disappears, and one is not sure from the appearance of the total pattern that two wavelengths are present.

Gratings actually used for spectroscopic purposes are almost always of the *reflection* type, consisting of parallel grooves in a metal surface. The source and observing point lie on the same side of the grating, and if the angles θ_1 and θ_2 are defined as in Fig. 7-24, formula (7-17) applies with the signs given. The grooves may be of any shape—that they all be of the same shape and be uniformly spaced are the only fundamental requirements. However, advantages accrue from giving them a saw-tooth profile with sides optically flat, as will be pointed out in Chap. 9 when the single-aperture pattern has been investigated. The spacing of the grooves may

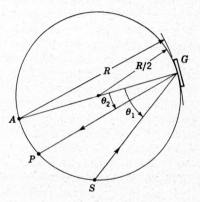

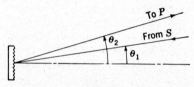

Fig. 7-24. *Definition of the angles θ_1 and θ_2 for a reflection-type grating.*

Fig. 7-25. *Concave grating G related to the Rowland circle. The radius of curvature of the grating and the diameter of the circle are equal.*

be anything from very many wavelengths, when high orders are to be observed, down to two or three wavelengths, when only the lowest orders are desired. Discussion of the rationale of the choices of N and d for various applications is best deferred to Chap. 9.

In the history of physics the diffraction grating stands out as one of the most important instruments, comparable with the present accelerating machines, for example. From around 1820, when the first gratings were made by Fraunhofer, until 1891, when Michelson introduced the interferometer, the grating with known spacing d was the only means of accurately measuring the characteristic wavelengths in atomic spectra in terms of a standard of length. A high point of this era was the work of H. A. Rowland, who not only developed engines for ruling finely spaced grooves with high accuracy, but discovered the principle of the concave grating. The latter consists in parallel and equally spaced grooves ruled in the metal surface of a concave spherical mirror of a large radius of curvature R, usually between 1 and 10 m. The unique properties of this grating are illustrated in Fig. 7-25, which shows the grating G tangent at its center to a circle of diameter (not radius) R. This circle is called the *Rowland circle*. The grooves are perpendicular to the plane of the figure. Let the source of the spectrum be a point S lying anywhere on the Rowland circle. (In practice, S is a narrow slit illuminated by light from the actual source.) Then the spectrum of this source is formed in various orders, all in sharp focus, on this same Rowland circle, and for each wavelength the formula (7-17) gives the locations of the principal maxima.[1] Thus the Fraunhofer diffraction pattern for a linear array is formed by virtue of the focal properties of the concave grating rather than with complicated and necessarily imperfect lenses; and because of the simple geometry involved (some of the consequences of which will not be entered into here), it is possible to determine accurately the difference between any two wavelengths. If a single spectrum line is exhaustively studied to determine its wavelength as the mean of many measurements with gratings, then all others can be referred to it as standard. On the basis of this principle Rowland published extensive tables of wavelengths in the spectra of the sun and various elements, and these tables were of inestimable value in the development of atomic physics and its applications to chemistry, astronomy, and other fields.

The role of the grating has been changed by the advent of interferometers, particularly that of Fabry and Perot (1899). These instruments, although they are difficult and tedious to use, can measure the absolute wavelength of a single line with an error of about one part in 10^8, some thousand times better than is possible with a grating, and they have provided a large number of standard wavelengths throughout the spectrum. These standards provide tests of the true capabilities of the best grating instruments, and the conclusion is that full advantage is taken of the sharpness of the fringes produced by a grating only when it is used to measure small differences between two wavelengths, for example, to compare an unknown line with a standard line of nearly the same wavelength. In Rowland's day gratings were used to compare widely different wavelengths, and it is now known that for various reasons errors always entered which were greater than anticipated on the basis of the resolving power of the grating.

The design and operation of spectroscopic instruments for use in various regions of the spectrum is a vast subject. For an introduction the reader may refer to Sawyer [80] and to Harrison, Lord, and Loofbourow [34].

7-16 Random Array The arrays considered so far have been regular. A very interesting problem is that in which a large number N of identical

---

[1] A way to avoid slipping into the common error of thinking of the Rowland circle as having radius R rather than diameter R is to note that if the source S is at point A in Fig. 7-25, then the zero-order spectrum is also at A and obviously will be in sharp focus only if A is at the *center of curvature* of the mirror.

apertures are placed at random in a diffracting screen, the only restrictions being that no two apertures are so far apart that the condition of Fraunhofer diffraction is not satisfied or so close together that they do not contribute independently to the diffracted wave. For definiteness, think of many small pinholes distributed in a circle of the order of a centimeter in diameter, and let the wavelength be in the visible range. For simplicity, let the incidence on the diffracting screen be normal ($\theta_1 = \phi_1 = 0$). This problem will now be discussed in great detail, not only because the pattern is of some interest in itself, but because the principles involved recur time and again in this book and in many other branches of physics, and there will be an advantage in having first become familiar with these principles in a simple context.

Referred to the standard coordinate system of Fig. 7-4, let the representative point of aperture j have coordinates x_j and y_j, and introduce the angle

$$\psi_j = -k(x_j \sin \theta_2 + y_j \sin \phi_2) \tag{7-19}$$

The problem is then to evaluate the function

$$F = \sum_{j=1}^{N} e^{i\psi_j} \tag{7-20}$$

In the forward direction ($\theta_2 = \phi_2 = 0$) all the ψ's are zero, and $F = N$. Well away from the forward direction the ψ's fall at random in the range zero to 2π (after reduction to this range by adding or subtracting appropriate integral multiples of 2π), and the vector diagram representing the sum in (7-20) appears as in Fig. 7-26. The resultant F can now have a magnitude equal to anything from zero to N, with either extreme value being very unlikely. Moreover, if one passes from one direction to another, even quite nearby, the ψ's all change by different amounts, and even though all these changes may be small, they can produce a large change in F when N is large. The result is that the diffraction pattern shows the finely mottled appearance seen in Fig. 7-27. Note the bright spot at the center, where $|F|^2$ is always equal to N^2. (The dark area immediately around the center is the result of the array being incompletely random. When many holes are crowded into a limited area, certain spacings between near neighbors inevitably become preferred.) As N is increased, the mottling becomes more complicated, but the magnitude of the fluctuation in irradiance does not decrease. If the pattern is smoothed out by averaging the irradiance over areas small enough that the single-aperture irradiance is essentially constant, but large enough to include a fair sample of the rapid fluctuations, this average irradiance is equal to N times that of the single aperture, except for the steep rise to the maximum in the central spot.

The theory of the pattern at points well away from the forward direction will be based on statistical arguments of a type introduced by J. W. Gibbs in connection with complicated mechanical systems having elements of randomness in their definitions, such as gases. The idea is that instead of attempting to treat the variation of irradiance on passing from point to point of the pattern for a given screen, one considers the irradiance at a *fixed* point P as one after another of a large number of

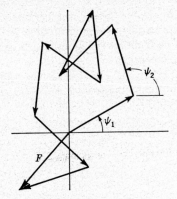

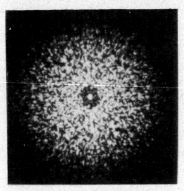

Fig. 7-26. *Vector addition of a number of unimodular complex numbers with random angles to give a resultant F.*

Fig. 7-27. *Fraunhofer diffraction pattern for a random array of 100 circular apertures.*

diffracting screens is put in place, each screen being prepared independently of the others and subject only to the constraints that it contain N apertures placed at random in a given area. The set of screens is called a *representative ensemble of systems.*

With P fixed, each screen of the ensemble will give rise to a vector diagram such as Fig. 7-26 with some set of angles ψ_j, all these angles falling at random in the range zero to 2π. For each screen let the end point of the resultant vector F be marked by a point; thereby we obtain a fine dust of points over the complex plane. The theory of the distribution of points in this dust is a famous problem known as the *random walk.* The essential results were first obtained by Lord Rayleigh [76], vol. I, p. 491 and vol. IV, p. 370, in the very connection of the superposition of waves. An exhaustive discussion has been given by Chandrasekhar [17]. For present purposes an excellent reference is Kennard [54], p. 268.

The probability $P_{\xi\eta}\,d\xi\,d\eta$ that a given screen will lead to a point in the dust having its real part between ξ and $\xi + d\xi$ and its imaginary part between η and $\eta + d\eta$ is the ratio of the number of points in the rectangle bounded by these values to the total number of points in the dust in the limit as the latter becomes infinite. This probability is

$$P_{\xi\eta} \, d\xi \, d\eta = \frac{1}{\pi N} \, e^{-(\xi^2+\eta^2)/N} \, d\xi \, d\eta \tag{7-21}$$

Note that the distribution function $P_{\xi\eta}$ depends only on $|F| = (\xi^2 + \eta^2)^{1/2}$ and is therefore symmetrical about the origin. For brevity introduce the notation

$$\rho \equiv |F|$$

Then $P_{\xi\eta}$ is a function of ρ and is plotted in Fig. 7-28.

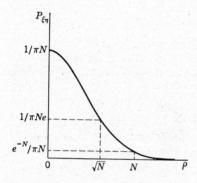

Fig. 7-28. *Probability distribution referring to variables ξ and η for the problem of the random walk in two dimensions.*

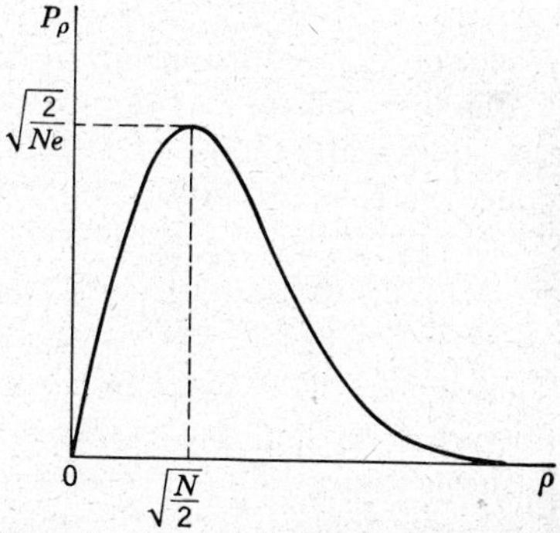

Fig. 7-29. *Probability distribution referring to the variable ρ for the problem of the random walk in two dimensions.*

The interpretation of this curve is that the density of points in the dust is greatest at the origin and falls off rapidly when ρ becomes large. A measure of the radius of the distribution is the value of ρ that gives an ordinate $1/e$ times the maximum; this value is $\sqrt{N}$. Hence the extent of the distribution increases more slowly than N.

The distributon (7-21) is satisfactory in so far as it meets the basic requirement of normalization:

$$\iint\limits_{-\infty}^{\infty} P_{\xi\eta} \, d\xi \, d\eta = 1$$

That is, the probability of the end point of the summation falling some-where on the complex plane is unity. It is unsatisfactory in that it gives finite probability of finding points at distances greater than N from the origin, N being the largest possible value. This defect enters when the problem is rendered mathematically tractable by introducing the Stirling approximation (see Kennard [54], p. 269). It is not a serious defect when N is large, since one easily shows by appropriate integration of (7-21) that the total probability of finding ρ greater than N is e^{-N}—a negligible fraction when N is large.

Another probability function, more pertinent to the diffraction problem, is P_ρ, having the significance that $P_\rho\, d\rho$ is the probability of finding the end point of the summation between the distances ρ and $\rho + d\rho$ from the origin. It is obtained by integrating (7-21) over the circular annulus between ρ and $\rho + d\rho$ and is

$$P_\rho\, d\rho = \frac{1}{\pi N}\, e^{-\rho^2/N}\, 2\pi\rho\, d\rho = \frac{2}{N}\, \rho e^{-\rho^2/N}\, d\rho \qquad (7\text{-}22)$$

A plot of P_ρ is shown in Fig. 7-29.

The distribution P_ρ can be used as a weighting function in calculating the statistical average of any function of ρ. (For more detail on this point, see Kennard [54], p. 48.) In particular, the average of $|F|^2 \equiv \rho^2$ is[1]

$$[\rho^2]_{\text{av}} = \int_0^\infty \rho^2 P_\rho\, d\rho = \frac{2}{N}\int_0^\infty \rho^3 e^{-\rho^2/N}\, d\rho = N$$

Thus if, at a fixed point in the diffraction pattern which is not near the forward direction, one averages the irradiances that would be observed with the many different screens of the ensemble, one would obtain just N times the single-aperture irradiance.

In the hypothetical observations just mentioned, one would find that any particular screen gives an irradiance which deviates more or less from the average, and the question is whether or not these deviations are appreciable compared with the average. As a measure, one takes the root-mean-square deviation from the mean, abbreviated *standard deviation* and denoted $\Delta(\rho^2)$. Now

$$\Delta(\rho^2) \equiv \{[(\rho^2 - [\rho^2]_{\text{av}})^2]_{\text{av}}\}^{1/2} = \{[\rho^4]_{\text{av}} - ([\rho^2]_{\text{av}})^2\}^{1/2}$$

The equivalence of these two expressions is easily shown (or see Kittel [55], p. 117). By a calculation analogous to that of $[\rho^2]_{\text{av}}$ one finds $[\rho^4]_{\text{av}} = 2N^2$, and hence

$$\Delta(\rho^2) = N$$

Thus the fluctuations are by no means small and are comparable with the average of $|F|^2$ itself, regardless of how large N may be.

Applying these statistical ideas to the point in the pattern lying exactly in the forward direction, one obtains $[\rho^2]_{\text{av}} = N^2$, and there are no fluctuations. The reason is that all the ψ's are zero with any screen of the

---

[1] This result can be obtained in an alternative way without resorting to the theory of the random walk (see, e.g., Kittel [55], p. 122). However, the random walk provides a broader view.

ensemble; this situation is characterized in that the sets of angles are *completely correlated* from one screen to another, with the result that there are no fluctuations. The opposite extreme occurs at points far from the forward direction; there the sets of angles are said to be *completely uncorrelated.*

At a point very nearly but not exactly in the forward direction, the angles θ_2 and ϕ_2 are so small that for any possible values of x_j and y_j the vector representing $e^{i\Psi_j}$ is nearly in the direction of the positive real axis. The N vectors are then roughly lined up, and the average of ρ^2 over the ensemble is some value intermediate between N and N^2, and the standard deviation is less than the average. This behavior is characterized in that the sets of angles ψ_j are *partially correlated.* In this region of partial correlation the theory becomes difficult and must take into account the size and shape of the area within which the array is confined and the fact that two apertures cannot be less than a certain distance apart.

The statistical behavior of the pattern at a fixed point is related to the mottling in the pattern for a given screen by the following argument: If one starts from a point far from the forward direction and moves across the pattern, it is not necessary to move very far before the ψ's will have assumed a set of values essentially uncorrelated with the initial set. Hence the spatial average of $|F|^2$ over a region of the pattern is the same as the statistical average at one point, and the spatial fluctuations in the mottling are of the same magnitude as the statistical fluctuations. This argument does not fix the fineness of the mottling or how far one must move in a given pattern to obtain a completely new set of random angles ψ_j. This question will not be pursued for the reason that the statistical treatment already given covers all the ideas that will be needed later. The main application will come in Chap. 12.

The essential content of this section can be summarized in somewhat generalized terms as follows: Let N monochromatic electromagnetic waves of the same frequency arrive at a point P traveling in the same direction. Let it be known from the physical processes by which the waves originated that all the waves have the same polarization, the irradiance I_1 of a single wave by itself is the same for all, and the phases of the waves are random. Then the irradiance of the resultant wave is $I = I_1|F|^2$, where F is given by (7-20) with the angles ψ_j falling at random in the range zero to 2π. If these angles are given a large number of independent sets of random values, $|F|^2$ evaluated for each, and the results averaged, then $[I]_{av} = NI_1$. Any individual value of I may depart from the average by a large amount, and the standard deviation is $\Delta I = NI_1$, just equal to the average itself.

At the opposite extreme to the case of random phases are problems in which the ψ's are known to have definite values. Examples occur in the forward direction in Fraunhofer diffraction with a random array and in any direction with a regular array (more generally, any definite array). It is superfluous to take a statistical average over an ensemble, since the fluctuations are zero; nevertheless, one can think of doing so and say that the sets of ψ's are completely correlated.

Intermediate between the two extremes are the cases in which it is known that the ψ's show some randomness and at the same time some regularity. Examples occur very near the forward direction with a random array and in any direction with an almost-regular array (that is, an array in which each aperture has a certain probability of being a small distance out of place). (Another example is given in the last of the problems.) One then averages over an ensemble, but the sets of ψ's are partially correlated. Generally, these problems are difficult to analyze.

Problems

7-1. In Sec. 7-3 it was stated that under the conditions of Fraunhofer diffraction the shift of the single-aperture pattern on changing from one aperture to another is small compared with the size of the pattern. Verify this statement by considering two circular apertures of diameter a separated by distance d, where d is the diameter of the circle C entering in Sec. 7-2. The incident wave can be taken to fall normally on the diffracting screen.

7-2. In performing Young's experiment in the laboratory, lenses in the arrangement of Fig. 7-16 are not usually employed, and one often observes the fringes from a distance which, compared with the separation of the apertures, is too small to give true Fraunhofer diffraction by a factor of 10 or more. Yet the pattern seems to show the "cosine-squared" distribution, and the separation of the maxima is according to the Fraunhofer theory within the experimental error. Explain these facts in the following way: Let the two apertures be on the x axis in Fig. 7-4 at equal distances from O, and let them be very small (essentially points). Assuming normal incidence, show that as the distance to the observing plane increases, the position on the X_2 axis of a maximum of given order traces an arc of a hyperbola whose focus is one of the two apertures and whose asymptote passes through O. (*Hint:* Recall the various geometric definitions of the hyperbola and the significance of the term "order.") From this result give a qualitative argument supported by a diagram as to why the condition of Fraunhofer diffraction can be substantially violated in this experiment without appreciable effect. One might elaborate with some quantitative estimates, perhaps taking the special case $d = 1$ mm and $\lambda = 5 \times 10^{-5}$ cm.

7-3. Draw a vector diagram and apply trigonometry to find $\dot{F}$ and $|F|^2$ for a linear array consisting of six apertures on the x axis of Fig. 7-4 at $x = 0, d, 2d, 6d, 7d$, and $8d$. Introduce δ defined by (7-10). Make a rough plot of $|F|^2$ as a function of δ. (*Answer:*

$$F = 2 \cos 6\pi\delta \, \frac{\sin 3\pi\delta}{\sin \pi\delta} \, e^{-i8\pi\delta}$$

In plotting $|F|^2$, first draw the function $4 \sin^2 3\pi\delta / \sin^2 \pi\delta$ as a dashed envelope whose ordinates are to be multiplied by $\cos^2 6\pi\delta$.)

7-4. Along the x axis of Fig. 7-4 lies an array of $2N$ apertures consisting of N pairs, with the members of any pair separated by a distance d and with corresponding apertures of successive pairs separated by the larger distance D. Introduce the quantity δ defined by (7-10), and define the analogous quantity Δ by replacing d by D. Find the expression for $|F|^2$, and note that it consists of a factor characteristic of a double aperture of spacing d and a second factor characteristic of a regular linear array of N apertures of spacing D. Show that when $D = 2d$ this expression can be reduced to that for a regular array of $2N$ apertures with spacing d. Draw a vector diagram to show how the $2N$ vectors giving F can be grouped into pairs such that F appears as the sum of resultants for N double apertures, and in another diagram show how F can appear as the sum of the resultants of two linear arrays of N apertures each. In these diagrams assume $N = 3$. Draw a rough plot of $|F|^2$ as a function of δ when $N = 3$ and $D = 6d$.

7-5. Generalize on the result of Prob. 7-4 by giving the form assumed by $|F|^2$ when a number of apertures can be regarded as a regular array of identically arranged subgroups. In terms of this statement comment on formula (7-16) for the rectangular array.

7-6. Show how the function F can be found for the regular rectangular array of Sec. 7-10 by graphical addition in the complex plane. In particular, draw diagrams yielding the resultants for the separate rows, and in a final diagram obtain the sum of these resultants for all the rows. The several diagrams must be properly related to each other with respect to angle. Take the case of three rows and two columns.

7-7. Let a plane wave be normally incident on a screen containing any array of identical apertures. Assume that the single-aperture pattern is confined to small values of θ_2 and ϕ_2 (referred to Fig. 7-4). Let the diffracting screen be stretched or compressed in the direction parallel to the x axis, so that an aperture originally at (x,y) shifts to (hx,y), with h a constant. Show that if, initially, the function $|F|^2$ has a certain value at (X_2,Y_2), after the deformation this same value occurs at $(X_2/h, Y_2)$. What is the significance of this result in terms of the change occurring in a system of fringes in the X_2Y_2 plane?

7-8. Show directly from formula (7-16) that when a square array is deformed into a rectangular one, the positions of the principal maxima (the spots) change in agreement with the result of the preceding problem.

7-9. Apply the result of Prob. 7-7 to draw the pattern for the array of Fig. 7-30. As far as this pattern depends on $|F|^2$, it consists in an array of spots extending indefinitely. Draw enough spots to give the character of the pattern, and, except for

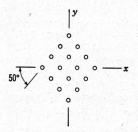

Fig. 7-30. *Array considered in Prob. 7-9.*

relative size, indicate the exact geometrical relations between the array of spots and the array of apertures.

7-10. An application of the double aperture is the *Rayleigh refractometer*, shown in Fig. 7-31. The tubes T_1 and T_2 are sealed at their ends by glass plates and are made to be identical. The simplest example of the use of the instrument is in measuring the refractive index of a gas. Initially, both tubes are evacuated, and the gas is then slowly admitted to one of them. Fringes, formed in monochromatic light, move across the field of view. Derive a formula for the change of order that will have occurred at the fixed central point of the field of view when the refractive index

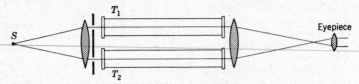

Fig. 7-31. *Rayleigh refractometer.*

of the gas reaches the value n. This change of order is then the number of fringes (plus a fraction, in general) that will have passed the reference point.

7-11. Find the linear separation of the fringes in a stellar interferometer when the two beams converge at what is considered the practical upper limit of 3°. Take the wavelength to be 5×10^{-5} cm (blue-green light). What are the focal length and the magnification of an eyepiece which images these fringes at infinity with an angular separation of 0.2°? (A reference on magnification of eyepieces is Jenkins and White [53], p. 174.) (*Answer:* Separation $\approx 10^{-3}$ cm; focal length ≈ 3 mm; magnification ≈ 80. A compound microscope is indicated!)

7-12. Show that if in the Michelson stellar interferometer illustrated in Figs. 7-18 and 7-19 the screen with apertures at separation d is replaced by a screen between the mirrors and the lens, the new screen having apertures at the fixed separation d', the conclusions about the function of the instrument are unchanged if the operation still consists in moving M_1 and M_4 in and out symmetrically. (In practical instruments, in which no screen is used, the one case corresponds to M_1 and M_4 being small enough compared with M_2 and M_3 that they constitute the effective apertures of the system, while the other corresponds to M_2 and M_3 being the effective apertures.)

7-13. Concerning the overlapping of orders in the diffraction pattern of a grating, as illustrated in Fig. 7-22, one defines the *free range* or *range without overlap* for a given order m to be the range λ_1 to λ_2 such that the fringe of order $m + 1$ for λ_1 coincides with that of order m for λ_2. If the spectrum being observed consists only of wavelengths confined to this range, then there will be no overlapping in orders 1 through m. Show that $(\lambda_2 - \lambda_1)/\lambda_1 = 1/m$. (For example, $\lambda_2 = 2\lambda_1$ when $m = 1$, so that the whole visible spectrum can be observed without overlap in the first order.)

7-14. In the pattern of a diffraction grating with N apertures, consider one of the two zeros immediately adjacent to the principal maximum of order m. By how many wavelengths does the difference of paths via the first and last aperture change on passing from the center of the principal maximum to this zero? To what is this difference approximately equal when N is very large? (*Answer:* For large N, one wavelength, with an error λ/N.)

7-15. Find F for the crossed array of Fig. 7-14 when the number of apertures counted either horizontally or vertically is an odd number N and the spacing in either direction is d. If N is large, it makes little difference if the center aperture is counted twice. Introduce δ_x and δ_y as in (7-16). [*Suggestion:* Choose the axes as shown in Fig. 7-14, so that the origin O is at the center aperture. Then for the horizontal row, $x_j = -\frac{1}{2}(N-1)d + (j-1)d$, where j enumerates the apertures from left to right. With this scheme, use can be made of the steps in (7-13). The same procedure can be applied to the vertical column.] From F write $|F|^2$ and show how the general appearance of the pattern in Fig. 7-13b and the quantitative statements in Sec. 7-11 follow. Continue with the next problem.

7-16. Let all the apertures in the horizontal row of Fig. 7-14 be covered by sheets of glass of the same small thickness such that an extra half wavelength is added to the optical paths from source to viewing point via these apertures. Show that the diffraction pattern looks like Fig. 7-13b, except that where the fringes cross, the value of $|F|^2$ drops to zero instead of rising to $4N^2$.

The Mills Cross. A paper by Mills and Little [66] pointed out the properties of the arrays considered in the last two problems and described an ingenious application to radio astronomy. Antennas were arranged in the form of a cross over level ground. They were connected in the usual additive fashion to a receiver, except that the resultant voltage signal from one arm was passed through a switching device which suddenly changed the polarity many times per second. This switching is analogous to alternately placing and removing the glass plates of Prob. 7-16. In terms of a sensitivity pattern mapped on the celestial sphere, this pattern consists of a grid of fringes along which the sensitivity is constant in time and proportional to N^2. At the intersections of the fringes, the sensitivity is alternately zero and proportional to $4N^2$. Hence a source lying at an intersection will appear to the receiver to be flickering at the switching frequency, and if the receiver is constructed to be insensitive to any steady component in the signal entering it, but to register an alternating component, the effective pattern of sensitivity becomes an array of spots, as would be given by a complete rectangular array. The advantage of a pattern of small spots and the disadvantage of obtaining it with a rectangular array were pointed out near the end of Sec. 7-14.

7-17. Starting with a random array of N pinholes in a screen, let a second set of N holes be punched such that for each hole in the first set there is one in the second at a distance d in the x direction. Describe the appearance and statistical properties of the pattern. In passing from one screen in an ensemble to another, the $2N$ angles ψ_j associated with a fixed point in the pattern are partly correlated. Discuss this correlation in terms of vectors in the complex plane.

chapter 8

Treatment of Diffraction in the Scalar Approximation. The Kirchhoff Integral

In the last chapter a number of important conclusions about diffraction patterns were deduced from a strictly electromagnetic point of view. The calculation of a pattern was incomplete only in that the irradiance I_1 in the single-aperture pattern was not calculated for any particular size and shape of aperture, but was regarded as something that could, in any event, be determined by experiment. The complete calculation of a diffraction pattern by finding appropriate solutions of the Maxwell equations has proved feasible only in a few simple and highly idealized situations. One of these is a monochromatic plane wave incident on a semi-infinite plane diffracting screen with a straight edge, made of a sheet of perfectly conducting metal of zero thickness, a problem which is still extremely difficult and was solved by Sommerfeld (see Sommerfeld [85], p. 247, and Born and Wolf [9], p. 557). The results for this particular problem are highly instructive in that one can see in detail how the incident wave induces oscillating currents in the sheet which then contribute radiation to the reflected and diffracted light. The solution is good for all points of space, and one can see the behavior of the fields even in the immediate vicinity of the diffracting edge. However, such calculations have not been extended to all the various shapes of apertures that are of interest in optics, and it is fortunate that there exists an approximate theory which is applicable with comparative ease to any shape, and which predicts diffraction patterns with high accuracy, except in very extreme cases to be mentioned later.

8-1 Scalar Theory of Light The approximate theory involves a radical simplification in that a light wave is represented by a single scalar field rather than two coupled vector fields. The only types of diffraction patterns one can hope to calculate with such a simplified theory are those that are essentially or completely independent of the polarization of the incident light, but the most important patterns—those due to apertures large compared with the wavelength and viewed at points not too near an edge of an aperture—are found by experiment to be of this type.

In setting up a scalar theory, it is necessary to conjure up some law governing the behavior of the scalar field to take the place of the Maxwell equations, some model of a source to replace the dipole oscillators of the Lorentz model, and finally some relation between the observed irradiance and the scalar amplitude to replace the Poynting vector. The basis for choice in these matters is that the scalar theory is to have as many features of the electromagnetic theory as possible, and the ultimate check is a comparison of predictions with experiment.

Before proceeding, it would be well to assure a proper perspective. Historically, the first wave theories of light were scalar theories. They originated in Huygens' ideas on the propagation of wave fronts and Young's idea of interference, and they reached a high development in the prize essay of Fresnel in 1818. About this same year the idea of transverse waves was introduced by Young and was incorporated in theories of reflection and double refraction, but the treatment of diffraction continued (and for the most part still continues) to be on the basis of a purely scalar theory. The latter was given a particularly satisfactory form by Kirchhoff in 1882. The historical development will not be traced in detail. In this section some heuristic arguments will be invoked whereby the scalar theory in its best form will emerge in a more or less satisfactory way from the higher point of view of the electromagnetic theory.

A clue to the appropriate equation to be satisfied by the scalar waves is found in the wave equations (3-21) and (3-22). In free space both **e** and **b** satisfy the homogeneous equation (3-23), and it is reasonable to try the assumption that if u represents the amplitude of any wave in the scalar theory, then at points in free space u must satisfy

$$\nabla^2 u - \frac{1}{c^2}\frac{\partial^2 u}{\partial t^2} = 0 \qquad (8\text{-}1)$$

Evidence that (8-1) is a good choice comes from acoustics. Acoustic waves are scalar by their very nature, and on good physical grounds the pressure in an acoustic wave satisfies (8-1).   Moreover, acoustic waves at ultrasonic frequencies (at which the wavelength can be made small compared with laboratory apparatus) are found to undergo diffraction in the same way as does light.   In fact, whenever one solves a problem in the diffraction of light by use of the scalar theory, one has also solved a problem in acoustics.   Equation (8-1) is rather formidable, and the main part of this chapter will be devoted to finding an easy way to solve it for problems of diffraction.

As to the question of sources, the scalar theory contains no physical basis for defining some analogue of the charge density and current density and specifying the way in which it gives rise to waves, nor is it necessary to seek any detailed hypotheses along these lines.   In the subject of diffraction the only feature of the source that enters is the wave it emits, and the hypothesis in the scalar theory can be limited to this aspect.

A scalar wave whose amplitude is independent of direction, which propagates outward from a point with the velocity c, and which satisfies (8-1) is

$$u(r,t) = \frac{1}{r} f(r - ct) \qquad (8\text{-}2)$$

where r is the distance from the point, and f stands for an arbitrary function of the expression in parentheses.   To verify that (8-1) is satisfied (everywhere except at $r = 0$, where u is infinite), one uses the expression (1-23) for the laplacian in spherical polar coordinates, of which only the first term is different from zero in the present case, and carries out the indicated differentiations of (8-2).   To represent a monochromatic wave of frequency ω, one takes the function f to be sinusoidal and writes

$$u(r,t) = \frac{a}{r} \cos \left[k(r - ct) + \theta \right]$$

where a is a constant fixing the amplitude, $k = \omega/c$, and θ is a phase angle. Finally, one introduces the complex representation

$$u(r,t) = \frac{A}{r} e^{i(kr - \omega t)} \qquad (8\text{-}3)$$

where A is the complex amplitude $ae^{i\theta}$.

One can now speak of monochromatic point sources in the scalar theory by saying that they emit waves of the type (8-3).   Note that in its dependence on r the wave (8-3) behaves like the vector waves in the wave zone of a dipole oscillator.   On the other hand, (8-3) shows no angular dependence and is therefore appropriate for representing a source radiating equally in all directions (in which case the source is said to be *isotropic*).   Waves from point sources satisfying (8-1) and showing angular dependence could be written, and they would have the same dependence on r as does (8-3), at least at distances greater than a few wavelengths from the source. For a discussion of diffraction it is sufficient to limit attention to isotropic sources.

Finally, in postulating the relation between the amplitude of a monochromatic scalar wave at a point where it falls on a screen and the irradiance there (the one point of contact of the scalar theory with physical reality), one proceeds by analogy with the electromagnetic case. There it was found that if the electric vector at the screen is $(\mathbf{A} + i\mathbf{B})e^{-i\omega t}$, the irradiance is $(c/8\pi)(A^2 + B^2)$. It is now assumed that if the scalar u at the screen is $u_0 e^{-i\omega t}$, the irradiance is $K|u_0|^2$, where K is a constant of proportionality. There is no basis for assigning a universal value to K, and the scalar theory will give only the ratios of the irradiances at various points of a diffraction pattern. In a given physical situation the absolute irradiance at points of the pattern would have to be determined either by a measurement at any one point or from a knowledge of the total power that passes through the apertures and must be accounted for in the pattern.

A deduction from the scalar theory is that the principle of superposition holds, just as in the electromagnetic theory. For if u_1 and u_2 are any two waves which satisfy (8-1), then from the linearity of this equation it follows that $u_1 + u_2$ is also a solution and represents a possible light wave.

8-2 Kirchhoff Integral Suppose any number of point sources of monochromatic scalar waves, all having the same frequency ω, are distributed in space. From a knowledge of the positions, amplitudes, and phases of the sources, the resultant amplitude $u(P,t)$ at any time t and at any point P that does not coincide with a source can be found by superposition of waves of type (8-3). However, there is a way to find $u(P,t)$ which does not require a knowledge of the sources, but requires only the values of u and its spatial derivative in the normal direction at all points of an arbitrary closed surface Σ surrounding P but not enclosing any source. The method is known as that of the Kirchhoff integral, and it will be seen that it provides a basis for a scalar theory of diffraction.

The derivation of the Kirchhoff integral and the steps leading to a special form appropriate for application to diffraction by plane screens involve rather long and formal calculations which are given in the rest of this section and which need be read with only sufficient care to gain some idea of the origin of the final results. These results are given in brief and self-contained statements in the paragraph following (8-8) (this equation being the general form of the Kirchhoff theorem) and in the last paragraph of the section.

The derivation of the integral makes use of Green's theorem, which states the following: Let U and V be arbitrary scalar fields. Let τ be a region of space bounded by the surface Σ. Then

$$\int_{\Sigma} \left(V \frac{dU}{dn} - U \frac{dV}{dn} \right) d\Sigma = \int_{\tau} (V \, \nabla^2 U - U \, \nabla^2 V) \, d\tau \qquad (8\text{-}4)$$

where d/dn indicates a directional derivative in the direction of the outward normal to Σ at the element $d\Sigma$. This formula is obtained by steps outlined in Probs. 1-12 and 1-13. [The directional derivatives are introduced by use of (1-7).]

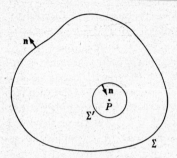

The Kirchhoff integral is obtained by the following application of (8-4): Take the surface Σ to which Green's theorem refers to consist of two parts, which will be denoted Σ and Σ', where Σ is the surface mentioned in the opening paragraph of this section, and Σ' is a small sphere about the point P at which the field is to be found as a surface integral over Σ. The volume τ is the region between Σ and Σ'. The two surfaces and the normals pointing outward from τ are illustrated in Fig. 8-1.

Fig. 8-1. *Closed surface, consisting of two parts Σ and Σ', used in obtaining the Kirchhoff integral from Green's theorem.*

Since the scalar light wave inside Σ is monochromatic, its amplitude is of the form

$$u = u_0 e^{-i\omega t} \qquad (8\text{-}5)$$

where u_0 is a function of position only. Then since u satisfies (8-1), u_0 satisfies

$$\nabla^2 u_0 = -k^2 u_0 \qquad (8\text{-}6)$$

where $k = \omega/c$. Let the function V in (8-4) equal u_0. For U take the function

$$U = \frac{1}{r} e^{ikr}$$

where r is the distance from P. Since U is the spatial part of a monochromatic wave that would be emitted from a point source of unit amplitude at P, U satisfies the same equation as u_0; that is,

$$\nabla^2 U = -k^2 \frac{1}{r} e^{ikr} \qquad (8\text{-}7)$$

except at the infinite singularity at P; hence (8-7) holds throughout τ.

On substitution of these values of U and V in (8-4), the integrand of the volume integral vanishes throughout τ (which was the objective in defining U in such a way as to satisfy $\nabla^2 U = -k^2 U$), and the equation reduces to

$$\int_\Sigma \left[u_0 \frac{d}{dn} \left(\frac{1}{r} \; e^{ikr} \right) - \frac{1}{r} \, e^{ikr} \frac{du_0}{dn} \right] d\Sigma$$

$$+ \int_{\Sigma'} \left[-u_0 \frac{d}{dr} \left(\frac{1}{r} \; e^{ikr} \right) + \frac{1}{r} \, e^{ikr} \frac{\partial u_0}{\partial r} \right] d\Sigma' = 0$$

where use has been made of the fact that over Σ', d/dn is equivalent to $-\partial/\partial r$. The integral over Σ' becomes, after the differentiation in the first term,

$$\int_{\Sigma'} \left(\frac{u_0}{r^2} - \frac{iku_0}{r} + \frac{1}{r} \frac{\partial u_0}{\partial r} \right) e^{ikr} \, d\Sigma'$$

Now let r, the radius of Σ', shrink to zero. When it has become very small, $e^{ikr} \approx 1$, and u_0 at any point of Σ' is practically equal to $u_0(P)$, the value at the center. The integral of the first term becomes $4\pi \, u_0(P)$ in the limit, while that of the second vanishes as r itself. The integral of the last term also vanishes at least as fast as r, since its absolute value is not greater than the value obtained by replacing $\partial u_0/\partial r$ by the maximum absolute value of this derivative on Σ', and the latter remains less than some finite upper bound as r decreases. The final result is then the Kirchhoff theorem:

$$u_0(P) = -\frac{1}{4\pi} \int_\Sigma \left[u_0 \frac{d}{dn} \left(\frac{1}{r} \; e^{ikr} \right) - \frac{1}{r} \, e^{ikr} \frac{du_0}{dn} \right] d\Sigma \qquad (8\text{-}8)$$

To summarize, it is supposed that inside a closed surface Σ surrounding a point P there exists a monochromatic scalar wave $u = u_0 e^{-i\omega t}$ originating in some distribution of sources, all of which lie outside Σ. It is further supposed that in some way the spatial factor u_0 and its directional derivative du_0/dn in the direction of the outward normal are known at all points of Σ. Then the value of u_0 at any point P inside Σ can be found as the right side of (8-8) in which r is the distance from P to the element of surface $d\Sigma$, and $k = \omega/c$.

As the first step toward applying (8-8) to diffraction with a single point source, consider the form the integral can be given when the position and amplitude of the source are known but there is no diffracting screen. The geometry is indicated in Fig. 8-2a, while Fig. 8-2b defines the angles $(\mathbf{n},\mathbf{r}_1)$ and $(\mathbf{n},\mathbf{r}_2)$. The source sends out a spherical wave whose amplitude at $d\Sigma$ will be

$$u_0 = \frac{A}{r_1} e^{ikr_1}$$

Since the level surfaces of this field are perpendicular to $\mathbf{r}_1$, (1-5) gives

$$\frac{du_0}{dn} = \frac{du_0}{dr_1} \cos (\mathbf{n},\mathbf{r}_1) = A \cos (\mathbf{n},\mathbf{r}_1) \left(-\frac{1}{r_1{}^2} + \frac{ik}{r_1} \right) e^{ikr_1} \quad (8\text{-}9)$$

Similarly,

$$\frac{d}{dn} \left(\frac{1}{r_2} e^{ikr_2} \right) = \cos (\mathbf{n},\mathbf{r}_2) \left(-\frac{1}{r_2{}^2} + \frac{ik}{r_2} \right) e^{ikr_2} \quad (8\text{-}10)$$

In all applications the distance from S to P will be many wavelengths,

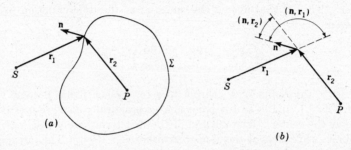

Fig. 8-2. *Geometry involved in applying the Kirchhoff theorem to the special case of a single point source and no diffracting screen.*

and the surface Σ will be such that, for any position of the element $d\Sigma$, the lengths r_1 and r_2 will also be many wavelengths. Then $1/r_1{}^2$ is small compared with k/r_1, and the former can be neglected in (8-9). Similarly, $1/r_2{}^2$ can be neglected in (8-10). With these approximations the Kirchhoff theorem takes the form

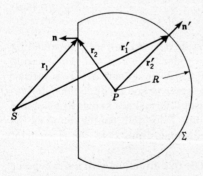

$$u_0(P) = -\frac{ikA}{4\pi} \int_\Sigma \frac{1}{r_1 r_2} [\cos (\mathbf{n},\mathbf{r}_2)$$
$$- \cos (\mathbf{n},\mathbf{r}_1)] e^{ik(r_1+r_2)} \, d\Sigma \quad (8\text{-}11)$$

For application to diffraction by a plane screen, it is advantageous to find the consequences of taking the surface Σ in the special form shown in Fig. 8-3, that is, as a plane circular disk, which will ultimately be located just behind the diffracting screen, and part of a sphere having radius R and center at P. It will now be shown that if R becomes infinite,

Fig. 8-3. *Surface which leads to a form of the Kirchhoff integral appropriate for application to diffraction by plane screens.*

the contribution to the integral from the spherical portion of Σ vanishes, and one is left with an integral over an infinite plane.

Denote the spherical part of Σ by Σ' and the contribution to the integral from it by I'. Then

$$I' = \int_{\Sigma'} \frac{1}{r_1' R} [1 - \cos(\mathbf{n}', \mathbf{r}_1')] e^{ik(r_1'+R)} \, d\Sigma'$$

To show that I' vanishes as R becomes infinite, it is sufficient to show that its absolute value vanishes. Now the absolute value of the integral is at most equal to the integral of the absolute value of the integrand, since the integral can be regarded as a sum of infinitesimal complex numbers, and (2-16) applies. Thus

$$|I'| \leqq \int_{\Sigma'} \frac{1}{r_1' R} [1 - \cos(\mathbf{n}', \mathbf{r}_1')] \, d\Sigma'$$

If d is the distance between S and P, the law of cosines gives

$$d^2 = r_1'^2 + R^2 - 2r_1' R \cos(\mathbf{n}', \mathbf{r}_1')$$

whence $1 - \cos(\mathbf{n}', \mathbf{r}_1') = \dfrac{d^2 - (R - r_1')^2}{2r_1' R} < \dfrac{d^2}{2r_1' R}$

When R is very large, $r_1' \approx R$, and

$$|I'| < \int_{\Sigma'} \frac{d^2}{2R^4} \, d\Sigma < \frac{2\pi d^2}{R^2}$$

which approaches zero as R becomes infinite.

The final result, ready for application to diffraction by plane screens, is thus the following: Let a point source at S and a point P be many wavelengths apart. Let an infinite plane surface Σ pass between these points such that the perpendicular distances from Σ to S and to P are also many wavelengths. If the source sends out the wave

$$u = \frac{A}{r} e^{i(kr-\omega t)}$$

where r is the distance from S, and if the oscillation of the field at P is

$$u(P,t) = u_0(P) \, e^{-i\omega t}$$

in the absence of any diffracting screen, then $u_0(P)$ can be found by the formula (8-11) in which the integration extends over the whole plane, the vectors $\mathbf{r}_1$ and $\mathbf{r}_2$ extend to the element $d\Sigma$ from S and P, respectively, $\mathbf{n}$ is the unit normal at $d\Sigma$ pointing out of the region in which P lies, and the angles are defined by Fig. 8-2b.

8-3   Application to Diffraction   Consider a monochromatic point source in front of a plane diffracting screen with apertures of any size and shape, as indicated by Fig. 8-4. The amplitude $u_0(P)$ at any point

P behind and not too near the screen can be found by evaluating the Kirchhoff integral over an infinite plane surface Σ lying against the back side of the screen. In contrast to the case considered at the end of Sec. 8-2, the amplitude u_0 and its normal derivative have the unobstructed values only over the parts of Σ covering openings in the screen and are zero in the shadow of the opaque area. Hence the amplitudes at points in the diffraction pattern are calculated by (8-11) *with the integral extending only over the open areas.* Consideration of specific cases in the Fraunhofer class will be the subject of Chap. 9, and the Fresnel class is taken up in Chap. 10. The next section will be devoted to some comments about the method just described.

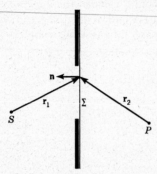

Fig. 8-4. *Geometry involved in applying the Kirchhoff integral to diffraction by plane screens with a point source.*

8-4 Comments on the Kirchhoff Method The assumption that the amplitude and its derivative over Σ are the same as in the unobstructed wave at points in the apertures and zero elsewhere does not correspond exactly with what is known about diffraction of electromagnetic waves. Measurements at microwave frequencies (at which the measurements can be on a scale small compared with a wavelength), as well as the few exact solutions of the Maxwell equations that have been obtained, show that at points within an aperture and less than a few wavelengths from the edge the fields differ markedly from those in the unobstructed wave, and over the back side of the screen the fields are not zero at points near the edge. However, it is reasonable to expect that these edge effects can be neglected if all but a small fraction of the area of an aperture is made up of points more than a few wavelengths from an edge, that is, if all dimensions of an aperture are large compared with the wavelength. Predictions based on this approximation are grossly in error in such cases as very small holes or very narrow slits, but for large apertures the calculated diffraction patterns agree very well with experiment.

It is interesting to note in what way the Kirchhoff method corresponds to the physical ideas set forth in Chap. 6. According to those ideas, the amplitude of the electric or magnetic field at P is the summation of amplitudes due to the source and the oscillators in the diffracting screen; it can be expressed alternatively as the negative of the sum of amplitudes due to oscillators which would be set into action over pieces of opaque screen just filling the apertures. The Kirchhoff method is a scalar theory which corresponds to this alternative view of the electromagnetic problem. It is seen from (8-11) that the contribution to $u_0(P)$ of an element $d\Sigma$ lying in an aperture is

$$du_0(P) = \frac{B\,d\Sigma}{r_2}\,e^{ikr_2}$$

where the amplitude $B\,d\Sigma$ is given by

$$B\,d\Sigma = -\frac{ikA}{4\pi r_1}\,[\cos(\mathbf{n},\mathbf{r}_2) - \cos(\mathbf{n},\mathbf{r}_1)]e^{ikr_1}\,d\Sigma$$

Thus the Kirchhoff integral in effect prescribes a distribution over the apertures of nonisotropic oscillators whose fields superpose to give the amplitude at P. Interpreted in this way, the Kirchhoff integral is the precise formulation of the earlier ideas of Huygens and Fresnel, according to which each small area in the aperture of a diffracting screen becomes the seat of a secondary wave, and only these secondary waves need be considered in finding the amplitude at P.

As a matter of terminology, the factor $\cos(\mathbf{n},\mathbf{r}_2) - \cos(\mathbf{n},\mathbf{r}_1)$, which gives the angular dependence of the contribution from $d\Sigma$, is called the *obliquity factor*. As an aid in remembering (8-11), one can note the significance of the several factors in the above expression for $B\,d\Sigma$. The incident wave arrives at $d\Sigma$ with amplitude $(A/r_1)e^{ikr_1}$. The latter is multiplied by $-i$, which subtracts $\pi/2$ from the phase angle. Finally, it is multiplied by $k\,d\Sigma/4\pi = d\Sigma/2\lambda$ and by the obliquity factor, which changes the magnitude and gives it an angular dependence.

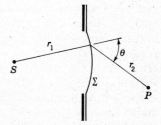

Fig. 8-5. *Alternative surface of integration that could be used in the case of a circular aperture with source on the axis.*

With regard to the choice of the surface Σ, taking it to be an infinite plane (together with a hemisphere at infinity, from which there comes no contribution) will prove to be suitable for all cases involving plane diffracting screens. However, one is always free to choose some other shape of surface as long as the behavior of the amplitude all over it can be stated with sufficient accuracy. For example, if the screen contains a circular aperture and the source is on the perpendicular through its center, the part of the surface covering the aperture could be chosen as in Fig. 8-5, that is, as a spherical cap of radius r_1. The unit normal $\mathbf{n}$ points toward the source, and with the amplitude over this cap taken to be the same as the unobstructed amplitude, (8-11) becomes

$$u_0(P) = -\frac{ikA}{4\pi r_1}\,e^{ikr_1}\int_\Sigma \frac{1}{r_2}[1 + \cos\theta]e^{ikr_2}\,d\Sigma$$

where θ is the angle defined in Fig. 8-5, and the integration extends over the spherical cap. A simplification in the appearance of the integral has resulted, but rather than seek the advantages inherent in any special case, we shall take the surface Σ to be a plane in all later work.

Before this section is closed, some other approaches to the problem of diffraction should be mentioned. Observations in the simple experiment mentioned in Chap. 6 suggest that a formula most closely related to the physical processes would express the amplitude at P as a superposition of contributions from the luminous edges of the apertures when P is inside the geometrical shadow, and as a superposition of the direct wave from the source and contributions from the luminous edges when P is outside the geometrical shadow. A theory along these lines was attempted by Thomas Young in 1802, but the idea could not be given quantitative expression at that time. Later the ideas of Huygens, as successfully applied to diffraction by Fresnel and further developed as the Kirchhoff integral, took over the field, and only recently has Young's idea been revived. A. Rubinowicz, in papers beginning in 1914, succeeded in transforming the surface integral of Kirchhoff into a line integral around the edge of the aperture, which in effect prescribes a set of nonisotropic sources distributed around this edge. The reader interested in following up this point can refer to Sommerfeld [85], p. 311. The surface integral of Kirchhoff remains the dominant method of solving diffraction problems.

In another approach, the solution of the Maxwell equations at any point P has been expressed as a surface integral over a closed surface Σ containing P but no charges or currents. As boundary conditions it is necessary to know the tangential components of $\mathbf{e}$ and $\mathbf{b}$ over all Σ. In applying this result to diffraction, the same difficulty arises as in the scalar theory, namely, these tangential components are not known except in the approximation that neglects edge effects. The formulas are complicated and are not easy to apply, but they are of some value in assessing the scalar theory. A reference is Sommerfeld [85], p. 325.

8-5 Reciprocity Theorem The reciprocity theorem, introduced in Sec. 7-9, states that the irradiance at P with a source at S is the same as the irradiance at S when the identical source is at P. In the scalar theory this theorem is proved for any diffracting screen by noting that the right side of (8-11) remains unchanged on interchange of the subscripts 1 and 2 and reversal of the direction of the unit normal $\mathbf{n}$. (When the source is shifted, the surface Σ must also be shifted to the other side of the screen, and the unit normal must always point into the region containing the source.)

8-6 Babinet's Principle When a problem of diffraction has been solved by evaluating the Kirchhoff integral, the solution to a related problem can be obtained by a simple algebraic subtraction.

Let two diffracting screens be such that, when superimposed, the opaque areas of one just cover the open areas of the other. Such screens are said to be *complementary*. With one screen in place, let the amplitude at a point P in the diffraction pattern be $u_0'(P)$; and with the other screen, let it be $u_0''(P)$. Since the sum of the Kirchhoff integrals giving these two amplitudes is the integral holding in the case of no screen,

$$u_0'(P) + u_0''(P) = u_0(P) \qquad (8\text{-}12)$$

where $u_0(P)$ is the unobstructed amplitude at P and is known from the position and amplitude of the source without evaluating an integral. The relation (8-12) between the amplitudes for complementary screens and the amplitude of the unobstructed wave is *Babinet's principle*. Applications will be discussed in the next two chapters.

Babinet's principle can be generalized in the following way: Suppose one has found the amplitude $u_0(P)$ in the pattern formed with a given diffracting aperture of any shape, and suppose there are two screens which can be placed over this aperture and which contain smaller apertures. If the two screens are complementary, and the amplitudes at P when they are in place are $u_0'(P)$ and $u_0''(P)$, respectively, then (8-12) holds. With any two of the amplitudes in this relation known from evaluation of the Kirchhoff integral, the third is found by simple addition or subtraction of complex numbers. In this generalization Babinet's principle will be useful in a number of cases, particularly in problems of the Fraunhofer class.

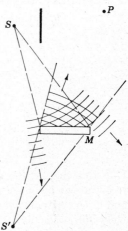

Fig. 8-6. *Behavior of the wave fronts from a point source as they are reflected by a plane mirror.*

8-7 Diffraction by Plane Mirrors If a point source S lies in front of a plane mirror M, assumed to be perfectly reflecting, then Fig. 8-6 shows how parts of the wave fronts from S are reflected and behave as though they came from a source at the geometrical image point S' and passed through an aperture of the same shape as M. The reflected wave arriving at an observing point P shows effects of diffraction and can be calculated by the Kirchhoff integral applied to the equivalent aperture with source at S'. (Direct radiation from S will also arrive at P unless a suitable shade is introduced, as shown in the figure.)

chapter **9**

Application of the Kirchhoff Integral to Fraunhofer Diffraction

In this chapter the method of the Kirchhoff integral will be applied to diffraction by one or more apertures of arbitrary shape when the source and observing point are far enough away that the conditions for Fraunhofer diffraction, as defined in Sec. 7-1, are satisfied. The results will be valid only if all the dimensions of each aperture are large compared with the wavelength.

9-1   General Formulas   The diffracting screen will be assumed to be plane, and for the initial discussion no lenses or other auxiliary devices will be used for achieving the conditions of Fraunhofer diffraction. The surface Σ to which the Kirchhoff formula (8-11) refers will be taken to be a plane just behind the screen, as in Fig. 8-4. The evaluation of $u_0(P)$ involves carrying the integration in (8-11) only over the open areas. The first problem is to find the special form the integrand assumes in the case of Fraunhofer diffraction.

Let the position of the element $d\Sigma$ in an aperture be referred to cartesian axes in the plane of the screen in the manner shown in Fig. 9-1. The orientation of S and P with respect to the screen is specified by completing the coordinate system as in Fig. 7-4.

If the origin O is within the area on the screen which includes the apertures and over which the Fraunhofer conditions hold, the directions from S to O and from S to any point in an aperture are essentially the same, and $\cos (\mathbf{n},\mathbf{r}_1) \approx \cos (\mathbf{n},\mathbf{R}_{10})$. Similarly, $\cos (\mathbf{n},\mathbf{r}_2) \approx \cos (\mathbf{n},\mathbf{R}_{20})$. Moreover, a negligible error is committed by replacing the factor $1/r_1 r_2$ by $1/R_{10}R_{20}$. For $r_1 + r_2$, appearing in the exponential, one writes

$$r_1 + r_2 = R_{10} + R_{20} + (r_1 - R_{10}) + (r_2 - R_{20})$$
$$= R_{10} + R_{20} - (x \sin \theta_1 + y \sin \phi_1) - (x \sin \theta_2 + y \sin \phi_2)$$

where the last step uses (7-2) and (7-3).

Further simplifying approximations can be made on the basis that the angular spread of the diffracted radiation will be small. Specifically,

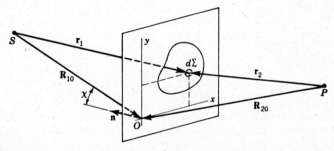

Fig. 9-1. *Geometry involved in applying the Kirchhoff integral to Fraunhofer diffraction.*

suppose the pattern is observed on the X_2Y_2 plane of Fig. 7-4, and let P_0 be the point in the forward direction (defined by $\theta_2 = -\theta_1$ and $\phi_2 = -\phi_1$). Then for apertures of sizes to which the Kirchhoff theory is applicable, the irradiance will be negligible at all points P whose angular distance from P_0 as seen from the apertures is greater than only a small number of degrees. If the angle of incidence χ is defined as in Fig. 9-1, the obliquity factor is practically constant over the pattern and equal to its value for the point P_0, so that

$$\cos (\mathbf{n},\mathbf{R}_{20}) - \cos (\mathbf{n},\mathbf{R}_{10}) \approx 2 \cos \chi$$

Another consequence is that the factor $1/R_{10}R_{20}$ can be regarded as constant over the pattern.

In writing the final form of the Kirchhoff integral, it will be convenient to regard the integration in (8-11) as extending over the whole of the infinite plane Σ; this can be done by introducing as a factor in the integrand a function $T(x,y)$ defined over all Σ and equal to unity at points (x,y) lying in an open aperture, and to zero elsewhere. Then the amplitude at P is given by

$$u_0(P) = - \frac{ikA}{4\pi R_{10}R_{20}} 2 \cos \chi \; e^{ik(R_{10}+R_{20})}$$

$$\int\!\!\!\int_{-\infty}^{\infty} T(x,y) \; e^{-ik[x(\sin \theta_1 + \sin \theta_2)+y(\sin \phi_1 + \sin \phi_2)]} \, dx \, dy \quad (9\text{-}1)$$

This formula is reduced to a condensed form by comparing $u_0(P)$ with $u_0(P_0)$, the latter being the amplitude at the point lying in the forward direction, given by (9-1), with the exponential in the integrand equal to unity. Thus

$$u_0(P) = u_0(P_0) \, G(P) \quad (9\text{-}2)$$

where

$$G(P) = \frac{\displaystyle\int\!\!\!\int_{-\infty}^{\infty} T(x,y) \; e^{-ik[x(\sin \theta_1 + \sin \theta_2)+y(\sin \phi_1 + \sin \phi_2)]} \, dx \, dy}{\displaystyle\int\!\!\!\int_{-\infty}^{\infty} T(x,y) \, dx \, dy} \quad (9\text{-}3)$$

The denominator in (9-3) has the effect of normalizing $G(P)$ in such a way that $G(P_0) = 1$. The numerator is easily remembered through its similarity to the function F defined by (7-9). The normal irradiance at P is obtained in terms of that at P_0 by squaring the absolute value of (9-2):

$$I(P) = I_0|G(P)|^2 \quad (9\text{-}4)$$

where I_0 is a brief notation for $I(P_0)$.

The interpretation of the final formula (9-4) is that if the normal irradiance in the forward direction I_0 is known, then the normal irradiance at any point P is obtained by multiplying by the factor $|G|^2$, which depends only on the shapes and arrangements of the apertures and on the directions to S and P. This formula bears a strong resemblance to (7-8). The relation between the two is such that if several identical apertures are involved, and (9-4) is evaluated for one such aperture whose representative point is at the origin O, then the resulting $I(P)$ becomes the factor I_1 in (7-8).

There is a simple and oftentimes convenient relation between I_0 and the normal irradiance of the incident wave as it arrives at the apertures. The latter is $E = A^2/R_{10}{}^2$. Noting that the integral appearing in the denominator of (9-3) is just the total area of the apertures and can be denoted by $\mathcal{A}$,

$$I_0 = |u_0(P_0)|^2 = \left(\frac{kA\mathcal{A}}{4\pi R_{10}R_{20}} 2 \cos \chi \right)^2 = \frac{E\mathcal{A}^2 \cos^2 \chi}{\lambda^2 R_{20}{}^2} \quad (9\text{-}5)$$

This formula is easily remembered by giving it the following interpretation: $\alpha \cos \chi$ is the projected area of the apertures as seen from S, and hence $E\alpha \cos \chi$ is the total power W passing through the apertures and appearing in the diffraction pattern. This power is not uniformly distributed in the pattern, but (9-5) results from the rough approximation that the power is spread uniformly throughout the solid angle

$$\Omega = \frac{\lambda^2}{\alpha \cos \chi}$$

and hence that the normal irradiance is uniform over a projected area of the observing screen equal to ΩR_{20}^2. Thus

$$I_0 = \frac{W}{\Omega R_{20}^2}$$

It will be seen later from specific examples (see particularly Prob. 9-1) that in the case of a single aperture of simple shape, such as a circle, the area ΩR_{20}^2 is in fact a good measure of the size of the diffraction pattern. It certainly shows the proper dependence on the parameters, since in every case the linear dimensions of the pattern are proportional to λ and R_{20} and inversely proportional to the linear dimensions of the apertures.

From the way in which the function T was defined, the denominator of (9-3) could be written more simply as just α, the total area of the apertures. However, it will be well to remember this formula as it stands, since it is of a form that can be applied to a generalized class of problems in which the apertures are not merely open, but are covered by semitransparent sheets of various kinds. The function T is then the factor, in general complex, by which the incident amplitude is multiplied to give the emergent amplitude at each point of Σ. It will then be appropriate to call T the *transmission coefficient* for the diffracting screen. These generalized problems will not be taken up until Fourier integrals have been introduced in Chap. 11. In the rest of the present chapter the denominator of (9-3) will always be equal to α.

To summarize, the working formulas are (9-4) and (9-3). If one is interested only in relative irradiances at various points in the diffraction pattern, I_0 is just an arbitrary constant of proportionality. However, I_0 has the significance of being the normal irradiance at the point lying in the forward direction. If the normal irradiance E of the incident wave as it arrives at the apertures is given, then I_0 is found from (9-5).

9-2 Special Form of Babinet's Principle The generalized statement of Babinet's principle (Sec. 8-6) can be applied to the type of problem with which this chapter deals, and it takes a very simple form. Let an aperture of area α and associated function G be given, and con-

sider two complementary screens fitting in this aperture. For one, let
the total area of its apertures be $\mathcal{C}'$, and the associated function be G .
For the other, let the corresponding quantities be $\mathcal{C}''$ and G'' (where
$\mathcal{C}' + \mathcal{C}'' = \mathcal{C}$). If the terms in (8-12) are written in the form (9-1)
and common factors canceled,

$$\mathcal{C}'G' + \mathcal{C}''G'' = \mathcal{C}G \tag{9-6}$$

In accumulating solutions for standard shapes of apertures, it will be
well to preserve a record of the angles of the complex functions G as well
as their magnitudes in anticipation that (9-6) will sometimes be quite
useful.

9-3 Rectangular Aperture

Consider the rectangular aperture of
dimensions a by b shown in Fig. 9-2. Let

$$\alpha = \frac{ka}{2\pi} (\sin \theta_1 + \sin \theta_2) \qquad \beta = \frac{kb}{2\pi} (\sin \phi_1 + \sin \phi_2) \tag{9-7}$$

Then

$$G = \frac{1}{ab} \int_{-a/2}^{a/2} e^{-i2\pi\alpha x/a} \, dx \int_{-b/2}^{b/2} e^{-i2\pi\beta y/b} \, dy = \frac{\sin \pi\alpha}{\pi\alpha} \frac{\sin \pi\beta}{\pi\beta} \tag{9-8}$$

A picture of this function is obtained by plotting it as a function of α for
constant β, as in Fig. 9-3. The maximum height
is $(\sin \pi\beta)/\pi\beta$, since the value of $(\sin \pi\alpha)/\pi\alpha$ is
unity at $\alpha = 0$. The same curve, with α and β
interchanged, holds along any locus $\alpha = constant$.
Notice that G is always real and oscillates in sign.
Areas in the $\alpha\beta$ plane over which G is positive or
negative are shown in Fig. 9-4. Along the solid
lines, called *nodal lines*, $G = 0$.

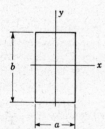

The irradiance in the pattern is

$$I = I_0 \frac{\sin^2 \pi\alpha}{(\pi\alpha)^2} \frac{\sin^2 \pi\beta}{(\pi\beta)^2} \tag{9-9}$$

Fig. 9-2. *Rectangular aperture referred to cartesian coordinates.*

where I_0 is the irradiance in the forward direction,
that is, for $\alpha = \beta = 0$. A plot of I along the locus
$\beta = constant$ is shown in Fig. 9-5 (a curve of the
same shape as in Fig. 7-11). The maximum height is $(I_0 \sin^2 \pi\beta)/(\pi\beta)^2$.

So far the discussion has been in terms of the dimensionless variables
α and β. To find the pattern formed on a screen with given position of
the source, one uses the relations (9-7). For example, let the source be
at O_1 in Fig. 7-4 (normal incidence), and let the observing screen be the
X_2Y_2 plane. The pattern will lie in a small region around O_2, and with
sufficient accuracy the relations between a pair of coordinates X_2, Y_2

and the corresponding values of α and β are

$$X_2 = \frac{\lambda L}{a}\,\alpha \qquad Y_2 = \frac{\lambda L}{b}\,\beta \qquad (9\text{-}10)$$

where L is the distance from O to O_2.   The nodal lines in the X_2Y_2 plane

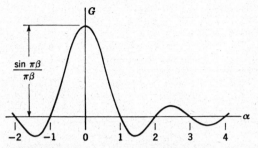

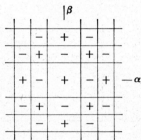

Fig. 9-3.   *Function G for a rectangular aperture plotted as a function of α for constant β.*

Fig. 9-4.   *Grid of nodal lines of the function G and the regions of the $\alpha\beta$ plane in which G is either positive or negative.*

form a grid similar to Fig. 9-4 except for being elongated in the direction *perpendicular* to the long axis of the rectangle.   A photograph of the pattern is shown in Fig. 9-6.   It is impossible in such a figure to show clearly that the irradiance at the center is more than 20 times greater than that of the brightest secondary maxima.   As a rough description, the pattern consists in a bright, elongated spot at the center, with the

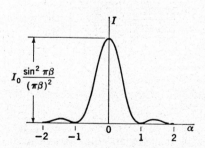

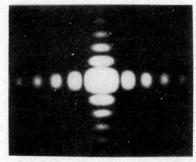

Fig. 9-5.   *Irradiance in the pattern of a rectangular aperture plotted as a function of α for constant β.*

Fig. 9-6.   *Fraunhofer pattern of a rectangular aperture.*

long direction at right angles to that of the aperture; radiating from this spot are four comparatively dim "spikes."   In white light (see Sec. 13-4) the secondary maxima fuse together, and this description becomes most apt.   In the case of a very long and narrow slit and a point source, the pattern formed in the focal plane of a lens is practically confined to a line at right angles to the slit.

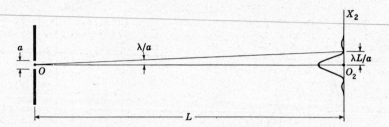

Fig. 9-7.   *Geometrical relation of the Fraunhofer pattern to the rectangular aperture producing it.*

Important quantities associated with the pattern are the angular widths of the bright central maximum.   In the plane defined by the X_2 axis and point O, the situation is as illustrated in Fig. 9-7.   Half the angular width of the central maximum is λ/a, in radians.   The same figure holds with X_2 replaced by Y_2, and a by b.   A nice way to think of these relations and bring them to mind quickly is illustrated in Fig. 9-8.

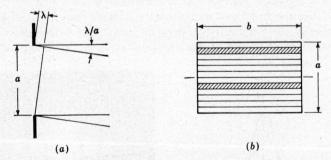

Fig. 9-8.   *Visualization of the destructive interference at the first zero in the pattern of a rectangular aperture.*

In (*a*), rays from the upper and lower edges of the aperture to a point P on the X_2 axis of the observing screen have been chosen to make the difference of path one wavelength.   In (*b*), the aperture has been divided into an even number of narrow strips.   The contributions to the amplitude at P from any two corresponding strips in the upper and lower half of the aperture, such as the shaded ones, are out of phase by π radians and cancel, and hence the amplitude at P is zero. The argument can be extended to account for the angles associated with other zeros in the diffraction pattern and to show the qualitative behavior of the amplitude and irradiance between zeros.

9-4 Circular Aperture   Calculation of the pattern for a circular aperture is complicated if the wave falling on it is not normally incident; hence only normal incidence will be considered. Referred to the coordinate system in Fig. 7-4 with the source at O_1 and the aperture centered at O, the problem has complete symmetry about the line from O_1 to O_2, and it is sufficient to consider only points on the X_2 axis, that is, $\theta_2 \geqq 0$ and $\phi_2 = 0$. Let the diameter of the aperture be D, and let

$$\alpha = \frac{kD}{2\pi} \sin \theta_2 \tag{9-11}$$

The integrand in the numerator of (9-3) is independent of y for points in the aperture, and if the aperture is divided into strips as in Fig. 9-9, integration over a strip introduces the factor $2(D^2/4 - x^2)^{\frac{1}{2}}$. Hence

$$G = \frac{1}{\pi D^2/4} \int_{-D/2}^{D/2} 2\left(\frac{D^2}{4} - x^2\right)^{\frac{1}{2}} e^{-i2\pi\alpha x/D} \, dx$$

$$= \frac{2}{\pi} \int_{-1}^{1} (1 - u^2)^{\frac{1}{2}} e^{-i\pi\alpha u} \, du$$

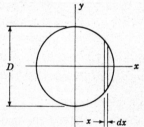

where $u = 2x/D$. The integrand can be written in a form involving only real quantities in the following way:

$$G = \frac{2}{\pi} \int_0^1 (1 - u^2)^{\frac{1}{2}} (e^{i\pi\alpha u} + e^{-i\pi\alpha u}) \, du$$

$$= \frac{4}{\pi} \int_0^1 (1 - u^2)^{\frac{1}{2}} \cos(\pi\alpha u) \, du$$

Fig. 9-9. *Circular aperture referred to cartesian coordinates and divided into infinitesimal strips parallel to the y axis.*

The last integral is not elementary, but it can be expressed in terms of a transcendental function whose values are available in tables:

$$G = \frac{2J_1(\pi\alpha)}{\pi\alpha} \qquad \alpha \geqq 0 \tag{9-12}$$

where J_1 is the Bessel function of order 1; a table can be found, for example, in Jahnke and Ende [50] or Jahnke-Emde-Lösch [51]. A plot of G is shown in Fig. 9-10a. Note that the function is real, but oscillates in sign.

Finally, the irradiance is

$$I = I_0 \left[\frac{2J_1(\pi\alpha)}{\pi\alpha} \right]^2 \tag{9-13}$$

Figure 9-10b is a plot of this function. A photograph of the pattern can be seen in Fig. 7-6a. It is usual to refer to the Fraunhofer pattern of a circular aperture as the *Airy pattern* after the astronomer G. B. Airy, who first obtained (9-13) in 1835. The main feature is the bright central region, called the *Airy disk*. It extends to the first dark ring defined

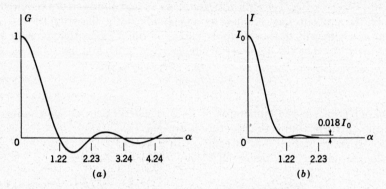

Fig. 9-10. *Function G and irradiance I for the pattern of a circular aperture with normal incidence.*

by $\alpha = 1.22$ and contains about 84 per cent of the total power. The angular radius of the nodal circle at $\alpha = 1.22$ is given by (9-11) to be approximately $1.22\lambda/D$, in radians. Hence it is slightly larger than the angle λ/D applying to a rectangular aperture of width D.

9-5 Diffraction Gratings with Rectangular Apertures The gratings used in spectroscopy can be thought of in the first instance as linear arrays of rectangular apertures, and the results of Sec. 9-3 can be used to complete the discussion begun in Sec. 7-15.

Consider first a transmission grating consisting of N slits parallel to the y axis of Fig. 7-4 with centers along the x axis at spacing d. Let the width of the slits be a. For most effective use of the grating as a spectroscope, the source is placed on the X_1 axis, and the pattern is observed on the X_2 axis. As long as a is a substantial number of wavelengths, the single-aperture irradiance to substitute in (7-8) is

$$I_1 = I_0 \frac{\sin^2 \pi\alpha}{(\pi\alpha)^2} \tag{9-14}$$

where α is given by the left of (9-7). For a monochromatic source with wavelength λ, the diffraction pattern, plotted as a function of $d(\sin \theta_1 + \sin \theta_2)$ as in Fig. 7-22, takes the form of Fig. 9-11, where only those secondary maxima flanking the zero-order principal maximum have been indicated. For the usual case of very large N, the secondary maxima are crowded together much more closely than Fig. 9-11 indicates.

If d/a happens to be the ratio of two whole numbers without common factor, say p/q, then the principal maxima of order np, with n any non-vanishing integer, will be reduced to zero by the factor I_1. This effect is known as the *phenomenon of missing orders*. An interesting case is

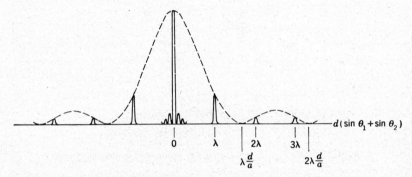

Fig. 9-11. *Diffraction pattern of a grating of rectangular slits. The dashed envelope is the single-aperture pattern.*

$a = d$. Then all orders but the zeroth are missing, and an interpretation comes from noting that the grating has become a single aperture of width Nd. In fact, if (7-15) is compared with (9-14), it is seen that when N is large, each principal maximum and its associated secondary maxima form a pattern of the same shape as for a single aperture of width Nd. The reader should now consider how the pattern for small N, say $N = 3$, goes over into a single-aperture pattern as a approaches d (see Prob. 9-11).

In the transmission grating just discussed, the maximum in the single-aperture pattern falls at the zeroth order. In reflection gratings there is an added flexibility in that the maximum for the single aperture can be placed anywhere with respect to the zeroth order. Suppose the grooves have the ·shape shown in Fig. 9-12. Angles specifying directions to S and P can be referred either to the normal to the plane of the grating, this plane being indicated by the ·horizontal dashed line in the figure, or to the normal to one of the faces of width a. The relation between these pairs of angles is

$$\psi_1 = \theta_1 - \gamma \qquad \psi_2 = \theta_2 - \gamma$$

Let $\qquad \alpha = \dfrac{ka}{2\pi} (\sin \psi_1 + \sin \psi_2) \qquad \delta = \dfrac{kd}{2\pi} (\sin \theta_1 + \sin \theta_2)$

The zeroth order is given by $\delta = 0$, or $\theta_2 = -\theta_1$, while the maximum in the pattern due to one of the faces of width a is given by $\alpha = 0$, or $\theta_2 = -\theta_1 + 2\gamma$. Hence by adjustment of γ, the maximum of the single-aperture pattern can be made to fall on any order, and most of the light will fall in this order rather than in the useless zeroth order. A grating of this type is said to be *blazed* for a given order at a given wavelength. An analogue of the blazed grating is seen in the array of antennas in

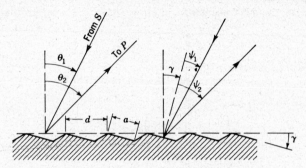

Fig. 9-12. *Reflection grating with grooves of sawtooth profile.*

Fig. 7-21. In that system a given blaze is achieved by tilting the individual antennas.

Practically all reflection gratings have the type profile shown in Fig. 9-12, and the dimensions fall between two extremes. In one, the spacing d is made only a few wavelengths, so that only a few orders fall in the whole range $-\pi/2 < \theta_2 < \pi/2$. For visible wavelengths, typical gratings have as many as 1200 grooves per millimeter. An engine ruling this finely can be relied upon to produce good grooves, equally spaced, only over a total length of some 15 cm, for a total of some 180,000 grooves. The theoretical resolving power in the first order would then be 180,000. However, inevitable small variations in shape and spacing of grooves result in the principal maxima in the diffraction pattern being wider than the theoretical curve shown in Fig. 7-11; the actual resolving power is rarely better than about half the theoretical, and is often much less.[1]

A question of principle arises when the width of a groove becomes comparable with the wavelength, for then the oscillators in the surface of one groove do not behave independently of those in adjacent grooves.

[1] These statements regarding finely ruled gratings must be regarded as subject to continual revision as techniques of producing gratings improve, and the improvements are put into general practice (see Stroke [87]). The figures quoted represent about the optimum for engines depending solely on the excellence of mechanical construction.

Nevertheless, the only difference between one groove and another is the difference of path length from S to P via the two grooves, and the arguments in Chap. 7 on which the function F was based still hold, except that in speaking of the single-aperture irradiance I_1, one must think in different terms.   It makes no sense to speak of measuring I_1 by covering all but one groove, since the oscillators in that groove would be altered. However, in principle one can say that I_1 is the irradiance of a wave which is the superposition of the waves from just the oscillators in any one groove when all are uncovered, even though one may not be able to make

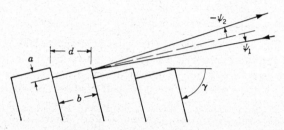

Fig. 9-13.   *Reflection echelon.*

an actual calculation.   The conclusion is that the previous arguments giving the shapes and positions of the principal maxima for a grating are good for all cases, but the relative heights of the maxima of different orders may not be calculable.   Even with such close spacing it turns out that shaping the grooves as in Fig. 9-12 will throw most of the light into any one desired order for a given wavelength, but the best shape must be found somewhat empirically.

The other extreme in geometry is to make d thousands of wavelengths and to make the dihedral angle between the faces of a groove 90°, as in Fig. 9-13.   Gratings of this type are called *reflection echelons*, and typical dimensions for use at visible and ultraviolet wavelengths are $a = 2$ mm, $b = 10$ mm.   The grating is constructed by bringing a number of plane-parallel plates of quartz into optical contact and aluminizing the surfaces. The great technical difficulties in making such a grating limit the number of steps to about 40.

In practice the angle ψ_1 is made very small, so that the light is nearly normally incident on the narrower faces, and practically the full width a is effective.   The single-aperture pattern is very narrow and is made to fall immediately beside the source (the source, of course, being a narrow slit through which the light to be studied passes).   It can easily be shown from the formulas to be obtained below that the angular separation of orders is practically equal to λ/a, which is the angle between the center of the single-aperture pattern and its first zero; hence for a given wavelength there are in general just two orders within the central peak of the single-aperture pattern. If an order happens to fall exactly at the center, all others are missing.

Now if θ_1 and θ_2 have the significance indicated in Fig. 9-12,

$$d \sin \theta_1 = d \sin (\psi_1 + \gamma) = a \sin \psi_1 + b \cos \psi_1$$

and the same applies with subscript 2. Hence

$$\delta = \alpha + \frac{b}{\lambda} (\cos \psi_1 + \cos \psi_2)$$

At the center of the single-aperture pattern ($\alpha = 0$) the order is

$$\delta = \frac{2b}{\lambda} \cos \psi_1 \approx \frac{2b}{\lambda}$$

If $b = 10$ mm and $\lambda = 5000$ A, the order is about 40,000, and with 40 plates the resolving power is 1.6×10^6. This high value justifies the effort of making an echelon. The instrument is not easy to use, and for further details the reader is referred to such treatises as Tolansky [90].

9-6 Resolving Power of Telescope and Microscope The discussion to be given in this section covers only the most elementary aspect of the broad subject of the diffraction theory of image formation by systems of lenses or reflecting surfaces or combinations of both. This subject is a most valuable adjunct to the method of geometrical ray tracing in understanding the fundamental nature of defects in optical systems and finding methods of ameliorating them. No attempt will be made to cover this general topic, and the discussion will be confined to the inherent limitations in the performance of a system that is assumed to be already perfect from the standpoint of geometrical optics.

One of the properties of a system perfect in the geometrical sense is that it is *stigmatic;* that is, for a monochromatic point source S there is a point P in the image space such that any ray from S which passes through the lens system according to the laws of geometrical optics ultimately passes through P. The number of wavelengths counted along such rays between S and P is exactly the same for all, or in other words, the optical lengths of the rays between S and P are all equal. The idea of the last point is illustrated by Fig. 7-15, which is special in that the point P is at infinity. In completing the definition of a geometrically perfect system, one considers the change in position of the stigmatic image P when the position of the source changes. If it is required that as S describes a three-dimensional figure, P is to describe a geometrically similar figure, it can be shown that the only perfect instrument is the trivial one whose longitudinal and lateral magnifications are equal to the ratio of the refractive indices of the object and image spaces. (An example is a plane mirror, for which the image is virtual, and the magnification is unity.) Hence the requirement is relaxed to the extent that as S describes a figure in a plane perpendicular to the axis of the system, the image P is to describe a geometrically similar figure in a plane perpendicular to the axis. Such a system is described as having a *flat field* and showing *no distortion*, and in the following it will be assumed that these two conditions, plus stigmatic imaging, hold for a pair of conjugate planes. In principle a system can be designed to satisfy these conditions for a given pair of conjugate planes and to have any magnification.

The problem to be considered is the following: At some distance outside the front focal point of a positive lens (or system of lenses, to be represented as a simple thin lens) are two monochromatic point sources of equal intensities, one on the axis, and one just off it. In the image

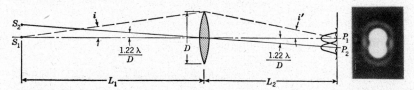

Fig. 9-14. *Rayleigh criterion for the resolution of two point sources by a lens. At extreme right is the image of the two sources just resolved.*

plane will appear a diffraction pattern, and the question is how close together the objects can be and still be recognized as two objects by observation of the pattern. For the moment let the media on the two sides of the lens be the same.

The solution is very simple in the case of incoherent sources. In the image plane the diffraction pattern due to each is the Fraunhofer pattern for a circular aperture, and the irradiance in the pattern with both sources is the sum of the irradiances in the separate patterns. As the criterion as to when the sources are resolved, one takes the Rayleigh criterion as illustrated in Fig. 9-14 (maximum of one pattern over first dark ring of the other). The angular separation between sources that are just resolved is then

$$\text{Minimum angle} = \frac{1.22\lambda}{D} \qquad (9\text{-}15)$$

When the distance L_1 is very great, essentially infinite (the case of a telescope), the angle between the sources is usually the desired quantity. On the other hand, when L_1 is only slightly greater than the focal length of the lens (the case of a microscope), the important datum is the distance between the sources, and from (9-15) one has, with sufficient accuracy,

$$\text{Minimum distance} = \frac{1.22\lambda L_1}{D} \qquad (9\text{-}16)$$

Thus the capability of a microscope objective can be specified by the ratio L_1/D when L_2 is some standard value adopted by manufacturers of microscopes. However, it is customary to replace this ratio by a quantity to which it is equal and which depends on a single parameter associated with the lens and the standard distance L_2. To arrive at this quantity, one uses the *sine condition*, an important property of perfect lenses (of which the proof will be given in the next section). This condition states that if y is the distance between S_1 and S_2, and y' is that between the geometrical image points P_1 and P_2, and if i and i' are the angles in Fig. 9-14, then

$$y \sin i = y' \sin i' \tag{9-17}$$

Since $y' = L_2 y / L_1$, the sine condition gives $L_1 \sin i = L_2 \sin i'$. When i' is small (the case in a microscope), $\sin i' \approx i' \approx D/2L_2$. Combining all these results, (9-16) becomes

$$\text{Minimum distance} = \frac{1.22\lambda}{2 \sin i} = \frac{0.61\lambda}{\text{N.A.}} \tag{9-18}$$

where N.A. stands for $\sin i$, is called the *numerical aperture* of the objective, and is the indication of resolving power marked on microscope objectives. Stated explicitly, the significance of i is that it is the half-angle of the cone of rays accepted by the objective from a point source on the axis.

In a microscope with an oil-immersion objective, the object space is filled with oil of refractive index n. The angular separation of the sources, as seen from the lens when the Rayleigh condition holds, becomes $1.22(\lambda/n)/D$, and the right side of (9-16) must be divided by n. Also, the right side of (9-18) becomes $1.22\lambda/(2n \sin i)$, since the sine condition takes the form $ny \sin i = y' \sin i'$, but the relation $L_1 \sin i = L_2 \sin i'$ still holds. The numerical aperture is now $n \sin i$ and may achieve a value greater than unity.

Both (9-15) and (9-18) must be regarded as rules of thumb which are subject to various qualifications in particular cases. In a telescope, (9-15) holds only if the medium between the lens and the sources is homogeneous, but the theoretical resolving power is not attained through a long path of turbulent atmosphere, as remarked in Sec. 7-13 on the stellar interferometer. The large diameters of the lenses or mirrors in the important astronomical telescopes are for the purpose of gathering large amounts of light, and do not give a measure of resolution of celestial objects.[1] In the microscope, formula (9-18) holds only for self-luminous

[1] As the diameter D of the objective of an astronomical telescope viewing a star through the turbulent atmosphere is increased from a small initial value to a very large value, the image passes from one given by the theory of diffraction (the Airy pattern), and therefore having a diameter proportional to $1/D$ and a central irradiance proportional to D^4, to one which ceases to decrease in size and has a central irradiance proportional to D^2. Under the best conditions, the critical diameter separating these two regimes is about 10 in.

objects, the only case in which the rule for incoherent sources holds exactly. The question of resolution when the object is illuminated in the various ways employed by microscopists has been investiₐated extensively, and the conclusion is that in each case (9-18) must be multiplied by a correction factor which is never far from unity. Hence (9-18) as it stands is a fairly good over-all rule.

9-7 Sine Condition From the definitions of a geometrically perfect optical system follow a number of theorems. One of the most important is the sine condition, which was used in the last section. To prove it, consider Fig. 9-15, in which the system of lenses is represented by its

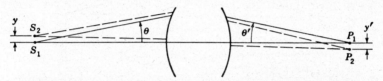

Fig. 9-15. *Construction for the proof of the sine condition.*

first and last surfaces. A source S_1 is on the axis, and a second source S_2 is a small distance y from it. The geometrical images are at P_1 and P_2, separated by distance y'. Two pairs of rays are drawn. One pair, which will be referred to as *paraxial* rays and distinguished by superscript (p), consist of a ray from S_1 to P_1 along the axis, and one from S_2 to P_2 such as to cross the axis somewhere in the system. Let the optical lengths of these rays be $l_1{}^{(p)}$ and $l_2{}^{(p)}$, respectively. The other pair, to be referred to as *extra-axial* and labeled superscript (e), leave S_1 and S_2 at angle θ (essentially the same for both) and arrive at P_1 and P_2 with angle θ'. The extra-axial rays have been chosen to cross somewhere in the system. Let their optical lengths be $l_1{}^{(e)}$ and $l_2{}^{(e)}$.

Since the system is stigmatic, $l_1{}^{(e)} = l_1{}^{(p)}$, and $l_2{}^{(e)} = l_2{}^{(p)}$. Since y and y' are small, the lengths $l_1{}^{(p)}$ and $l_2{}^{(p)}$ clearly differ by an amount proportional only to the second and higher powers of y, and as an approximation they can be set equal to each other. Then, to the same degree of approximation,

$$l_1{}^{(e)} = l_2{}^{(e)} \tag{9-19}$$

From Fig. 9-16 it is seen that (9-19) is equivalent to

$$\frac{y \sin \theta}{\lambda} = \frac{y' \sin \theta'}{\lambda'} \tag{9-20}$$

where λ and λ' are the wavelengths in the media filling the object and image spaces, respectively. (Recall the sense in which the term "optical length" is being used in this book. The definition is given in Sec. 7-12.)

Relation (9-20) is the statement of the sine condition. It holds exactly for a perfect system only in the limit as y and y' go to zero, but is certainly very nearly satisfied for the small distances (relative to L_1 and L_2) involved in discussing limits of resolution. The great importance of (9-20) in the theory of optical instruments is that it must be satisfied for all admissible values of θ if the system is to be stigmatic. Departures from the condition shown by any particular design can be related to

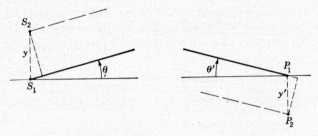

Fig. 9-16. *Additional construction for the proof of the sine condition.*

certain types of errors in the geometrical image of a point source that lies any distance off the axis. The sine condition is also used in deriving theorems on the illumination in optical instruments when the source is extended and diffraction plays no role. For the latter subject, see Hardy and Perrin [33], chap. 19.

Problems

9-1. To follow up the discussion immediately following (9-5), assume that the total power falling in the diffraction pattern for a circular aperture of diameter D with normal incidence is uniformly distributed over a circular area with constant irradiance equal to I_0, where I_0 is the irradiance at the center of the actual pattern. Prove that the angular radius of this area as seen from the aperture is $2\lambda/\pi D$ radians, or approximately one-half the angular radius of the first dark ring.

9-2. If the Fraunhofer pattern is formed in the focal plane of a lens placed a short distance behind the diffracting screen, give an argument whereby formula (9-5) holds if R_{20} is replaced by f, the focal length of the lens.

9-3. Consider the rectangular aperture of Fig. 9-2, and let the incident wave fall normally on it. Check the balance of energy by integrating the irradiance I over the pattern formed on the X_2Y_2 plane of Fig. 7-4 and making use of (9-5) to show that this integral is equal to the power passing through the aperture. Make the usual approximations (9-10). The definite integrals involved can be found in standard tables. [The balance happens to come out exactly, in spite of the approximations. Note that the approximations involved are not just those in (9-10); others enter through the way the obliquity factor and the factor $1/R_{20}$ were treated in getting (9-1). Finally, the irradiance at each point of the X_2Y_2 plane (the power per unit area) is really not the normal irradiance of the diffracted wave (see definition in Sec. 7-6), but is this quantity multiplied by the cosine of the angle of incidence at each point. There happens to be exact compensation among all these approximations.]

9-4. Deduce the formula

$$\int_{-a/2}^{a/2} e^{-i2\pi\alpha x/a}\, dx = a\,\frac{\sin \pi\alpha}{\pi\alpha}$$

[see (9-8)] by a graphical addition of the infinitesimal complex numbers $e^{-i2\pi\alpha x/a}\, dx$. When the vectors representing these numbers are drawn end to end beginning at the lower limit, the result is an arc of a circle whose tangent at the midpoint is parallel to the real axis. Base the derivation on the case $\alpha < 1$. Draw also the case $\alpha = 1$.

9-5. Consider the two apertures of areas α_1 and α_2 shown in Fig. 9-17. For the first aperture let G_1 be the function defined by (9-3), except that it is referred to the x_1 and y_1 axes rather than the x and y axes. Similarly define G_2 for the second aperture. Let G be the function for both apertures referred to the x and y axes. Show that

$$G = \frac{\alpha_1 G_1 e^{-i\psi_1} + \alpha_2 G_2 e^{-i\psi_2}}{\alpha_1 + \alpha_2}$$

where $\psi_1 = k[\xi_1(\sin \theta_1 + \sin \theta_2) + \eta_1(\sin \phi_1 + \sin \phi_2)]$, and similarly for ψ_2. (Clearly, this formula extends to any number of apertures.)

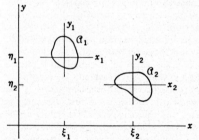
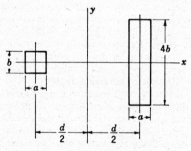

Fig. 9-17. *Apertures referred to in Prob. 9-5.* **Fig. 9-18.** *Apertures referred to in Prob. 9-6.*

9-6. Let a plane wave of wavelength λ be normally incident on a screen containing the pair of apertures shown in Fig. 9-18. Apply the formula of Prob. 9-5 to find an expression for the irradiance along the X_2 axis of Fig. 7-4. Plot roughly the result as a function of $\sin \theta_2$, and indicate all the characteristic dimensions of the figure.

9-7. Show that for N identical apertures the formula (9-4) with G obtained as in Prob. 9-5 is equivalent to (7-8), provided the apertures are identically related to their respective coordinate systems.

9-8. A Fraunhofer pattern is formed with a plane diffracting screen having an aperture of any shape. Let the incidence be normal. Referred to the standard coordinate system of Fig. 7-4, let the coordinates of any point p on the rim of the aperture be (x_p, y_p). Show by an argument based on (9-3) to (9-5) that if the aperture is deformed by changing x_p to hx_p for all points p, where h is a constant (so that, for example, a circle becomes an ellipse), then the irradiance at (X_2, Y_2) after the deformation is h^2 times that at (hX_2, Y_2) before the deformation. It is necessary to assume that only small values of θ_2 and ϕ_2 are of interest. (Compare Prob. 7-7.)

9-9. Show directly from (9-9) and (9-5) that the general behavior described in Prob. 9-8 holds when a square aperture is deformed into a rectangle.

9-10. As an application of Prob. 9-8, draw figures to show how the dark rings in the Fraunhofer pattern for a circular aperture change as the circle is deformed into an ellipse.

9-11. Consider a diffraction grating with three slits of width a having centers lying on the x axis of Fig. 7-4 at spacing d. Let the incident wave fall normally. The problem will be to investigate the limiting case $a = d$. Draw a curve of the function $|F|^2$ against $d \sin \theta_2$ (see Sec. 7-8). Directly below and to the same horizontal scale draw I_1 for a single slit of width d, and for $\phi_2 = 0$. Below these two curves draw by eye the product $I_1|F|^2$, and note that it has the appearance of the irradiance for a single slit of width $3d$. Obtain this result analytically from the formulas for I_1 and $|F|^2$.

9-12. In contrast to Prob. 9-11, draw the curves for three slits with spacing d and widths $a = d/2$. Include the range of orders -5 to $+5$. Which orders are missing?

9-13. For the reflection echelon, as for any grating, the principal maxima are defined by $\delta = m$, where m is an integer. Show that for the echelon the maxima are given by $\alpha = m - m_0$, where m_0 is the order (not necessarily an integer) at the center of the single-aperture pattern. From this result show that the angular separation of the important principal maxima (the ones for small ψ_1 and ψ_2) is approximately λ/a. Draw two figures as follows: In each draw a dashed envelope curve representing the single-aperture pattern. Include several secondary maxima in these curves. In one figure draw the principal maxima of the grating pattern when one order falls at the center of the single-aperture pattern, and in the other draw the case in which the center of the single-aperture pattern falls midway between two orders.

9-14. A plane monochromatic wave is normally incident on a lens of diameter D. At the center of the lens is an opaque disk whose diameter d is a small fraction of D, say one-tenth. Use Babinet's principle to find the effect of the small disk on the Fraunhofer diffraction pattern. It is intended that the treatment be essentially qualitative and based on a drawing of appropriate curves to represent terms in the formula (9-6). Conclusions which should come out are that the first dark ring is reduced in diameter, the second increased, etc., and that the central maximum in the irradiance is reduced, the first secondary maximum is increased, the second reduced, etc. Calculate exactly how much the central maximum is reduced. (If it were not for distortion in the incident wave fronts due to atmospheric turbulence, the images of stars formed by reflecting telescopes would show the pattern of this problem, since the secondary mirror acts as a small disk in the entrance aperture. Curves showing the change in the pattern as d varies between zero and D can be found in Born and Wolf [9], p. 416.)

9-15. In astronomical photographs made with a reflecting telescope, any heavily exposed stellar images in the field show four radial spikes spaced at 90° (see, for example, Baker [2], pp. 232, 508, and 524). They are due to four radial supports of the secondary mirror. These supports are made of the thinnest possible plates oriented to be seen edgewise by the incoming light, the reason being not so much to admit maximum light as to minimize the spikes. Elucidate these spikes with the aid of Babinet's principle. In the discussion one can neglect the presence of the secondary mirror and can consider the effect of two thin strips along perpendicular diameters of the aperture. What is the effect of removing one of the strips?

9-16. Use Babinet's principle to describe the effect on the Fraunhofer pattern of stretching two parallel wires across a lens. Let the wires be at equal distances from the center, let their diameters be equal and small compared with their separation, and let the separation be small compared with the diameter of the lens.

9-17. The Fraunhofer pattern for a random array of small circular holes is formed in the focal plane of a lens. What is the principal change in the pattern if the diffracting screen is replaced by its complement (that is, the aperture of the lens is open except for an array of small opaque disks)?

9-18. Show that the Fraunhofer pattern formed by a narrow slit bent into an equilateral triangle (or equivalently, a triangular hole containing an opaque triangle almost as large) has the general appearance of six equally spaced spikes radiating from a central bright spot. (*Hints:* Do not attempt to use Babinet's principle, but rather consider the straight segments of the slit one at a time, and note what can be said at once when all three are considered. Do not attempt to describe the complicated secondary maxima and minima immediately around the central spot.)

chapter 10

Application of the Kirchhoff Integral to Fresnel Diffraction

According to the definitions given in Sec. 7-1, Fresnel diffraction occurs when the aperture is too large compared with the distance.to the source or to the observing point, or both, to satisfy the conditions for Fraunhofer diffraction. The simplifications by which the Kirchhoff integral led to concise formulas to represent Fraunhofer patterns no longer hold, and Fresnel patterns can be found only by tedious numerical or graphical computations.

The problem of the rectangular aperture is simple enough that it will be treated completely. The main objective will be to see the transition from the case in which the observing screen is near the aperture, and the diffraction pattern is roughly uniform within the geometrically defined boundary of the shadow, to the Fraunhofer case, in which the geometrical shadow ceases to have any evident relation to the diffraction pattern.

The circular aperture is much more difficult, both in the derivation of the relevant formulas and in their numerical evaluation. The pattern has circular rather than rectangular symmetry, but otherwise is not qualitatively different from that of the rectangular aperture, except at the center, where a very interesting phenomenon occurs. The theory of the behavior of the irradiance at this special point is very simple and will be given. Historically, it is of great importance, since the ability of Fresnel's theory to account for this striking and easily observed phenomenon is said to have convinced the last skeptics that light must be of the nature of waves.

10-1   Rectangular Aperture   Let a plane diffracting screen contain a rectangular aperture of dimensions a by b, as shown in Fig. 10-1.   Let a monochromatic point source be at S, and let SO be the perpendicular from S to the diffracting screen.   Let P be the point on the observing screen lying on the extension of this perpendicular.

Rather than to find the irradiance at various points of the observing screen with the aperture fixed, the procedure will be to consider the fixed point P and to cause the pattern to sweep over it by translating the aperture in its own plane, so that the origin O will assume various positions with respect to the bounding contour.   Strictly speaking, these

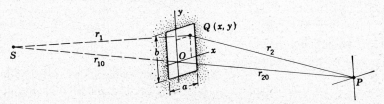

Fig. 10-1.   *Geometry for treating Fresnel diffraction by a rectangular aperture.   Line SOP is perpendicular to the plane of the aperture.*

two approaches to the problem are not equivalent, since the pattern on the observing screen changes both in size and in distribution of irradiance when the aperture is moved.   However, these changes are negligible if the aperture is moved only through distances small compared with the distance r_{10} to the source.   This restriction admits the following cases to which the discussion can be limited without significant loss of generality: (1) The dimensions a and b are small compared with r_{10}; the entire pattern can be calculated.   (2) The dimension a is small, but b is large (long slit); the pattern can be investigated as the aperture is translated parallel to the x axis.   (3) Both a and b are large, but the pattern is investigated only for the origin O lying near one edge of the aperture and P, therefore, being near the edge of the geometrical shadow; when a and b are infinite this is the problem of a semi-infinite screen with a straight edge.

Consider first the case in which a and b are small compared with r_{10}; let Q be an arbitrary point in the aperture at which is situated an element of surface

$$d\Sigma = dx\,dy$$

In evaluating the Kirchhoff integral (8-11), it is sufficiently accurate to set the obliquity factor equal to 2 and to set $1/r_1r_2$ equal to $1/r_{10}r_{20}$. Then the amplitude at P is given by

$$u_0(P) = -\frac{iA}{\lambda r_{10}r_{20}} \int_{y_1}^{y_2} \int_{x_1}^{x_2} e^{ik(r_1+r_2)}\,dx\,dy \qquad (10\text{-}1)$$

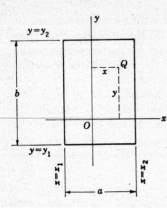

Fig. 10-2. *Rectangular aperture referred to cartesian coordinates.*

where the limits define the edges of the aperture, as shown in Fig. 10-2. Now

$$r_1 = (r_{10}{}^2 + x^2 + y^2)^{1/2} \approx r_{10} + \frac{x^2 + y^2}{2r_{10}}$$

Let r_2 be evaluated to the same degree of approximation, which implies that r_{20}, as well as r_{10}, is large compared with a and b. (The nature of the corrections when this condition does not hold will be discussed later.) Then

$$r_1 + r_2 \approx r_{10} + r_{20} + (x^2 + y^2)\,\frac{r_{10} + r_{20}}{2r_{10}r_{20}}$$

$$(10\text{-}2)$$

The formula obtained by substituting (10-2) in (10-1) is given a simple form by substituting for x and y the dimensionless variables

$$\xi = x\left[\frac{2(r_{10} + r_{20})}{\lambda r_{10}r_{20}}\right]^{1/2} \qquad \eta = y\left[\frac{2(r_{10} + r_{20})}{\lambda r_{10}r_{20}}\right]^{1/2} \qquad (10\text{-}3)$$

The result is

$$u_0(P) = -\frac{iA}{2(r_{10} + r_{20})}\,e^{ik(r_{10}+r_{20})}\int_{\xi_1}^{\xi_2} e^{i\pi\xi^2/2}\,d\xi \int_{\eta_1}^{\eta_2} e^{i\pi\eta^2/2}\,d\eta \qquad (10\text{-}4)$$

The factor outside the integrals is just $-i/2$ times the unobstructed amplitude at P. The latter will be denoted henceforth by $u_{00}(P)$.

The integrals in (10-4) are not elementary and can be evaluated only in terms of the standard integrals:

$$C(v) = \int_0^v \cos\frac{\pi t^2}{2}\,dt \qquad S(v) = \int_0^v \sin\frac{\pi t^2}{2}\,dt \qquad (10\text{-}5)$$

Tables of the functions C and S, which are called *Fresnel integrals*, are given in Appendix C. For more extensive tables see Jahnke-Emde-Lösch [51]. Formula (10-4) is given its final form in terms of these functions by writing each integral as the sum of its real and imaginary parts:

$$u_0(P) = -\frac{iu_{00}(P)}{2}\,\{C(\xi_2) - C(\xi_1)$$
$$+ i[S(\xi_2) - S(\xi_1)]\}\{C(\eta_2) - C(\eta_1) + i[S(\eta_2) - S(\eta_1)]\} \qquad (10\text{-}6)$$

It will now be shown how (10-6) can be evaluated in a very simple way by graphical measurements.

Figure 10-3 shows the curve obtained by plotting points in the complex plane whose real coordinates with respect to a fixed origin are $C(v)$ and whose imaginary coordinates are $S(v)$. This curve is called *Cornu's spiral*. The point at the origin corresponds to $v = 0$, and the part of the curve for positive v lies in the upper right-hand quadrant. The curve is symmetrical about the origin, since it is evident from (10-5) that C

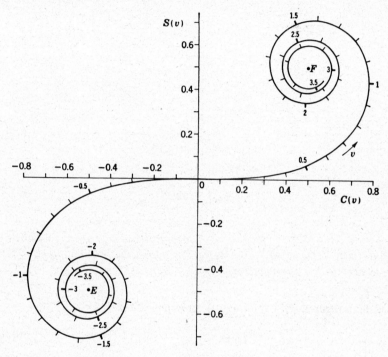

Fig. 10-3. *Cornu spiral. A scale of the parameter v is marked along the curve.*

and S are odd functions of v. As v increases indefinitely, the curve spirals in to the limit point labeled F whose coordinates are

$$C(\infty) = S(\infty) = \tfrac{1}{2} \tag{10-7}$$

The spiral can be thought of as being constructed by placing end to end the infinitesimal vectors $e^{i\pi v^2/2}\,dv$ as v increases from $-\infty$ to $+\infty$. Each of these vectors has length dv, and hence the parameter v has the geometrical significance that the length of arc along the spiral from the origin (where $v = 0$) to the point associated with a given value of v is $|v|$. A scale of v is marked along the curve in Fig. 10-3.

The use of the Cornu spiral in evaluating (10-6) is as follows: Mark the points $v = \xi_1$ and $v = \xi_2$ and join them by a vector, as in Fig. 10-4. The vector represents a complex number whose magnitude A and angle ψ

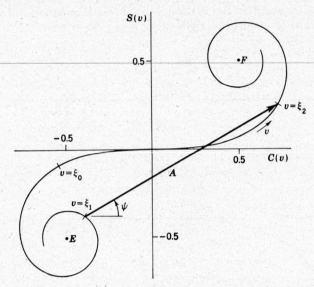

Fig. 10-4.   *Use of the Cornu spiral in finding the complex number $Ae^{i\psi}$ associated with a rectangular aperture.*

can be measured with ruler and protractor.   Then

$$C(\xi_2) - C(\xi_1) + i[S(\xi_2) - S(\xi_1)] = Ae^{i\psi} \qquad (10\text{-}8)$$

In the same way one finds

$$C(\eta_2) - C(\eta_1) + i[S(\eta_2) - S(\eta_1)] = Be^{ix} \qquad (10\text{-}9)$$

The irradiance at P is then

$$I(P) = \tfrac{1}{4}A^2B^2\,I_0(P) \qquad (10\text{-}10)$$

where $I_0(P)$ is the irradiance at P in the absence of a diffracting screen. The angles ψ and χ do not appear in (10-10), and a record of them need be preserved only if one contemplates an application of Babinet's principle in a manner to be discussed in the next section.

Consider now the effect on $I(P)$ of translating the aperture parallel to the x axis. The factor (10-9) appearing in (10-6) remains constant, and the only variation occurs in (10-8). The investigation of (10-8) by the graphical method is facilitated by introducing the parameters

$$\Delta v = \xi_2 - \xi_1 = a \left[\frac{2(r_{10} + r_{20})}{\lambda r_{10} r_{20}} \right]^{\frac{1}{2}} \tag{10-11}$$

$$\xi_0 = \tfrac{1}{2}(\xi_2 + \xi_1) = x_0 \left[\frac{2(r_{10} + r_{20})}{\lambda r_{10} r_{20}} \right]^{\frac{1}{2}} \tag{10-12}$$

where a is the width of the aperture, and x_0 is the x coordinate of the center of the aperture. In relation to the curve in Fig. 10-4, Δv is the length of arc between the points $v = \xi_1$ and $v = \xi_2$, and ξ_0 defines the midpoint of this arc. As the aperture is translated, Δv remains constant, while ξ_0 moves along the curve through a distance proportional to the distance of translation and falls at the center of symmetry of the spiral when the center of the aperture is on the y axis.

It is now evident that the most economical expression of the data on Fresnel diffraction by rectangular apertures is a family of curves of A^2 as a function of ξ_0, each curve being associated with a given value of Δv. The same set of curves then applies for translation of the aperture parallel to the y axis, that is, for the factor B^2 in (10-10), since (10-9) is of the same form as (10-8). Figure 10-5 shows several members of this family. The curves are symmetrical about $\xi_0 = 0$, and only half of each curve is shown. To recapitulate the way in which these curves are obtained, two points on the Cornu spiral which mark off an arc of fixed length Δv slide along the spiral. The positions of these points are specified by the single variable ξ_0 defining the midpoint of the arc. For each value of ξ_0 the end points of the arc are joined by a straight line whose length is measured to be A. Then A^2 is plotted as a function of ξ_0. All lengths are measured in terms of the unit to which $C(v)$ and $S(v)$ were laid off in plotting the spiral.

The diffraction pattern is obtained from the standard curves of Fig. 10-5 in the following way: The parameters a, b, λ, r_{10}, and r_{20} are given. The curve belonging to the Δv calculated by (10-11) then gives the factor A^2 in (10-10) as a function of ξ_0. In the same way, the Δv calculated with a replaced by b selects a curve which gives B^2 as a function of η_0, the latter being defined in analogy with (10-12). Imagining $A^2 B^2$ plotted as ordinate above a plane referred to cartesian coordinates ξ_0 and η_0, one has a surface which represents the irradiance at the fixed point P as the aperture is translated into various positions and, alternatively, which represents, apart from scale, the irradiance over the observing screen when the aperture is fixed. Note that B^2 is constant along lines parallel to the ξ_0 axis, and A^2 is constant along lines parallel to the η_0 axis. This type behavior is evident at the bottom of Fig. 6-1b. The simplest way to relate the scale of the three-dimensional plot just described to that of the pattern on the observing screen is to draw a rectangle on the $\xi_0 \eta_0$

plane to correspond to the boundary of the geometrically defined shadow on the observing screen. Since P is at this boundary whenever O in Fig. 10-1 is at the edge of the aperture, the sides of this rectangle parallel to the η_0 axis are at $\xi_0 = \pm \Delta v/2$, the Δv being given by (10-11). The

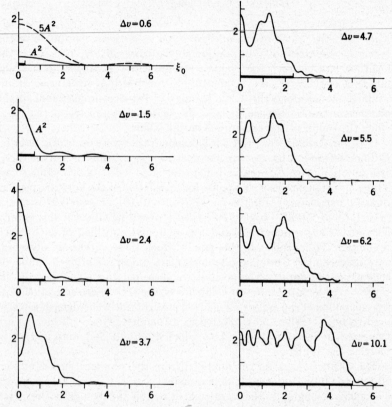

Fig. 10-5. *Function A^2 associated with a rectangular aperture as a function of ξ_0 for several values of Δv. The complete curves are symmetrical about $\xi_0 = 0$, and only half of each is shown. A heavy segment along the horizontal axis indicates the boundary of the geometrical shadow.*

other two sides are found analogously. For each curve of Fig. 10-5 a heavy segment along the ξ_0 axis marks off the extent of this rectangle.

From Fig. 10-5 one gets a quite complete idea of the nature of the Fresnel patterns. When Δv is greater than 10, the pattern is roughly that predicted by geometrical optics, the principal difference being the prominent fringes near the edge of the pattern. In the next section it will be shown that these fringes do not become less prominent as the size of the aperture increases. When Δv is less than unity, the pattern shows roughly the profile characteristic of Fraunhofer diffraction, but the spreading of the pattern far into the geometrical shadow, also characteristic of the Fraunhofer case, does not occur until Δv is substantially less than unity. In the intermediate range $1 < \Delta v < 10$, the pattern undergoes pronounced and complicated changes. In connection with the curves plotted in Fig. 10-5, the significance of the six choices of Δv beginning with 2.5 and ending with 10.1 is that, with respect to variation of Δv, the ordinate at the center is passing through a maximum or a minimum in each case, as is seen by examining the Cornu spiral.

It is worthwhile to point out explicitly the effects on the pattern as actually seen on the observing screen when certain of the parameters of the problem are varied. Let r_{10} and r_{20} be kept fixed. Let b be greater than a, and consider first the effect of varying the size of the aperture, keeping b/a constant. Associated with the problem are the two quantities Δv_a, defined by (10-11), and Δv_b, defined analogously. When both these quantities are greater than 10, the pattern is roughly as predicted by geometrical optics and covers a rectangular area of the same shape and orientation as that of the aperture, that is, broader in the y direction. As the aperture shrinks, the pattern shrinks roughly in proportion, but the system of fringes becomes complicated. When Δv_a passes a value of about 2, the pattern ceases to shrink in the x direction and begins to expand, while it continues to shrink in the y direction. Finally, when Δv_b passes the same value of 2, expansion sets in in the y direction. Ultimately the pattern goes over into the Fraunhofer type, which is broader in the x direction. Note that when Δv_a and Δv_b are greater than unity, the irradiance in the bright part of the pattern hovers about the unobstructed value I_0, but after Δv_a becomes less than unity, the maximum irradiance falls rapidly because a decreasing amount of power is being spread over an increasing area.

Consider now the effect of decreasing the wavelength, keeping a and b constant. Both Δv_a and Δv_b increase as $1/\sqrt{\lambda}$, but the outline of the geometrically defined shadow remains fixed. Clearly, the pattern becomes more and more nearly uniform within this outline, and the fringes around the edge, while they do not decrease in contrast, become finer and finer, and the region of appreciable fluctuation extends a smaller and smaller distance in from the edge. This result, drawn from a somewhat special problem, illustrates the general principle that diffraction becomes insignificant and the predictions of geometrical optics are realized in the limit of vanishing wavelength.

The discussions of this section and in sections to follow should be supplemented with numerical calculations to gain a feeling for the magnitudes involved. Some of the problems will suggest appropriate exercises.

**10-2   Limiting Case of a Large Aperture.   Long Slit and
Straight Edge**   Refer to Fig. 10-1; suppose the center of the aperture
is held fixed at the origin O, and a and b are allowed to become very large.
The variable point Q can now advance to large distances from O, and all
the approximations made in the last section concerning the obliquity
factor, the factor $1/r_1 r_2$, and the value of $k(r_1 + r_2)$ (particularly the
last—see Prob. 10-6) break down.   One should proceed to a more exact
analysis, but it is too difficult to carry through.   One of its awkward
features would be that the double integral in the Kirchhoff formula for
$u_0(P)$ would not separate into a product of single integrals as in (10-4).

Now if one ignores this failure of the approximations and formally
applies the results of the last section even in the limit as a and b become
infinite, the results are as follows: The evaluation of (10-8) is

$$A e^{i\psi} = C(\infty) - C(-\infty) + i[S(\infty) - S(-\infty)] = 1 + i = \sqrt{2}\, e^{i\pi/4}$$

Here (10-7) has been used.   Similarly,

$$B e^{i\chi} = \sqrt{2}\, e^{i\pi/4} \tag{10-13}$$

Then (10-6) becomes

$$u_0(P) = u_{00}(P)$$

which is the correct result, since when a and b become infinite, the wave
from the source arrives at P unobstructed by a diffracting screen.

On the one hand, it is surprising that this formal procedure has given
exactly the right result, but on the other, it is to be expected that it should
give at least a very good approximation, for a fundamental restriction in
the Kirchhoff theory is that r_{10} and r_{20} be very large compared with the
wavelength.   In ordinary laboratory arrangements for observing Fresnel
patterns with visible light, this restriction is more than met.   Numerical
examples (such as are called for in the problems) show that the aperture
can be large enough to give very large values of Δv (essentially infinite)
while the angles subtended by the aperture as seen from either S or P
are still of the order of a degree.   Under these conditions the approximations in the last section are still valid, and since the calculated amplitude at P is already very close to the unobstructed value, it certainly
cannot undergo any appreciable change as a and b are allowed to go to
infinity.

The conclusion is that the approximate formulas of the last section
will give quite accurate results when applied to apertures of any size.
It appears that the problem of diffraction apologizes for its difficulty by
offering cases in which several approximations exactly or very nearly
balance.   Another example was cited in Prob. 9-3.

As a first application of this extended view of the validity of (10-6)
and (10-10), consider the case in which b is large and a is small (long,
narrow slit).   Let the center of the aperture be held on the x axis of

Fig. 10-1, and let translation occur in the x direction. The Δv correspond-ing to the long dimension is practically infinite, so that (10-9) becomes (10-13), and

$$u_0(P) = \frac{1}{\sqrt{2}} u_{00}(P) A e^{i(\psi - \pi/4)} \tag{10-14}$$

$$I(P) = \tfrac{1}{2} I_0(P) A^2 \tag{10-15}$$

Translation in the y direction through small distances would not change this result. Thus the pattern is confined to a long region parallel to the slit, and the profile of the irradiance along a line perpendicular to the long axis of the slit and passing through or near the center of the pattern is one of the curves of the family illustrated in Fig. 10-5. The fringes in this central region are parallel bands along which the irradiance does not vary.

The results just obtained are the basis of a very beautiful laboratory experiment. An eyepiece is placed a meter or so from a pinhole strongly illuminated by nearly monochromatic light (commonly obtained by pass-ing the light from a mercury arc through a filter which passes only the green line 5461 A). Midway from the pinhole is placed a slit some centimeter or two in length and adjustable in width. The jaws must be straight and parallel and free of dirt. (A high-quality slit is cleaned by gently stroking it lengthwise with the sharpened end of a soft match-stick.) As the slit is varied in width, the fringes pass continuously through the configurations represented by the curves in Fig. 10-5. Photographs cannot adequately convey the impression obtained visually. If the pinhole is replaced by a very narrow fixed slit made parallel to the adjustable one by finding the adjustment that gives the best contrast to the fringes, the pattern is brightened without other alteration except near the ends.

Consider next a semi-infinite diffracting screen with a straight edge. Let the opaque part cover those points of the xy plane of Fig. 10-1 for which $x > x_1$, and suppose $|x_1|$ is small compared with r_{10}, so that P will always be near the edge of the geometrical shadow. To x_1 corre-sponds the dimensionless quantity ξ_1, and (10-6) can be applied by setting $\xi_2 = -\infty$, $\eta_1 = \infty$, and $\eta_2 = -\infty$. Then $u_0(P)$ and $I(P)$ are given by (10-14) and (10-15) if

$$A e^{i\psi} = C(\xi_1) - C(-\infty) + i[S(\xi_1) - S(-\infty)]$$

This quantity is evaluated graphically by drawing in Fig. 10-3 a vector from the asymptotic point E at $C = S = -\tfrac{1}{2}$ to the point $v = \xi_1$. Figure 10-6 shows A^2 as a function ξ_1. The abscissa $\xi_1 = 0$ corresponds to P being at the edge of the geometrical shadow, and at this point the amplitude is one-half and the irradiance one-fourth of the unobstructed value. As x_1 increases from zero, a series of fringes paralleling the diffracting edge and showing decreasing contrast and decreasing separation sweep over the observing point P. It is evident how Fig. 10-6 relates to the curves of Fig. 10-5 as a limiting case.

To conclude this section, consider how Babinet's principle is applied to find the pattern for a rectangular obstacle once the problem has been solved for an aperture of the same size and shape. The most instructive

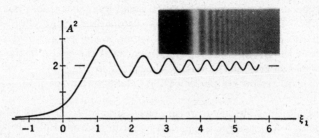

Fig. 10-6. *Function A^2 for the pattern of a straight edge. The abscissa $\xi_1 = 0$ corresponds to the edge of the geometrical shadow. Inset is the diffraction pattern.*

case, and one that is not inordinately tedious, is that of a long opaque strip, complementary to a long slit of the same width. If $u_0(P)$ is the amplitude at P for a given position of the slit, and $u_0'(P)$ is that for the strip, then the general expression of Babinet's principle is

$$u_0'(P) = u_{00}(P) - u_0(P)$$

Substituting from (10-14),

$$u_0'(P) = u_{00}(P) \left(1 - \frac{1}{\sqrt{2}} A e^{i(\psi - \pi/4)} \right)$$

Let this relation be rewritten as

$$u_0'(P) = -\frac{i}{\sqrt{2}} e^{i\pi/4} u_{00}(P) A' e^{i\psi'}$$

where
$$A' e^{i\psi'} = \sqrt{2} e^{i\pi/4} - A e^{i\psi} \tag{10-16}$$

The irradiance at P when the diffracting screen is the strip is then

$$I'(P) = \tfrac{1}{2} I_0(P) A'^2 \tag{10-17}$$

The problem of finding A' from (10-16) is one of vector subtraction in the complex plane. The first term on the right is represented by a vector of length $\sqrt{2}$ forming an angle of 45° with the real axis; it is, in fact, the vector joining the asymptotic points E and F in Fig. 10-3. The second term is represented by the vector drawn in Fig. 10-4, and its magnitude and angle will have been measured in solving the problem of the slit. The vector subtraction is then done graphically as in Fig. 10-7. (For an alternative method of calculation see Prob. 10-8.)

As for the slit, it is appropriate to represent the pattern for the strip by a plot of A'^2 as a function of ξ_0 for a given Δv. A very interesting case is that of small Δv. Figure 10-8 shows one-half the curve for $\Delta v = 0.6$. This curve, when compared with the corresponding one in Fig. 10-5, emphasizes in a striking way that Babinet's principle involves a subtraction of amplitudes, and not irradiances. When Δv is greater than 10, the two edges of the strip become essentially independent of each other, and a pattern of fringes as represented by Fig.

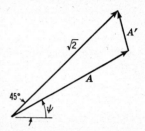

Fig. 10-7. *Vector subtraction involved in applying Babinet's principle to a long strip complementary to a slit.*

10-6 extends out from either side of the shadow. For $1 < \Delta v < 10$ the pattern is very complicated, just as for the complementary slits.

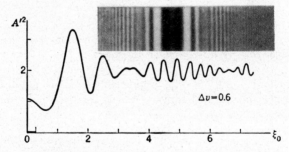

Fig. 10-8. *Profile of the pattern of a narrow strip with $\Delta v = 0.6$. Inset is the diffraction pattern.*

10-3 Transition to the Fraunhofer Case Qualitatively it is already evident from Fig. 10-5 how the Fraunhofer pattern for a rectangular aperture emerges as a limiting case when the dimensions of the aperture become sufficiently small compared with r_{10} and r_{20}. It will now be shown quantitatively how the Fraunhofer formulas are obtained asymptotically from the Fresnel formulas.

For simplicity let r_{10} be infinite, so that a plane wave is normally incident on the aperture. Let the center of the aperture be initially at O in Fig. 10-1, and let it be translated along the x axis until one has the situation shown in Fig. 10-9. As long as a remains large compared with λ, only small values of θ will be of interest. If the Fraunhofer conditions are to hold, a must be very small compared with r_{20}, and Δv, which is now given by

$$\Delta v = a \left(\frac{2}{\lambda r_{20}} \right)^{\frac{1}{2}} \tag{10-18}$$

must be small compared with unity.   With the x in Fig. 10-9, define v by

$$v = x \left(\frac{2}{\lambda r_{20}} \right)^{\frac{1}{2}} \tag{10-19}$$

which is just (10-3) with $r_{10} = \infty$ and v in place of ξ.
  One must now evaluate

$$A e^{i\psi} = C(v + \Delta v) - C(v) + i[S(v + \Delta v) - S(v)]$$

From the Cornu spiral, it is evident that when Δv is small compared with

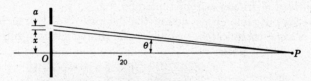

Fig. 10-9. *Geometry for investigating the transition from the Fresnel to the Fraunhofer case for a rectangular aperture.*

unity, the chord A will not differ appreciably from the arc Δv until v has become large compared with unity.   When v is large, the Fresnel integrals can be approximated by

$$C(v) \approx \frac{1}{2} + \frac{\sin (\pi v^2 / 2)}{\pi v} \qquad S(v) \approx \frac{1}{2} - \frac{\cos (\pi v^2 / 2)}{\pi v} \tag{10-20}$$

The error in these formulas is less than 1 per cent when v is equal to about 3 and decreases thereafter roughly as $1/v^3$.   Using (10-20),

$$
\begin{aligned}
C(v + \Delta v) - C(v) &\approx \frac{1}{\pi v} \left[\sin \frac{\pi}{2} (v + \Delta v)^2 - \sin \frac{\pi}{2} v^2 \right] \\
&= \frac{2}{\pi v} \sin \frac{\pi}{4} [(v + \Delta v)^2 - v^2] \cos \frac{\pi}{4} [(v + \Delta v)^2 + v^2] \\
&\approx \frac{2}{\pi v} \sin \frac{\pi v \, \Delta v}{2} \cos \frac{\pi v^2}{2}
\end{aligned}
$$

Similarly, $S(v + \Delta v) - S(v) \approx \dfrac{2}{\pi v} \sin \dfrac{\pi v \, \Delta v}{2} \sin \dfrac{\pi v^2}{2}$

Squaring and adding the last two results and substituting from (10-18) and (10-19) gives

$$A^2 = \frac{2a^2}{\lambda r_{20}} \frac{\sin^2 \pi\alpha}{(\pi\alpha)^2} \tag{10-21}$$

where

$$\alpha = \frac{v\,\Delta v}{2} = \frac{xa}{\lambda r_{20}} \approx \frac{a\theta}{\lambda}$$

so that α is essentially the quantity defined by (9-7) with $\theta_1 = 0$, $\theta_2 = \theta$, and θ small.

Consider next a translation of the aperture in the y direction. Figure 10-9 applies with x, a, and θ replaced by y, b, and ϕ, respectively. A calculation similar to the above then gives

$$B^2 = \frac{2b^2}{\lambda r_{20}} \frac{\sin^2 \pi\beta}{(\pi\beta)^2} \tag{10-22}$$

where $\beta \approx b\phi/\lambda$.

Substituting (10-21) and (10-22) in (10-10),

$$I(P) = I_0(P) \frac{a^2 b^2}{\lambda^2 r_{20}^2} \frac{\sin^2 \pi\alpha}{(\pi\alpha)^2} \frac{\sin^2 \pi\beta}{(\pi\beta)^2}$$

This formula agrees with the Fraunhofer formulas (9-4), (9-5), and (9-8) if it is noted that in the present problem the unobstructed irradiance $I_0(P)$ is the same as the irradiance E of the incident plane wave falling on the aperture.

10-4   Circular Aperture   Consider a circular aperture of radius c, and let S and P lie on the normal through its center, as shown in Fig. 10-10. Only this special configuration will be treated in connection with the circular aperture.

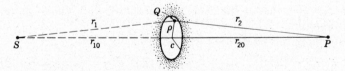

Fig. 10-10. *Geometry for finding the amplitude at the center of the pattern of a circular aperture. Line SP is perpendicular to the plane of the screen and passes through the center of the aperture.*

Suppose first that c is small compared with r_{10} and r_{20}; the usual approximations that the obliquity factor is equal to 2 and $1/r_1 r_2$ is equal to $1/r_{10}r_{20}$ can be made in the Kirchhoff integral. The cylindrical symmetry about the axis SP suggests using polar coordinates in the integration. Then

$$u_0(P) = -\frac{iA}{\lambda r_{10} r_{20}} \int_0^c e^{ik(r_1 + r_2)} 2\pi\rho \, d\rho$$

Now it is easily shown that

$$\rho \, d\rho = r_1 \, dr_1 = r_2 \, dr_2$$

whence

$$d(r_1 + r_2) = \left(\frac{1}{r_1} + \frac{1}{r_2}\right) \rho \, d\rho$$

or

$$\rho \, d\rho = \frac{r_1 r_2}{r_1 + r_2} d(r_1 + r_2) \tag{10-23}$$

This expression can be approximated by

$$\rho \, d\rho = \frac{r_{10} r_{20}}{r_{10} + r_{20}} d(r_1 + r_2)$$

Then

$$u_0(P) = -\frac{i2\pi A}{\lambda(r_{10} + r_{20})} \int_{l(0)}^{l(c)} e^{ik(r_1 + r_2)} d(r_1 + r_2) \tag{10-24}$$

where $l(0) = r_{10} + r_{20}$, and $l(c)$ is equal to $r_1 + r_2$ when $\rho = c$, that is, when the point Q in Fig. 10-10 lies on the rim of the aperture.

It is appropriate to introduce the dimensionless variable q defined by

$$r_1 + r_2 = r_{10} + r_{20} + \frac{q\lambda}{2} \tag{10-25}$$

Thus q measures the excess of the path $r_1 + r_2$ over the path $r_{10} + r_{20}$ in *half-wavelengths* and is a function of ρ. The idea of defining q in this particular way originated with Fresnel. Its usefulness will appear in Sec. 10-7. Substituting (10-25) in (10-24) and noting the emergence of the unobstructed amplitude $u_{00}(P)$ as a factor,

$$u_0(P) = -i\pi \, u_{00}(P) \int_0^{\zeta} e^{i\pi q} \, dq \tag{10-26}$$

where $\zeta = q(c)$, that is, the value of q associated with a point on the rim of the aperture.

Performing the integration in (10-26) finally gives

$$u_0(P) = u_{00}(P) \, (1 - e^{i\pi\zeta}) \tag{10-27}$$

and

$$I(P) = |u_0(P)|^2 = 2 \, I_0(P) \, (1 - \cos \pi\zeta) = 4 \, I_0(P) \sin^2 \frac{\pi\zeta}{2} \tag{10-28}$$

The conclusion is that as the radius of the aperture increases, the irradiance at P oscillates between zero and four times the unobstructed irradiance. The photographs in Fig. 10-11 show this phenomenon as ζ passes through integral values starting with $\zeta = 1$. The center is bright when ζ is an odd integer. The large pattern below is especially interesting. For this pattern $\zeta = 71$, and if one looks at it with the eyes slightly out of focus, the central region appears uniform except for a bright spot at the center. Since the profile of the irradiance near the edge of the pattern must approach that of the straight edge as the radius of the

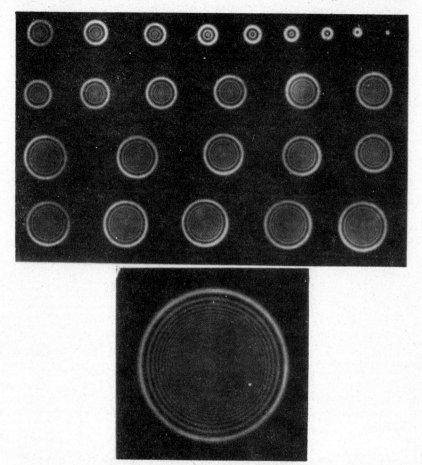

Fig. 10-11. *Fresnel patterns of circular apertures for various integral values of ζ. For the large pattern below, $\zeta = 71$. (Photographs by Hufford. See references 45 and 47.)*

aperture increases, it is to be expected that the coarse outer fringes will remain prominent for large ζ.

The relation between ζ and c is found as follows: From Fig. 10-10 with $\rho = c$,

$$r_1 = (r_{10}{}^2 + c^2)^{1/2} \approx r_{10} + \frac{c^2}{2r_{10}}$$

Treating r_2 similarly,

$$\zeta = 2 \frac{r_1 + r_2 - (r_{10} + r_{20})}{\lambda} = c^2 \frac{r_{10} + r_{20}}{\lambda r_{10} r_{20}} \tag{10-29}$$

The behavior of the diffraction pattern as c decreases from a fairly large value is similar to the case of the rectangular aperture. The pattern decreases in size until ζ reaches a value about equal to unity and then increases and passes over to the Fraunhofer pattern. Lord Rayleigh investigated this matter, to determine the size of aperture that gives the sharpest image in a pinhole camera, and concluded that the optimum radius is obtained by setting $\zeta = 0.9$. If the light is not monochromatic, then λ must be set equal to some average wavelength, depending on the spectral sensitivity of the photographic plate, in calculating the best aperture for a pinhole camera.

10-5 Limiting Case of a Large Aperture The irradiances at the centers of the patterns for a circle and for a square behave quite differently as the sizes of the apertures increase. To make a comparison, consider a circle of radius c and a square of edge $2c$.

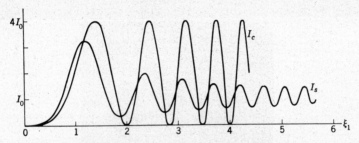

Fig. 10-12. *Comparison of the irradiance at the center of the pattern for a circular aperture of radius c (curve I_c) with that for a square of edge $2c$ (curve I_s). The parameter ξ_1 is proportional to c.*

Consider first the square aperture; in (10-8) through (10-10), one has $\xi_1 = -\xi_2 = \eta_1 = -\eta_2$, and

$$\xi_1 = c \left[\frac{2(r_{10} + r_{20})}{\lambda r_{10} r_{20}} \right]^{1/2}$$

The irradiance at the center of the pattern for the square is then

$$I_s(P) = 4 I_0(P) [C^2(\xi_1) + S^2(\xi_1)]^2 \tag{10-30}$$

For the circle, ζ is given by (10-29), and hence $\zeta = \xi_1^2/2$. The irradiance at the center is

$$I_c(P) = 4 I_0(P) \sin^2 \frac{\pi \xi_1^2}{4} \tag{10-31}$$

Both (10-30) and (10-31) are expressed in terms of the variable ξ_1, which is simply proportional to c. These two functions are compared in Fig. 10-12.

Formulas (10-30) and (10-31) involve essentially the same approximations, and while it was shown in Sec. 10-2 that as ξ_1 increases indefinitely, I_s converges to I_0, it is clear that I_c would continue to oscillate with undiminished amplitude, and convergence would result only from a more exact treatment of the Kirchhoff integral. However, the reduction in oscillation amplitude resulting from an exact treatment would not be perceptible until ξ_1 became very large, long after I_s had become practically constant at the value I_0. A point to note is that in the absence of a diffracting screen, the evaluation of the Kirchhoff integral over the infinite plane Σ leads to entirely different rates of convergence for integration with respect to rectangular coordinates and with respect to polar coordinates. This contrast in behavior occurs frequently, and there are even integrals that converge for one method of integrating and not for another, as was pointed out in the comments on Prob. 3-16.

The physical origin of the difference in the oscillations of the curves in Fig. 10-12 can be seen by cutting, in a sheet of black paper, a circle of some 2 cm diam (very round and smooth), and in another sheet a square of the same size. Holding each of the apertures at arm's length in turn and looking through it at a small source of light (which may be white), one observes that when the eye is on the axis of the system, the square shows four bright segments at the midpoints of the edges, while the circle has a bright edge all the way around. Hence the diffracted wave (which interferes with the direct wave) is much stronger in the case of the circle, and the difference becomes more pronounced as the sizes of the apertures increase. When the eye is off the axis, the circle shows only a short luminous crescent at one side, and the situation is then not essentially different from that of the square.

10-6 Opaque Disk   The amplitude $u_0'(P)$ at the center of the pattern for an opaque circular disk is found by applying Babinet's principle to formula (10-27) for a circular aperture of the same size. The result is

$$u_0'(P) = u_{00}(P) - u_0(P) = u_{00}(P)\, e^{i\pi\zeta}$$

The irradiance is then

$$I'(P) = |u_0'(P)|^2 = I_0(P)$$

This remarkable result indicates that at the center of the shadow of an opaque disk there must be a bright spot, and that at the exact central point the irradiance must have the unobstructed value I_0 for any values of r_{10}, r_{20}, and λ, except those which give exceedingly large values of ζ, that is, values for which (10-27) is not accurate. This spot is easily observed using a smooth-edged coin or a small bearing ball for obstacle. The spot, which is surrounded by faint luminous rings somewhat similar to the Airy pattern (Sec. 9-4), becomes smaller and contains less total power and is therefore harder to locate as the size of the disk increases, other parameters being held constant (see Hufford [45,46]).

The bright spot is one of the diffraction phenomena easily seen to be sensitive to edge effects. In Raman [74], p. 130, it is pointed out that the spot is fainter with a rounded edge than with a sharp edge, the difference becoming greater as the angle of diffraction at the edge increases.

10-7   Zone Plate   Let r_{10}, r_{20}, and λ have assigned values, and let ζ in (10-29) assume positive integral values. This equation then defines a series of radii

$$c_n = \left(\frac{\lambda r_{10} r_{20} n}{r_{10} + r_{20}} \right)^{\frac{1}{2}} \qquad n = 1, 2, 3, \ldots \qquad (10\text{-}32)$$

which increase as the square roots of whole numbers. If circles with these radii, all having centers at O, are drawn on the plane of the diffracting screen, the plane is divided into what are called *Fresnel half-period zones*, since the path $r_1 + r_2$ for a point on one circle differs from that for a point on the next by $\lambda/2$.

Suppose now that the diffracting screen is constructed by making alternate half-period zones opaque. The conclusions now to be drawn are independent of whether one starts with the central zone open or opaque, but for definiteness, let it be open, as shown in Fig. 10-13. The outer boundaries of the open zones then correspond to odd n; let the screen be opaque at all radii greater than c_N, with N a fairly large odd integer. Such a screen is called a *zone plate* of N zones.

The amplitude at the center of the diffraction pattern is obtained from formula (10-26) if the integral is replaced by the sum of $(N + 1)/2$ integrals with limits $(0,1)$, $(2,3)$, $(4,5)$, . . . , $(N - 1, N)$. Each of these integrals has the value $-2/i\pi$, and hence

$$u_0(P) = (N + 1) \, u_{00}(P) \qquad I(P) = (N + 1)^2 \, I_0(P) \qquad (10\text{-}33)$$

The conclusion is that there is a very intense bright spot at P.

With the same screen and the same values of r_{10} and λ, consider a point P' on the axis just inside or just outside the point P just considered. The limits of the $(N + 1)/2$ integrals in the formula for $u_0(P')$ are no longer integers. The integrals give complex numbers whose magnitudes are less than the maximum possible value $2/\pi$, and their angles are all different. The vector summation appears as in Fig. 10-14. Clearly, when N is large, $|u_0(P')|$ is much less than $u_0(P)$, the latter resulting from a figure similar to 10-14 except that all the vectors are in line along the imaginary axis and have length $2/\pi$. As P' moves farther from P, the vector diagram curls up on itself more and more, with the result that the irradiance along the axis shows a sharp maximum at P. Thus the zone plate shows the longitudinal focal properties of an ordinary lens and in this respect differs from the simple opaque disk, for which the bright spot can be found anywhere along the axis. It also shows the same lateral focal properties as a lens. In fact, when N is about 200, the diffraction pattern in the plane perpendicular to the axis and passing through the focal point P is essentially the Airy pattern. This property

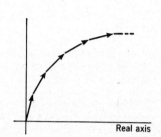

Fig. 10-13. *Zone plate of fifteen zones with the central zone open.*

Fig. 10-14. *Typical vector addition giving the amplitude on the axis of a zone plate near the focal point.*

has been demonstrated by Boivin [6]. The similarity to an ordinary lens is further brought out by setting $n = 1$ in (10-32) and rewriting this formula as

$$\frac{1}{r_{10}} + \frac{1}{r_{20}} = \frac{\lambda}{c_1{}^2}$$

This is just the ordinary lens formula with the focal length $f = c_1{}^2/\lambda$. The strong dependence of f on λ means that the zone plate shows serious chromatic aberration and must be used with nearly monochromatic light.

For possible applications of zone plates as lenses operating in the extreme ultraviolet and long X-ray region, where no transparent materials for making ordinary lenses exist, see Baez [1].

10-8 Concluding Remarks on Fresnel Diffraction In limiting the treatment of diffraction of the Fresnel type, we have omitted many topics which have been of great interest and value in optics. Of chief importance have been the many developments in the diffraction theory of the formation of images in optical instruments. A typical problem is the following: A monochromatic point source is on the axis of a geometrically perfect system of lenses. In the plane perpendicular to the axis and passing through the point conjugate to the source, a Fraunhofer pattern is formed. In planes on one side or the other of the conjugate plane, the patterns are of the Fresnel type and are poorer as images of the source. The detailed study of the wave field in the vicinity of the focal point is a matter of enormous labor, and the beautiful results can be found described and illustrated in Born and Wolf [9], beginning on p. 434. Such calculations have been extended to systems with various aberrations, and results are given in Born and Wolf [9], chap. 9. Another reference for essentially the same material is Linfoot [58], beginning on p. 35.

Problems

10-1. As a multiple of the unobstructed value, what is, approximately, the largest irradiance that can occur in the Fresnel pattern of a rectangular aperture? Specify the general conditions under which this value is attained. Evaluate these conditions to find the dimensions of the aperture when the source is at infinity, the observing point is 50 cm from the aperture, and $\lambda = 5000$ A. What are the angular dimensions (in degrees) of the aperture as seen from the observing point?

10-2. Two parallel slits have equal lengths l. Their widths are a and b, respectively, and the width of the strip between them is d, where a, b, and d are small compared with l, and l is large enough that the corresponding Δv is essentially infinite. Explain how the Cornu spiral can be used to find the profile of the pattern along a line perpendicular to the long axes of the slits and midway between the ends of the pattern.

10-3. Considering a rectangular aperture as discussed in Sec. 10-1, let a, b, λ, and the distance from source to observing screen be fixed. Given a value of r_{10}, there is in general one other value for which the diffraction pattern is essentially the same except for size. What is the relation between these two distances, and what is the relation between the sizes of the pattern? The qualification "essentially" is meant to imply that certain conditions must hold if the statement is to be reasonably valid for patterns as they would actually be observed. What are these conditions?

10-4. As values typical of arrangements for observing Fresnel patterns in the laboratory, let $r_{10} = r_{20} = 100$ cm and $\lambda = 5000$ A. Let one of the dimensions of a rectangular aperture be a, and let the corresponding angular width as seen from P be ϕ. Making approximations appropriate to small values of ϕ, find Δv as a numerical multiple of ϕ when the latter is expressed in degrees.

10-5. Assume the numerical values given in Prob. 10-4. Let the aperture be a square of such size as to have an angular width as seen from P of 1°. How long is the side of the square defining the geometrical shadow on the observing screen? Let the aperture increase slightly in size so that the irradiance at the center of the pattern oscillates about I_0 through one cycle. What is the amplitude of the oscillation in terms of I_0? [*Hints:* Use (10-30) and (10-20). Note that when v is large, one revolution of the Cornu spiral is practically a circle of radius $1/\pi v$, and hence finding the maximum and minimum of (10-30) with sufficient accuracy becomes simple. *Answer:* Side of square ≈ 3.5 cm; amplitude of oscillation $\approx 0.018\, I_0$.]

10-6. Of the various approximations which led to (10-4), the pattern is most sensitive to (10-2). Carry this expansion to the next term, which involves $(x^2 + y^2)^2$. Taking $y = 0$, $r_{10} = r_{20} = 100$ cm, and $\lambda = 5000$ A, calculate the value of x which makes k times this added term equal to $\pi/2$ (so that the error in the path length neglecting this term is one-quarter wavelength). (*Answer:* $x = 2.66$ cm.) Calculate the corresponding value of ξ from (10-3). Repeat when $r_{20} = 10$ cm. [These results give a measure of the maximum size of aperture, relative to the other parameters, for which (10-4) will give accurate values. It should be remarked, however, that the corrections resulting from higher approximations never amount to a major alteration of the pattern as calculated by the formulas in the body of the chapter—the conclusion in Sec. 10-2 is valid. Similar conclusions hold for the circular aperture, for which the approximation in question enters through (10-29).]

10-7. Let r_{10} and r_{20} be large compared with λ, but otherwise arbitrary. Let the diffracting screen be semi-infinite with a straight edge. Find an expression for the linear distance on the observing screen between the edge of the geometric shadow and the first maximum in the pattern, and find an expression for the angle subtended by this segment as seen from the diffracting edge. Write the limiting forms of these expressions as r_{10} becomes infinite, and note what then happens as r_{20} becomes infinite. Comment on the significance of the manner in which λ enters these formulas. Evaluate the general expressions using the numerical data of Prob. 10-4, giving the angle in degrees. (*Answer to last part:* Distance ≈ 0.45 mm; angle $\approx 0.026°$.)

10-8. Show that a formula equivalent to (10-17) is

$$I'(P) = \tfrac{1}{2} I_0(P) (A^2 - 2\,\Delta C - 2\,\Delta S + 2)$$

where ΔC and ΔS are the real and imaginary parts of (10-8), respectively. (This formula is convenient if one obtains the diffraction pattern for an opaque strip directly from a table of Fresnel integrals by use of a calculating machine.)

10-9. The oscillations in Fig. 10-8 for $\xi_0 > 3.5$ can be plotted from rather few calculated points if one first plots the envelope curves which must be touched by the oscillating curve at its upper and lower extremities. Explain how such envelope curves can be found from a knowledge of A^2 for the complementary slit.

10-10. Let r_{10} in Fig. 10-10 be infinite. Show that as the radius of the circular aperture becomes very small and the diffraction pattern goes over into the Fraunhofer type, formula (10-28) becomes equivalent to (9-5).

10-11. Using the asymptotic expressions (10-20), find the asymptotic form of (10-30) for large ξ_1. Strive to put the result in the most concise and elegant form. Evaluate the result for $\xi_1 = 5.5$ (a fairly large value chosen at random), and compare with the value obtained by substituting in (10-30) from the table of Fresnel integrals in Appendix C. (The disagreement should be less than 1 per cent. The formula should show that the amplitude of oscillation in the curve of I_s ultimately goes to zero as $1/\xi_1$.)

10-12. As a problem very similar to Prob. 10-11, find the asymptotic expression for the factor A^2 in the irradiance of the pattern for a straight edge (see Fig. 10-6) as ξ_1 becomes large in the positive sense and in the negative sense.

chapter *11*

Fourier Analysis and Its Application to Optical Problems

This chapter will set forth the general principles of Fourier analysis and its applications to optical problems. Of the applications to be made, the most important will be to nonmonochromatic waves, the subject of Chaps. 12 and 13, and among the results will be the justification and certain generalizations of the rule for incoherent sources and an understanding of the natures of polarized and unpolarized beams. Other results will be an understanding of when and why certain sources can be treated as though they were perfectly monochromatic and, at the other extreme, the extent to which the departure from monochromaticity, that is, the spectrum, can be observed. Since these questions arise in connection with any problem in physical optics when fully formulated in a realistic way, it is apparent that Fourier analysis is one of the most important mathematical techniques in the subject. The procedure in the present chapter will be to give the fundamental theorem of Fourier and some of its corollaries as propositions in pure mathematics and to illustrate with a number of physical problems.

11-1 Fourier Theorem The method of Fourier analysis derives from the following remarkable theorem: Let $f(x)$ be a real function defined for $-\infty < x < \infty$. Let this function be arbitrary except for the following restrictions:

1. $f(x)$ is everywhere finite, and if it has discontinuities, they are finite jumps occurring at a finite number of points in any finite range of x.

2. $f(x)$ has a derivative everywhere except possibly at a finite number of points in any finite range of x, and at each of these points it has a derivative on the right and on the left. [If x_0 is one of the points in question, the derivative on the right is defined by

$$\lim_{\Delta \to 0} \frac{f(x_0 + \Delta) - f(x_0 + 0)}{\Delta}$$

where Δ takes *positive* values only, and $f(x_0 + 0)$ is the limit of $f(x_0 + \Delta)$ as Δ approaches zero. The derivative on the left is defined analogously.] This condition allows the curve of the function to have sudden changes of slope.

3. $f(x)$ is absolutely integrable, that is, $\int_{-\infty}^{\infty} |f(x)| \, dx$ is finite.

Then $f(x)$ can be written as a superposition of sinusoidal functions in the form

$$f(x) = \int_0^{\infty} a(\xi) \cos [\xi x - \theta(\xi)] \, d\xi \tag{11-1}$$

If the integrand is written

$$a(\xi) \cos [\xi x - \theta(\xi)] = a \cos \theta \cos \xi x + a \sin \theta \sin \xi x \tag{11-2}$$

then the dependence of the amplitude a and phase angle θ on ξ is given by

$$a \cos \theta = \frac{1}{\pi} \int_{-\infty}^{\infty} f(x) \cos \xi x \, dx \qquad a \sin \theta = \frac{1}{\pi} \int_{-\infty}^{\infty} f(x) \sin \xi x \, dx \tag{11-3}$$

This theorem is called the *Fourier integral theorem*. It has been stated for a class of functions that is not the most general for which the theorem can be proved, but that includes practically all functions arising in physical problems. A proof of the theorem as stated is given in Churchill [18], p. 88. This reference also gives the heuristic arguments whereby Fourier integrals emerge as a limiting case from Fourier series; the arguments are helpful in understanding the integrals. Another reference, which has excellent graphical illustrations, is Carslaw [16]. It is not essential for what follows to have pursued these references. It might be remarked that Fourier series express a function $f(x)$, periodic over the whole range $-\infty < x < \infty$ with period X, as a sum of sinusoidal functions with periods X/n, $n = 0, 1, 2, \ldots$. The functions to be considered in the following will be either completely nonperiodic or, at most, periodic over only a finite number of periods and zero over the rest of the infinite range. Such functions are representable only as integrals, and a knowledge of series will not be required.

Formulas (11-1) to (11-3) can be put in a more convenient and simpler form by introducing the complex exponential. Formula (11-1) can be written

$$f(x) = \frac{1}{2} \int_0^\infty a(e^{i\theta}e^{-i\xi x} + e^{-i\theta}e^{i\xi x}) \, d\xi$$

or

$$f(x) = \frac{1}{\sqrt{2\pi}} \int_{-\infty}^\infty A(\xi) \, e^{-i\xi x} \, d\xi \tag{11-4}$$

where

$$A(\xi) = \sqrt{\frac{\pi}{2}} \, ae^{i\theta} \qquad \xi > 0$$

and

$$A(-\xi) = A^*(\xi) \tag{11-5}$$

The reason for writing (11-4) with the factor $1/\sqrt{2\pi}$ will be seen presently. If both sides of the right-hand relation in (11-3) are multiplied by i and the result is added to the left-hand expression, one obtains, by Euler's formula,

$$A(\xi) = \frac{1}{\sqrt{2\pi}} \int_{-\infty}^\infty f(x) \, e^{i\xi x} \, dx \tag{11-6}$$

The remarkably simple and similar formulas (11-4) and (11-6) constitute the form of the Fourier integral theorem that will be used in all the following work. The formulas (11-1) to (11-3) served only as introduction and will not appear again.

A great advantage of the complex formulation of the Fourier theorem is that if $f(x)$ is a complex function of the real variable x, (11-4) and (11-6) still hold, as is seen by applying the theorem to the real and imaginary parts of $f(x)$ separately and combining. However, (11-5) holds when and only when $f(x)$ is real, the proof coming from (11-4) and (11-6) in the following way: Let $f(x)$ be real. The complex conjugate of (11-6) is

$$A^*(\xi) = \frac{1}{\sqrt{2\pi}} \int_{-\infty}^\infty f(x) \, e^{-i\xi x} \, dx = A(-\xi)$$

Conversely, suppose (11-5) is satisfied. The complex conjugate of (11-4) is

$$f^*(x) = \frac{1}{\sqrt{2\pi}} \int_{-\infty}^\infty A(-\xi) \, e^{i\xi x} \, d\xi = \frac{1}{\sqrt{2\pi}} \int_{-\infty}^\infty A(\xi) \, e^{-i\xi x} \, d\xi = f(x)$$

and $f(x)$ is therefore real.

The following terminology is used in Fourier analysis: Given the function $f(x)$, the function $A(\xi)$ is called its *Fourier transform*. The sinusoidal function of x, $A(\xi) \, e^{-i\xi x}$, perhaps also with the factor $1/\sqrt{2\pi}$, is called the *Fourier component of $f(x)$ with frequency ξ*. The variable ξ is said to be *conjugate* to the variable x. The process of superposition of Fourier components defined by (11-4) for a given $A(\xi)$ is called a *Fourier synthesis*, and, in contrast, the process of finding the components through the operation in (11-6) is sometimes called a *Fourier analysis* (in a restricted sense, since the term also signifies the whole discipline of this chapter).

The choice of the negative sign in the exponential in (11-4), which then requires a positive sign in (11-6), is arbitrary. Equally good formulas result from changing both these signs. With given $f(x)$, the result is to change $A(\xi)$ [to the complex conjugate if $f(x)$ is real], but it will be seen that no physical conclusion is ever affected thereby. Moreover, it is perfectly correct to speak of $f(x)$ as the transform of $A(\xi)$. Which function is to be regarded as the original, and which the transform, and which signs are to be taken in the exponents are fixed either arbitrarily or by the context of the individual problem. If it is established that $f(x)$ is the original, and $A(\xi)$ the transform, then $f(x)$ is sometimes referred to as the *inverse transform* of $A(\xi)$. The transform is defined in such a way that the factor $1/\sqrt{2\pi}$ appears in (11-4) merely to symmetrize the formulas. If this factor is omitted in (11-4), then the factor in (11-6) becomes $1/2\pi$.

The physical significances of the two conjugate variables depend on the problem. Most often in the following these variables will be the time t and the temporal frequency ω. Then, in keeping with previous convention, the signs in the exponents will be chosen so that

$$ f(t) = \frac{1}{\sqrt{2\pi}} \int_{-\infty}^{\infty} A(\omega)\, e^{-i\omega t}\, d\omega \qquad (11\text{-}7) $$

In examples to be given, other physical variables will enter. Note that because of the limits in (11-7), one is led to speak of negative temporal frequencies. At first sight this seems strange, but these negative frequencies entered through the mathematical device of passing from the original formulation (11-1), which involved only positive frequencies, to the complex representation. All physical results, such as the spectrum of an arbitrary wave, can and will be ultimately expressed in terms of positive frequencies only. On the other hand, in many problems not involving time, it will be perfectly natural and even physically required to let both conjugate variables assume negative as well as positive values.

11-2 Examples of Fourier Transforms Several examples will now be worked out in which a function $f(x)$ is given and its transform $A(\xi)$ is found by (11-6). Substitution of $A(\xi)$ in (11-4) will then give back $f(x)$. It will appear that in most cases the integrals do not yield to elementary methods of evaluation, and the examples will be limited to those for which one can resort to collections of definite integrals in standard tables such as Dwight [26]. While the examples are simple, they will be seen to have interesting optical applications.

Example 1 Let $f(x)$ be the gaussian function

$$f(x) = be^{-x^2/a^2} \qquad (11\text{-}8)$$

A plot is shown in Fig. 11-1a. The Fourier transform is

$$A(\xi) = \frac{b}{\sqrt{2\pi}} \int_{-\infty}^{\infty} e^{-x^2/a^2} e^{i\xi x}\, dx$$

$$= \sqrt{\frac{2}{\pi}}\, b \int_{0}^{\infty} e^{-x^2/a^2} \cos \xi x\, dx = \frac{ab}{\sqrt{2}}\, e^{-a^2\xi^2/4} \qquad (11\text{-}9)$$

where the last result is from tables. Thus the transform, which is plotted in Fig. 11-1b, is another gaussian, and the synthesis will obviously give back $f(x)$.

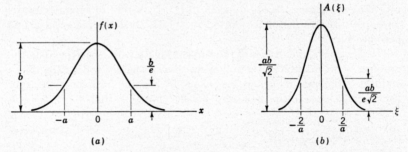

Fig. 11-1. a. *Gaussian function of x.* **b.** *Fourier transform, which is also a gaussian function.*

An important point to note is that if one takes the width of the curve in Fig. 11-1a to be the distance $\Delta x = 2a$ between the abscissas for which the ordinate is $1/e$ times the maximum, and if one similarly takes the width of the transform to be $\Delta \xi = 4/a$, one has $\Delta x\, \Delta \xi = 8$, a constant. (A different constant would result if the widths were measured at some other fraction of the maximum ordinate, say one-half.) Hence if the given function is made wider, the transform becomes narrower, and vice versa. This will be seen to be a general behavior of transform pairs.

Example 2 Consider the function

$$f(x) = \begin{cases} b & (x^2 < a^2) \\ 0 & (x^2 > a^2) \end{cases} \qquad (11\text{-}10)$$

illustrated in Fig. 11-2a. The transform is

$$A(\xi) = \frac{b}{\sqrt{2\pi}} \int_{-a}^{a} e^{i\xi x}\, dx = \sqrt{\frac{2}{\pi}}\, \frac{b \sin \xi a}{\xi} \qquad (11\text{-}11)$$

and is shown in Fig. 11-2b. The synthesis is

$$\frac{b}{\pi} \int_{-\infty}^{\infty} \frac{\sin \xi a}{\xi} e^{-i\xi x} \, d\xi = \frac{2b}{\pi} \int_{0}^{\infty} \frac{\sin \xi a \cos \xi x}{\xi} \, d\xi = f(x)$$

The last step is made with the use of tables. If one takes the width of the function $f(x)$ to be $\Delta x = 2a$, and that of the transform to be $\Delta \xi = 2\pi/a$,

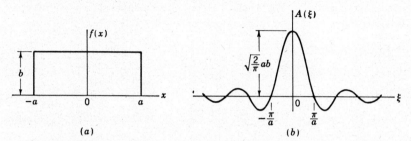

Fig. 11-2. **a.** *Square-topped function.* **b.** *Fourier transform.*

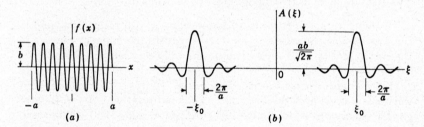

Fig. 11-3. **a.** *Finite length of a sinusoidal function.* **b.** *Fourier transform.*

as suggested by Fig. 11-2b, then $\Delta x \, \Delta \xi = 4\pi$, again a constant.

Example 3 Let

$$f(x) = \begin{cases} b \cos \xi_0 x & (x^2 < a^2) \\ 0 & (x^2 > a^2), \ (\xi_0 a \gg 1) \end{cases} \tag{11-12}$$

The plot is shown in Fig. 11-3a. The condition $\xi_0 a \gg 1$ implies that many cycles of the cosine function lie in the range $-a < x < a$. The transform is

$$\begin{aligned} A(\xi) &= \frac{b}{\sqrt{2\pi}} \int_{-a}^{a} \cos \xi_0 x \, e^{i\xi x} \, dx = \frac{b}{2\sqrt{2\pi}} \int_{-a}^{a} (e^{i(\xi+\xi_0)x} + e^{i(\xi-\xi_0)x}) \, dx \\ &= \frac{b}{\sqrt{2\pi}} \left[\frac{\sin(\xi+\xi_0)a}{\xi+\xi_0} + \frac{\sin(\xi-\xi_0)a}{\xi-\xi_0} \right] \end{aligned} \tag{11-13}$$

A plot of $A(\xi)$ is given in Fig. 11-3b. Note that the condition $\xi_0 a \gg 1$ now implies that the curve of $A(\xi)$ consists of two well-separated parts. As the width $\Delta x = 2a$ varies, the widths of the two parts of $A(\xi)$ vary inversely, but the positions of the maxima at $\xi = \pm \xi_0$ remain fixed. The significant measure of the width of the transform is thus $\Delta\xi = 2\pi/a$, and again $\Delta x \, \Delta\xi$ is constant. On the other hand, the separation of the two maxima in Fig. 11-3b is inversely proportional to the separation of successive maxima in Fig. 11-3a. Hence this example shows two inverse relationships.

Example 4   Let

$$f(x) = \begin{cases} be^{-i\xi_0 x} & (x^2 < a^2) \\ 0 & (x^2 > a^2),\ (\xi_0 a \gg 1) \end{cases} \tag{11-14}$$

The transform is

$$A(\xi) = \sqrt{\frac{2}{\pi}}\ \frac{b\,\sin\,(\xi - \xi_0)a}{\xi - \xi_0} \tag{11-15}$$

which is represented graphically by the right half of Fig. 11-3b, except that the ordinates in that figure must be multiplied by two.

All these examples happen to have resulted in real transforms, and in the case of real $f(x)$, the relation (11-5) reduces to simple symmetry in the curves of $A(\xi)$. Complex transforms will occur later.

11-3   Theorems on Fourier Integrals   In this section a number of theorems of wide applicability will be gathered together. In all the discussion, the symbols and choice of signs in (11-4) and (11-6) will be used. For the opposite choice of signs, wherever i appears explicitly (which is only in Theorems 2 and 3), it should be changed to $-i$. In all the theorems the functions of x can be complex. The notation $f(x) \to A(\xi)$ is to be read "$f(x)$ has the transform $A(\xi)$," while $A(\xi) \leftarrow f(x)$ is to be read "$A(\xi)$ is the transform of $f(x)$."

Theorem 1a (*First similarity rule.*)   If $f(x) \to A(\xi)$, then $f(ax) \to (1/a)\,A(\xi/a)$, $a > 0$.

PROOF: The transform of $f(ax)$ is

$$\frac{1}{\sqrt{2\pi}} \int_{-\infty}^{\infty} f(ax)\,e^{i\xi x}\,dx = \frac{1}{\sqrt{2\pi}a} \int_{-\infty}^{\infty} f(y)\,e^{i(\xi/a)y}\,dy = \frac{1}{a}\,A\left(\frac{\xi}{a}\right)$$

where $y = ax$.

Theorem 1b (*Second similarity rule.*)   If $A(\xi) \leftarrow f(x)$, then $A(a\xi) \leftarrow (1/a)\,f(x/a)$, $a > 0$.

The proof is similar to that of Theorem 1a.

Theorem 2a (*First shift rule.*)   If $f(x) \to A(\xi)$, then $f(x - b) \to e^{ib\xi}\,A(\xi)$.

PROOF: The transform of $f(x - b)$ is

$$\frac{1}{\sqrt{2\pi}} \int_{-\infty}^{\infty} f(x - b)\, e^{i\xi x}\, dx = \frac{1}{\sqrt{2\pi}}\, e^{ib\xi} \int_{-\infty}^{\infty} f(y)\, e^{i\xi y}\, dy = e^{ib\xi}\, A(\xi)$$

where $y = x - b$. Note that this theorem means that if the curve representing $f(x)$ is translated along the x axis through distance b, in the positive direction if b is positive, the function of x which it then represents has a transform which differs from the transform of the original $f(x)$ only by the unimodular factor $e^{ib\xi}$.

Theorem 2b (*Second shift rule.*) If $A(\xi) \leftarrow f(x)$, then $A(\xi - b) \leftarrow e^{-ibx} f(x)$.

The proof is similar to that of Theorem 2a.

Theorem 3 (*Differentiation and integration rules.*) If $f(x) \rightarrow A(\xi)$, then

$$\frac{df(x)}{dx} \rightarrow -i\xi\, A(\xi) \qquad \int f(x)\, dx \rightarrow \frac{i}{\xi}\, A(\xi)$$

These formulas are obtained by differentiating or integrating the integrand in (11-4). It should be remarked that the integration rule is always valid, but in the case of the differentiation rule one must ascertain in each case that df/dx belongs to the class of functions specified in the fundamental theorem in Sec. 11-1. For example, one obviously encounters difficulty in applying the differentiation rule to Example 2 of Sec. 11-2. In the few applications of this rule to be made, the functions in question will be continuous and have continuous derivatives of sufficiently high order.[1]

Theorem 4 (*Folding rule. Also called theorem of the "convolution integral," or of the "composition product," or of the "Faltung," the last being the German word for folding.*) If $f_1(x) \rightarrow A_1(\xi)$ and $f_2(x) \rightarrow A_2(\xi)$, then

$$\int_{-\infty}^{\infty} f_1(\tau)\, f_2(x - \tau)\, d\tau \rightarrow \sqrt{2\pi}\, A_1(\xi)\, A_2(\xi)$$

The integral on the left is called a folding integral.

PROOF: The steps involve writing the formula for the transform of the function of x defined by the integral on the left, multiplying and dividing the integrand in this formula by $e^{i\xi\tau}$, and interchanging the order of

---

[1] For a formulation of Fourier analysis in which these qualifying remarks can be omitted, see Lighthill [57]. The essence of this method is to define a very general class of functions for which the Fourier integral theorem can be shown to hold and which is closed under various limiting processes such as differentiation. For the purposes of this book, the more restricted class of functions considered in this chapter will be adequate.

integration. Thus

$$\frac{1}{\sqrt{2\pi}} \int_{-\infty}^{\infty} \left[\int_{-\infty}^{\infty} f_1(\tau) f_2(x - \tau) \, d\tau \right] e^{i\xi x} \, dx$$

$$= \frac{1}{\sqrt{2\pi}} \int_{-\infty}^{\infty} f_1(\tau) e^{i\xi \tau} \left[\int_{-\infty}^{\infty} f_2(x - \tau) e^{i\xi(x-\tau)} \, d(x - \tau) \right] d\tau$$

$$= \int_{-\infty}^{\infty} f_1(\tau) e^{i\xi \tau} A_2(\xi) \, d\tau = \sqrt{2\pi} \, A_1(\xi) \, A_2(\xi)$$

Corollary (*Other forms of the folding rule.*)

$$\int_{-\infty}^{\infty} f_1(\tau) f_2(\tau - x) \, d\tau \to \sqrt{2\pi} \, A_1(\xi) \, A_2(-\xi)$$

$$\int_{-\infty}^{\infty} f_1(\tau) f_2(\tau + x) \, d\tau \to \sqrt{2\pi} \, A_1(-\xi) \, A_2(\xi)$$

If f_1 and f_2 *are real functions, then by* (11-5) *the transforms in the last two formulas can be written* $\sqrt{2\pi} \, A_1(\xi) \, A_2^*(\xi)$ *and* $\sqrt{2\pi} \, A_1^*(\xi) \, A_2(\xi)$, *respectively.*

On the significance of the folding integral in its various forms, see Prob. 11-7. Whenever a folding integral arises later in the book, it will have the form in Theorem 4 or the first form in the corollary.

Theorem 5 (*Transform of a product.*)   If $f_1(x) \to A_1(\xi)$ and $f_2(x) \to A_2(\xi)$, *then*

$$f_1(x) f_2(x) \to \frac{1}{\sqrt{2\pi}} \int_{-\infty}^{\infty} A_1(\xi') \, A_2(\xi - \xi') \, d\xi'$$

That is, the transform of the product is a folding integral of the separate transforms.

PROOF: The transform of the product is

$$\frac{1}{\sqrt{2\pi}} \int_{-\infty}^{\infty} f_1(x) f_2(x) e^{i\xi x} \, dx = \frac{1}{2\pi} \int_{-\infty}^{\infty} \left[\int_{-\infty}^{\infty} A_1(\xi') e^{-i\xi' x} \, d\xi' \right] f_2(x) e^{i\xi x} \, dx$$

$$= \frac{1}{2\pi} \int_{-\infty}^{\infty} A_1(\xi') \left[\int_{-\infty}^{\infty} f_2(x) e^{i(\xi - \xi')x} \, dx \right] d\xi'$$

$$= \frac{1}{\sqrt{2\pi}} \int_{-\infty}^{\infty} A_1(\xi') \, A_2(\xi - \xi') \, d\xi'$$

Theorem 6 (*Parseval's theorem.*)   If $f(x) \to A(\xi)$, *then*

$$\int_{-\infty}^{\infty} |f(x)|^2 \, dx = \int_{-\infty}^{\infty} |A(\xi)|^2 \, d\xi$$

PROOF: In the left-hand integral, $|f(x)|^2$ can be written ff^*, the second factor replaced by its Fourier integral, and the order of integration interchanged:

$$\frac{1}{\sqrt{2\pi}} \int_{-\infty}^{\infty} f(x) \left[\int_{-\infty}^{\infty} A^*(\xi) \, e^{i\xi x} \, d\xi \right] dx$$

$$= \frac{1}{\sqrt{2\pi}} \int_{-\infty}^{\infty} A^*(\xi) \left[\int_{-\infty}^{\infty} f(x) \, e^{i\xi x} \, dx \right] d\xi$$

$$= \int_{-\infty}^{\infty} A^*(\xi) \, A(\xi) \, d\xi$$

Theorem 7 *(Generalization of Parseval's theorem.)*   *If $f_1(x) \rightarrow A_1(\xi)$ and $f_2(x) \rightarrow A_2(\xi)$, then*

$$\int_{-\infty}^{\infty} f_1(x) \, f_2^*(x) \, dx = \int_{-\infty}^{\infty} A_1(\xi) \, A_2^*(\xi) \, d\xi$$

11-4 Multiple Integrals   The ideas of Fourier analysis can be extended to functions of several variables. Consider a function $f(x,y)$ depending on two variables, each of which ranges over the interval $-\infty$ to $+\infty$. The formula for the analysis can be found by successively analyzing with respect to a single variable.

Let ξ and η be the variables conjugate to x and y, respectively. Then the given function can be written first as

$$f(x,y) = \frac{1}{\sqrt{2\pi}} \int_{-\infty}^{\infty} A_1(\xi, y) \, e^{-i\xi x} \, d\xi$$

where y can be regarded as merely a parameter. Treat next the variable y; the partial transform $A_1(\xi, y)$ can be written

$$A_1(\xi, y) = \frac{1}{\sqrt{2\pi}} \int_{-\infty}^{\infty} A(\xi, \eta) \, e^{-i\eta y} \, d\eta$$

Combining gives the final formula:

$$f(x,y) = \frac{1}{2\pi} \iint_{-\infty}^{\infty} A(\xi, \eta) \, e^{-i(\xi x + \eta y)} \, d\xi \, d\eta \tag{11-16}$$

By a similar stepwise procedure, the transform is given by

$$A(\xi, \eta) = \frac{1}{2\pi} \iint_{-\infty}^{\infty} f(x,y) \, e^{i(\xi x + \eta y)} \, dx \, dy \tag{11-17}$$

Clearly, these arguments can be extended to any number of variables.

11-5   Vector Functions   Let $\mathbf{F}(x)$ be a vector function, perhaps complex, of the variable x. Each cartesian component of $\mathbf{F}$ can be expressed as a Fourier integral according to the theorem of Sec. 11-1 and the results can be combined as a vector relation independent of the coordinate system:

$$\mathbf{F}(x) = \frac{1}{\sqrt{2\pi}} \int_{-\infty}^{\infty} \mathbf{A}(\xi) \, e^{-i\xi x} \, d\xi \qquad (11\text{-}18a)$$

The transform $\mathbf{A}(\xi)$, which is in general a complex vector function, is given by

$$\mathbf{A}(\xi) = \frac{1}{\sqrt{2\pi}} \int_{-\infty}^{\infty} \mathbf{F}(x) \, e^{i\xi x} \, dx \qquad (11\text{-}18b)$$

In most applications, $\mathbf{F}$ will be real (for example, the electric field as a function of time at a fixed point over which passes an arbitrary electromagnetic wave). In such a case the transform satisfies

$$\mathbf{A}(-\xi) = \mathbf{A}^*(\xi) \qquad (11\text{-}19)$$

All the theorems of Sec. 11-3 carry over to vector functions if, in Theorems 4, 5, and 7, the products of functions are either scalar or vector products. In the form of Parseval's theorem for vector functions which reads

$$\int_{-\infty}^{\infty} |\mathbf{F}(x)|^2 \, dx = \int_{-\infty}^{\infty} |\mathbf{A}(\xi)|^2 \, d\xi$$

the integrands are to be understood in the sense

$$|\mathbf{F}|^2 = \mathbf{F} \cdot \mathbf{F}^* = F'^2 + F''^2$$

where F' and F'' are the magnitudes of the real and imaginary parts of $\mathbf{F}$.

11-6   Occurrence of Fourier Integrals in Fraunhofer Diffraction
Consider the fundamental formula (9-1) for calculating the amplitude in a Fraunhofer pattern in the scalar approximation. The integral in this formula can be thought of as a Fourier integral in several ways. For example, define variables ξ and η by

$$\xi = k(\sin \theta_1 + \sin \theta_2) \qquad \eta = k(\sin \phi_1 + \sin \phi_2)$$

Then
$$u_0(P) = C \iint_{-\infty}^{\infty} T(x,y) \, e^{-i(\xi x + \eta y)} \, dx \, dy$$

where C is the expression multiplying the integral in (9-1) and is essentially a constant over the diffraction pattern. Thus $u_0(P)$, which can be thought of as a function of ξ and η, is, apart from a constant, the Fourier transform of the function $T(x,y)$.

Thinking in terms of Fourier integrals in this way does not really add anything to the theory of Fraunhofer diffraction, but it is always satisfying to arrive at a unifying point of view, and there is always the possibility that a result in one field will suggest an important analogue in the other. Moreover, one can look over the results already obtained in diffraction and see illustrations of the examples in Sec. 11-2 and the theorems in Sec. 11-3. For example, formula (9-8) for a rectangular aperture is clearly related to (11-11). In the case of several identical apertures, the factor F defined by (7-9) can be thought of as arising through the shift rule of Sec. 11-3. The proposition stated in Prob. 9-8 can be proved by means of the similarity rule. The fact that the power passing through an aperture must appear in the diffraction pattern is none other than Parseval's theorem for double integrals.

11-7 Snell's Law. Resolving Power of a Prism

Another way in which (9-1) can be thought of as involving a Fourier integral is to define the variables

$$\xi_2 = k \sin \theta_2 \qquad \eta_2 = k \sin \phi_2 \qquad (11\text{-}20)$$

and define the function

$$v(x,y) = T(x,y) \, e^{-ik(x \sin \theta_1 + y \sin \phi_1)}$$

Apart from a constant factor, $v(x,y)$ is the complex amplitude over the surface of integration Σ lying just behind the diffracting screen. If one is interested only in relative amplitudes in the diffraction pattern, formula (9-1) can be simplified to read

$$u_0(\xi_2,\eta_2) = \int\!\!\int_{-\infty}^{\infty} v(x,y) \, e^{-i(\xi_2 x + \eta_2 y)} \, dx \, dy \qquad (11\text{-}21)$$

so that, apart from a constant factor, the amplitude u_0 at the point in the pattern specified by given values of ξ_2 and η_2 is the Fourier transform of the amplitude $v(x,y)$ over the surface Σ.

Formula (11-21) can be applied to any problem in which the amplitude $v(x,y)$ can be inferred from an examination of the optical system. As an application of this point of view, consider a prism covering a rectangular aperture of width a, as shown in cross section in Fig. 11-4. Let the apex angle be θ_1, and let a plane wave of wavelength λ (*in vacuo*) be normally incident on the first face. For this wavelength let the refractive index of the prism be n, so that the wavelength in the medium is λ/n. Figure 11-4b shows how the wave fronts obliquely incident on the second face define a spacing $d = \lambda/(n \sin \theta_1)$, which suggests that a prism might be regarded as acting as a kind of grating.

Let the diffracting screen be referred to cartesian coordinates with origin at the center of the aperture and the x axis in the plane of Fig. 11-4.

Let the dimension of the aperture in the y direction be h.   Define ξ_0 by

$$\xi_0 = \frac{2\pi}{d} = \frac{2\pi n \sin \theta_1}{\lambda} \tag{11-22}$$

Then over the aperture

$$v(x,y) = e^{i\xi_0 x} \qquad \frac{-a}{2} < x < \frac{a}{2}, \frac{-h}{2} < y < \frac{h}{2}$$

and $v = 0$ elsewhere.   Formula (11-21) becomes

$$
\begin{aligned}
u_0(\xi_2,\eta_2) &= \int_{-a/2}^{a/2} e^{i(\xi_0-\xi_2)x}\,dx \int_{-h/2}^{h/2} e^{-i\eta_2 y}\,dy \\
&= ah\,\frac{\sin\left[(\xi_0 - \xi_2)a/2\right]}{(\xi_0 - \xi_2)a/2}\frac{\sin\,(\eta_2 h/2)}{\eta_2 h/2}
\end{aligned}
$$

One notes the similarity to Example 4, Sec. 11-2.   In fact, if one had inquired what optical problems could bear a resemblance to this example,

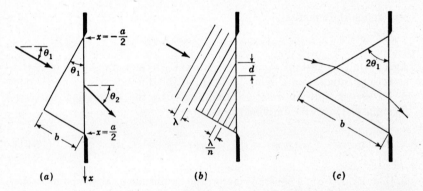

Fig. 11-4.   a. *Prism with a monochromatic plane wave normally incident on the first face.* **b.** *Set of wave fronts outside and inside the prism.   The geometry defines a spacing d on the second face.* **c.** *Isosceles prism with a ray passing through at minimum deviation.*

one would have been led to examine the prism along the lines being pursued.

The irradiance in the diffraction pattern, which is proportional to $|u_0|^2$, shows one principal maximum at

$$\xi_2 = \xi_0 \qquad \eta_2 = 0 \tag{11-23}$$

Thus this maximum lies in the plane of Fig. 11-4 and occurs at the angle $\theta_2^{(0)}$ given by substituting from (11-20) and (11-22) in the left relation of (11-23). The result is

$$\sin \theta_2{}^{(0)} = n \sin \theta_1 \tag{11-24}$$

which is Snell's law. Note that this substitution also leads to

$$d \sin \theta_2{}^{(0)} = \lambda \tag{11-25}$$

so that the pattern can be thought of as being produced by a grating of spacing d of such a nature that it gives only a single principal maximum of order 1.

This principal maximum shows dispersion since λ appears in (11-25), and, moreover, d depends on λ. More simply, the dispersion is inferred from the occurrence in (11-24) of the refractive index n, which depends on λ. The resolving power of the prism is obtained by applying the Rayleigh criterion as in Sec. 7-15. Consider the wavelength λ; the first zero adjacent to the principal maximum occurs when

$$\frac{(\xi_0 - \xi_2)a}{2} = \pi$$

Denoting the corresponding value of θ_2 by $\theta_2{}^{(1)}$, this relation leads to

$$n \sin \theta_1 - \sin \theta_2{}^{(1)} = \frac{\lambda}{a}$$

By Snell's law,

$$\delta(\sin \theta_2) \equiv \sin \theta_2{}^{(0)} - \sin \theta_2{}^{(1)} = \frac{\lambda}{a} \tag{11-26}$$

Let the principal maximum for $\lambda + \delta\lambda$ fall at this first zero. Differentiating (11-24),

$$\delta(\sin \theta_2{}^{(0)}) = \frac{dn}{d\lambda} \delta\lambda \sin \theta_1 \tag{11-27}$$

Equating (11-26) and (11-27), the resolving power is

$$\mathcal{R} \equiv \frac{\lambda}{\delta\lambda} = a \frac{dn}{d\lambda} \sin \theta_1 = b \frac{dn}{d\lambda} \tag{11-28}$$

where b is the length of the base of the prism, as indicated in Fig. 11-4a. Note that the simple formula (7-19) for the resolving power of an ordinary grating cannot be applied to the prism because $N \equiv a/d$ varies with wavelength.

If the cross section of the prism is made isosceles, as shown in Fig. 11-4c, and the incident wave is such that the rays inside the prism are parallel to the base, one has the usual case of a prism spectroscope operating at minimum deviation.[1] All the preceding arguments apply,

---

[1] The condition of minimum deviation results in the most favorable imaging when the source is an illuminated slit rather than a point. See Sawyer [80], p. 59.

except that in (11-27) the right side must be multiplied by 2, since equal refractions take place at two surfaces rather than at one.   Then the last expression in (11-28) again gives the resolving power if b is interpreted as the whole base of the prism, as in Fig. 11-4c.   For the more conventional derivation of this result see, for example, Jenkins and White [53], p. 301.

11-8   Abbe's Theory of the Formation of Images in the Microscope

Section 9-6 treated the theory of the microscope when the objects are self-luminous points.   In ordinary applications of the instrument, the object does not emit and is a thin translucent layer.   Light from an external source passes through this layer and enters the objective. Ultimately an image is formed from which the structure of the object is to be inferred.   It has been demonstrated by many experiments that near the limit of resolution the image can be profoundly altered by changing the method of illumination, by slightly altering the focus, by misalignment of the optical elements, or by introducing diaphragms with various shapes of apertures at critical points in the system.   Many of these effects can be used to advantage in arriving at a complete delineation of the object, but the interpretation of the image is not always straightforward and must be based on a sound theory.

The basis for such a theory was laid by Ernst Abbe in 1873.   All the subsequent developments cannot be covered here, and the discussion will be limited to very simple objects and a simple type of illumination.   In this way it is possible to bring out the main ideas and to explain their spectacular application in the phase-contrast microscope (Sec. 11-9). Excellent references for collateral reading are Rossi [79], p. 230, Ditchburn [25], p. 242, and an article by F. Zernike, the originator of the phase-contrast method, appearing as Appendix K in Strong [88].   A more detailed account is given in Born and Wolf [9], p. 418.

Consider the system shown in Fig. 11-5 in which the lens represents a microscope objective.   As object take a screen containing a long narrow slit with the long axis perpendicular to the plane of the figure.   The object is illuminated by a plane wave, assumed monochromatic, falling at normal incidence.   This case is referred to as *coherent illumination*, since the amplitudes and phases at various points of the object are in definite relationship at all times (the full significance of this characterization will not be seen until Chap. 13).

The lens can be thought of as producing two distinct images.   One occurs in the plane passing through the point O' in Fig. 11-5, this point being the back focal point of the lens.   The image is the Fraunhofer pattern corresponding to the object slit.   The amplitude in this pattern is indicated in the figure.   This pattern also has extension in the direction perpendicular to the figure, but since the slit is long in this direction, the pattern is practically confined to the line labeled x'.   The problem will be simplified by considering only phenomena in the plane of the figure, that is, the plane containing the axis of the system and perpendicular to the long axis of the slit.

The second image occurs in the plane through O'', the plane conjugate to the object plane.   Ideally, and even practically, provided the slit is many wavelengths wide and the objective has large numerical aperture (see Sec. 9-6 for definition), this image has uniform amplitude over the geometrically defined image of the slit and is zero elsewhere.   The amplitude for such an essentially perfect image is indicated by the rectangular curve in the figure.

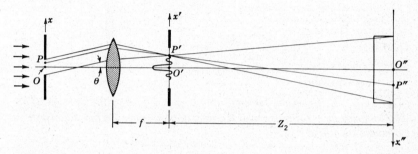

Fig. 11-5. *Optical system to illustrate the Abbe theory of the formation of images in the microscope when the object is illuminated by a plane monochromatic wave.*

A preliminary statement of Abbe's idea is the following: The amplitude in the final image at O'' is to be thought of as coming about in two stages. First, the Fraunhofer pattern at O' is formed, and in terms of appropriate variables its amplitude is the Fourier transform of the amplitude over the object plane.   Then since, for a slit that is not too narrow, the amplitude in the image at O'' is a faithful magnified image of the amplitude over the object plane, the former must be the inverse transform of the amplitude in the pattern at O'.   This conclusion is now generalized to say that if a diaphragm at O' (or the lens itself) cuts off a significant part of the Fraunhofer pattern, then the amplitude in the final image is still the inverse transform of the amplitude over the plane at O' but of the amplitude as it is actually seen from O''.   The generalization applies also to more complicated changes in the amplitude over the plane at O' (as seen from O'') that can be brought about by covering this plane by a thin sheet of glass of nonuniform thickness, perhaps coated with a semitransparent metal film of nonuniform absorption.   The Abbe theory allows one to study systematically the changes of irradiance in the final image brought about by altering the amplitude and phase over the plane at O'. Such a study led to the phase contrast method, discussed in the next section.

To express the ideas of the last paragraph quantitatively, define coordinates x, x', and x'' measured positively in the directions indicated in Fig. 11-5. Let P be a point in the object plane with coordinate x. Associated with it is the image point P'' whose coordinate is

$$x'' = Mx \tag{11-29}$$

where M is the magnification. Consider a ray emanating from P at angle θ with the axis of the system. This ray and all rays parallel to it pass

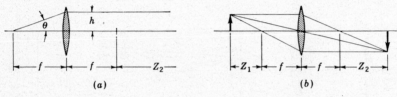

Fig. 11-6. **a.** *Geometry for obtaining a special form of the sine condition.* **b.** *Geometry for obtaining one of the several expressions for the magnification produced by a lens.*

through a point P' on the x' axis whose coordinate x' depends only on θ according to

$$x' = f \sin \theta \tag{11-30}$$

where f is the focal length of the lens. This relation is a special form of the sine condition (Sec. 9-7) holding when the image plane in Fig. 9-15 is at an infinite distance. The argument is based on Fig. 11-6a. First let the image be at a large distance Z_2 to the right of the second focal point. The source is then practically at the first focal point. Equation (9-20), with $\lambda = \lambda'$, becomes $\sin \theta = (y'/y) \sin \theta' = M \sin \theta'$. Now the magnification can be written $M = Z_2/f$, as is seen from Fig. 11-6b. Also, $\sin \theta' \approx h/Z_2$. Thus $h \approx f \sin \theta$; this relation becomes exact as Z_2 becomes infinite. The connection of this result with (11-30) is obvious. (Note that Fig. 11-6a suggests that $h = f \tan \theta$, but this conclusion is drawn from a figure involving a simple thin lens. Such a lens gives stigmatic imaging only for small θ, when the sine and tangent are about equal. For good imaging at large numerical aperture, a combination of thick lenses is required. In any case, stigmatic imaging implies precisely the sine condition.)

Let the amplitude along the x axis in the object plane be $v(x)$. In the case of the slit being considered, $v(x)$ is a constant over the aperture, and zero elsewhere. Let the amplitude falling on the x' axis be $v'(x')$. Formula (11-21) can now be applied to find $v'(x')$, and for simplicity the integration with respect to y, which only contributes a constant factor along the x' axis, can be omitted. Replace ξ_2 appearing in (11-21) by its original expression in (11-20), and replace $\sin \theta_2$ by $\sin \theta$ and finally by x'/f, as given by (11-30). The result is

$$v'(x') = \int_{-\infty}^{\infty} v(x) \, e^{-ikxx'/f} \, dx \qquad (11\text{-}31)$$

Note that many constant factors have been omitted, so that $v'(x')$ is only proportional to the amplitude in question and is not absolutely related to $v(x)$. While (11-31) formally defines v' for all values of x', there is a physical limitation set by the largest value of θ admitted by the lens. As far as the amplitude v' contributes to the final image, there may be a further limitation by a diaphragm in the plane through O', as indicated in Fig. 11-5. Suppose for the moment that the slit is wide enough that all points x' for which v' is appreciably different from zero are physically admitted and are visible from O''. The amplitude $v''(x'')$ along the x'' axis must then be a faithful but magnified image of $v(x)$; that is

$$v''(x'') = v\left(\frac{x''}{M}\right) \qquad (11\text{-}32)$$

Now (11-31) is a Fourier integral, and if constant factors are omitted, its inversion gives

$$v(x) = \int_{-\infty}^{\infty} v'(x') \, e^{ikxx'/f} \, dx'$$

With the above assumption on v', the value of the integral is essentially unaltered if the limits are replaced by x_1' and x_2', the lower and upper bounds of the range over which v' can contribute to the final image. Substitution in (11-32) then gives

$$v''(x'') = \int_{x_1'}^{x_2'} v'(x') \, e^{ikx'x''/fM} \, dx' \qquad (11\text{-}33)$$

Formulas (11-31) and (11-33) are the fundamental expressions of the Abbe theory. They are now taken to apply even when v' as given by (11-31) is a broad function extending with appreciable amplitude beyond the physically determined limits in (11-33). This case arises when the slit becomes sufficiently narrow; the theory then says that v'' fails to be a faithful replica of the object in ways that can be studied. A few examples will now be worked out.

Let the object slit extend over the range $-a/2 < x < a/2$. Formula (11-31) gives

$$v'(x') = a \, \frac{\sin \, (kax'/2f)}{kax'/2f} \qquad (11\text{-}34)$$

Plots of $v(x)$ and $v'(x')$ are shown in Fig. 11-7a and b. Suppose that a is large enough that v' is essentially zero outside the range marked off by the limits in (11-33). Then with small effect these limits can be

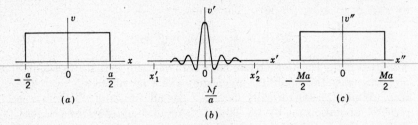

(a)   (b)   (c)

Fig. 11-7. **a.** *Amplitude over the object plane when the object is a slit in an opaque screen.* **b.** *Amplitude in the back focal plane of the objective. The points x_1' and x_2' define the edges of the aperture stop of the system and are assumed such that essentially perfect imaging results.* **c.** *Amplitude over the image plane.*

replaced by $-\infty$ and ∞, and the integral can be evaluated as in Example 2, Sec. 11-2, to give

$$v''(x'') = \frac{2\pi f}{k} \qquad \frac{-Ma}{2} < x'' < \frac{Ma}{2} \tag{11-35}$$

This function is shown in Fig. 11-7c; the conclusion is that the image is essentially perfect and shows magnification by the factor M.

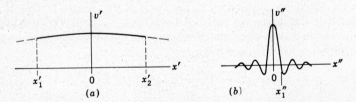

(a)   (b)

Fig. 11-8. **a.** *Amplitude in the back focal plane of the objective when the object slit is very narrow.* **b.** *Amplitude over the image plane.*

At the opposite extreme, suppose a is small enough that the characteristic dimension $\lambda f/a$ indicated in Fig. 11-7b is large compared with the upper limit x_2' in (11-33). The situation is then as shown in Fig. 11-8a. As an approximation, v' can be considered constant, say unity, between the limits of integration. Let these limits be $-D'/2$ and $D'/2$, as determined by a circular diaphragm A at the back focal plane of the lens (Fig. 11-9). Evaluation of (11-33) then gives

$$v''(x'') = D' \frac{\sin (kD'x''/2fM)}{kD'x''/2fM}$$

The curve is shown in Fig. 11-8*b*, and the first zero falls at x_1'', obtained by setting the argument of the sine equal to π, whence

$$x_1'' = \frac{fM\lambda}{D'} = \frac{\lambda Z_2}{D'} = \frac{\lambda L}{D}$$

where the new symbols are defined by Fig. 11-9, and the relation $M = Z_2/f$ has been used. Thus the final image is characteristic only of the microscope and gives no information about the object except that it is so narrow that no detail can be resolved. If (11-31) and (11-33) had

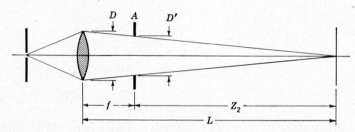

Fig. 11-9. *Circular aperture A in the back focal plane of the objective. The diameter of the aperture is taken in a special relation to the diameter of the objective lens.*

been completely formulated as double integrals and the object were a very small pinhole rather than a narrow slit, then the amplitude would be constant over the whole circular aperture A in Fig. 11-9, and the final image would be the Airy pattern (Sec. 9-4) with the radius of the first dark ring equal to $1.22\lambda L/D$, the same as in the case of a self-luminous point source. It should be pointed out, however, that one cannot then assume that the calculation of resolving power in Sec. 9-6 applies when the object is a pair of pinholes, for with coherent illumination it is necessary to find *first* the resultant amplitude at each point of the image and *then* the irradiance. A calculation, which can be found in Born and Wolf [9], p. 423, gives the minimum resolvable separation (according to a criterion which cannot be the Rayleigh criterion but is essentially the same) to be the formula (9-18) with the factor 0.61 changed to 0.77, an unimportant difference.

When the width of the slit is intermediate between the two extremes just considered, the integral in (11-33) becomes difficult, and it is customary to study such cases by taking the object to be a grating of many parallel slits of width a separated by opaque strips, taken to be also of width a. Let the number of slits be N. Then $v(x)$ is as shown in Fig. 11-10*a*, and the amplitude over the apertures can be taken to be unity.

Evaluation of (11-31) gives

$$v'(x') = a \frac{\sin (kax'/2f)}{kax'/2f} \frac{\sin (Nkax'/f)}{\sin (kax'/f)} \tag{11-36}$$

[This formula can be written at once by a simple adaptation of the calculation in Sec. 7-8 and by using the single-aperture formula (11-34). The spacing of the grating is $d = 2a$.] A plot of $v'(x')$ for large N is shown in Fig. 11-10b, in which the dashed envelope is the first factor in

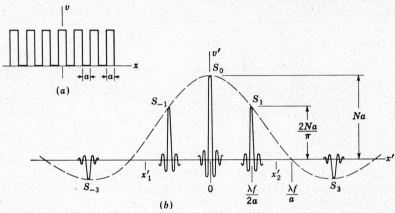

Fig. 11-10. **a.** *Amplitude across the object when the latter is a number of parallel slits in an opaque screen.* **b.** *Amplitude in the back focal plane of the objective.*

(11-36) multiplied by N. The curve consists of a number of well-separated parts, each made up of a principal maximum and several secondary oscillations. It is usual to refer to these parts as *spectra* of various orders and to denote them by $S_0, S_1, S_{-1}, \ldots$ (With the grating having $d = 2a$, all the spectra of even order happen to be missing.) If one looked down the tube of the microscope with eyepiece removed, one would see these spectra as a row of small spots of light in the back focal plane of the objective.

The final image is a good reproduction of the object only if a large number of spectra are passed by the instrument. As an intermediate case, suppose the width a is such that only the zeroth and two first spectra fall within the limits x_1' and x_2', as indicated in Fig. 11-10b. Then within the range of integration in (11-33), one can write to good approximation,

$$v'(x') = \frac{2Na}{\pi} \frac{\sin [Nka(x' - \lambda f/2a)/f]}{Nka(x' - \lambda f/2a)/f} + Na \frac{\sin (Nkax'/f)}{Nkax'/f}$$
$$+ \frac{2Na}{\pi} \frac{\sin [Nka(x' + \lambda f/2a)/f]}{Nka(x' + \lambda f/2a)/f} \tag{11-37}$$

That is, N is assumed large, and each spectrum is expressed in an approximation after the manner of (7-15). The relative heights of the spectra are fixed by the ordinates of the dashed envelopes at the points touched by the principal maxima, the factor being $2/\pi$. In evaluating (11-33), one substitutes (11-37) and makes the approximation of integrating between infinite limits. (The *essential* effect of the finite limits is to cut off completely all spectra higher than the first.) Making appropriate changes of variable in the two first-order terms and comparing with (11-34) and (11-35), one obtains

$$v''(x'') = a\left(\frac{2}{\pi}e^{-i\pi x''/Ma} + 1 + \frac{2}{\pi}e^{i\pi x''/Ma}\right)$$

$$= A\left(1 + \frac{4}{\pi}\cos\frac{\pi x''}{Ma}\right) \quad -NMa < x'' < NMa \quad (11\text{-}38)$$

and $v'' = 0$ elsewhere. The constant factor represented by A is unessential. A plot of v'' is shown in Fig. 11-11a, and v''^2, which is proportional·

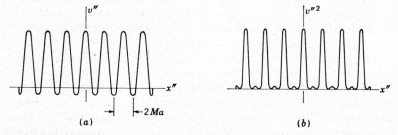

Fig. 11-11. *Amplitude* (**a**) *and irradiance* (**b**) *in the final image of the object of Fig.* 11-10 *when the system passes only the zeroth and two first spectra.*

to the irradiance in the image, is shown in Fig. 11-11b. From such an image one might read spurious detail into the object.

If the width a is made smaller, even the first spectra will eventually fall outside the limits x_1', x_2'. The zeroth spectrum alone gives a final image which is that of a single slit whose width is the total width of the grating. All resolution of the grating has vanished, and the critical condition is seen from Fig. 11-10b to be $x_2' = \lambda f/2a$. Substituting $d = 2a$ and $x_2' = f \times$ N.A., where N.A. is the numerical aperture of the objective, the minimum resolvable spacing is

$$d_{\min} = \frac{\lambda}{\text{N.A.}}$$

which is not far different from (9-18).

As one example of the many ways in which the final image can be altered by modifying the spectra, let the object be the grating just considered, and suppose again that the instrument transmits only the zeroth and two first spectra. Let the zeroth spectrum be covered by a small opaque disk at the center of the back focal plane of the objective. (The field of view would than be dark if the object were removed—this case is known as *dark-field* illumination.) The effect on the amplitude in the final image is to eliminate the constant term in (11-38), and Fig. 11-11*b* is then modified to the extent that the small subsidiary maxima become equal to the others, and the object appears to be twice as fine and have twice as many slits as it actually has. Further examples will occur in the problems and in the next section. Abbe and successors performed many experiments to demonstrate these effects, to the surprise of the microscopists of the time.

11-9 Phase-contrast Method   An object of the type considered in the preceding section is called an *amplitude object*, by which one understands that it impresses variations on the magnitude of the complex amplitude of the incident light, but not on the phase angle. Many of the objects examined by microscopists are *phase objects*, perfectly transparent, but varying from point to point in optical thickness, either through variation of refractive index, variation of geometrical thickness, or both. Their effect is to impress variations in phase on the complex amplitude of the incident light. If the microscope produces a perfect image, the irradiance in this image is everywhere the same, since it is independent of phase, and no detail appears. The method of phase contrast, introduced into microscopy by F. Zernike in 1935, is a means of converting changes of phase over the object plane into changes of irradiance over the final image. The method is most easily explained if the variation in optical thickness of the object is confined to a small range, say less than one-twentieth of a wavelength. This condition is usually achieved in applications if the specimen is embedded in a homogeneous medium of nearly the same refractive index.

As an object on which to base the discussion, take a glass plate covering a rectangular aperture in an opaque screen, and let the plate contain parallel shallow grooves of rectangular profile to make a phase grating, as shown in Fig. 11-12*a*. This particular object is chosen to make possible a comparison with the grating of the last section.

The object is to be introduced in the arrangement of Fig. 11-5. Take the x axis to be just above the raised areas (Fig. 11-12*a*), and suppose that at a point of this axis lying over a groove, the amplitude v is real and unity. Then at a point over a raised area, the incident wave will have traversed a greater optical path, and the amplitude will be $e^{i\delta}$, with δ positive (predicated on the time factor being $e^{-i\omega t}$). As a function of x, the amplitude over the whole object can be written

$$v(x) = e^{i\,\phi(x)} \tag{11-39}$$

where $\phi(x)$ is the discontinuous function shown in Fig. 11-12b.   When δ is small (very shallow grooves in the object), $v(x)$ can be approximated by

$$v(x) = V(x) + i\,\phi(x)$$

where $V(x)$ is the function of unit height and of a width equal to that of the whole transparent part of the object, as shown in Fig. 11-12b.

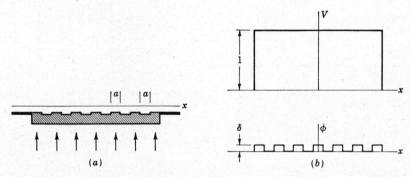

Fig. 11-12.   a. *Phase object consisting of a glass plate with shallow grooves of rectangular cross section.* **b.** *Real part V and imaginary part ϕ of the amplitude along the x axis of (**a**) when the incident wave has unit amplitude. The optical paths through the raised areas and through the grooves differ by δ radians.*

Substitution of $v(x)$ in (11-31) gives the amplitude $v'(x')$ in the Fraunhofer pattern at the back focal plane of the objective.   The imaginary part of this amplitude is the transform of $\phi(x)$ and has the shape of Fig. 11-10b.   The heights of the various spectra are proportional to δ, and for purposes of comparing with the real part, assume that the maximum of the zeroth spectrum is equal to δ.   The real part of v' is the transform of $V(x)$, and if the grating has a large number of grooves, this transform has the same shape as just the zeroth spectrum in Fig. 11-10b, but its maximum ordinate is 2, much larger than the maximum in the imaginary part.   The total amplitude v' is therefore characterized in that all spectra but the zeroth are imaginary and proportional to δ, while the zeroth is much larger, almost purely real, and almost independent of δ.

The amplitude $v''(x'')$ can now be calculated.   Putting infinite limits on the integral in (11-33), which is equivalent to assuming perfect imaging, gives just the function (11-39) on a magnified scale, and hence a uniform irradiance over the whole image of the grating.   The first and most important step in the phase-contrast method is to place over the zeroth spectrum a thin sheet of refracting material of such thickness that it adds to the optical path for this order alone an extra one-quarter wavelength. After passing through the plate, called a *phase plate* or *diffraction plate*, the amplitude for the zeroth spectrum becomes essentially pure imaginary and is therefore in phase with the other spectra.

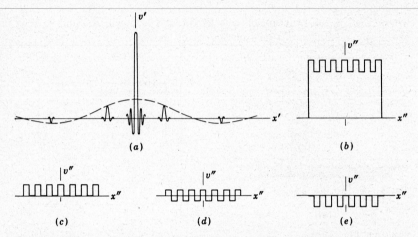

Fig. 11-13.   a. *Amplitude in the back focal plane of the objective when the object is that of Fig.* 11-12 *and a phase plate adding one-quarter wavelength to the optical path covers the zero-order spectrum.* **b.** *Amplitude in the final image corresponding to* (**a**). **c.** *Final image when the phase plate has optimum absorption.* **d.** *Final image when the phase plate is opaque.* **e.** *Final image when the phase plate has optimum absorption and adds three-quarters wavelength to the optical path.*

Then without the factor i, v' becomes as in Fig. 11-13a. The final amplitude v'' is then given, apart from a constant factor and to good approximation, by

$$v''(x'') = V\left(\frac{x''}{M}\right) + \phi\left(\frac{x''}{M}\right)$$

where M is the magnification. A plot is shown in Fig. 11-13b. Square, and neglect ϕ^2; the irradiance in the final image is proportional to $V(x''/M) + 2\phi(x''/M)$. Thus the jumps in irradiance are proportional to the jumps in optical path in the object when the latter are a small fraction of a wavelength.

The image is still unsatisfactory in the sense that the details appear as small fluctuations in a strong general illumination; that is, the contrast is poor. Hence the second step in the phase-contrast method is to add absorption to the phase plate to reduce the magnitude of the zeroth spectrum. Ideally, this spectrum is brought down to touch the dashed curve in Fig. 11-13a, in which case the amplitude in the final image is as in Fig. 11-13c, and the grooves (regions of shorter optical path) appear black.

If one eliminates the zeroth spectrum altogether, one has *dark-field* illumination; that is, the field of view is dark in the absence of an object. The amplitude v'' then becomes as in Fig. 11-13d, and the irradiance is constant. Actually, because of the finite numerical aperture, the imaging is not perfect, and some detail shows up, but the image is not nearly as satisfactory as when the right amount of zeroth spectrum is present.

If the zeroth spectrum is reduced by the right amount to give Fig. 11-13c and is then changed in sign by addition of an extra half-wavelength to the optical path in the phase plate, the result is Fig. 11-13e; that is, the contrast is reversed, the grooves now being bright.

The optimum amount of absorption in the phase plate depends on the height of the dashed curve in Fig. 11-13a and hence increases as δ decreases. A complete phase microscope provides an assortment of phase plates, so that almost any object can be viewed with nearly optimum contrast. The sensitivity of the method is such that differences of optical path of less than $\lambda/100$ have been detected.

The phase-contrast method is more versatile than the above discussion indicates. For example, suppose the object is a grating of open slits separated by strips which are not opaque, but only slightly absorbing, and which have negligible optical thickness (for example, metal can be deposited in thin, semitransparent strips on a glass plate). Then in the ordinary microscope one has the situation in Fig. 11-13a and b. A phase plate with the right absorption but no optical thickness or with thickness $\lambda/2$ will produce the optimum contrast of Fig. 11-13c or e, respectively, by appropriately reducing the zeroth spectrum, and with it the average illumination in the image.

More generally, the absorbing area in the object may introduce an additional optical path simultaneously (for example, let absorbing layers cover the ridges in Fig. 11-12a), and this additional path may be of any length up to a wavelength (or longer, but then an ambiguity enters in the interpretation). It is always possible to design a phase plate with such absorption and optical thickness that the area in question appears dark on a bright surround or bright on a dark surround, and the characteristics of the phase plates which produce ideal contrasts give indication of the characteristics of the object. To fully exploit this idea, it is clear that a continuous range of absorption and optical thickness in the phase plate should be available. As a compromise, manufacturers supply a number of combinations which have been found to meet most requirements reasonably well. For descriptions of actual instruments and the theory and practice when the objects and the imaging are not as ideal as assumed here, reference can be made to the treatise by Bennett, Osterberg, Jupnik, and Richards [3].

11-10 Rationale of the Fourier Analysis of Linear Systems
Sections 11-6 to 11-9 have treated interesting optical problems and, at the same time, have illustrated the ideas of a Fourier transform and its inversion. However, the real power of the Fourier theorem has not yet been brought out, but will be the subject of the present section. Applications of these new ideas will occur throughout the rest of the book and

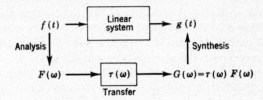

Fig. 11-14. *Schematic diagram to illustrate the Fourier analysis of linear systems.*

will be of the following nature: A physical system is stimulated in some way to give a response. In general the stimulus is very complicated, and the response correspondingly so. Fourier analysis simplifies the problem of finding the response to a given stimulus. Since most applications will involve the time t as independent variable and the temporal frequency ω as the conjugate variable in a Fourier analysis, the discussion to be given will refer to this single pair of variables, but the ideas carry over to other problems in a way that will be obvious.

Consider the schematic diagram in Fig. 11-14. The upper box in the figure, labeled "linear system," represents the physical constituents of the problem at hand, for example, a spectrograph, an antenna, an antenna connected to an amplifier, or an electron and a nucleus forming a dipole. To the system is applied some real input function $f(t)$, which may be the electric field as a function of time at the entrance aperture of a spectrograph or an antenna, the instantaneous dipole moment of an atom, or the voltage applied to an amplifier. From the system comes an output function $g(t)$, for example, the electric field at the detector in a spectrograph, the voltage at the output terminals of an antenna or an amplifier to which it is connected, or the electric field of a dipole oscillator at some given point of space.

The system is said to be linear if it obeys the principle of superposition, so that if $f_1(t)$ and $f_2(t)$ are any two input functions for which the outputs are $g_1(t)$ and $g_2(t)$, respectively, then for the input $c_1f_1 + c_2f_2$ the output is $c_1g_1 + c_2g_2$, where c_1 and c_2 are arbitrary constants.

The fundamental problem is: Given a linear system and an input $f(t)$, find the output $g(t)$. In some cases a direct solution is easiest. For example, if the system is a resistance R, the input is an applied voltage $V(t)$, and the output is the current $I(t)$, then $I = V/R$. But in a complicated system such as a spectrograph, the direct solution for the output when the input is a complicated function is at best very difficult, and the indirect method of Fourier analysis is a great help in getting at the quantities of interest.

The method consists in the three steps indicated by the lower path from f to g in Fig. 11-14. First, the Fourier transform of $f(t)$, denoted $F(\omega)$, is found. A single Fourier component $F(\omega)\,e^{-i\omega t}$ is applied to the system as a hypothetical input function, and the monochromatic output $G(\omega)\,e^{-i\omega t}$ is found. This part of the problem is comparatively easy, and much of the work in previous chapters actually dealt with it, although the problems were formulated as dealing with real monochromatic functions in complex representation. Since

$$f(t) = \frac{1}{\sqrt{2\pi}} \int_{-\infty}^{\infty} F(\omega)\,e^{-i\omega t}\,d\omega$$

that is, $f(t)$ is the summation of its Fourier components, it follows from the linearity of the system that

$$g(t) = \frac{1}{\sqrt{2\pi}} \int_{-\infty}^{\infty} G(\omega)\,e^{-i\omega t}\,d\omega$$

so that $G(\omega)$ *is just the Fourier transform of* $g(t)$.

In all cases $G(\omega)$ can be written as the product of $F(\omega)$ and a function $\tau(\omega)$, called the *transfer function*. The transfer function completely characterizes the performance of the linear system. If $f(t)$ and $g(t)$ are scalar quantities, $\tau(\omega)$ is just a complex scalar function. For example, if $f(t)$ is the current through a self-inductance L, and $g(t)$ is the voltage across it, then $\tau(\omega) = -i\omega L$ by the differentiation rule. If f and g are vector functions, then F and G are also vectors, and τ transforms one vector into another. In general, τ is then a tensor of second rank, as will be shown in later chapters, but in some cases it may reduce to a vector function of ω which acts on F through vector multiplication, as in the example to be worked in the next section. Finally, if the input is a vector and the output is a scalar (for example, if a vector wave is incident on an antenna, and a scalar voltage appears across its terminals), then τ relates a vector to a scalar, usually through τ being a vector and the multiplication being scalar. The proper terminology to cover all cases is that $\tau(\omega)$ is an *operator* which operates on $F(\omega)$ to give $G(\omega)$, the

operation being written as multiplication in Fig. 11-14 (but this multiplication is of a kind that is different for different types of operators).
In some problems the transfer function cannot be calculated, but can be
measured experimentally with sufficient accuracy by application of real
sinusoidal inputs of different frequencies and observation of the magnitudes and phase angles of the outputs.

11-11   Examples   An example to illustrate the discussion of the last
section will now be worked out in detail, and a few more will be cited
in outline only.

Consider an electron moving about a fixed nucleus such that the vector
from the center of the nucleus to the center of the electron is $\mathbf{s}(t)$, any
given real function of time which is continuous, has continuous derivatives, and is zero outside some finite interval of time.   A further restriction will be imposed below.   The problem will be to find the electric
and magnetic fields $\mathbf{e}(t)$ and $\mathbf{b}(t)$ at a fixed point far from the atom when
these fields are known for a sinusoidal motion of the electron.

Write $\mathbf{s}(t)$ as a Fourier integral:

$$\mathbf{s}(t) = \frac{1}{\sqrt{2\pi}} \int_{-\infty}^{\infty} \mathbf{s}_0(\omega)\, e^{-i\omega t}\, d\omega$$

so that $\mathbf{s}_0(\omega)$ is the transform.   Take the component $\mathbf{s}_0(\omega)\, e^{-i\omega t}$ as the
input function; the fields $\mathbf{e}(\omega)$ and $\mathbf{b}(\omega)$ at a large distance r in the direction of the unit vector $\hat{\mathbf{r}}$ are given by (5-13).   In order to apply these
formulas to all components, it must be assumed that there is some posi-
tive frequency ω_L such that $\mathbf{s}_0(\omega)$, hence also $\mathbf{s}_0(-\omega) = \mathbf{s}_0^*(\omega)$, is zero
for $0 \leq \omega \leq \omega_L$, and that the maximum wavelength involved in the
problem, namely, $\lambda_M = 2\pi c/\omega_L$, is small compared with r.   Then the
point in question is in the wave zone for all nonvanishing components.

Formulas (5-13) already contain the factor $e^{-i\omega t}$; the required electric
field is

$$\mathbf{e}(t) = \frac{1}{\sqrt{2\pi}} \int_{-\infty}^{\infty} \mathbf{e}(\omega)\, d\omega = \frac{e}{\sqrt{2\pi}\, c^2 r} \hat{\mathbf{r}} \times \left[\hat{\mathbf{r}} \times \int_{-\infty}^{\infty} \omega^2\, \mathbf{s}_0(\omega)\, e^{-i\omega(t-r/c)}\, d\omega \right]$$

$$= -\frac{e}{c^2 r} \hat{\mathbf{r}} \times \left[\hat{\mathbf{r}} \times \ddot{\mathbf{s}}\left(t - \frac{r}{c}\right) \right] \qquad (11\text{-}40)$$

where each k in (5-13) has been replaced by ω/c, and the differentiation
rule (Sec. 11-3) has been applied.   By $\ddot{\mathbf{s}}(t - r/c)$ is meant the second
derivative of $\mathbf{s}(t)$, that is, the acceleration of the electron, evaluated at
the retarded time $t - r/c$ (Sec. 3-14).   In the same way the magnetic
field is

$$\mathbf{b}(t) = \frac{e}{c^2 r} \hat{\mathbf{r}} \times \ddot{\mathbf{s}}\left(t - \frac{r}{c}\right) \qquad (11\text{-}41)$$

[Recall that (5-13) was given in Chap. 5 without proof, and reference was made to Appendix B, in which the relevant formulas are (B-32). The above calculation has gone in reverse to get back the last terms in (B-32). Problem 11-17 calls for the remaining terms.]

The transfer operator for the electric field is

$$\tau(\omega) = \frac{e\omega^2}{c^2 r} e^{i\omega r/c} \hat{\mathbf{r}} \times [\hat{\mathbf{r}} \times$$

since applying this operator to $\mathbf{s}_0(\omega)$ gives the transform of $\mathbf{e}(t)$, that is, the first formula of (5-13) with the factor $e^{-i\omega t}$ omitted. The transfer operator for the magnetic field is

$$\tau(\omega) = - \frac{e\omega^2}{c^2 r} e^{i\omega r/c} \hat{\mathbf{r}} \times$$

Fourier analysis is an invaluable tool in studying the formation of images by optical instruments. For example, in extending the Abbe theory (Sec. 11-8) to more general objects, one procedure is the following: The amplitude of the wave just after passing through the object is some function $v(x,y)$, in general complex, defined over the object plane. Rather than calculate at once the amplitude $v'(x',y')$ in the back focal plane of the objective and then the amplitude $v''(x'',y'')$ in the final image, one makes a two-dimensional Fourier analysis of $v(x,y)$, the conjugate variables being spatial frequencies k_x and k_y, and the transform being $V(k_x,k_y)$. Let the unit of length in the image plane be that in the object plane multiplied by the magnification. The amplitude in the image can be analyzed to yield a transform $V''(k_x'',k_y'')$. It is then possible to define and (in principle, at least) calculate a transfer function $\tau(k_x,k_y)$ such that $V''(k_x,k_y) = \tau(k_x,k_y) \ V(k_x,k_y)$. The transfer function is characteristic of the optical system and can be altered by altering the system. For example, the effect of the phase plate in the phase microscope on the images of various kinds of objects can be studied in this way. The introduction of the phase plate or any generalization of it is called *spatial filtering*, since it is exactly analogous to filters introduced in electric networks to alter Fourier components of functions of time. In terms of filtering, a microscope can be thought of as a low-pass filter, since τ shows a high-frequency cutoff which determines the resolution. Introducing an absorbing layer over a small area at the center of the back focal plane of the objective reduces the lowest Fourier components, and hence the general level of illumination in the image, without seriously affecting the fine detail, which is carried by higher frequencies. The contrast is sometimes improved thereby, as pointed out in the simple case in Sec. 11-9. If the object is self-luminous, the rule for incoherent sources applies, and the Fourier analysis is made, not in terms of amplitudes, but in terms of irradiances (more correctly, long-time averages of irradiances), since it is now in terms of the latter that the problem is linear. The points raised in this paragraph will not be pursued further. A good introductory account with bibliography has been given by O'Neill [68].

Problems

11-1. Let $f(x)$ be real, and consider the complex function

$$\phi(x) = \sqrt{\frac{2}{\pi}} \int_0^\infty A(\xi) \, e^{-i\xi x} \, d\xi$$

where $A(\xi)$ is the transform defined by (11-6). Show that $f(x)$ is the real part of $\phi(x)$. [Thus $\phi(x)$ is a complex representation of $f(x)$ analogous to writing $e^{-i\xi x}$ as the representation of $\cos \xi x$.]

11-2. Let $f(x) = be^{-x^2/a^2} \cos \xi_0 x \; (-\infty < x < \infty)$, with $\xi_0 a \gg 1$. Plot $f(x)$ roughly. Find and plot the transform. Discuss the significance of $\xi_0 a \gg 1$.

11-3. If in the function (11-12) the parameter ξ_0 approaches zero, $f(x)$ approaches (11-10), and Fig. 11-3b goes into Fig. 11-2b. Illustrate this transition by drawing roughly the curve of the transform (11-13) at that stage when $\xi_0 a = \pi/2$. [*Suggestion:* Draw curves for the separate terms in (11-13) and draw the sum by eye.] Draw also $f(x)$ at that stage.

11-4. Repeat Prob. 11-2 for $f(x) = b \cos^2 \xi_0 x/2 \; (x^2 < a^2)$, $f(x) = 0 \; (x^2 > a^2)$, with $\xi_0 a \gg 1$.

11-5. Find the transform of $f(x) = b_0 + b_1 \cos \xi_0 x \; (x^2 < a^2)$, $f(x) = 0 \; (x^2 > a^2)$, with $\xi_0 a \gg 1$. Note that when $b_1 = 0$ or $b_0 = 0$, one has Example 2 or Example 3, Sec. 11-2. Plot $f(x)$ and its transform for the additional cases (1) $b_0 = b_1$ (essentially Prob. 11-3), (2) $b_0 = b_1/2$, (3) $b_0 = -b_1/2$, and (4) $b_0 = -b_1$. Take b_1 positive in each case. Give the ordinates of the principal maxima in the transforms.

11-6. Let $f(x) = b(1 - |x|/a) \; (x^2 < a^2)$, $f(x) = 0 \; (x^2 > a^2)$. Plot $f(x)$ and find and plot the transform. The answer should agree with that of Prob. 11-8.

11-7. Show by a figure how the folding integral (Theorem 4, Sec. 11-3) receives a geometrical interpretation according to which $f_1(\tau)$ is represented by a fixed curve while $f_2(x - \tau)$ slides along the τ axis and the integral is the area under the curve of the product at each stage. Contrast the integral in Theorem 4 with those in the corollary.

11-8. Consider the function $g(x) = (b/a)^{1/2} \; (x^2 < a^2/4)$, $g(x) = 0 \; (x^2 > a^2/4)$. Calculate the folding integral of g with itself (i.e., both functions in the integrand are the same and equal to g). Use the geometrical idea of Prob. 11-7 to simplify the evaluation. The answer is the function in Prob. 11-6; hence use the folding rule as an alternative method of finding the transform of this function.

11-9. With the function f defined in Prob. 11-6, calculate the folding integral of f with itself (see Prob. 11-8). Plot the result, and use the folding rule to find the transform.

11-10. Calculate the folding integral of the gaussian functions $f_1(x) = be^{-x^2/a^2}$ and $f_2(x) = de^{-x^2/c^2}$. (*Hint:* Use the folding rule to find the transform of the integral, and then calculate the inverse transform.) The result is important enough to be remembered in words: The folding integral of two gaussians whose widths between $1/e$ points are $2a$ and $2c$ is a gaussian of width $2\sqrt{a^2 + c^2}$. It is sometimes useful to know also that, with the maximum values of the given functions being b and d, the maximum of the folding integral is $\sqrt{\pi} \, abcd/\sqrt{a^2 + c^2}$.

11-11. Use Parseval's theorem to show that

$$\int_{-\infty}^{\infty} \frac{\sin^2 x}{x^2}\, dx = \pi$$

11-12. With regard to the resolving power of a glass prism, take a rather large but realizable value of $dn/d\lambda$ to be 10^3 cm^{-1} and the base of the prism to be 15 cm. Calculate the resolving power, and calculate the number of grooves in a grating which gives the same resolving power in the first order. The conclusion is that a modest grating is superior to the largest prism. The grating is superior in other respects: On a fair basis of comparison, a grating instrument transmits more light in many applications (see Jacquinot [48]), and the task of converting positions of lines on a spectrographic plate to wavelengths is much easier in a grating (Sawyer [80], pp. 236 and 246). There is the disadvantage of overlapping of orders, but this can be overcome by suitable auxiliary devices if desired. Since well-made gratings became generally available, there has been a tendency for the proportion of grating instruments to increase.

11-13. Let a grating of many slits of width a and spacing d (the slits being separated by opaque strips) be examined with a microscope with coherent illumination, and suppose that all spectra having appreciable amplitude are passed by the instrument, so that the image is essentially perfect. Discuss the effect on the final image of covering the zeroth spectrum with a glass plate which adds one-half wavelength to the optical path. Discuss the cases $d > 2a$, $d = 2a$, and $d < 2a$.

11-14. Figure 11-11 resulted when the microscope transmitted only the spectra of orders 0, ± 1. Suppose that, in addition, the orders ± 3 are transmitted. (The second orders are missing with the grating being considered, that is, when $d = 2a$.) Find and plot v'' and v''^2. These plots need only be rough and such as to show the trend of improvement in the image as more spectra are passed by the microscope. (Curves which can be interpreted as applying to this problem and its extension as more and more spectra are included, although they illustrate points on Fourier series, are given by Carslaw [16], pp. 238 and 300.)

11-15. Let a grating of many slits of width a and spacing $d = 2a$ be examined with a microscope. Let a plane monochromatic wave fall on the object at such an angle of incidence that the zeroth spectrum falls just inside the edge of the aperture A in Fig. 11-9. Let a be such that the first spectrum falls just inside the opposite edge. Calculate the irradiance in the final image, and illustrate with a figure similar to Fig. 11-11b. What is the limit of resolution in this case? (*Answer to last question:* $d_{\min} = 0.5\lambda/\text{N.A.}$)

11-16. Let the raised areas of the grating in Fig. 11-12a be covered with absorbing layers which reduce the modulus of the amplitude of the incident wave by the factor $g < 1$ Let the extra optical path through the thicker parts be δ radians, with δ having any value between zero and 2π. Let the central area of the phase plate in a phase microscope add optical path Δ radians (for the zeroth order only) and have absorption (again for the zeroth spectrum only) such that the modulus of the amplitude incident on it is reduced by the factor G. Find the relation between $ge^{i\delta}$ and $Ge^{i\Delta}$ such that the final image of the transparent grooves in the object is black. [*Hint:* One way of starting is to write $v(x)$ as $V(x) + W(x)$, where $V(x)$ is the function defined in Sec. 11-9, and $W(x)$ equals zero over a groove and beyond the ends of the grating, and $ge^{i\delta} - 1$ over a raised area. Assume that there are very many grooves.] Find G and Δ in the special cases (1) $g = 1$, $\delta \ll 1$, and (2) $g < 1$, $\delta = 0$, and note that the results are consistent with conclusions drawn in Sec. 11-9. [*Answer to last parts:* (1) $G \approx \delta/2$, $\Delta \approx \pi/2$; (2) $G = (1-g)/(1+g)$, $\Delta = \pi$.]

11-17. If in the dipole oscillator considered in Sec. 11-11 the motion has Fourier components of arbitrarily low frequency, then (5-13) breaks down as an approximation, and the complete formulas (5-4) and (5-5) must be used in finding the Fourier components of the fields. Find the fields $e(t)$ and $b(t)$ in this case, and note that the result is the whole of (B-32).

11-18. Consider a voltage amplifier to which is applied an arbitrary input voltage $V_1(t)$, and from which comes an output voltage $V_2(t)$. The amplifier is said to be distortionless if $V_2(t) = cV_1(t - b)$ for any input, where b and c are constants. Describe by words and graphical illustration the relation of $V_2(t)$ to $V_1(t)$, and in particular the significances of b and c. Why can b never be negative? Find the transfer function for the amplifier, and describe in words the behavior of its modulus and angle as functions of ω.

Radiation from Lorentz Atoms

In this chapter the Lorentz theory will be pushed as far as it will go in giving a theoretical interpretation of the radiation actually observed to come from a discharge tube containing atoms excited by collisions. The first section will give a brief description of the Geissler tube as generating the typical discharge with which the rest of the chapter attempts to deal. The second section reduces this description to terms that have meaning in the purely classical theory of Lorentz and that can therefore serve as premises for the later calculations. The most important steps in these calculations will be to introduce the idea of the spectrum of the radiation and to find a theoretical form of this spectrum. Assessment of the results as they arise will show that in certain well-defined aspects they are surprisingly close to observed facts, and the final chapter will show that in these aspects the quantum theory leads merely to adjustment of constants in the classical formulas, even though the quantum theory involves fundamentally different ideas concerning the processes of atomic radiation. This happy circumstance explains the many instances in the modern literature in which an author relaxes into a classical or semiclassical manner of speaking, reference being precisely to the theory in the present chapter.

12-1 The Geissler Tube Figure 12-1 shows the usual form of the Geissler tube as it is used in the laboratory to generate radiation from atoms which occur naturally in the gaseous form. The sealed glass envelope, some 20 cm long, consists of a capillary tube with the ends blown out into bulbs containing electrodes. The gas is at the low pressure of a few millimeters of mercury. The electrodes are connected to a voltage generator which applies a few thousand volts and has a high internal resistance. The first action of the applied voltage is to ionize some of the atoms of the gas, whereupon a current flows; because of the resistance just mentioned, the voltage across the tube drops to a few hundred volts, and the current is limited to a few milliamperes. The gas glows and is brightest in the capillary section, where the current density is highest. Under these conditions of operation only a very small

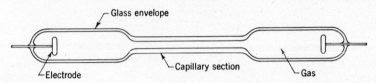

Fig. 12-1.   *Common design of Geissler tube.   The glass envelope is some 20 cm long.*

fraction of the atoms in the gas are split into positive ions and free electrons, and the radiation arising in the capillary section comes from and is characteristic of the neutral atoms.

The process giving rise to the excitation of atoms and ultimately to radiation is as follows: The voltage across the tube results in an electric field inside the gas which accelerates the positive ions in one direction, and the free electrons in the other. The kinetic energy gained by the ions is transferred through elastic collisions to the kinetic energy of thermal agitation of the neutral atoms, thereby raising the temperature of the gas. The motion of the ions consists of thermal motions at the elevated temperature, as though they were neutral atoms, together with a slow drift in the direction of the electric field. No characteristic atomic radiation comes from collisions with ions. The electrons as well as the ions suffer elastic collisions with the neutral atoms, but because of the great disparity of masses, very little kinetic energy is transferred. The electrons lose kinetic energy chiefly through *inelastic collisions* in which the struck atom absorbs energy in the form of excitation of its electronic structure.

An excited atom soon returns to its initial state, and the energy of excitation appears as radiation. A spectroscope shows that the radiation emitted by the tube consists of a number of sharp lines with which are associated certain frequencies or wavelengths; the distribution and relative strengths of these lines are characteristic of the chemical identity of the atoms in the tube. If the spectroscope has sufficiently high resolution, the radiated wave giving rise to any one of the lines cannot be interpreted as being perfectly monochromatic, but rather has to be thought of in the spirit of Fourier analysis as a superposition of mono-chromatic waves with frequencies filling a small continuous range. The total energy falling in the line is distributed over the range of frequencies in a manner partly characteristic of the internal motions in the atom and partly characteristic of the over-all physical conditions in the tube, such as temperature, pressure, and degree of ionization; once a reliable theory is at hand, the observation of the spectral distribution of the radiated energy is a powerful tool for determining the conditions existing in the discharge.

It will be advantageous to leave further observational details to be taken up piecemeal as predictions from the classical theory become available for comparison. In the end there will be a residue of facts that can be understood only on the basis of the quantum theory, and some attention to these points will be given in the final chapter.

The program before us is threefold: First, a classical model of the gaseous discharge will be formulated. Second, the theoretical spectrum of the radiation will be precisely defined and calculated. Third, the question of measurement of the spectrum will be taken up. The third part is more involved than might be imagined. A beginning in the subject was made in the earlier discussions of the diffraction grating and prism, but only discrete monochromatic waves were considered. Extension must now be made, firstly to continuous distributions of frequencies, and secondly to the interferometric spectroscopes that are usually required for observing spectra of the type to be found in the next few sections. This whole subject of spectroscopy is taken up in general terms as part of Chap. 13, and it will be found that some of the ideas presented there will be more quickly appreciated with the aid of the preliminary background provided by the specific results of the present chapter.

12-2 Classical Model of the Gaseous Discharge The first step in reducing the ideas of the last section to classical formulation is to assume that the atoms are Lorentz atoms containing elastically bound electrons. In the unexcited state the electrons are at rest with respect to the nucleus, but the whole atom may be in motion due to thermal agitation. The process of excitation through inelastic collisions with electrons must be introduced in a phenomenological way, since the Lorentz theory says nothing about the details of such encounters. The assumption is that an atom receives an impulsive blow which leaves one or more electrons displaced from their equilibrium positions, moving with some set of initial velocities relative to the nucleus. Thereafter the electrons vibrate in close analogy with the prong of a tuning fork, except that since the elastic binding of an electron is isotropic about the equilibrium position (that is, the binding force is independent of the direction of the displacement), its oscillation will in general be other than linear and will turn out to be elliptical.

The voltage applied to the tube defines a preferred direction in the discharge, and one might expect that the elliptical paths of the electrons should be taken to have a preferred orientation. The result would be a polarization of the radiation, but no more than a very slight polarization is ever observed, and so it will be assumed that the planes of the ellipses and the directions of the principal axes fall at random. All eccentricities will be assumed equally probable. Finally, the initial amplitude of oscillation can be taken to fall in a range according to some probability law. The classical theory cannot be specific even about the upper limit of the possible amplitudes, but let it be assumed for the sake of a comfortable picture that an electron is to remain within the accepted volume of an atom—of order 10^{-8} cm radius. It will be seen that assumptions concerning amplitude play no essential role.

Once an electron is set into oscillation, it will radiate according to the laws of dipole radiation. The energy radiated must be compensated by a gradual reduction to zero of the amplitude of oscillation. It will turn out that the oscillation lasts only a very short time, and yet this interval includes a very large number of oscillations, and the emitted wave is therefore almost monochromatic. The exact departure from monochromaticity will be an important question, but it is so small as to be very difficult to observe.

The frequency of the wave emitted by a given electron depends on the mass of the electron and the stiffness of its binding. A value can be assigned to the stiffness only as an *ad hoc* assumption which makes the frequency of oscillation correspond to that of some spectrum line observed to come from the discharge. To follow up this idea and reconstruct an entire atomic spectrum with its infinite number of lines would require assuming an infinite number of electrons with appropriate stiffnesses. To anticipate some points in the final chapter, the quantum theory yields formulas, formally identical to the classical ones, according to which an atom can be regarded in classical terms except that each oscillator has associated with it only a certain fraction of an electron such that the sum of all the fractions equals the actual number of electrons in the atom. These points will not concern us here, and any required number of electrons will be assumed. For the most part the arguments will deal with hypothetical spectra involving only one or a few lines, since the important results will be the spectral distributions in individual lines.

The calculation of the spectrum of a line will begin with the simplifying assumption that the radiating atoms are stationary. The results will be refined in Secs. 12-7 and 12-8 by taking into account the thermal motions of the atoms and the effects of collisions when the pressure is high.

12-3 Equation of Motion and Its Solution This section will deal with the motion of an electron in an atom whose nucleus is at rest. The motion of the electron is governed by Newton's law, which sets the product of the mass of the electron and its acceleration equal to the sum of all the forces acting on the electron. If $s(t)$ is the vector from the nucleus to the instantaneous position of the electron, then according to the Lorentz model, one of the forces is an elastic binding force $-k\mathbf{s}$, where k is a constant of proportionality. In addition there may be a force $\mathbf{F}_e(t)$ arising from causes external to the atom. On first thought one would then write the equation of motion

$$m\ddot{\mathbf{s}} = -k\mathbf{s} + \mathbf{F}_e \qquad (12\text{-}1)$$

This cannot be the complete equation, as will now be shown.

Suppose the external force results from an impulsive blow occurring at $t = 0$, of such a nature that immediately after it the electron has some displacement $\mathbf{s}(0)$ and some velocity $\dot{\mathbf{s}}(0)$. Starting with these initial conditions, the motion during all positive times must satisfy the homogeneous equation

$$\ddot{\mathbf{s}} + \omega_0{}^2\mathbf{s} = 0 \qquad (12\text{-}2)$$

where $\omega_0{}^2 = k/m$. The general solution of (12-2) is the sinusoidal motion

$$\mathbf{s}(t) = \mathbf{A}\cos\omega_0 t + \mathbf{B}\sin\omega_0 t \qquad (12\text{-}3)$$

where $\mathbf{A}$ and $\mathbf{B}$ are constant vectors determined by the initial conditions; in fact, $\mathbf{A} = \mathbf{s}(0)$ and $\mathbf{B} = \dot{\mathbf{s}}(0)/\omega_0$. That is (compare Sec. 2-3), the solution is in general an elliptical motion with constant amplitude. The solution can equally well be given in the complex representation

$$\mathbf{s}(t) = \mathbf{s}_0 e^{-i\omega_0 t} \qquad (12\text{-}4)$$

where $\mathbf{s}_0 = \mathbf{A} + i\mathbf{B}$. (By earlier convention the same symbol $\mathbf{s}$ will stand for either the real displacement or its complex representation.) Now the electron will radiate energy at the rate given by (5-18) and, according to the solution obtained, will do so forever without compensating energy being supplied to the atom, which is physically absurd.

The conclusion is that (12-1) is not the complete equation of motion, and the fact is that there is an additional force $\mathbf{F}_r$, called the *radiation reaction*, given by

$$\mathbf{F}_r = \frac{2e^2}{3c^3}\frac{d}{dt}\ddot{\mathbf{s}} \qquad (12\text{-}5)$$

Before we discuss this force, note that it is proportional to e^2 (therefore independent of the sign of the charge) and to the rate of change of acceleration (therefore to the *third* time derivative of $\mathbf{s}$).

The question of radiation reaction is one of the most difficult in the theory of electrons. The expression (12-5) was obtained directly from the Maxwell equations (3-1) to (3-5) by Lorentz, but his calculation, which is very involved and will not be reproduced here, raises side questions which are still the subject of investigation and which persist in the quantum theory. Two references on the subject which the reader should certainly plan to study eventually are Heitler [37], chap. 1, sec. 4, and Wheeler and Feynman [97]. (Some optical ideas in the second reference are covered later in this book.) To these references should be added the paper by Plass [72] which discusses some interesting general consequences of adding (12-5) to the equation of motion.[1] As a last reference, see Rohrlich [77].

The significance of (12-5), irrespective of how one comes to understand it, is that when a small charged particle (which can even be taken in the limit as a point particle) executes some accelerated motion, it radiates an electromagnetic wave. Through some mechanism this process of radiation results in a force of reaction on the particle, given by (12-5). While formulas (11-40) and (11-41) show that there is a radiated wave whenever the acceleration is different from zero, there is a force of reaction only when the acceleration is changing. Since the need for some additional term in the equation of motion was inferred from the failure of conservation of energy, parts of later calculations will be devoted to showing that the assumption of (12-5) does lead to conservation of energy in cases to arise.

Taking (12-5) to be the term that completes the equation of motion, and returning to the problem of an electron left in an excited state at $t = 0$, the motion during positive times is governed by

$$\frac{d^2\mathbf{s}}{dt^2} + \omega_0^2\mathbf{s} - \frac{2e^2}{3mc^3}\frac{d^3\mathbf{s}}{dt^3} = 0 \tag{12-6}$$

The general solution, obtained by the standard method found in any elementary text on differential equations, is

$$\mathbf{s} = \mathbf{C}_1 e^{\xi_1 t} + \mathbf{C}_2 e^{\xi_2 t} + \mathbf{C}_3 e^{\xi_3 t} \tag{12-7}$$

where the $\mathbf{C}$'s are constant vectors to be chosen to fit the physical conditions, and the ξ's are the three roots of

$$\xi^2 + \omega_0^2 - \frac{2e^2}{3mc^3}\xi^3 = 0 \tag{12-8}$$

This equation, which is commonly called the *characteristic equation*, is related to (12-6) in the obvious way.

---

[1] It should be emphasized that the full contents of these three references are not suggested for immediate reading on the level of the present book, yet some of the qualitative discussions and summaries contained in them will be found to give at least some feeling for the problem and the various ways in which it has been treated.

In Fig. 12-2 the solid curve is a qualitative plot of the left side of (12-8) as a function of ξ. (The three dashed curves represent the terms that must be added together.) This curve shows that the characteristic equation has only one real root, and it is positive. Since the coefficients are real, the two complex roots must be conjugates of each other, by a theorem of algebra. The real root, let it be ξ_3, would lead to an exponentially increasing term in the solution, and hence the coefficient C_3 must be zero on physical grounds.

The complex roots can be found to sufficient accuracy by a process of successive approximations. Such a process leads quickly to usable values because the coefficient of ξ^3 in (12-8) has the small value of about 6×10^{-24}; hence the cubic term has only a small effect on the roots. (The physical equivalent is that the radiation reaction is small compared with the sum of the forces of inertia and binding appearing in the equation of motion, as will be seen.) The first approximation is obtained by neglecting the cubic

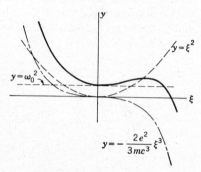

Fig. 12-2. *Qualitative plot of the function on the left of Eq. (12-8). The dashed curves represent the three separate terms in this function. Their sum is the solid curve.*

term in (12-8). The result is $\xi_1^{(1)} = i\omega_0$, $\xi_2^{(1)} = -i\omega_0$. The next approximation to ξ_1 is obtained by substituting $\xi_1^{(1)}$ for the ξ in the cubic term and solving the resulting quadratic equation to obtain

$$\xi_1^{(2)} = \left(-\omega_0^2 - i\,\frac{2e^2}{3mc^3}\,\omega_0^3\right)^{1/2} = i\omega_0\left(1 + \frac{i\gamma}{\omega_0}\right)^{1/2}$$

where γ, which will assume special significance, is defined by

$$\gamma = \frac{2e^2\omega_0^2}{3mc^3} \tag{12-9}$$

The correction in the second approximation appears in the quantity γ/ω_0, which is only of order 10^{-8} for visible light and increases only linearly with ω_0. Higher approximations bring in corrections involving higher powers of γ/ω_0. Hence at all frequencies of interest to us, the second approximation is certainly adequate and can be written

$$\xi_1^{(2)} \approx i\omega_0\left(1 + \frac{i\gamma}{2\omega_0}\right) = -\frac{\gamma}{2} + i\omega_0$$

The root ξ_2 is then the complex conjugate.

Substitute these roots in (12-7) and use Euler's formula; the solution takes the final form

$$\mathbf{s} = (\mathbf{A} \cos \omega_0 t + \mathbf{B} \sin \omega_0 t)e^{-\gamma t/2} \qquad (12\text{-}10)$$

where $\mathbf{A}$ and $\mathbf{B}$ are again constant vectors which must be chosen such that $\mathbf{s}$ and $\dot{\mathbf{s}}$ have given values at $t = 0$. The solution is similar to (12-3) and represents an elliptical spiral which converges exponentially to the equilibrium position as the atom radiates. The beginning of this motion is shown in Fig. 12-3a, although the rate of spiraling in is greatly

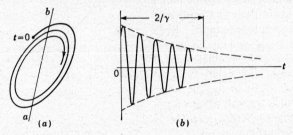

Fig. 12-3. **a.** *Elliptical spiral described by an electron which is suddenly excited at $t = 0$.* **b.** *Projection of the instantaneous position of the electron onto the line ab as a function of time. The decrease in amplitude per cycle is greatly exaggerated.*

exaggerated, as will be seen presently. If the motion is projected onto any line such as ab, it generates a function of time shown in Fig. 12-3b. The ordinates of the dashed envelope are proportional to the exponential function $e^{-\gamma t/2}$. A motion that decays in this exponential fashion is said to be a *damped oscillation*. A similar motion occurs in the case of a freely swinging pendulum subject to the friction of the air, although in this case the damping enters the equation of motion through a term proportional to the first derivative of the displacement, rather than the third.

As a measure of the rate of decay of the motion, we can take the time required for the factor $e^{-\gamma t/2}$ to decrease from its initial value of unity to the value $1/e$. This time is $2/\gamma$, which for frequencies of visible light is of order 10^{-8} sec and varies as ω_0^{-2}. The number of cycles occurring in this time is $(\omega_0/2\pi)(2/\gamma)$, which for visible light is of order 10^7 and varies as ω_0^{-1}. Thus the motion decays very rapidly, but because of the smallness of the period of oscillation compared with the characteristic time $2/\gamma$, the fractional decrease in amplitude in one cycle is very small (see Prob. 12-2), and the motion is really very close to monochromatic. The forces of inertia and binding are the major determinants of the motion, and the radiation reaction has only a comparatively small (but not unimportant) effect.

12-4 Radiated Fields and Energy The motion of the electron is described by (12-10) for $t > 0$; for $t < 0$ the electron is at rest in the equilibrium position $s = 0$. The electric and magnetic fields in the wave zone are found by substitution in (11-40) and (11-41). Since only the linear operation of differentiation is involved, it is permissible and simplest to use the complex representation

$$s = s_0 e^{-(\gamma/2 + i\omega_0)t} \qquad t > 0 \qquad (12\text{-}11)$$

where $s_0 = A + iB$. With approximations allowable because of the smallness of γ/ω_0 in comparison with unity,

$$\ddot{s} \approx -\omega_0^2 s_0 e^{-(\gamma/2 + i\omega_0)t}$$

and the complex representations of the fields are

$$e = \frac{e\omega_0^2}{c^2 r} \, \hat{r} \times (\hat{r} \times s_0) e^{-\gamma(t - r/c)/2} e^{i(k_0 r - \omega_0 t)}$$

$$(12\text{-}12)$$

$$b = -\frac{e\omega_0^2}{c^2 r} \, \hat{r} \times s_0 e^{-\gamma(t - r/c)/2} e^{i(k_0 r - \omega_0 t)}$$

where $k_0 = \omega_0/c$. These formulas represent the fields only for $t > r/c$, and the fields are zero for $t < r/c$. That is, the atom begins to emit at $t = 0$, but the wave first appears at a distance r only after it has had time to propagate through this distance with velocity c.

The geometrical interpretation of the fields (12-12) is essentially the same as in Sec. 5-4. Consider a point P at distance r in the direction of the unit vector $\hat{r}$, and let the real field e at P be represented by an arrow beginning at P. Then the end point of this arrow describes an elliptical spiral which begins at $t = r/c$, lies in the plane perpendicular to $\hat{r}$, and converges exponentially to P. This spiral is identical, except for scale, to the projection of the spiral motion of the electron onto a plane perpendicular to $\hat{r}$. (In particular, if $\hat{r}$ lies in the plane of motion of the electron, the electric vector executes a damped linear oscillation.) The arrow representing b describes the same spiral as e except for its being rotated through 90° about the axis $\hat{r}$ in the sense which makes $e \times b$ point in the direction of $\hat{r}$. At all times e and b have the same magnitude (a special feature of the gaussian units, be it recalled) and are perpendicular to each other, exactly as in the monochromatic case illustrated in Fig. 5-11.

To calculate the Poynting vector averaged over any given cycle, it is permissible to use (5-14). Strictly speaking, this formula applies only to undamped sinusoidal waves, and the correct procedure is to evaluate (4-7), using the real damped fields, and average over any desired cycle. When this is done, and certain terms neglected because of the smallness of γ/ω_0, the result is just that given by (5-14). Another view of the matter is that the fractional decrease of amplitude in one cycle is so small as to be negligible in calculating $\langle \mathbf{S} \rangle$ for that cycle. We thus have

$$\langle \mathbf{S} \rangle = \frac{e^2 \omega_0^4}{8\pi c^3 r^2} \left[(\hat{\mathbf{r}} \times \mathbf{A})^2 + (\hat{\mathbf{r}} \times \mathbf{B})^2 \right] e^{-\gamma(t-r/c)} \hat{\mathbf{r}} \qquad (12\text{-}13)$$

Again, this formula applies only for $t > r/c$. The total power passing through a sphere of radius r averaged over one cycle is given by the same calculation as led to (5-18) and is

$$P = \frac{e^2 \omega_0^4}{3c^3} (A^2 + B^2) e^{-\gamma(t-r/c)} \qquad (12\text{-}14)$$

Note that both $\langle \mathbf{S} \rangle$ and P decrease exponentially and fall by a factor $1/e$ in the time

$$\tau = \frac{1}{\gamma} \qquad (12\text{-}15)$$

(In contrast, the amplitudes of the fields require a time 2τ to reduce by a factor $1/e$.) This time τ is called the *lifetime* of the excited state of the atom. Its magnitude is of order 10^{-8} sec for frequencies in the visible range and varies as $1/\omega_0^2$ or as λ^2. It will be seen in the final chapter of this book that in the quantum theory a lifetime is defined in a very similar way, and its magnitude is in remarkable agreement with the classical value.

The question of whether or not energy is conserved in the radiation process can be investigated in various ways. The simplest is to calculate the total energy W carried away by the radiation and to compare it with the sum of the kinetic and potential energies of excitation of the electron immediately after the exciting impulse. Integrating (12-14) from $t = r/c$ to $t = \infty$ and using (12-9) gives

$$W = \tfrac{1}{2} m \omega_0^2 (A^2 + B^2)$$

The kinetic energy of excitation is

$$T = \tfrac{1}{2} m \, \dot{\mathbf{s}}(0)^2 = \tfrac{1}{2} m \omega_0^2 B^2$$

The potential energy is

$$V = \tfrac{1}{2} k \, \mathbf{s}(0)^2 = \tfrac{1}{2} m \omega_0^2 A^2$$

where k is, of course, the constant of the binding force, and not the wave number. We thus have the balance $W = T + V$; that is, all the energy of excitation imparted to the atom is ultimately converted into radiant energy.

12-5 Spectrum of the Radiation This section will treat a situation in which a stationary atom is excited once and emits a damped wave. At a point P in the wave zone a certain total energy will arrive per unit area. By means of Fourier analysis this flux density of energy will be broken into a distribution over frequencies, this distribution being the *energy spectrum* of the wave.

It will be convenient to refer the problem to cartesian coordinates with the atom at the origin and the point P on the z axis. Let the origin of the time scale be adjusted such that the wave first appears at P at time $t = 0$. For times $t > 0$ the components of the real fields at P are then of the form

$$e_x = Ce^{-\gamma t/2} \cos (\omega_0 t - \theta)$$
$$e_y = De^{-\gamma t/2} \cos (\omega_0 t - \phi) \qquad (12\text{-}16)$$
$$e_z = 0 \qquad b_x = -e_y \qquad b_y = e_x \qquad b_z = 0$$

The constants C, D, θ, and ϕ are related to the components of **A** and **B** appearing in (12-10) and specifying the motion of the electron, but for deriving the shape of the spectrum it is not necessary to carry along these complicated relations, and C, D, θ, and ϕ can be regarded as a new set of arbitrary constants.

The total flux density of energy w at P can be found by integrating the z component of the Poynting vector:

$$w = \int_{-\infty}^{\infty} S_z \, dt = \frac{c}{4\pi} \int_{-\infty}^{\infty} (e_x{}^2 + e_y{}^2) \, dt$$

The second form of the integral comes from (4-7), (1-15), and (12-16). Let $V_x(\omega)$ and $V_y(\omega)$ be the Fourier transforms of e_x and e_y, respectively. Then by Parseval's theorem and symmetry of the type of (11-5),

$$w = \frac{c}{2\pi} \int_0^{\infty} [|V_x(\omega)|^2 + |V_y(\omega)|^2] \, d\omega$$

The flux density of energy has thus been written as an integral over positive frequencies of the form

$$w = \int_0^{\infty} \mathcal{S}(\omega) \, d\omega \qquad (12\text{-}17)$$

where

$$\mathcal{S}(\omega) = \frac{c}{2\pi} [|V_x(\omega)|^2 + |V_y(\omega)|^2] \qquad \omega \geqq 0 \qquad (12\text{-}18)$$

The function $\mathcal{S}(\omega)$ defined by the right side of (12-18) is called the *theoretical energy spectrum* of the wave arriving at P, and as suggested by the form of (12-17), its physical significance is that it *equals the energy arriving at the observing point per unit area per unit frequency interval*.[1] In the next chapter this physical interpretation of $\mathcal{S}$ will be strengthened by showing how it can be measured with a spectrograph, or rather it will

---

[1] An important point in connection with the definition of spectra is made in Prob. 12-6.

be shown how a spectrograph yields an *observed spectrum* that can be compared with the theoretical.

In calculating the transforms of (12-16), the simplest procedure is to express the cosines in terms of exponentials. The limits of the integral are zero and infinity, and the transform of $e_x(t)$ is easily shown to be

$$V_x(\omega) = \frac{C}{2\sqrt{2\pi}} \left[\frac{e^{-i\theta}}{\gamma/2 - i(\omega + \omega_0)} + \frac{e^{i\theta}}{\gamma/2 - i(\omega - \omega_0)} \right] \quad (12\text{-}19)$$

The same formula with C replaced by D, and θ by ϕ, gives $V_y(\omega)$. It will be seen in a moment that the condition $\gamma \ll \omega_0$ carries the implication

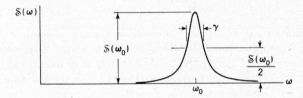

Fig. 12-4. *Theoretical energy spectrum for a single emission from a stationary Lorentz atom. In cases of actual interest the ratio γ/ω_0 is much smaller than shown in this figure.*

that the modulus of either transform consists of two narrow peaks centered at ω_0 and $-\omega_0$, the situation being analogous to Fig. 11-3. Then in calculating $|V_x(\omega)|^2$ for positive ω, only the second term in (12-19) need be considered; the same applies to the y component. The spectrum is therefore

$$S(\omega) = \frac{c}{16\pi^2} (C^2 + D^2) \frac{1}{(\omega - \omega_0)^2 + \gamma^2/4} \quad (12\text{-}20)$$

For purposes of discussing the shape of the spectrum, let this result be written

$$S(\omega) = S(\omega_0) \frac{\gamma^2/4}{(\omega - \omega_0)^2 + \gamma^2/4} \quad (12\text{-}21)$$

A plot of (12-21) is shown in Fig. 12-4. It is easily verified that the width of the peak at half-maximum is γ, which is very small compared with ω_0 (much smaller than indicated in the figure), and the earlier remark as to the nature of the transforms is valid. It is usual to refer to the curve in Fig. 12-4 as a *resonance profile* or as a *Lorentz profile* and to speak of the denominator in (12-21) as a *resonance denominator*. Note that far out in the wings of the profile the ordinates fall off as $1/(\omega - \omega_0)^2$, since the term $\gamma^2/4$ in the resonance denominator is effective only near the resonant frequency ω_0. Note also the reciprocal relationship (12-15) between the width γ and the lifetime τ, a most important example of the general reciprocal relationship between the width of a function and the width of its transform pointed out several times in Chap. 11.

12-6 Spectrum in the Case of Many Emissions   The next step in developing the classical theory of a gaseous discharge is to suppose that a large number of atoms in the source undergo excitations at a random sequence of instants. Let it be assumed that all the atoms are identical and that each contains just one electron free to oscillate, the resonant frequency being ω_0. The source is *steady* in the sense that if a temporal interval of given duration is long enough to include many excitations, then except for negligible fluctuations the sum of all the energies of excitation absorbed by the atoms during this interval is independent of the time at which the interval begins. According to classical notions, the energy of a single excitation is determined only to the extent that it falls in a range according to a probability distribution. If an interval of observation is long enough to include a good statistical sample of the excitations, then the number of them as well as the total energy will be essentially independent of the time at which the interval begins.

In this section we shall continue to impose the restriction that the atoms are stationary; it will be assumed further that they are far enough apart (that is, that the density of the gas is low enough) that a wave emitted by any one atom induces negligible motion of electrons in neighboring atoms. Under this assumption the total emitted wave is the superposition of waves from individual atoms; an individual wave is the same as it would be if the atom emitting it were alone in space. (The subject of induced motions will be taken up in the chapter on scattering.) Finally, it will be assumed that the excitations result in all types of spiral motions of the electrons and all orientations of the plane of the motion, without preference. An immediate consequence is that on averaging over many emissions, a volume of the gas radiates equally in all directions. Another consequence, which will not be fully investigated until the next chapter, is that the radiation is unpolarized.

Consider now a point of observation P which is far enough from the source that the latter subtends only a small solid angle as seen from P; then the individual waves arrive at P traveling in essentially the same direction. Let this direction define the positive z axis of a cartesian system. Let a screen just in front of P contain a shutter which opens at time $t = 0$ and closes at $t = T$. A certain number N of elementary waves of the type (12-16) will arrive at P, but they will begin at the random sequence of instants

$$0 < t_1 < \cdots < t_j < \cdots t_N < T$$

It will be assumed that T is very large compared with the lifetime of excitation τ. For example, T may be seconds or longer, while τ may be of order 10^{-8} sec. As a further assumption, take N to be very large.

The components of the electric field of the jth wave are

$$
\begin{aligned}
\mathrm{e}_{jx} &= C_j e^{-\gamma(t-t_j)/2} \cos\left[\omega_0(t - t_j) - \theta_j\right] \\
\mathrm{e}_{jy} &= D_j e^{-\gamma(t-t_j)/2} \cos\left[\omega_0(t - t_j) - \phi_j\right]
\end{aligned}
\tag{12-22}
$$

for $t_j < t < T$ and zero outside this interval. The phase angles θ_j and ϕ_j fall at random in the range zero to 2π. The initial amplitudes C_j and D_j fall in some positive range according to some probability distribution which must be the same for both C_j and D_j because of the isotropic nature assumed for the excitation, but the details of this distribution will turn out to be unimportant.

The Fourier transform of the x component of the resultant electric field at P is

$$
V_x(\omega) = \sum_{j=1}^{N} V_{jx}(\omega)
$$

where $V_{jx}(\omega)$ is the transform of e_{jx}. To derive the spectrum we need $|V_x(\omega)|^2$ at positive frequencies, and this quantity is

$$
|V_x(\omega)|^2 = \frac{1/8\pi}{(\omega - \omega_0)^2 + \gamma^2/4} \left| \sum_{j=1}^{N} C_j \, e^{i(\omega t_j + \theta_j)} \right|^2
\tag{12-23}
$$

[In applying the general formula for finding $V_{jx}(\omega)$, first express the cosine in terms of exponentials, and then multiply and divide the integrand by $e^{i\omega t_j}$ so that the integration can be performed with respect to the variable $x = t - t_j$ with limits zero and infinity. Actually, because of the closing of the shutter, the upper limit should be $T - t_j$, but for almost all the elementary waves this quantity is large enough compared with $1/\gamma$ to be effectively infinite, so that all but a negligible fraction of the waves will have decayed practically to zero by the time T.]

Attention must now be given to the factor

$$
\left| \sum_{j=1}^{N} C_j \, e^{i(\omega t_j + \theta_j)} \right|^2
\tag{12-24}
$$

The sum is very similar to the sum (7-21) arising in the problem of the random array of diffracting apertures, the new feature being that the moduli C_j of the complex terms are not all equal. The theory of the two-dimensional random walk can be applied by drawing a vector diagram analogous to Fig. 7-26 for any given value of ω and then redrawing it many times with new sets of random values assigned to the t_j and θ_j and new values assigned to the C_j according to the probability law governing these quantities. Kennard [54], p. 271, gives the argument applying to this generalized case, and the result is that if ρ denotes the modulus of the sum for any one set of parameters, so that (12-24) equals ρ^2, then the probability of finding ρ between the values ρ and $\rho + d\rho$ is the following slight modification of (7-23):

$$P_\rho \, d\rho = \frac{2}{Nl^2} \, \rho \, e^{-\rho^2/(Nl^2)} \, d\rho \tag{12-25}$$

where l^2 is the average of the squares of the C's; that is, if N is large enough to include a good statistical sample,

$$l^2 = \frac{1}{N} \sum_{j=1}^{N} C_j^2 = [C^2]_{\text{av}} \tag{12-26}$$

By the same calculations as those below (7-23),

$$[\rho^2]_{\text{av}} = Nl^2 \tag{12-27}$$

and

$$\Delta(\rho^2) = [\rho^2]_{\text{av}} \tag{12-28}$$

The first result gives the statistical average of (12-24), and the second shows that the standard deviation of this factor from its average is just equal to the average itself, regardless of how large N may be.

These statistical considerations, *which refer to a fixed value of* ω, can be applied to give the qualitative behavior of (12-24) when the C_j, t_j, and θ_j have given values and ω varies. In the vector diagram representing the sum, the angle between the jth and kth vectors is

$$\omega(t_j - t_k) + \theta_j - \theta_k \tag{12-29}$$

Since T is very large compared with $1/\gamma$, practically all the differences $t_j - t_k$ are very large compared with $1/\gamma$, and if ω changes by an amount that may even be quite small compared with γ, the angle (12-29) will undergo a change of many radians. This change is different for different pairs of vectors, and hence the angles of the summands in (12-24) rapidly pass from one random set to a different and essentially uncorrelated set. The resulting fluctuations of (12-24) are therefore of the same magnitude as the statistical fluctuations just found, and a plot of (12-23) has the appearance of Fig. 12-5. The same curve, with the fluctuations differing in their fine details, represents the component $|V_y(\omega)|^2$, and the spectrum (12-18) therefore also has the appearance of Fig. 12-5. This behavior of the spectrum is analogous to the mottling in the diffraction pattern of the random array (Sec. 7-16).

When the capabilities of the best spectrographs are considered in the next chapter, it will be seen that it is just possible to measure a spectrum of the shape shown in Fig. 12-4 with γ/ω_0 as small as 10^{-8}, but it is certainly out of the question to observe the very fine fluctuations in Fig. 12-5. For practical purposes it is therefore appropriate to take as the theoretical energy spectrum the result of smoothing out these fluctuations,

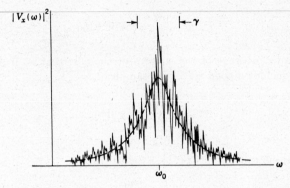

Fig. 12-5. *Qualitative plot of the function (12-23). The dashed curve is the resonance profile resulting from smoothing out the rapid fluctuations.*

which is equivalent to replacing the factor (12-24) by its statistical average (12-27). The result is

$$[\mathcal{S}(\omega)]_{\mathrm{av}} = [\mathcal{S}(\omega_0)]_{\mathrm{av}} \frac{\gamma^2/4}{(\omega - \omega_0)^2 + \gamma^2/4} \tag{12-30}$$

where

$$[\mathcal{S}(\omega_0)]_{\mathrm{av}} = \frac{c}{4\pi^2\gamma^2} \sum_{j=1}^{N} (C_j^2 + D_j^2) \tag{12-31}$$

This smoothed spectrum has a resonance profile and is just the sum of the spectra of the N elementary waves, each considered in the absence of the others.

The total flux density of energy at P during the time the shutter is open is the area under the curve of the spectrum, and as long as T is very large compared with τ and N is very large, this area is the same whether the spectrum is taken to be the true one with its fine fluctuations or the smoothed one. Again there is simple additivity; that is, *the total flux density of energy is the sum of the flux densities due to the elementary waves taken separately.*

With this total flux density of energy denoted by w, integration of (12-30) with respect to ω between the limits $-\infty$ and $+\infty$ (strictly speaking, between zero and $+\infty$, but the integrand is essentially zero at negative frequencies, and changing the lower limit to $-\infty$ has no effect and leads to a standard definite integral) gives

$$w = \frac{c}{8\pi\gamma} \sum_{j=1}^{N} (C_j{}^2 + D_j{}^2) \qquad (12\text{-}32)$$

From (12-30) through (12-32), the smoothed spectrum can be written in terms of w in the form

$$[\mathcal{S}(\omega)]_{\mathrm{av}} = w \frac{\gamma/2\pi}{(\omega - \omega_0)^2 + \gamma^2/4} = w\,\mathcal{L}(\omega - \omega_0;\gamma) \qquad (12\text{-}33)$$

The function $\mathcal{L}(\omega - \omega_0;\gamma)$, defined by (12-33) and called a *resonance function* or a *Lorentz function*, has a curve as shown in Fig. 12-6 (the same

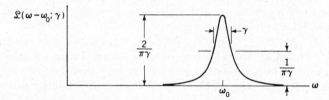

Fig. 12-6. *Normalized resonance function defined by (12-33).* *The area under the curve is unity.*

shape as Fig. 12-4), the width at half-maximum being γ, and it is *normalized* such that the area under the curve is unity. The interpretation of this function as it appears in (12-33) is that it specifies the manner in which the total flux density of energy w is distributed over frequencies.

The forms (12-30) and (12-33) of the smoothed energy spectrum differ only in that the first exhibits explicitly the maximum ordinate, while the second exhibits the area under the curve of the spectrum, this area having the significance of being the total flux density of energy arriving during the time of observation. Each form has its usefulness. Unlike the individual amplitudes C_j and D_j, the quantities $[\mathcal{S}(\omega_0)]_{\mathrm{av}}$ and w are observable, and hence the distribution law for the amplitudes plays no essential role, as stated earlier.

The two statements given above in italics break down as general propositions when N is small. Problem 12-9 gives insight into this matter by calling for a study of the case $N = 2$. Problem 12-10 gives support to the statements made above that when T and N are large, smoothing a given spectrum is equivalent to taking a statistical average and that the area under a given spectrum with its fine fluctuations is the same as the area under the smoothed spectrum. These two problems contain important points that should certainly be looked into. In particular, the replacing of a smoothing operation by statistical averaging over random variables occurs many times in physics. An example was seen earlier in connection with the diffraction pattern of a random array of apertures. Other examples of the greatest importance occur in the smoothing of the complicated temporal functions arising in kinetic theory by the equivalent device of averaging over an ensemble after the methods of J. W. Gibbs. The case in the present section is one of the few that are simple enough that the equivalence can be seen easily.

In the final chapter it will be pointed out that the quantum theory predicts that a line in the spectrum of a large number of emissions from stationary atoms has, after fluctuations are averaged out, the same shape as Fig. 12-4, and for most of the bright lines the width is very near the classical value γ. Moreover, the spectrum is predicted to show fluctuations closely analogous to those indicated in Fig. 12-5, and even quantitatively there is good agreement with the classical theory as long as many emissions are involved.

12-7 Thermal Broadening of Spectrum Lines Atoms never remain at rest with respect to an observer, and their motions are often such as to produce observable optical effects. A vessel containing gas may be stationary, but the individual atoms are subject to thermal agitation. In addition to the random thermal motions there may be a motion of the whole system, an example being a star in rapid motion with respect to the earth; or there may be organized motion of a part of the system containing many atoms, as in the turbulence, prominences, and other mass motions observed in the atmosphere of the sun.

If an atom at rest with respect to the observer emits a wave whose spectrum is narrow and is peaked at frequency ω_0, then, when the atom emits while moving with velocity $\mathbf{v}$ relative to the observer, the spectrum is shifted so that the peak frequency becomes

$$\omega_0' = \omega_0 \left(1 - \frac{\mathbf{v} \cdot \hat{\mathbf{r}}}{c} \right) \tag{12-34}$$

where $\hat{\mathbf{r}}$ is a unit vector in the direction *from the observer to the atom*. Denoting the change $\omega_0' - \omega_0$ by $\Delta\omega$, (12-34) takes the simpler form

$$\frac{\Delta\omega}{\omega_0} = - \frac{\mathbf{v} \cdot \hat{\mathbf{r}}}{c} \tag{12-35}$$

The quantity $\mathbf{v} \cdot \hat{\mathbf{r}}$ is the component of the velocity in the direction $\hat{\mathbf{r}}$ and is usually called the *radial velocity;* if it is positive, the atom is receding from the observer, and the spectrum is shifted to lower frequencies. This shift is called the *Doppler effect* and is the optical analogue of the change of pitch of a whistle that moves rapidly by an observer. Problems 12-12 to 12-14, and the comments therein, give sufficient background on the origin of formula (12-34), and it will be seen in these problems that when v is comparable to c, additional terms proportional to the second and higher powers of v/c must be added, but (12-34) is adequate in the usual case $v \ll c$.

Applications of the Doppler formula to determining radial velocities of sources are especially numerous in astronomy, the most striking examples occurring in the spectra of very distant galaxies. Here a spectrum line that would appear in the blue or ultraviolet with a stationary source appears shifted to the red by an amount that may be 1000 A or more. The shift is attributed to the Doppler effect and in turn to a general expansion of the universe. The application to be made in the rest of this section is to the small shifts resulting from thermal motion of atoms in gaseous discharges. The net effect when many atoms in chaotic motion are considered is a broadening and change in shape of a spectrum line in a way that reveals the temperature of the source.

When a large number of atoms, each of total mass M, are in thermal equilibrium at absolute temperature T, the probability $P(v_z)\, dv_z$ that at a given time any one atom has the z component of velocity between v_z and $v_z + dv_z$ is given by the *maxwellian distribution*

$$P(v_z)\, dv_z = \left(\frac{M}{2\pi kT}\right)^{\!\!1/2} e^{-Mv_z^2/2kT}\, dv_z \tag{12-36}$$

where k is the Boltzmann constant, about 1.38×10^{-16} erg °K^{-1}. This formula is derived in books on the kinetic theory of gases, such as Kennard [54].

Let the atoms have natural frequency ω_0 and be subject to random excitations in a discharge. Suppose that the pressure is low enough that once an atom is excited, there is very little probability that it will suffer a collision with another atom before its vibration decays to a very low amplitude; thus its velocity is constant and its vibration undisturbed during practically all the time of emission. Let the source be at the origin of a cartesian system, and let an observer be located some distance along the positive z axis. Then by the Doppler formula, v_z in (12-36) can be replaced by $c(\omega_0' - \omega_0)/\omega_0$ to give as the probability $P(\omega_0')\, d\omega_0'$ that the wave emitted by an individual atom with resonant frequency ω_0 would be observed to have a spectrum (with the shape shown in Fig. 12-4) whose maximum lies between ω_0' and $\omega_0' + d\omega_0'$

$$P(\omega_0')\, d\omega_0' = \frac{2}{\sqrt{\pi}\,\Lambda} e^{-4(\omega_0'-\omega_0)^2/\Lambda^2}\, d\omega_0' = \mathcal{G}(\omega_0' - \omega_0; \Lambda)\, d\omega_0' \tag{12-37}$$

where
$$\Lambda = \frac{2\omega_0}{c}\left(\frac{2kT}{M}\right)^{\!\!1/2} \tag{12-38}$$

The function $g(\omega_0' - \omega_0; \Delta)$ defined by (12-37) is the normalized gaussian function whose width between "$1/e$ points" is Δ. This relationship is illustrated in Fig. 12-7. Note particularly that the value of Δ given by (12-38), which will turn out to be an observable quantity, is proportional to $(T/M)^{1/2}$, so that with atoms of given mass, a measurement of Δ gives the kinetic temperature of the atoms in the gas. It will be found (see Prob. 12-15) that even with the lightest atoms at any attainable temperature, Δ is a very small fraction of ω_0.

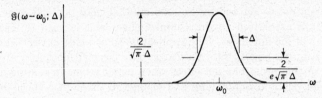

Fig. 12-7. *Normalized gaussian function defined by (12-37). The area under the curve is unity.*

The calculation of the energy spectrum of the superposition of a large number N of elementary waves is the same as in the last section except for a new feature introduced by the thermal motions. The components of the electric field in the jth wave are again given by (12-22), but with ω_0 replaced by the shifted frequency ω_{0j}' given by (12-34) after $-\mathbf{v} \cdot \hat{\mathbf{r}}$ is set equal to the z component of the velocity of the atom emitting this wave. (Recall the sense in which $\hat{\mathbf{r}}$ is defined here, and recall that the observer is in the positive z direction from the source.) Then in (12-23) a common resonance denominator cannot be drawn outside the vertical bars, and we have

$$|V_x(\omega)|^2 = \frac{1}{8\pi} \left| \sum_{j=1}^{N} \frac{C_j e^{i(\omega t_j + \theta_j)}}{(\omega - \omega_{0j}')^2 + \gamma^2/4} \right|^2 \tag{12-39}$$

If we denote (12-39) by ρ^2, the statistical average of this quantity and the standard deviation can be calculated by the theory of the random walk using (12-25), (12-27), and (12-28) if, instead of (12-26), we take

$$l^2 = \frac{1}{8\pi} \left[\frac{C^2}{(\omega - \omega_0')^2 + \gamma^2/4} \right]_{av} \tag{12-40}$$

Now the fluctuations in the amplitude constants C_j are uncorrelated with those of the frequencies ω_{0j}', and it is an elementary principle of statistics that in such a case (12-40) can be written as the product of two statistical averages in the form

$$l^2 = [C^2]_{av} \left[\frac{1/8\pi}{(\omega - \omega_0')^2 + \gamma^2/4} \right]_{av} \tag{12-41}$$

The first average can, if desired, be written in the form of the middle expression in (12-26) as long as N is large enough; that is, the average of the C^2 found in one observation that includes many emissions would not be significantly changed on further averaging over many repetitions of the observation. As in the last section, it is not necessary to know more about this average.

The second average in (12-41) can be found by use of the probability distribution (12-37), this use of a distribution being illustrated in Sec. 7-16. Introduce the resonance function $\mathcal{L}(\omega - \omega'_0; \gamma)$ defined in analogy with (12-33) by

$$\mathcal{L}(\omega - \omega'_0; \gamma) = \frac{\gamma/2\pi}{(\omega - \omega'_0)^2 + \gamma^2/4} \qquad (12\text{-}42)$$

Then we have

$$l^2 = \frac{1}{4\gamma N}\left(\sum_{j=1}^{N} C_j^2\right) \int_{-\infty}^{\infty} P(\omega'_0)\, \mathcal{L}(\omega - \omega'_0; \gamma)\, d\omega'_0$$

and $[|V_x(\omega)|^2]_{\text{av}} = N l^2$. (It is convenient to take the lower limit to be $-\infty$ rather than zero, and it is permissible to do so since both P and $\mathcal{L}$ are essentially zero at negative frequencies.) Adding the analogous result for the y component, substituting in the general formula for the smoothed spectrum, namely,

$$[\mathcal{S}(\omega)]_{\text{av}} = \frac{c}{2\pi}\left[|V_x(\omega)|^2 + |V_y(\omega)|^2\right]_{\text{av}}$$

and finally using (12-32) and (12-37), the smoothed energy spectrum is

$$[\mathcal{S}(\omega)]_{\text{av}} = w \int_{-\infty}^{\infty} \mathcal{G}(\omega'_0 - \omega_0; \Delta)\, \mathcal{L}(\omega - \omega'_0; \gamma)\, d\omega'_0 \qquad (12\text{-}43)$$

In contrast to the case of stationary atoms, for which the spectrum (12-33) is determined by the resonance function $\mathcal{L}$, the spectrum taking into account thermal agitation is determined by the folding integral of $\mathcal{L}$ and the gaussian function $\mathcal{G}$. Since both these functions are normalized, it is easily seen that the integral of (12-43) over all frequencies ω is equal to w (interchange the order of integration with respect to ω and ω'_0), so that w still has the significance of being the total flux density of energy, a fact that is also evident on physical grounds.

We have now to look into the shape of the spectrum. In any low-pressure gaseous discharge only one case arises, namely, that in which the width Δ of the gaussian function $\mathcal{G}$ is orders of magnitude greater than the width γ of the resonance function $\mathcal{L}$. The numerical examples in Prob. 12-15 will bear out this point. With this great disparity of widths, the first factor in the integrand in (12-43) is practically constant at the value $\mathcal{G}(\omega - \omega_0; \Delta)$ over the range of values of ω'_0 for which the second factor is appreciably different from zero. The first factor can then be taken outside the integral, and because of the normalization of $\mathcal{L}$, the spectrum becomes

$$[\mathcal{S}(\omega)]_{\mathrm{av}} \approx w \, \mathcal{G}(\omega - \omega_0; \Delta) \tag{12-44}$$

The effect of thermal motions in a gaseous discharge is to change the spectrum from the very narrow resonance profile shown in Fig. 12-4 to a much wider gaussian profile whose shape and width are shown in Fig. 12-7. Lines in the spectra of low-density gaseous discharges that are free of turbulence and other mass motions are always wide enough to be observed, and they show the gaussian profile. In principle, the spectrum still has fine fluctuations showing large excursions of the type indicated in Fig. 12-5, but they are not resolved by spectrographs.

12-8   Pressure Broadening of Spectrum Lines   When the pressure in a gaseous discharge is high, the atoms are so close together and collide so often that there is a significant effect on the time dependence of the emitted wave, and hence on the spectrum. The classical theory is unable to treat these effects in any way other than to make plausible hypotheses. A theory developed mainly by Lorentz takes as its first assumption that the influence on an oscillating atom during a collision is of very short duration compared with the lifetime τ and can therefore be treated as an essentially instantaneous impulse. The second assumption is that a collision changes the phase angle of the oscillation by an amount falling at random between zero and 2π. The third assumption is that with some types of atoms the amplitude of the oscillation is not changed by a collision, but with other types the amplitude drops suddenly to zero, and the energy of excitation existing at the time of collision is added to the kinetic energy of the colliding atoms, such encounters being called *collisions of the second kind.* The third assumption means that with some types of atoms all the energy of excitation absorbed by collision with electrons is converted into radiation, but with others this conversion has a certain efficiency that decreases as the pressure increases. Such reduction of efficiency is known to occur, and the phenomenon is called *quenching of radiation.* It is best studied as an aspect of scattering. In the case of emission, the shape of the spectrum, as distinct from its absolute intensity, is the same whether quenching occurs or not.

The calculation of the smoothed energy spectrum taking into account collisions as well as thermal motions is only an extension of the last section in that no new principles of averaging are involved. An additional averaging is required, since the time between two successive collisions suffered by a given atom enters, and this is a fluctuating quantity for which a complete characterization is given by the kinetic theory of gases. The algebra becomes rather lengthy, and the details are relegated to Appendix D. In this section the problem will be described briefly, and the results discussed.

At a point of observation P, that contribution to the resultant electric field that comes from an excited atom executing undisturbed oscillations during the interval between two successive collisions is given by (12-22). This contribution begins at P at the time t_j and ends at the time $t_j + \tau_{cj}$, where τ_{cj} is the interval between the two collisions. If the atom has a component of radial velocity during the time it gives rise to this contribution, then ω_0 in (12-22) must be replaced by the shifted frequency ω'_{0j} given by the Doppler formula. The resultant field is a superposition of a very large number of these truncated damped oscillations, and the new feature added to those of the last two sections is the fluctuation of the intervals τ_{cj}. The smoothed spectrum is found by taking the statistical average over all the fluctuating quantities C_j, D_j, θ_j, ϕ_j, ω'_{0j}, t_j, and τ_{cj}, making full use of the fact that all these quantities fluctuate independently of each other. To average over τ_{cj}, it is necessary to know the probability $P(\tau_c)\,d\tau_c$ that the interval of time between two collisions falls between τ_c and $\tau_c + d\tau_c$. The kinetic theory of gases gives this probability as

$$P(\tau_c)\,d\tau_c = \frac{1}{a}\,e^{-\tau_c/a}\,d\tau_c \qquad (12\text{-}45)$$

where a is a constant equal to the statistical average of τ_c:

$$a = [\tau_c]_{\text{av}} \qquad (12\text{-}46)$$

[This fact is seen by multiplying (12-45) by τ_c and integrating from zero to infinity.]

The final result, calculated in Appendix D, is that the smoothed energy spectrum is

$$[\mathcal{S}(\omega)]_{\text{av}} = w \int_{-\infty}^{\infty} \mathcal{G}(\omega'_0 - \omega_0; \Delta)\,\mathcal{L}(\omega - \omega'_0; \Gamma)\,d\omega'_0 \qquad (12\text{-}47)$$

That is, the distribution over frequencies ω of the total flux density of energy w at the point of observation is again given by the folding integral of the gaussian $\mathcal{G}$ [whose width is Δ given by (12-38)] and the resonance function $\mathcal{L}$, which differs from that in (12-43) by having a different width Γ between half-maximum points. This width turns out to be

$$\Gamma = \gamma + \frac{2}{[\tau_c]_{\text{av}}} = \gamma + \gamma_c \qquad (12\text{-}48)$$

where γ is the natural width (12-9) and γ_c is the additional width due to collisions. It is clear that collisions will have an observable effect on the spectrum only when $[\tau_c]_{\text{av}}$ is so much shorter than the natural lifetime $\tau = 1/\gamma$ that the width Γ becomes at least comparable with the thermal width Δ.

To see what values of Γ are possible, it is necessary to resort again to the kinetic theory for a relation between $[\tau_c]_{av}$ and the pressure, temperature, and size of an atom. This relation, expressed as the "collision width," is

$$\gamma_c = \frac{2}{[\tau_c]_{av}} = \frac{8 \sqrt{\pi} \, D^2 p}{(MkT)^{1/2}} \qquad (12\text{-}49)$$

where p is the pressure, D is the diameter of an atom, M is the mass of an atom, T is the absolute temperature of the gas, and k is the Boltzmann constant. When these quantities are expressed in cgs units, the pressure is in dynes per square centimeter. It is more convenient to express the pressure in millimeters of mercury or in atmospheres, the relations being

$$p \ (\text{dyne cm}^{-2}) = 1.33 \times 10^3 p \ (\text{mm Hg}) = 1.01 \times 10^6 p \ (\text{atm})$$

Pressures of practical interest range from a small fraction of a millimeter of mercury to many atmospheres, and numerical examples, with the diameter of an atom taken to be about 10^{-8} cm, show that one encounters conditions all the way from $\gamma_c \ll \gamma$ to $\gamma_c \gg \Delta$. In the former extreme, which can obtain in ordinary Geissler tubes, effects of collisions are completely negligible, and the spectrum shows only thermal broadening. In the latter extreme the argument used in the last section to get (12-44) gives the shape of a spectrum dominated by collisional broadening as

$$[\mathcal{S}(\omega)]_{av} = w \, \mathcal{L}(\omega - \omega_0; \Gamma) \qquad (12\text{-}50)$$

Spectra of this resonance shape are observed to occur, and if T and p are known, as can be the case in some experimental arrangements to be discussed in the chapter on scattering, a measurement of Γ gives a measure of the diameter of an atom, or more correctly, the range of interaction between two atoms.

By "range of interaction" one understands here the distance within which the centers of two atoms must approach each other in order to produce the effects on the oscillations assumed by Lorentz. Experiments show this range to be of order 10^{-8} cm, but to be larger by a factor of 2 or 3 than the range determined from measurements of viscosity, diffusion, etc. The reason for the discrepancy is that different types of physical consequences of a collision are in question in the different measurements. In particular, viscosity depends on encounters being intimate enough to produce significant deflections of path, but observations indicate that a collision contributing to broadening of the spectrum need not involve a close enough approach to give a deflection. The main point is that an atom does not have a definite diameter, but can be assigned various effective diameters by a combination of measurement and theory applied to various physical phenomena in which collisions play a role.

When Γ and Δ in (12-47) are comparable in magnitude, the folding integral cannot be expressed or even well approximated by a simple function of ω and the parameters Γ and Δ. The functions defined by this integral are called *Voigt functions* and are important enough (not only in the present connection, but in others as well) that they have been tabulated and their elegant properties summarized by Van de Hulst and Reesinck [93]. One use of this reference is as follows: Suppose one has observed a spectral profile that can be shown by the method prescribed in the article to fit one of the Voigt functions. Then an auxiliary table

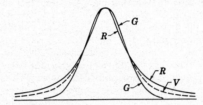

Fig. 12-8. *Comparison of the shapes of the gaussian function G, the resonance function R, and the intermediate Voigt function V for which* $\Gamma = \Delta$.

gives Γ and Δ, so that the degrees of pressure and thermal broadening are obtained separately. The Voigt functions include the gaussian and resonance functions as limiting cases when Δ/Γ is very large and very small, respectively. Figure 12-8 shows the difference in shapes of the gaussian function, the resonance function, and that one of the Voigt functions for which $\Gamma = \Delta$. For purposes of comparison, the curves have been plotted to have equal maxima and equal widths at half-maximum.

Lorentz's theory of pressure broadening, which successfully accounts for the shapes of some observed spectra, is about as far as the classical theory can go on this subject. With some types of discharge the lines in the emitted spectra have shapes and widths that can be deduced theoretically only by appeal to the quantum theory. An important and striking example occurs when a discharge is operated under conditions producing a high density of positive ions. These ions interact with radiating atoms through their electrostatic fields and give rise to a type of perturbation known as the Stark effect. The result can be to broaden a line that occurs, say, in the visible spectrum until it covers 100 A or more, and if the whole spectrum of the source contains many lines, they fuse together to give a continuous spectrum, showing appreciable radiation at all wavelengths. (In contrast, the classical unbroadened width of a line is about 10^{-4}A, as pointed out in Prob. 12-7.)

Problems

12-1. Discuss the solution of Eq. (12-2) along the lines employed in dealing with (12-6). That is, write the equation analogous to (12-8), find its roots, substitute in the equation analogous to (12-7) [which in this case involves only two terms with constant vectors C_1 and C_2, since (12-2) is of only second order], and finally apply Euler's formula to obtain the solution in the form (12-3), but with A and B replaced by certain expressions involving C_1 and C_2. Find C_1 and C_2 (which must be complex) in terms of the initial values $s(0)$ and $\dot{s}(0)$. Make this evaluation twice, once before applying Euler's formula, and again after. The results must, of course, be the same. What relation holds between C_1 and C_2? Show that the final solution is real and identical to (12-3) with the values of A and B stated in connection with that formula. Substitute the solution in (12-2) to show that the equation of motion is indeed satisfied for all times after the exciting impulse. [For this check any form of the solution, such as (12-3), can be used.]

12-2. Referring to the motion depicted in Fig. 12-3a, consider the positions of the electron at the two times t_1 and $t_1 + T$, where t_1 is any time after the motion begins, and T is the period of the oscillation. The displacement vector s points in the same direction at these two times, but has different magnitudes. Show that the fractional decrease in magnitude, defined by $[s(t_1) - s(t_2)]/s(t_1)$, is approximately $\pi\gamma/\omega_0$. Compute this quantity for the frequency corresponding to the visible wavelength 5000 A (blue-green).

12-3. According to the quantum theory, an elementary process of atomic emission at frequency ω_0 gives rise to a total radiated energy in the definite amount $\hbar\omega_0$, where $\hbar$ is Planck's constant divided by 2π and has a value very near 10^{-27} erg-sec, which happens to be very nearly equal numerically to the mass of the electron in grams. Consider a classical atom in which an electron executes the motion (12-10) with $B = 0$. Calculate the order of magnitude of A when ω_0 is in the visible range and the total radiated energy is $\hbar\omega_0$. State the dependence of this magnitude on ω_0. (*Partial answer:* A is of the order of the size of actual atoms when the frequency is in the visible range.)

12-4. For a slightly damped, freely oscillating system, whether mechanical or electrical, it is common to define a "quality factor" Q by

$$Q = \frac{2\pi(\text{energy stored in system})}{\text{energy lost per cycle}} = \frac{\omega_0(\text{energy stored in system})}{\text{average power loss}}$$

where ω_0 is the resonant frequency of oscillation, and the quantities in numerator and denominator refer to any given instant of time. For such systems the stored energy (always the sum of two different kinds) can be represented by $W = W_0 e^{-\alpha t}$ if additional terms proportional to the first and second powers of the small quantity α/ω_0 are neglected (see Prob. 12-5). Find an expression for Q in terms of ω_0 and α. Evaluate Q for a freely swinging pendulum that has a period of 1 sec and is damped by friction of the air such that the amplitude (not the energy) decreases from unity to $1/e$ in 1 hr. For contrast with this "high-quality" mechanical system, calculate the Q of a Lorentz atom at the visible frequency corresponding to wavelength 5000 A. How does Q for the atom vary with ω_0? [*Partial answer:* Q for the atom is ω_0/γ, with γ given by (12-9). This exceedingly high value of Q is another manifestation of the extreme smallness of the radiation reaction in comparison with the forces of binding and inertia.]

12-5. Calculate the instantaneous value of the energy W stored in a Lorentz atom with an oscillating electron, this energy being the sum of the kinetic and potential energies. Use the real (!) representation (12-10) of the motion and carry the calculation far enough to yield the dominant terms plus those additional terms that are smaller by a factor γ/ω_0, but neglect those that are smaller by a factor $(\gamma/\omega_0)^2$. Show that the additional terms are oscillatory with frequency $2\omega_0$ and that with the dominant terms alone, W is in the form stated in Prob. 12-4. [The physical origin of these oscillatory terms can be seen by calculating the rate at which the radiation reaction (12-5) does work on the moving electron, that is, by calculating $\mathbf{F}_r \cdot \mathbf{s}$. This quantity can then be shown to equal dW/dt. The calculation can be kept short by retaining only terms of lowest order in γ, being careful not to overlook any.]

12-6. In discussions of spectra in this book, emphasis is placed on angular frequency ω; however, other variables could be used, namely, the ordinary frequency $\nu = \omega/2\pi$, the wavelength $\lambda = 2\pi c/\omega$, and the wave numbers $k = 2\pi/\lambda$ and $\sigma = 1/\lambda$. In practice, λ and σ are especially convenient, and spectra can be expressed in terms of them by writing (12-17) in the alternative ways

$$w = \int_0^\infty \mathcal{S}_\omega(\omega) \, d\omega = \int_0^\infty \mathcal{S}_\lambda(\lambda) \, d\lambda = \int_0^\infty \mathcal{S}_\sigma(\sigma) \, d\sigma$$

where the integrals are related by ordinary changes of variable, and the subscripts distinguish different functions of the quantities in parentheses ($\mathcal{S}_\omega$ is denoted $\mathcal{S}$ in the text). Find the expression for $\mathcal{S}_\lambda(\lambda)$ when $\mathcal{S}_\omega(\omega)$ is known, and similarly find $\mathcal{S}_\sigma(\sigma)$. [*Partial answer:* $\mathcal{S}_\lambda(\lambda) = (2\pi c/\lambda^2)\mathcal{S}_\omega(2\pi c/\lambda)$.]

12-7. Using the result of Prob. 12-6, convert the spectrum (12-21) to the spectrum $\mathcal{S}_\lambda(\lambda)$. Show that since the spectrum is appreciably different from zero only in the immediate vicinity of the resonant wavelength $\lambda_0 = 2\pi c/\omega_0$, a slight approximation can be made which reduces $\mathcal{S}_\lambda(\lambda)$ to the form of (12-21) with $(\omega - \omega_0)^2$ replaced by $(\lambda - \lambda_0)^2$, and $\mathcal{S}(\omega_0)$ and γ replaced by new values $\mathcal{S}_\lambda(\lambda_0)$ and γ_λ. Use (12-9) to show that the width γ_λ is independent of λ_0 and equal to about 10^{-4} A.

12-8. Check the result of Prob. 12-7 by substituting the expression obtained for $\mathcal{S}_\lambda(\lambda)$ in the second integral for w given in Prob. 12-6 and showing that the same value of w is given by substituting (12-21) in the first integral. With negligible effect the lower limits can be changed from zero to $-\infty$, since the integrands are effectively zero at all negative values of the variables.

12-9. Suppose a source emits just two damped waves whose fields at a point P are of the type (12-22); that is, $j = 1, 2$. For simplicity take $C_1 = C_2 = 1$, $D_1 = D_2 = 0$, and $\theta_1 = \theta_2 = 0$. Consider the three cases (1) $t_2 - t_1 = 0$, (2) $t_2 - t_1 = \pi/\omega_0$, and (3) $t_2 - t_1 \gg 1/\gamma$. (In the third case the two wave trains are very far from overlapping.) Draw curves of the resultant electric field as a function of time for all three cases, and calculate and draw the theoretical spectra. Show that the concept of a smoothed spectrum and the two italicized statements near the end of Sec. 12-6 are applicable in the third case, but not in the first two. (Remarks on the idea of smoothing are given in the next problem.) Discuss the gradual transition of the spectrum from the first case to the third. The essential part of this discussion deals with the behavior of the factor (12-24) as $t_2 - t_1$ increases from zero, and the situation should be illustrated by typical curves of this factor properly related to a curve of the remaining factor in the formula for the spectrum. [Note that (12-24) can easily be rewritten as a sum of a constant term and a real sinusoidal term.]

12-10. Near the end of Sec. 12-6, reference was made to smoothing fluctuations in a curve similar to Fig. 12-5. The process consists in averaging the ordinates over a range $\Delta\omega$ centered about any given frequency ω and taking the ordinate of the smoothed spectrum at ω to be this average. $\Delta\omega$ is to be taken small enough compared with γ so that throughout $\Delta\omega$ the first factor in (12-23) is essentially constant, and yet large enough to include a good sample of the fluctuations in the second factor, that is, in (12-24). Show that when the time of observation T is larger than the lifetime τ by a factor of perhaps 10^8 and N is very large, such a $\Delta\omega$ can easily be chosen, and that with negligible error the smoothed curve is the same as results from taking a statistical average at each frequency. [*Hint:* Rewrite (12-24) as a sum of real terms, some of which are constant, while others are sinusoidal functions of ω.] As the second part of the problem (in which the above hint is again useful), show that, with negligible error, the area under a curve such as Fig. 12-5 is the same as the area under the smooth curve obtained by taking a statistical average, provided the above assumptions on T and N hold. Make it clear that in both parts of the problem there are always residual fluctuations, but that they become progressively less significant as T and N increase, with $\Delta\omega$ constant in the first part.

12-11. Convert the Doppler formula (12-34) to an expression involving wavelengths λ_0 and λ_0' rather than frequencies ω_0 and ω_0'. Show that as the relative change in wavelength is small, a sufficiently accurate formula analogous to (12-35) is $\Delta\lambda/\lambda_0 = \mathbf{v} \cdot \hat{\mathbf{r}}/c$.

12-12. Derive the Doppler formula (12-34) by the following arguments: An atom moves with constant velocity $\mathbf{v}$ relative to an observer located at point P. During the short interval $0 < t < \Delta t$ an electron in the atom oscillates sinusoidally with a frequency ω_0 as seen by an observer moving with the atom. The total number of cycles is $\omega_0 \Delta t/2\pi$. At $t = 0$ let the vector from P to the atom be $r\hat{\mathbf{r}}$, where $\hat{\mathbf{r}}$ is a unit vector. Make the assumption that the velocity of the wave is c with respect to the point P, and calculate the times t' and $t' + \Delta t'$ at which the wave begins and ends at P. Set $\omega_0 \Delta t = \omega_0' \Delta t'$ to find the frequency ω_0' seen by the observer. The result is not (12-34), but show that (12-34) is the first approximation when $v \ll c$. (See the next problem.)

12-13. Repeat Prob. 12-12 under the assumption that the velocity of the wave is c with respect to the atom. The result is exactly (12-34). (See the next problem.)

12-14. The different assumptions in the last two problems concerning the velocity of the wave are appropriate when the wave propagates with a definite velocity with respect to some all-pervading medium, as in the case of sound waves in air. The source or the observer may then be at rest with respect to the medium. The assumption of such a medium (ether) proved untenable in the case of light; this led to adopting the postulate that the velocity of light *in vacuo* is independent of the velocity of the source relative to the observer as part of the special theory of relativity. Without our going into details, this theory gives the following formula for the Doppler effect:

$$\omega_0' = \omega_0 \frac{1 - \mathbf{v} \cdot \hat{\mathbf{r}}/c}{(1 - v^2/c^2)^{1/2}}$$

Expand this formula as far as terms of order v^2/c^2. Show that (12-34) results from keeping only linear terms and that the second-order terms predict a shift of frequency even when the velocity has no radial component. (The correctness of the second-order terms was checked in 1938 by H. E. Ives by observing radiation from molecular ions of hydrogen artificially accelerated to high velocities.)

12-15. Evaluate the relative width Δ/ω_0, as defined by (12-38), for the following extreme cases: (1) hydrogen atoms at 10^6 degrees Kelvin and (2) mercury atoms at 100 degrees Kelvin. (Both cases are academic, the first because all the atoms would be ionized by collisions to electrons and bare protons, and the second because of the low vapor pressure.) Note that the results in both cases are very small compared with unity. Using (12-9), find the ratio of the second result to the relative unbroadened width γ/ω_0 for the visible wavelength 5000 A, and note that it is still an order of magnitude greater than unity.

chapter 13

Polychromatic Waves

This chapter will begin with a restatement in general terms of a number of the ideas concerning polychromatic waves that arose in the last chapter. These ideas will then be taken as basis for a discussion of the various modes of detection of radiation and of the theory of the passage of an arbitrary wave through any optical system. Finally, attention will be given to those particular systems—spectroscopes, interferometers, and polarizing devices—especially suited to studying the nature of a given sample of radiation. The treatment of these systems will be largely in terms of their basic functions; some of the details of their realization as practical instruments appropriate to various regions of the electro-magnetic spectrum will be deferred to later chapters, since an under-standing of these instruments generally requires a preliminary develop-ment of the macroscopic theory of dense optical media, such as glasses, crystals, and metals.

In the course of the later sections a sample of radiation will come to be characterized by certain gross features, namely, its spectrum, its coher-ence, and its polarization, and operational methods will be specified for measuring these quantities. The ideas will have been arrived at through the classical model of a light wave, but in the end the operational defini-tions will put them on an independent footing. One can then reverse and contemplate experimental measurements whose results are to be com-pared with one theory or another. The last chapter of the book (espe-cially Sec. 19-7) will show in a qualitative survey that the quantum theory of radiation leaves the classical predictions concerning inter-ference and coherence in general wave fields, the subject of the present chapter, unchanged.   The classical theory is much the simpler to apply, and the result of the present chapter will be a large step toward a simple working theory applicable to real situations, in which perfectly mono-chromatic waves and ideal point sources do not exist.

13-1   Polychromatic Waves and Their Sources   This section will give a brief survey of the types of waves to be considered and some of their properties.

Suppose a number of charged particles in a source execute accelerated motions and emit waves that travel through space to a point of observation P at which instruments can be placed to study the resultant wave. The source may be an incandescent body, a gaseous discharge, a radio antenna, etc., and the simplifying assumption will be made throughout that the source as seen from P is confined within a cone whose vertex is at P and whose angular radius is not greater than some 5°.

Let a line drawn from the middle of the source to P define a z axis. With the restriction on angular spread of the source, the resultant electric vector at P has a z component that is at all times relatively small; we shall simplify by ignoring this z component.   The electric vector at P can then be written

$$\mathbf{e}(t) = \mathrm{e}_x(t)\,\mathbf{a} + \mathrm{e}_y(t)\,\mathbf{b} \tag{13-1}$$

where $\mathbf{a}$ and $\mathbf{b}$ are unit vectors in the x and y directions.

In an elementary dipole wave represented by (11-40) and (11-41), the electric and magnetic vectors at a point have equal magnitudes and are perpendicular to each other and to the direction of propagation.   The waves we are now considering can be regarded as a superposition of waves of this elementary type propagating past P in various directions, all lying nearly along the z axis.   It is then a good approximation to take the resultant magnetic vector to be in the xy plane and to be equal in magnitude to the approximate electric vector (13-1) and perpendicular to it.   The direction must be such that $\mathbf{e} \times \mathbf{b}$ is in the z direction (away from the source).   Thus we take

$$\mathbf{b}(t) = -\mathrm{e}_y(t)\,\mathbf{a} + \mathrm{e}_x(t)\,\mathbf{b} \tag{13-2}$$

The Poynting vector formed with (13-1) and (13-2) has only a z component:

$$S_z(t) = \frac{c}{4\pi}\,[\mathrm{e}_x{}^2(t) + \mathrm{e}_y{}^2(t)] \tag{13-3}$$

The instantaneous fields and flow of energy at P are thus given to sufficient accuracy by the two scalar functions $\mathrm{e}_x(t)$ and $\mathrm{e}_y(t)$ pertaining to that point.

In general these two functions are very complicated.   In the range of radio frequencies they can easily be observed directly, and principles are available that will ultimately extend such observations up to visible frequencies (see Sec. 19-8). But there are other quantities associated with the wave that are readily observed regardless of the frequencies involved and which have important practical significance.

One such quantity is the total energy arriving at P per unit area in an interval of time from t_1 to $t_1 + T$. Denoting this quantity by w,

$$w = \int_{t_1}^{t_1+T} S_z(t)\, dt \tag{13-4}$$

To get at another quantity, an argument identical to that in Sec. 12-5 can be applied to reexpress w as an integral over positive frequencies of the form

$$w = \int_0^\infty \mathcal{S}(\omega)\, d\omega \tag{13-5}$$

where
$$\mathcal{S}(\omega) = \frac{c}{2\pi} [\,|V_x(\omega)|^2 + |V_y(\omega)|^2] \tag{13-6}$$

Here $V_x(\omega)$ is the Fourier transform of that function which is equal to $e_x(t)$ in the interval $t_1 < t < t_1 + T$ and zero outside this interval; similarly for the y component. As in the last chapter, $\mathcal{S}(\omega)$ will be called the theoretical energy spectrum of that part of the wave that arrives at P during the time of observation. So far $\mathcal{S}(\omega)$ is a mathematical construct—merely the integrand in a certain integral. It is one of the purposes of this chapter to show how this integrand can be given physical significance through actual measurement.

Any source, no matter what efforts are devoted to making it steady, involves in its inner workings uncontrollable random processes. At a given frequency ω these processes show up in the Fourier transforms and in the energy spectrum $\mathcal{S}$ as fluctuations from one to another of a series of repeated observations. This matter was thoroughly investigated in the last chapter for the classical model of a gaseous discharge (results from quantum theory are very similar in all respects). Each kind of source must be analyzed separately for the origin and magnitude (relative to the average) of the fluctuations in the theoretical energy spectrum. Recognition of this randomness in a source is essential to understanding the incoherence of two independent sources, as will be brought out in Sec. 13-6. On the other hand, it will be important to see when and why fluctuations from statistical mean values of irradiance and spectrum are not observed experimentally.

A final point about our waves must be noted before we proceed. In the vicinity of the fixed point of observation P, let there be a point P' in a variable position. Let the electric vectors at these points be $\mathbf{e}(t)$ and $\mathbf{e}'(t)$, respectively. A question of fundamental importance is the degree to which the function $\mathbf{e}'$ is characterized by a knowledge of $\mathbf{e}$, or the degree to which e' and e are *correlated* or are *coherent*. This degree of correlation is taken up from the point of view of its experimental measurement and its practical consequences in several sections beginning with Sec. 13-10. However, a certain preliminary feeling for this correlation is necessary now.

Consider first a single atom in which an electron undergoes some accelerated motion and radiates an electric field given by (11-40). As seen from the atom, let P and P' be at the same distance and be separated by angle α. The only difference between the values of the field at P and P' arises from the different directions that must be given the unit vector in evaluating (11-40). Clearly α must be at least several degrees before one can no longer predict $e'(t)$ with good accuracy when $e(t)$ is known. (Recall that from e one knows a projection of the acceleration vector, and not the vector itself.) Thus on a sphere centered at the atom and passing through P, there is a circular cap centered at P of some diameter such that there is almost complete correlation between the field at P and that at any other point of the cap.

Suppose now that P and P' lie in the same direction from the atom but at different distances by an amount δr. According to (11-40) the field at the two points differs in the same way as a projection of the acceleration vector differs at two times $\delta r/c$ apart. From continuity alone it follows that there is some nonvanishing δr within which correlation is high. How large such a δr can be depends on the degree of regularity in the electron's motion, and a relation to the width of the spectrum of the radiation will be found in Sec. 13-11. For the moment we have arrived at the conclusion that P is surrounded by a volume in the shape of a cap of some diameter cut from a spherical shell of some thickness such that the field anywhere in the volume is known with good accuracy if it is known at P. Such a volume surrounding P is called a *region of coherence*.

If one has a large number of atoms constituting an extended source, and all the atoms undergo motions independently of each other, then for the field from each atom alone there is a region of coherence around P of the sort just described. The volume common to all these separate regions is the region of coherence pertaining to the entire source. The sequence of deductions beginning in Sec. 13-3 will take as a starting premise the existence of such a region of coherence. The linear extension of the region in directions perpendicular to the line from source to P will be assumed large enough that the region can cover the entrance aperture of any given optical instrument if the source is far enough away and small enough in angular diameter. The ultimate justification of this starting premise will be the consistency of deductions with observations.

13-2 Integrating and Continuous Modes of Detection The subject of detectors of radiant energy or power is complicated by a number of facts. The sensitivity of any detector depends on the frequency of the radiation, and no one detector responds over the whole range from low radio frequencies to hard X rays. Some detectors, notably the photographic emulsion, are nonlinear in response. Every detector introduces a certain amount of fluctuation, or "noise," into its final indication over and above the fluctuation inherent in the incident radiation. This noise introduced by the detector limits the sensitivity with which an input signal can be detected, but with some types of detectors the art has advanced to the point where the spurious fluctuations are almost negligible. In this book these complications will be passed over, and a detector will be assumed linear and uniformly sensitive to all frequencies in question and ideally free of internal noise. The reader interested in the problems of actual detectors can consult the following references: A brief and excellent survey has been given in an article by Harold W. Yates appearing as Appendix I in Strong [88]. A treatise on detectors for the infrared is Smith, Jones, and Chasmar [84]. A treatise on photoelectric detectors is Zworykin and Ramberg [106]. Radiometry with the photographic plate is treated in chapters in Sawyer [80] and in Harrison et al. [34]. A text on noise with sections on physical instruments and the detection of radiation is Van der Ziel [94].

There are two modes of observation. One, typified by exposing a photographic plate for a certain length of time, is called the *integrating mode;* it would be used for measuring the quantity w defined by (13-4), whether this quantity represents flux density of energy arriving directly from the source or arriving at an output point in an instrument. The other is called the *continuous mode* and gives as a continuous record some approximation to the instantaneous irradiance at the point of observation. It will now be shown that these two modes have much in common.

A continuous detector consists of a sensitive element, an amplifier, and a recorder. The output of the sensitive element is a feeble voltage or current that must be amplified before a deflection can be produced in a pen recorder or on the screen of a cathode-ray oscilloscope. Such a combination will be considered as a unit and called a *detecting system*, and by *response* we shall understand the observed deflection.

The response of a detecting system can be characterized in various ways; the one most convenient for us is the response to a short pulse of radiation. If radiation from a steady source reaches the detector through a shutter that opens for a certain duration, the response will be some function of the time. As the open time of the shutter is decreased, this response function relative to the maximum deflection will ultimately cease to change shape. A typical limiting form of the function is shown in Fig. 13-1a. A time of duration T can be defined as indicated in this figure, the precise way in which the definition is formulated being of no great importance, and the test pulse need only be confined to 1 per cent or so of T.

Contributions to this sluggishness of response can come from any or all of the three parts of the detecting system. With some types of systems the time T can be made short compared with the natural lifetime of an excited atom (see, for example, the reference in Sec. 19-6), but more commonly it ranges from several milliseconds to several seconds. Let us consider only those detectors that are linear, so that the height of the curve in Fig. 13-1a is proportional to the energy in the pulse.

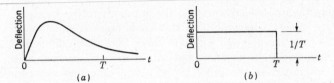

Fig. 13-1. a. *Typical deflection of the indicator as a function of time when a detecting system is exposed at $t = 0$ to a short pulse of radiation.* **b.** *Idealization of the curve of* (**a**).

Suppose now that radiation from a steady source falls continuously on a detector whose sensitive surface is of unit area and whose response time is, say, 1 sec. Let the time axis be divided into intervals of length Δt small compared with 1 sec. The energy $E(t'')$ falling on the detector in the interval t'' to $t'' + \Delta t$ acts as a pulse which, by itself, would give a deflection at time t equal to $E(t'') \, r(t - t'')$, where $r(t)$ is the response function for a pulse of unit energy occurring at $t = 0$ and has a curve as in Fig. 13-1a. Taking the radiation to travel in the z direction,

$$E(t'') = \int_{t''}^{t'' + \Delta t} S_z(t') \, dt'$$

where S_z is the magnitude of the Poynting vector. The total deflection D at time t is the sum of the deflections due to the individual pulses and can be written

$$D(t) = \int_{-\infty}^{\infty} S_z(t') \, r(t - t') \, dt' \tag{13-7}$$

The deflection is thus expressed as a folding integral (Sec. 11-3), and the operation of folding in the slowly varying function r has the effect of smoothing out rapid variations in the Poynting vector. This effect reduces to very simple terms if we make the idealization that the response function is as shown in Fig. 13-1b, that is, a constant equal to $1/T$ for a duration T. The deflection then becomes

$$D(t) = \frac{1}{T} \int_{t-T}^{t} S_z(t') \, dt' \tag{13-8}$$

which is just the average of the Poynting vector taken over the interval of duration T preceding the time t at which the deflection is observed.

We thus reach the conclusion that *a continuous detector essentially performs a time averaging of the instantaneous irradiance, and if the effective time of averaging is long enough to include a good sample of the fluctuations of irradiance from a steady source, the deflection of the recorder is steady.*   In other words, both the integrating and continuous detector involve a time of integration, the only difference being that with the continuous detector a weighting function r appears in (13-7), although when the detector is slow and the source is steady, it is permissible to think in terms of the idealization (13-8).

13-3   Propagation of a Wave from a Small Source through an Optical System   As a general conception, an optical system consists of an entrance aperture behind which lies some combination of optical elements—lenses, gratings, etc.   A wave is incident on the system, and the basic problem is to find the modified wave arriving at any point of interest P behind the system.   The wave at P is determined by the characteristics of the incident wave at the different points of the entrance aperture and by the structure of the system.

This section will deal with a source small enough in angular size that the entrance aperture is covered by a region of coherence as defined in Sec. 13-1.   The simplification is that the behavior of the fields all over the entrance aperture is known if it is known at any one reference point P_r in or near the aperture.   The fields at P are then uniquely related to those at P_r.

Let the line from the source to P_r define the positive z axis with P_r as origin, and choose x and y axes in any angular orientation about the z axis.   Let the discussion be confined to systems that are *optically slow,* which means that any two rays that can be traced through the system so as to pass through the point of observation P and through the entrance aperture have an angle of convergence at P not greater than some 15°.   Then the wave arriving at P can be thought of as being essentially a transverse wave traveling in a unique direction.   (It is not absolutely necessary to impose this restriction, but it avoids tedious radiometric considerations that are necessary when accurate calculations are attempted with fast systems.)   Let the direction of arrival at P define a positive ζ axis of a cartesian system with P as origin, and choose ξ and η axes in arbitrary orientation.

Let us now consider an integrating type of observation in which a shutter in front of the entrance aperture opens for a time T and an integrating detector at P measures the total flux density of energy $w(P)$ arriving there.   The components of the electric field at P_r during the time of exposure will be some functions $e_x(t;P_r)$ and $e_y(t;P_r)$.   The components at P will be $e_\xi(t;P)$ and $e_\eta(t;P)$.   It will be pointed out in Probs. 13-8 and 13-9 that the signal at P extends over an interval somewhat longer than T, but this consideration is of no moment with an integrating detector allowed to integrate effectively from $t = -\infty$ to $t = \infty$.

A general relation between the fields at P and P_r can be written by the method of Fourier analysis, particularly the transfer function discussed in Sec. 11-10. Let the transforms of e_x and e_y at P_r be $V_x(\omega;P_r)$ and $V_y(\omega;P_r)$, respectively. We can think of $V_x(\omega;P_r)\,e^{-i\omega t}$ as the instantaneous amplitude at P_r of a monochromatic spherical wave emanating from the source and linearly polarized along the x axis. After passing through the system such a wave in general becomes an elliptically polarized wave at P with ξ and η components linearly related to the x component at P_r. In the same way we can think of the passage of a monochromatic wave linearly polarized in the y direction with amplitude $V_y(\omega;P_r)$. Superposing the two waves gives the following linear relation between the transforms of the components of the electric field at P and at P_r:

$$V_\xi(\omega;P) = \tau_{\xi x}(\omega;P,P_r)\, V_x(\omega;P_r) + \tau_{\xi y}(\omega;P,P_r)\, V_y(\omega;P_r)$$
$$V_\eta(\omega;P) = \tau_{\eta x}(\omega;P,P_r)\, V_x(\omega;P_r) + \tau_{\eta y}(\omega;P,P_r)\, V_y(\omega;P_r) \tag{13-9}$$

The τ's are transfer functions to be calculated from the geometry of the system. They are complex functions, in general all different, and they depend on the frequency, on the choice of the fixed reference point P_r, on the position of the point of observation P, and on the choice of axes. They also depend on the direction and distance from P_r to the source, although this fact is not indicated explicitly in the notation.

Formulas (13-9) are general relations through which any optical system can be studied. Whereas a scalar problem involves only a single scalar transfer function, a problem involving transverse vector waves in a coordinate representation involves four, although with most systems it is possible to orient the x, y, ξ, and η axes in such a way with respect to the system that some of the four vanish. The first systems to be examined are such that the axes can be chosen to make $\tau_{\xi y} = \tau_{\eta x} = 0$. Such systems form a broad class of which the following are examples:

1. The system consists of an axially symmetric series of lenses, and the source is on the axis. The lenses are such that any ray traced from the source through the system never makes an angle greater than about $10°$ with the axis. In this case the z and ζ axes practically coincide for any point P of interest, and a linearly polarized wave remains essentially linearly polarized, oscillating in the same direction, throughout the system. It is appropriate to choose the x and ξ axes to be parallel, but otherwise arbitrary. Then to a very good approximation the transfer functions satisfy, not only $\tau_{\xi y} = \tau_{\eta x} = 0$, but also $\tau_{\xi x} = \tau_{\eta y}$.

2. The system consists of a screen with diffracting apertures, the dimensions of the apertures being large compared with the wavelength.

A linearly polarized incident wave remains linearly polarized in the same direction, and when the x and ξ axes are chosen parallel, the τ's satisfy the same relations as in case 1.

3. The system consists of a prism preceded and followed by lenses to make a spectrograph (see Fig. 13-6). An incident wave linearly polarized either parallel or perpendicular to the apex edge of the prism remains linearly polarized in the same sense. Choosing the x and ξ axes parallel to the apex edge makes $\tau_{\xi y} = \tau_{\eta x} = 0$, but $\tau_{\xi x} \neq \tau_{\eta y}$. (The reason for the last condition will be seen later from the macroscopic theory.)

4. The system consists of a diffraction grating whose spacing is comparable with the wavelength corresponding to frequency ω. There may be one or two lenses to give proper imaging, or the grating may be of the concave type (Sec. 7-15). This case is the same as case 3, except that the preferred axes are defined by the grooves rather than by an apex edge.

The inequality of the nonvanishing τ's in the last two cases means that an unpolarized incident beam arrives at points in the image plane showing some polarization, a point on which more will be said later.

With proper choice of axes, the systems now being considered are characterized by

$$V_\xi = \tau_{\xi x} V_x \qquad V_\eta = \tau_{\eta y} V_y \qquad (13\text{-}10)$$

The flux density of energy $w(P)$ can be calculated by the formulas (13-5) and (13-6), the latter with x and y replaced by ξ and η. Thus,

$$w(P) = \frac{c}{2\pi} \int_0^\infty [\Im_{\xi x}(\omega;P,P_r)|V_x(\omega;P_r)|^2$$
$$+ \Im_{\eta y}(\omega;P,P_r)|V_y(\omega;P_r)|^2]\, d\omega \qquad (13\text{-}11)$$

where
$$\Im_{\xi x} = |\tau_{\xi x}|^2 \qquad \Im_{\eta y} = |\tau_{\eta y}|^2 \qquad (13\text{-}12)$$

The $\Im$'s, which are real functions, are called *transmission functions* in contrast to the τ's, which are complex and are called *transfer functions*. From (13-10), $\tau_{\xi x}$ is the complex amplitude at P divided by that at P_r when the incident wave is monochromtic and linearly polarized with **e** along the x axis. The transmission function $\Im_{\xi x}$ then has the physical significance of being the time average of the irradiance at P divided by that at P_r with the same type of incident wave. These interpretations are suitable for theoretical calculations, but the transmission functions can also be given interpretations by which they can be determined experimentally, although it will take several sections to bring out this point in full detail.

If the time T during which the system is exposed to radiation is very long compared with the duration of elementary processes in the source, then $|V_x|^2$ and $|V_y|^2$, whatever shape their smoothed curves may have, will show rapid fluctuations as functions of ω of the type shown in Fig. 12-5. On the other hand, it will turn out that the $\mathfrak{I}$'s have smooth curves and never vary so rapidly with ω that they are not essentially constant over ranges of frequencies that can be chosen large enough to contain a good sample of the fluctuations just mentioned. It is therefore permissible to smooth out the fine fluctuations in the integrand of (13-11) before integrating, and by arguments given in the last chapter, this smoothing can be done by taking a statistical average at each frequency. Taking the source to be unpolarized, and using the definition of the smoothed spectrum of the incident wave (equivalently, the statistical average of the spectrum), we have

$$[|V_x|^2]_{\text{av}} = [|V_y|^2]_{\text{av}} = \frac{\pi}{c}\,[\mathbb{S}]_{\text{av}} \tag{13-13}$$

Equation (13-11) becomes

$$w(P) = \int_0^\infty \mathfrak{I}(\omega;P,P_r)[\mathbb{S}(\omega;P_r)]_{\text{av}}\,d\omega \tag{13-14}$$

where
$$\mathfrak{I} = \tfrac{1}{2}(\mathfrak{I}_{\xi x} + \mathfrak{I}_{\eta y}) \tag{13-15}$$

The over-all transmission function $\mathfrak{I}$ is thus the average of the transmission functions associated with the two monochromatic incident waves that are linearly polarized in orthogonal directions and that remain linearly polarized on propagating through the system. The systems under consideration are restricted for the moment to those for which this type of propagation occurs, that is, those for which (13-9) can be reduced to (13-10) by suitable choice of axes. Recall that (13-13) and (13-15) refer to an unpolarized incident wave. Extension to polarized waves will be made in Sec. 13-12.

Formula (13-14) is a fundamental relation expressing in terms of real quantities the behavior of optical systems of the class being considered. (The theorem for general systems is called for in Prob. 13-10, which requires results from Sec. 13-6.) While it has been derived from a rather specific classical model of radiation, it can now be given a wider significance by assuming that it holds even when w, $\mathfrak{I}$, and $[\mathbb{S}]_{\text{av}}$ are given the values observed in actual experiments. Applications of the formula fall into three classes according as one seeks to find some one of the three quantities when the other two are known, either from theory or experiment. Calculating w at various points P, when $\mathfrak{I}$ and $[\mathbb{S}]_{\text{av}}$ are given, amounts to calculating the flux density of energy at points in an image formed with a given system and radiation of given spectrum. (The term image is meant to include all kinds of diffraction and interference patterns.) Finding $\mathfrak{I}$ when the other two quantities are given amounts to calibrating the instrument. Finally, finding $[\mathbb{S}]_{\text{av}}$ when w and $\mathfrak{I}$ are known is the fundamental problem of spectroscopy. In the next few sections these various aspects of (13-14) will be explored.

13-4   Examples of Transmission Functions and Calculation of Diffraction Patterns   Let us consider a system consisting merely of a plane opaque screen containing a rectangular aperture of dimensions a by b, as shown in Fig. 9-2.   Let the source and the point of observation P be far enough away that Fraunhofer diffraction obtains for any frequency present in the spectrum of the source, and assume that the aperture is large compared with the wavelength corresponding to any of these frequencies.   Experiments show that if the incident wave is linearly polarized, the diffraction pattern is independent of the direction of vibration and is given accurately enough by the scalar theory of Fresnel and Kirchhoff.   This means that the over-all transmission function $\mathfrak{J}$ can be drawn directly from the scalar calculations of Sec. 9-3 and need not be found as the average of two terms according to (13-15).   (This simplification does not apply to a slit whose width is comparable with the wavelength.   Such a slit shows higher transmission when the electric vector is perpendicular to the long axis of the slit than when it is parallel. A discussion of this difficult problem can be found in Sommerfeld [85], p. 273.)

Let the reference point be located at the center of the aperture.   The transmission function is the ratio of the irradiance at P to that at P_r when the source is a point emitting a monochromatic scalar wave of frequency ω; that is,

$$\mathfrak{J}(\omega;P,P_r) = \frac{I(\omega;P)}{I(\omega;P_r)} \tag{13-16}$$

If the problem is referred to the standard coordinate system shown in Fig. 7-4, and the aperture is centered about the origin O (so that O is the reference point P_r), then $I(\omega;P)$ is given by (9-9), (9-7), and (9-5). In the last, E has the significance of $I(\omega;P_r)$, and $\mathfrak{A} = ab$.   The transmission function is therefore

$$\mathfrak{J}(\omega;P,P_r) = \left(\frac{ab\omega\,\cos\,\chi}{4\pi c R_{20}}\frac{\sin\,\pi\alpha}{\pi\alpha}\frac{\sin\,\pi\beta}{\pi\beta}\right)^2 \tag{13-17}$$

where $\alpha = \dfrac{\omega a}{2\pi c}(\sin\,\theta_1 + \sin\,\theta_2)$ $\beta = \dfrac{\omega b}{2\pi c}(\sin\,\phi_1 + \sin\,\phi_2)$ (13-18)

In addition to depending on the frequency and the variables R_{20}, θ_2, and ϕ_2, the last three fixing the position of P, the transmission function depends on the angles θ_1 and ϕ_1, which fix the direction to the source and the angle of incidence χ (Fig. 9-1).   The way in which $\mathfrak{J}$ is defined eliminates dependence on the distance from P_r to the source when this distance is large enough to satisfy the condition for Fraunhofer diffraction.

Consider the special case $\theta_1 = \phi_1 = \chi = 0$ (normal incidence on the aperture).   In addition, let $\phi_2 = 0$, so that only points P on the X_2 axis of Fig. 7-4 are to be considered.   The distance R_{20} can be regarded as constant for points P to which the diffraction pattern is effectively confined. The transmission function now depends only on the two variables ω and $\sin \theta_2$, and (13-17) reduces to

$$\mathfrak{I}(\omega, \sin \theta_2) = B \frac{\sin^2 \pi\alpha}{\sin^2 \theta_2} \tag{13-19}$$

where $$B = \left(\frac{b}{2\pi R_{20}}\right)^2 \qquad \alpha = \frac{\omega a}{2\pi c} \sin \theta_2 \tag{13-20}$$

The value of the constant B is unimportant if one is interested only in relative values in the diffraction pattern.

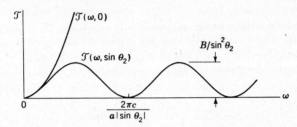

Fig. 13-2. *Transmission function for a rectangular aperture in the Fraunhofer arrangement with normal incidence. The parabolic curve refers to the center of the diffraction pattern, and the sinusoidal curve refers to an arbitrary point on an axis of symmetry.*

To see the nature of the function (13-19), consider it first as a function of ω for various fixed values of θ_2. In the special case $\theta_2 = 0$, one has an indeterminate form $0/0$. It is evaluated by taking the limit as θ_2 approaches zero. On making the approximation $\sin \pi\alpha = \pi\alpha$, which is good when θ_2 is small, and which becomes exact in the limit, one obtains

$$\mathfrak{I}(\omega,0) = \frac{a^2 B}{4c^2} \omega^2 \tag{13-21}$$

Figure 13-2 shows the function (13-21) and a typical curve representing (13-19) for a nonvanishing value of θ_2, either positive or negative. The latter curve oscillates with constant amplitude over the whole range of positive frequencies. Note that both curves start out the same at small ω, since, again, $\sin \pi\alpha \approx \pi\alpha$.

Alternatively, one can think of (13-19) as a function of $\sin \theta_2$ for fixed ω. In this view $\mathfrak{I}$ is proportional to the irradiance in the diffraction pattern formed with a monochromatic wave and has the shape of Fig. 9-5. Figure 13-3 indicates how $\mathfrak{I}$ can be pictured as a three-dimensional surface above the plane of the two variables ω and $\sin \theta_2$. The value of $\mathfrak{I}$ is zero whenever $\alpha = n$ with n an integer, positive or negative, that is, when

$\omega \sin \theta_2 = 2\pi c n/a$. The latter relation defines arcs of hyperbolas, indicated in Fig. 13-3 by dashed curves.

There is an upper limit to the range of frequencies for which the curves in Figs. 13-2 and 13-3 are valid, for ultimately the wavelength becomes so short that the pattern goes over into the Fresnel type. Even if the pattern is formed in the focal plane of a lens placed behind the aperture, so that there is no tendency to depart from the Fraunhofer case, there is

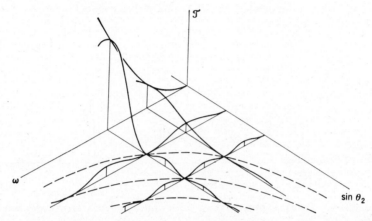

Fig. 13-3. *Dependence of the transmission function for a rectangular aperture on frequency and on the position of the point of observation along an axis of symmetry of the diffraction pattern. The dashed curves (arcs of hyperbolas) are loci along which the transmission function is zero. The figure should be imagined to extend symmetrically on both sides of the frequency axis.*

inevitably a frequency beyond which the lens is opaque. Thus $\mathfrak{I}$ evaluated at $\theta_2 = 0$ does not actually become infinite; nevertheless, it can follow the parabolic curve for a considerable distance and attain a high value for the reason that, as the wavelength decreases, the pattern is concentrated in a smaller area.

As a second example of a theoretical transmission function, consider a large number N of apertures of the same shape as the one just treated. Let them be arranged along the x axis of Fig. 7-4 at uniform spacing d to make a grating. The transmission function becomes (13-19) multiplied by the factor $|F|^2$ given by (7-14), in which

$$\delta = \frac{\omega d}{2\pi c} \sin \theta_2$$

Normal incidence is again assumed. A plot of $\mathfrak{I}$ as a function of ω for a given nonvanishing value of $\sin \theta_2$ is shown in Fig. 13-4. The principal maxima occur at frequencies obtained by setting δ equal to positive and negative integers (the order numbers), with negative integers being associated with negative values of $\sin \theta_2$. The transmission function can again be pictured as a three-dimensional surface analogous to Fig. 13-3, and it is easily seen that the locus on the plane of ω and $\sin \theta_2$ of the principal maximum of given order is an arc of a hyperbola similar to the dashed curves in Fig. 13-3. In fact, the surface indicated in Fig. 13-3, with all ordinates multiplied by N^2, becomes the envelope touched by the principal maxima of the grating.

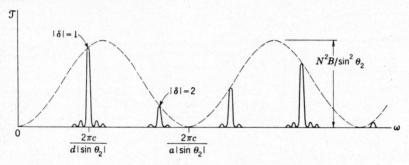

Fig. 13-4. *Transmission function for a grating of N slits of width a and spacing d.*

Not shown in Fig. 13-4 is the curve pertaining to the special point $\theta_2 = 0$. It is just N^2 times the $\mathfrak{I}(\omega,0)$ shown in Fig. 13-2, and at small ω it essentially coincides with the dashed envelope in Fig. 13-4. Since the point at $\theta_2 = 0$ falls at the center of the zero-order principal maximum ($\delta = 0$), one sees in a new light the phenomenon, noted in connection with Fig. 7-22, that the zeroth order has a unique location, and all frequencies contribute to it.

These two examples illustrate the procedure of calculating the transmission function for simple and exactly known geometries. In a practical spectrograph intended for the most precise work, it is important to know the transmission function as accurately as possible. It is always necessary to resort to experimental measurement, since in these instruments $\mathfrak{I}$ is very sensitive to any small defects such as imperfections in the ruling of a grating or in the design and manufacture of a lens. The problem of measuring the transmission function of a spectrograph and the use of the instrument to measure spectra are intimately related and will be discussed together in the next section.

Let us now calculate a diffraction pattern formed with polychromatic radiation. Take the system to be the rectangular aperture just considered, so that the transmission function for points on the X_2 axis when the incident wave falls normally on the aperture is (13-19). Take the energy spectrum to be

$$[\mathcal{S}(\omega;P_r)]_{av} = \begin{cases} 0 & (0 < \omega < \omega_1) \\ 1 & (\omega_1 < \omega < 2\omega_1) \\ 0 & (\omega > 2\omega_1) \end{cases} \tag{13-22}$$

Thus the spectrum extends over one octave of frequencies, which might be the visible octave, and is constant in this range.[1]

The flux density of energy w at any point in the diffraction pattern is found by substituting (13-19) and (13-22) in (13-14). The result will be compared with the irradiance in the monochromatic pattern formed with a wave having the mean frequency $3\omega_1/2$, and it will be advantageous to express w not as a function of $\sin \theta_2$, but as a function of

$$\xi = \frac{3\omega_1 a}{4c} \sin \theta_2$$

which is $\pi\alpha$ evaluated at the mean frequency. A straightforward but tedious calculation gives

$$\frac{w(\xi)}{w(0)} = \frac{27}{56\xi^2} \left(1 - \frac{3}{2\xi} \sin \frac{2\xi}{3} \cos 2\xi \right) \tag{13-23}$$

The irradiance in the monochromatic pattern for $\omega = 3\omega_1/2$ is

$$\frac{I(\xi)}{I(0)} = \frac{\sin^2 \xi}{\xi^2} \tag{13-24}$$

Figure 13-5 shows plots of the functions (13-23) and (13-24). The main feature is that when a spectrum covering a broad range of frequencies is involved, the secondary maxima and minima appearing in a mono-chromatic pattern are almost obliterated. An intuitive feeling for this phenomenon is gained from contemplating the family of curves repre-sented by Fig. 13-2. The value of w at a given point in the pattern is the area under the corresponding curve between the fixed frequencies ω_1 and $2\omega_1$, and it is easy to picture what happens as $\sin \theta_2$ increases from zero. One also sees why a visual observation with white light shows strong colors near the center of the pattern, but only white light farther out in

[1] Radiation from a source that radiates equally in equal frequency intervals over a range of frequencies is sometimes said to be ideally "white" in this range, but in a technical sense only. If the range covers the visible frequencies, such "white" light would actually be quite bluish. Another definition of ideal white light is that the source radiates equally in equal wavelength intervals; such light is nearly the same color as overcast daylight. For further reading on the subject of colorimetry, see Ref. 19. For the relation between the two definitions of ideal white light, see Prob. 12-6.

the wings. This coloring makes secondary maxima more prominent in a visual observation than on a black-and-white photograph.

By the same qualitative reasoning one sees that a photograph of the white-light pattern of a double slit shows only the lowest orders with rapidly decreasing contrast. On the other hand, if the spectrum is confined to frequencies whose total range is small compared with the mean frequency ω_0, then the low orders show essentially the same profile

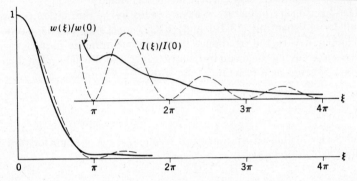

Fig. 13-5. *Comparison of the Fraunhofer diffraction patterns (13-23) and (13-24) for a rectangular aperture with monochromatic light (dashed curves) and white light covering one octave of frequencies (solid curves). The curves in the upper right are the same as the ones below, but referred to a vertical scale expanded five times. Only half of each pattern is shown.*

as would be calculated on the assumption of perfectly monochromatic radiation of frequency ω_0. At sufficiently high orders the nonvanishing width of the spectrum begins to have an effect, but the single-aperture pattern may prevent these high orders from being observed. When a diffraction pattern appears to be the same as though the radiation were perfectly monochromatic, the actual radiation is said to be *quasi-monochromatic*.

13-5 Spectrographs and the Measurement of Energy Spectra and Power Spectra The function of a spectrograph, of whatever kind, can be discussed on the basis of the fundamental relation (13-14). This formula was obtained with reference to an integrating type of observation, and for the moment only such observations will be considered. Later it will be shown how the arguments apply to continuous observations.

The only spectrographs introduced so far are those incorporating a grating or a prism. Let us keep these two types in mind pending subsequent introduction of interferometric instruments, to which the treatment now to be developed applies equally well.

When the source is small enough to be essentially a point, a spectrograph can in principle be as simple as the arrangement in Fig. 13-6. (The prism could be replaced by a grating, in which case the red rays would show greater deviation than blue in a given order.) In common practice, a spectrograph has as an entrance aperture a narrow slit at the location S in the figure, and this aperture is irradiated in one way or another by radiation from the source, located farther to the left.[1] This

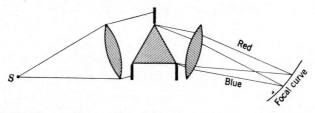

Fig. 13-6. *Schematic arrangement of a prism spectrograph with a point source of radiation at S.*

entrance aperture introduces complications which will be pointed out in Sec. 13-10.

A system involving lenses usually has chromatic aberration which results in the focal points for monochromatic rays of various wavelengths falling on a line that is inclined and curved, as indicated in Fig. 13-6. With a concave grating the focal curve is the Rowland circle (Sec. 7-15). When a spectrum is photographed, the emulsion is placed on thin glass plates or film bent to fit this curve.

The arrangement of Fig. 13-6, the source being essentially a point, would have the practical disadvantage that each monochromatic component in the spectrum of the source would give rise to just a small spot (a diffraction pattern) on the focal surface, and the whole spectrum would give a series of such spots with their centers ranged along a line in the focal surface. The discussion in this section will refer to flux densities of energy at points just along this line.

Suppose the source is nearly monochromatic, and let P be the center of the diffraction pattern formed on the focal surface. If the frequency of the source changes, P shifts, and the position of any point P can be specified in a most convenient way as the frequency ω_P of that monochromatic wave that makes P the center of the diffraction pattern. In a grating this specification is unique if attention is confined to a single

---

[1] A type of spectrograph having no entrance slit is used by astronomers. The objective of a telescope is covered by a glass wedge having a dihedral angle of some 5°. Images of stars then consist of short spectra suitable for classification preliminary to study with instruments of higher dispersion. For illustrations, see Baker [2], pp. 326 and 328.

order. The notation of formula (13-14) can now be simplified to read

$$w(\omega_P) = \int_0^\infty \Im(\omega,\omega_P) \, \mathcal{S}(\omega) \, d\omega \qquad (13\text{-}25)$$

That this formula depends on the choice of the reference point P_r is left understood. (In Fig. 13-6, P_r might be at the center of the first lens. In practical instruments, it is taken at the entrance slit.) It is also left understood that $\mathcal{S}$ is the energy spectrum of the radiation arriving at P_r with statistical fluctuations averaged out.

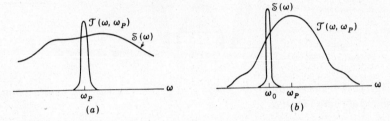

Fig. 13-7. *Extreme cases of the ratio of the width of a spectrum to the width of the instrumental profile.*

Consider now the two extreme cases shown in Fig. 13-7. The curve of $\Im(\omega,\omega_P)$ as a function of ω is called the *instrumental profile* associated with the point P. In the case shown at (a), the spectrum is very broad and slowly varying in comparison with the instrumental profile, and (13-25) can be approximated by

$$w(\omega_P) = \mathcal{S}(\omega_P) \int_0^\infty \Im(\omega,\omega_P) \, d\omega \qquad (13\text{-}26)$$

This situation is the simplest that can arise in spectroscopy. The spectrum at frequency ω_P is obtained by dividing the observed flux density of energy w by the integral on the right of (13-26). This integral is found by calibrating the instrument, the procedure being as follows: The source is replaced by a standard source whose spectrum and power output are precisely known. The ultimate standard is a cavity completely enclosed except for a small hole in one side, with walls held accurately at some high temperature. The formula of Planck for cavity radiation (Sec. 19-3), together with the solid angle subtended by the hole and the time of exposure, determine the energy spectrum at P_r exactly. An experimental measurement of w with this source then gives the integral in (13-26) by division. A cavity operating at the dull red heat appropriate to the infrared is not difficult to construct and use, but one suitable for the visible and near ultraviolet is so inconvenient that it is usually replaced by a standard lamp with a tungsten filament carrying a specified current.   Such a lamp is calibrated once and for all by comparison with a cavity operated at white heat in a standards laboratory.

In the extreme case shown in Fig. 13-7b, the spectrum is peaked at ω_0, and the instrumental profile is broad enough in comparison that it is essentially constant over the range of frequencies covered by the spectrum.   Then (13-25) reduces to

$$w(\omega_P) = \Im(\omega_0,\omega_P) \int_0^\infty \mathcal{S}(\omega) \, d\omega \qquad (13\text{-}27)$$

The integral on the right can be measured as the flux density of energy

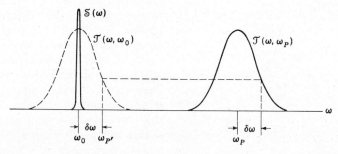

Fig. 13-8. *Measurement of the instrumental profile of a spectrograph with a single narrow spectrum line.   Only the dashed profile is actually measured, and immediately neighboring ones are taken to have the same shape.*

arriving at the reference point P_r during the exposure.   Simple division then gives the transmission function associated with point P at the one frequency ω_0.   In principle one could then vary ω_0 and find the whole transmission function for point P.   In 'the calibration of a prism or grating instrument this procedure is not feasible because the only spectra that are sufficiently narrow are the discrete lines from gaseous discharges operated at low temperature and pressure, and such lines are not available at all frequencies.   The practical procedure is to use a single narrow line whose central frequency ω_0 is near the frequency ω_P and to take advantage of the property of the instrumental profile that when ω_P moves along the frequency axis, the profile associated with ω_P moves with it and changes shape so slowly that it is essentially the same for all ω_P in a range many times the width of the profile.

Figure 13-8 illustrates the principle of the method.   Radiation with the narrow spectrum at ω_0 enters the instrument, and $w(\omega_{P'})$ is measured at various points P'.   This function w is then proportional to the transmission function associated with the point identified by the frequency ω_0 (dashed curve), the constant of proportionality being the integral of

$\mathcal{S}(\omega)$. The transmission function for neighboring points is then obtained through the equality indicated in the figure. In most applications of spectroscopy one wants only the relative ordinates of the spectrum, and not the absolute values. The integral in (13-27) can then be left as an undetermined constant—a great simplification, since the measurement of absolute values (which involves absolute calibration of the detector) is difficult.

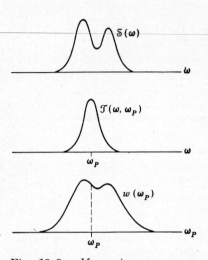

The final case to be considered is that in which a spectrum to be measured has a width comparable to the width of the instrumental profile. This case always arises in measuring the shapes of very narrow spectrum lines or spectra with very fine detail. Figure 13-9 is a typical illustration. Assume that the instrumental profile is known. Then the curve of $w(\omega_P)$ is obtained by sliding this profile along the ω axis and at each stage calculating the integral of $\mathcal{S}\mathcal{S}$ to obtain w at that stage. Now $w(\omega_P)$ is the observed quantity, called the *spectrogram*. It differs in shape from the spectrum, and the problem is to use formula (13-25) to get the spectrum from the spectrogram. Because of the invariance of the instrumental profile illustrated in Fig. 13-8, this formula can be rewritten in a simple form.

Fig. 13-9. *Measuring a very narrow spectrum. The upper curve is the spectrum. The middle curve is the instrumental profile for a point of observation P; the profile is assumed to have the property of invariance shown in Fig. 13-8. The lower curve is the observed spectrogram.*

For all points P of interest in the problem, the instrumental profile $\mathcal{S}(\omega,\omega_P)$ can be written as an unchanging function X of the difference $\omega - \omega_P$:

$$\mathcal{S}(\omega,\omega_P) = X(\omega - \omega_P)$$

Then (13-25) becomes

$$w(\omega_P) = \int_0^\infty X(\omega - \omega_P)\, \mathcal{S}(\omega)\, d\omega \tag{13-28}$$

Thus the spectrogram is a folding integral of the spectrum and the instrumental profile. When w and X have certain simple shapes, the folding rule (see corollary to Theorem 4, Sec. 11-3) gives the spectrum easily. An illustration is given in Prob. 13-7. For less simple cases the folding rule has been made the basis of numerical routines that allow one to get somewhat closer to the true spectrum than the original spectrogram, but detail substantially finer than the width of the instrumental profile is inevitably lost.

There is a difficulty in determining the instrumental profile of a spectrograph intended to measure the shapes of the narrowest spectra, since no narrower ones are available for calibration. The instrument par excellence for this work is the interferometer of Fabry and Perot; when this instrument is described, it will be seen that there is a special way to measure the instrumental profile that does not require exceedingly narrow spectra.

So far this section has mentioned only the integrating mode of observation. All the formulas remain formally identical in the continuous mode. Here one places at any point P of the focal curve a pinhole (in practice a narrow slit), and behind it a continuous detector which can be calibrated to read directly the irradiance $I(\omega_P)$ at P. Suppose the source is steady and the detector is slow enough to give a steady reading. Then in the fundamental formula (13-25), $w(\omega_P)$ can be replaced by $I(\omega_P)$, provided $\S(\omega)$ is understood to represent the *power spectrum*, that is, the average taken over a long time of the power arriving at the reference point P_r per unit area per unit frequency interval. The transmission function remains the same.

The power spectrum is a characteristic of the steady source itself, since, in contrast to the energy spectrum, it does not refer to some definite length of observation. The power spectrum has the same shape, as a function of ω, as the smoothed energy spectrum. In fact, if the energy spectrum associated with a long time of observation T is averaged over statistical fluctuations, then the power spectrum is this averaged energy spectrum divided by T. Obtaining a spectrogram with a steady source and continuous detector involves sweeping the pinhole and detector along the focal curve at a measured rate slow enough that the recorder always gives essentially the same deflection as it would if the pinhole were stationary.

13-6 Incoherence of Independent Sources Consider two small sources lying in nearly the same direction from a point of observation P. The sources may be completely separate, or they may be two small regions in the same incandescent body or in the same gaseous discharge, but in any case let us assume that the motions of the electrons in one source are completely uncorrelated with those in the other. An example of cases to be excluded is that in which the sources are two elements of conductor in a radio-frequency antenna when the currents in the elements are determined by a single generator.

Let the line from the sources to P be the z axis, and let the x components of the electric fields at P due to the two sources as observed during a certain interval be $e_x^{(1)}(t;P)$ and $e_x^{(2)}(t;P)$, with Fourier transforms $V_x^{(1)}(\omega;P)$ and $V_x^{(2)}(\omega;P)$; similarly for the y components.

Imagine that the observation is repeated many times under the same conditions, so that a statistical sample of the transforms is obtained. The modulus of, say, $V_x^{(1)}$ will show fluctuations, but, more important, its angle will fall at random in the range zero to 2π. Then the statistical average of the transform vanishes:

$$[V_x^{(1)}(\omega;P)]_{\text{av}} = 0 \tag{13-29}$$

(In contrast, the average of the modulus squared does not vanish, as has been seen in many examples.)

Now when the sources are unpolarized and independent, all four transforms $V_x^{(1)}, \ldots, V_y^{(2)}$ fluctuate independently. It follows that the statistical average of the product of any one of them and the complex conjugate of another is equal to the product of the averages of the factors and therefore vanishes:

$$[V_x^{(1)}V_y^{(1)*}]_{\text{av}} = [V_x^{(1)}V_x^{(2)*}]_{\text{av}} = [V_y^{(1)}V_y^{(2)*}]_{\text{av}} = 0 \tag{13-30}$$

More such relations could be added to the list; it is not essential that one factor be the complex conjugate, although the conjugate will appear in applications to be made of these important results.

The x component of the resultant of the electric fields has the Fourier transform

$$V_x(\omega;P) = V_x^{(1)}(\omega;P) + V_x^{(2)}(\omega;P)$$

Then $\qquad |V_x|^2 = |V_x^{(1)}|^2 + |V_x^{(2)}|^2 + 2\,\text{Re}\,(V_x^{(1)}V_x^{(2)*}) \tag{13-31}$

In a statistical average of (13-31), the third term on the right vanishes. The same result holds for the y component. The average energy spectrum of the resultant wave is then

$$[\mathcal{S}(\omega;P)]_{\text{av}} = \frac{c}{2\pi}\,[|V_x|^2 + |V_y|^2]_{\text{av}}$$

$$= [\mathcal{S}^{(1)}(\omega;P)]_{\text{av}} + [\mathcal{S}^{(2)}(\omega;P)]_{\text{av}} \tag{13-32}$$

By familiar arguments, the total flux density of energy $w(P)$ at the point P in a single observation when the sources are steady and the time of observation is long enough is equal to the integral of the averaged spectrum, and hence

$$w(P) = w^{(1)}(P) + w^{(2)}(P) \tag{13-33}$$

The last result states that the flux densities of energy observed when one or the other source is covered are to be simply added to obtain the result when both sources are uncovered. On movement from one point P

to another, no pattern with details attributable to interference of waves from the different sources is observed, and the sources are said to be *incoherent*. It does not follow that the instantaneous irradiance, considered at a particular instant and at various points P, fails to show any effects of interference of the two waves; but as time goes on, these effects result in a rapidly scintillating pattern, and on integration over a long time the effects disappear, and the additivity in (13-33) emerges. It is more difficult to establish (13-33) by considering instantaneous amplitudes and irradiances than by introducing Fourier transforms and applying Parseval's theorem.

13-7 Rule for Incoherent Sources In Sec. 7-12 the rule for incoherent sources was stated with reference to quasi-monochromatic radiation. The rule will now be proved, and the proof will apply for steady sources of arbitrary spectra.

Only slow optical systems for which the general relations (13-9) reduce to (13-10) will be considered, although it will be obvious how the argument can be extended to apply to the general case. Points P_r and P and the coordinate axes have the same significance as in Sec. 13-3. The new feature is the presence of two sources, each small enough in angular size that the entrance aperture is covered by a region of coherence for that source alone. It will be assumed that the angle between the sources is small enough (say, up to 10° or 15°) that the z axis at P_r is fairly definitely fixed, and the waves arriving there are essentially transverse to this axis. It is now necessary to note explicitly that the transfer functions for one source depend on the direction and distance of this source from P_r, and that there is therefore a different pair for each source.

The squared modulus of the Fourier transform of the ξ component of the resultant electric field at P, averaged over many observations of given duration, is

$$[|V_\xi|^2]_{\text{av}} = [|\tau_{\xi x}{}^{(1)}V_x{}^{(1)} + \tau_{\xi x}{}^{(2)}V_x{}^{(2)}|^2]_{\text{av}}$$
$$= \mathfrak{J}_{\xi x}{}^{(1)}[|V_x{}^{(1)}|^2]_{\text{av}} + \mathfrak{J}_{\xi x}{}^{(2)}[|V_x{}^{(2)}|^2]_{\text{av}}$$
$$+ 2\text{Re }(\tau_{\xi x}{}^{(1)}\tau_{\xi x}{}^{(2)*}[V_x{}^{(1)}V_x{}^{(2)*}]_{\text{av}})$$

where the transmission functions are defined as in (13-12). By (13-30), the last term vanishes, and the arguments leading from (13-11) to (13-14) can be applied to give

$$w(P) = \int_0^\infty \{\mathfrak{J}^{(1)}(\omega;P,P_r)\,[\mathfrak{S}^{(1)}(\omega;P_r)]_{\text{av}} + \mathfrak{J}^{(2)}(\omega;P,P_r)\,[\mathfrak{S}^{(2)}(\omega;P_r)]_{\text{av}}\}\,d\omega$$
$$= w^{(1)}(P) + w^{(2)}(P) \tag{13-34}$$

where the over-all transmission functions $\mathfrak{J}^{(1)}$ and $\mathfrak{J}^{(2)}$ are defined as in (13-15). The quantities $w^{(1)}$ and $w^{(2)}$ are the flux densities of energy at P that would be found in a single observation of a given and sufficiently long duration when one or the other source is covered, and w is the flux density that would be observed in an observation of the same duration when both sources are uncovered.

The additivity expressed by (13-34) is the rule for incoherent sources. The w's can be replaced by the long-time averages of the instantaneous irradiances, in which case the $\mathcal{S}$'s appearing in (13-34) are the power spectra of the two sources, rather than energy spectra. Clearly, the rule extends to any number of independent sources. A proof of the rule for those systems for which (13-9) cannot be reduced to (13-10) is called for in Prob. 13-11.

13-8 Diffraction with Quasi-monochromatic Sources

The difficulty generally encountered in calculating diffraction patterns when the radiation has a broad spectrum is quite evident even in the ideally simple example considered in Sec. 13-4. For this reason most calculations of diffraction phenomena assume quasi-monochromatic radiation. This assumption means that the spectrum has a width so small compared with its mean frequency ω_0 that at all points of the pattern to be considered, the relative irradiances (alternatively, flux densities of energy) would change insignificantly if the spectrum were taken still narrower. Equivalently, the assumption means that the transmission function associated with any point of the pattern to be considered is essentially constant over the range of frequencies covered by the spectrum. Then in (13-14), one commits negligible error by evaluating $\mathfrak{I}$ at the mean frequency ω_0 and taking it outside the integral. The integral that remains is just the flux density of energy arriving at the reference point P_r. Dividing by the time of observation to express the result in terms of irradiances, (13-14) reduces to

$$I(P) = \mathfrak{I}(\omega_0;P,P_r)\, I(P_r) \tag{13-35}$$

This formula refers to a single steady source of very small angular size as seen from P_r. If there are two such sources that are incoherent and have spectra of the same mean frequency but perhaps different intensities, the extension of (13-35) is found from (13-34) to be (with the superscripts lowered)

$$I(P) = \mathfrak{I}_1(\omega_0;P,P_r)\, I_1(P_r) + \mathfrak{I}_2(\omega;P,P_r)\, I_2(P_r) \tag{13-36}$$

Formula (13-35) is formally the same as what would be written if the source were assumed to be a point emitting a perfectly monochromatic wave of frequency ω_0. For example, if apertures in a screen are referred to the coordinate system in Fig. 7-4 with point O taken as the reference point P_r, and if the conditions for Fraunhofer diffraction are satisfied, then the general formula (9-4) with I_0 replaced by the expression in (9-5) is seen to be of the form (13-35) when E in (9-5) is recognized as $I(P_r)$. On the other hand, (13-36) is not a formula of the monochromatic theory and had to be introduced *ad hoc* as the rule for incoherent sources in Sec. 7-12. This rule cannot be proved by any argument that begins with the assumption that the sources emit strictly monochromatic waves of the same frequency; rather it must be recognized that any source is polychromatic and involves randomness of some sort, and that there is no correlation between the random processes in two independent sources. Nothing short of the elaborate statistical consideration of this and the preceding chapter suffices to make (13-34) and (13-36) understandable.

13-9 Extended Sources Formula (13-36) can be enlarged, by adding any number of terms to the right side, to calculate a diffraction pattern when there are any number of discrete quasi-monochromatic sources, each of very small angular size, and all independent and therefore incoherent. Consider now a source that is not small in angular dimensions but is continuous and quasi-monochromatic, for example, an incandescent body covered by a filter that isolates a very narrow band of frequencies, or a gaseous discharge from whose spectrum a single line is isolated. In such a case the projected area of the source as seen from the diffracting apertures can be divided into parts, each small enough to be treated as essentially a point source and yet large enough to contain many radiating elements and be a steady source independent of the other parts. Calculation of the diffraction pattern then consists in finding the irradiance in the pattern due to each part alone and adding these irradiances for all the parts. The process is simplified analytically by treating each part as infinitesimal and replacing summation by integration. Let us now work out a simple and important example.

Figure 13-10 shows an extended quasi-monochromatic source in front of a diffracting screen containing two identical pinholes at separation s. One hole is centered at a reference point P_r, which is also the origin of a cartesian coordinate system. The other hole is at (x,y), so that $s^2 = x^2 + y^2$. The point P_0 on an observing screen is on the normal through P_r and at a distance very large compared with s. A ξ axis is drawn in the observing plane to be parallel to the line joining the pinholes. It is to maintain this relationship when the hole at (x,y) is subsequently imagined to move about while that at P_r is held fixed. Only points P on the ξ axis need be considered, since any fringes that form will be parallel bands perpendicular to the ξ axis.

The source is assumed to be at a distance L very large compared with s and to be confined within some $10°$ about the normal. It is represented in the figure by a plane surface referred to X and Y axes. This surface is to be regarded as the projection onto a distant plane of the actual source, which may be a three-dimensional body or a volume of gas; its distance may be indefinite or unknown. The assumption of a plane source at a definite distance L is convenient, but L will disappear from the final result, and only the angular spread of the source will remain.

The area of the source is to be divided into small elements such as $d\sigma$ in the figure. The position of an element can be specified either by the

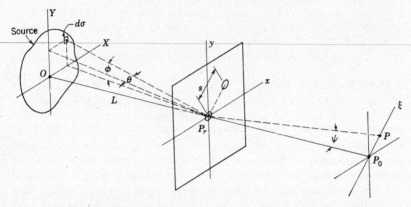

Fig. 13-10. *Extended quasi-monochromatic source irradiating a diffracting screen containing two identical pinholes at separation s. The distances OP_r and P_rP_0 are to be imagined large enough that Fraunhofer diffraction would result if the source were a point. The ξ axis is parallel to the line joining the pinholes.*

coordinates (X,Y) or by the angles (θ,ϕ). The latter will always be sufficiently small to admit the approximations

$$X = L\theta \qquad Y = L\phi \qquad d\sigma = dX\,dY = L^2\,d\theta\,d\phi \qquad (13\text{-}37)$$

The irradiance at the reference point P_r due to the part of the source contained in $d\sigma$ is proportional to $d\sigma$ and to L^{-2}, so that from (13-37),

$$dI(P_r) = N(\theta,\phi)\,d\theta\,d\phi \qquad (13\text{-}38)$$

where N is the factor of proportionality and is called the *radiance* of the source, expressed as power per unit area per unit solid angle. Dependence of N on θ and ϕ enters when the source is not uniform over its area. Moreover, it will be convenient to define N for all values of θ and ϕ between $-\infty$ and $+\infty$ by setting it equal to zero outside the range of small values subtended by the source.

Let the position of the point of observation P be specified by the angle ψ, of which only small values need be considered. The transmission function associated with a given configuration of the apertures and with the element $d\sigma$ as source depends on the position of P_r and the mean frequency as fixed parameters; it involves as variable parameters the coordinates (x,y) of the movable pinhole, the angles (θ,ϕ) specifying the position of $d\sigma$, and the angle ψ specifying the position of P. If it is assumed that the pinholes are small enough that the irradiance in the single-aperture pattern is essentially constant over the range of ψ to be considered, the transmission function can be written at once from the principles of Chap. 7. With approximations appropriate to small angles, the result is

$$\Im(x,y;\theta,\phi;\psi) = A|1 + e^{-ik(x\theta+y\phi+s\psi)}|^2$$
$$= 2A[1 + \mathrm{Re}\ (e^{-ik(x\theta+y\phi+s\psi)})]$$

where A is an unimportant constant.

This transmission function is to be multiplied by (13-38) and integrated to obtain the total irradiance at P. Thus,

$$I(P) = 2A \left\{ \iint_{-\infty}^{\infty} N(\theta,\phi)\ d\theta\ d\phi \right.$$

$$\left. + \mathrm{Re}\left[e^{-iks\psi} \iint_{-\infty}^{\infty} N(\theta,\phi)\ e^{-ik(x\theta+y\phi)}\ d\theta\ d\phi \right]\right\} \quad (13\text{-}39)$$

The first integral on the right is just the total irradiance at the reference point P_r, and (13-39) can be written in the concise form

$$I(P) = 2A\ I(P_r)\ \{1 + \mathrm{Re}\ [\gamma(x,y)\ e^{-iks\psi}]\} \quad (13\text{-}40)$$

where
$$\gamma(x,y) = \frac{\displaystyle\iint_{-\infty}^{\infty} N(\theta,\phi)\ e^{-ik(x\theta+y\phi)}\ d\theta\ d\phi}{\displaystyle\iint_{-\infty}^{\infty} N(\theta,\phi)\ d\theta\ d\phi}$$

$$= \Gamma(x,y)\ e^{i\,\beta(x,y)} \quad (13\text{-}41)$$

In the last expression, Γ is the magnitude of the complex quantity γ, and β is its angle. The relation (13-40) can now be written in the particularly significant form

$$I(P) = 2A\ I(P_r)\ [1 + \Gamma \cos\ (ks\psi - \beta)] \quad (13\text{-}42)$$

The significance of (13-42) is that whenever Γ is different from zero, there will be fringes with the angular separation $\Delta\psi = \lambda/s$, just as in Sec. 7-7. The value of β fixes the positions of the maxima on the ξ axis and can be determined, apart from an additive multiple of 2π, by observation if the position of P_0 can be accurately located (often not possible). The value of Γ can be determined from observation by the relation

$$\Gamma = \frac{I_{\max} - I_{\min}}{I_{\max} + I_{\min}} \quad (13\text{-}43)$$

where I_{max} and I_{min} are the maximum and minimum irradiances in the pattern of fringes and are given by (13-42) on setting $ks\psi - \beta$ equal to zero and π, respectively, whence (13-43) follows. The quantity on the right of (13-43) was introduced by Michelson and named the *visibility* of the fringes. Since I_{min} cannot be negative, Γ takes values only between zero and unity, a fact also evident from (13-41).

Suppose a source has unknown distribution of radiance, and suppose Γ and β have been observed as functions of x and y by varying the position of one of the pinholes. The complex quantity γ is then known, and (13-41) shows that apart from an irrelevant constant, $\gamma(x,y)$ is the Fourier transform of $N(\theta,\phi)$, and the latter can in principle be found by inversion. We thus have a very complete theory of the stellar interferometer. In practice, β cannot be determined, and Γ alone gives useful but incomplete information about N. An example will be cited in a moment.

Now γ has a significance in addition to its being proportional to the Fourier transform of N. By (13-37),

$$x\theta = \frac{xX}{L} = X\theta' \qquad y\phi = \frac{yY}{L} = Y\phi'$$

where θ' and ϕ' are angles fixing the direction of the pinhole at (x,y) from the point O in Fig. 13-10 in the same way that θ and ϕ fix the direction of $d\sigma$ from P_r. The radiance N can be expressed as a function of X and Y, and $d\theta\, d\phi = dX\, dY/L^2$. Then (13-41) can be rewritten

$$\gamma(\theta',\phi') = \frac{\displaystyle\iint_{-\infty}^{\infty} N(X,Y)\, e^{-ik(X\theta'+Y\phi')}\, dX\, dY}{\displaystyle\iint_{-\infty}^{\infty} N(X,Y)\, dX\, dY}$$

Comparison with (9-3) shows that γ at the point (x,y) of the screen containing the apertures is proportional to the complex amplitude of the Fraunhofer diffraction pattern formed on this screen in the following way: The source in Fig. 13-10 is replaced by an aperture of the same shape in an opaque screen. A plane monochromatic wave of the same frequency as the source, traveling in the direction O to P_r, is incident on this aperture. The aperture is covered by a semitransparent plate whose optical thickness is everywhere the same and whose transmittance is such that the magnitude of the complex amplitude of the emergent wave at (X,Y) is proportional to $N(X,Y)$ Finally, if the aperture is too large compared with L to give Fraunhofer diffraction, it is covered by a lens whose axis is the line OP_r and whose focal point is P_r. With this interpretation of γ, it follows that Γ is the square root of the irradiance in the diffraction pattern.

As an example to illustrate this interpretation of γ, suppose the problem is to measure the angular diameter α of a star with the stellar interferometer. Let it be assumed that the star is effectively a circular disk with uniform radiance. If the star is at the hypothetical distance L, its linear diameter is $D = \alpha L$. With an aperture of this diameter and distance, the Fraunhofer pattern formed on the plane of the double aperture of the instrument has an amplitude whose first zero is at the radius $1.22\lambda L/D = 1.22\lambda/\alpha$ from the center of the pattern. (See Sec. 9-4, noting that a different α appears there.) Fringes first disappear ($\Gamma = 0$) when the separation of the apertures equals this radius, a fact that was stated without proof in Sec. 7-13.

13-10 Coherent and Partially Coherent Sources. Lateral Coherence in Wave Fields The general subject of coherence and incoherence is of prime importance in physical optics and has received the attention of many scientists in the nineteenth and twentieth centuries. It is essential to recognize the role of statistical fluctuations, but the real problem is to arrive at a set of working rules that is not unnecessarily encumbered with complicated and repetitious statistical arguments. A successful solution was given in an important and beautiful paper by Zernike [105], and for application to a wide class of optical problems Zernike's ideas were reduced to still simpler terms in three papers by Hopkins [42, 43, 44]. The present section will deal, mostly in qualitative terms, with some of the main ideas in these papers.

In Sec. 13-6 the criterion whereby two small steady sources lying in nearly the same direction from an observer are said to be incoherent is that they give rise to no persistent interference fringes. Incoherence results when the statistical fluctuations, inevitably present in the sources, are uncorrelated. When the sources are nearly monochromatic with the same mean frequency, the case to which all the following discussion will be confined, one has the simple picture in which the wave from each source as it arrives at an observing screen is sinusoidal with the mean frequency, except that the amplitude and phase angle undergo slow and erratic changes, more slowly as the wave is made more nearly monochromatic. At any instant, fringes appear as though the sources were perfectly monochromatic, but as time goes on, the maxima shift about, and on the average the fringes disappear.

If, on the other hand, the sources are completely correlated, changes of amplitude and phase are the same in the two waves as they arrive at any point of the observing screen near a point equidistant from the sources. Fringes then remain stationary and fluctuate in irradiance by a time-dependent factor which is the same for all points of observation. After a time average, the fringes are just those that would be calculated on the assumption that the sources are perfectly monochromatic with some definite phase difference; in this case the sources are said to be *coherent.*

Finally, there are intermediate cases in which fringes appear but have less contrast, or visibility, than they would have with monochromatic sources. The sources are then said to be *partially coherent;* this case arises through some partial correlation of the random processes in the sources. A given maximum in the instantaneous pattern of fringes moves, but remains most of the time in the immediate vicinity of a mean position.

The most common occurrence in optics of these various cases is in diffraction. Consider the example of the two pinholes treated in the last section. The wave from the primary source induces motions of charges in the diffracting screen, and some of them constitute luminous edges around the holes, as described in Chap. 6. These luminous edges are the two sources, *secondary* sources, of the waves behind the screen, and since the holes are identical and are irradiated by a distant primary source of fairly small angular extent, the secondary sources are of equal intensities. There is clearly a good chance for some correlation between the motions of charges at the edge of one pinhole and those at the edge of the other, since the part of the primary wave originating in any one moving charge in the primary source affects the motions at both pinholes. If these secondary sources happen to be completely correlated, and therefore coherent, then when waves from them fall on a distant observing screen and form fringes, the visibility Γ as defined by (13-43) is unity, since these fringes must be the same as though the pinholes were perfectly mono-chromatic points. If the secondary sources are incoherent, $\Gamma = 0$; if they are partially coherent, $0 < \Gamma < 1$.

Now the motions of charges in the secondary sources are determined entirely by the primary incident wave, and any coherence of these sources is really a property of the incident wave and indicates correlation between the amplitudes and phases at the locations of the two pinholes. It was Zernike's idea to take the complex quantity γ, whose magnitude Γ and angle β are experimentally observable by means of identical pinholes as described in the last section, as the most useful measure of this correlation. He called γ the *complex degree of coherence,* and the magnitude Γ the *degree of coherence.* Both quantities refer to two separate points on a surface transverse to the direction of propagation of the incident wave, and choosing these points variously gives γ as a function of four coordinates, two for each point. Ordinarily the magnitude Γ depends only on the distance and direction from one point to the other, and not on the absolute positions. It is important to note that these diffraction problems involve a primary source divisible into small incoherent elements, and for this class of problems statistical considerations are disposed of once and for all in obtaining the rule for incoherent sources. This point was made explicitly by Hopkins.

A feeling for the various degrees of coherence comes easily from the interpretation of γ as being proportional to the amplitude in a certain diffraction pattern, as was brought out in the last section. Suppose the source is a distant circular disk of uniform radiance. Then the circular symmetry makes Γ a function only of the distance s between the two points to which it refers. The character of this function can be drawn from Sec. 9-4, as called for in Prob. 13-14. For any nonvanishing angular diameter α of the source, Γ approaches unity as s approaches zero, and Γ becomes and remains arbitrarily small when s becomes sufficiently large. When α is very small, Γ remains near unity, say greater than 0.9, for $0 < s < s_0$, where s_0 may be quite large and varies as α^{-1}. The value of s_0 is the diameter of the region of coherence defined in Sec. 13-1.

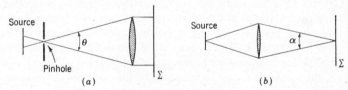

Fig. 13-11. *Two modes of irradiating a surface. At (a) the oscillations at any two irradiated points of Σ are approximately coherent if the pinhole is small enough, and at (b) they are approximately incoherent if the angle α is large.*

When α is large, say 90°, Γ is practically zero for all s greater than about two wavelengths, and it is often an adequate approximation to say that coherence vanishes altogether.

In Fig. 13-11a, an observer at any point of the irradiated part of the surface Σ sees a virtual image of the pinhole at an infinite distance with an angular diameter equal to that of the actual pinhole as seen from the center of the lens. This virtual image becomes the effective source, and the pinhole can readily be made small enough that Σ is irradiated almost coherently, even when the angle θ is as large as 10° or 20°. The test for coherence is, of course, to cover Σ with a screen with two small holes separated by the diameter of the lens and to measure the visibility of fringes formed in the focal plane of a second lens behind the screen. When Σ is irradiated essentially coherently, it is a good approximation to treat the wave falling on it as a monochromatic plane wave.

In Fig. 13-11b the situation is essentially different, for now the degree of coherence between two points of Σ is determined entirely by diffraction introduced by the lens. From the standpoint of geometrical optics, each point of the source is imaged as a point on Σ, and any two points on the latter are then incoherent. Physically, each point of the source gives rise to a diffraction pattern on Σ whose linear extent is of order λ/α. There will be some correlation, and hence some coherence, between the oscillations at any two points of Σ lying within such a pattern. A quantitative determination of γ requires the general methods developed by Zernike and Hopkins; the result is that γ is the same as it would be if the actual source and lens were replaced by a distant circular source subtending the angular diameter α. Hence the region of partial coherence surrounding any given point of Σ extends only a very small number of wavelengths when α is large.

The surface Σ in Fig. 13-11 might be the plane of a translucent object to be examined with a microscope. The lens would then be called a *condenser*. Case (*a*) is the coherent illumination assumed in Secs. 11-8 and 11-9. Case (*b*) is called *critical illumination*, and the fact that partial coherence extends over several wavelengths even when α is large, together with the fact that the minimum resolvable distance for a microscope of large numerical aperture is also of the order of a wavelength, means that one cannot conclude that the object can be regarded as a distribution of incoherent points, although it can be so regarded when the angular diameters of the condenser and objective are equal.

Again, the surface Σ might be the plane of the entrance slit of a spectrograph. The width and ordinate of the instrumental profile depend on the width of the slit in different ways for (*a*) and (*b*). Van Cittert solved this problem, taking (*b*) to represent complete incoherence of all pairs of points in the aperture of the slit; the results are given in Sawyer [80], p. 111, and Harrison et al. [34], p. 121. These considerations are important in choosing the optimum width of the slit.

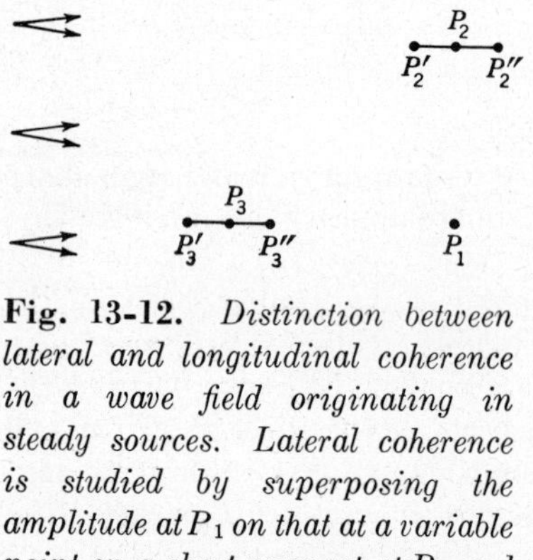

Fig. 13-12. *Distinction between lateral and longitudinal coherence in a wave field originating in steady sources. Lateral coherence is studied by superposing the amplitude at P_1 on that at a variable point on a short segment at P_2 and looking for persistent interference. Longitudinal coherence is studied similarly with reference to points P_1 and P_3. The arrows at the left indicate a range of directions from sources.*

13-11 Longitudinal Coherence in Wave Fields. Michelson Interferometer and Its Use as a Spectrograph

The last section dealt with what might be called the *degree of lateral coherence* in a quasi-monochromatic wave field, since the item of interest was the correlation between the oscillations in the field at two points on a plane surface transverse to the direction of arrival of the wave. This correlation was characterized by the visibility and the positions of maxima in the fringes observed when identical pinholes are placed at the points in question. Only a few fringes are to be observed in the vicinity of a point on the observing screen equidistant from the apertures. The essential nature of this observation is illustrated by Fig. 13-12. The degree of coherence between two points P_1 and P_2 is to be determined. Points P_2' and P_2'' mark off a segment a few wavelengths long at P_2. The experiment with the pinholes amounts to superposing the instantaneous amplitude at P_1 on that at a variable point on the segment at P_2 and measuring the time average of the irradiance resulting from this superposition as the variable point assumes positions between P_2' to P_2''.

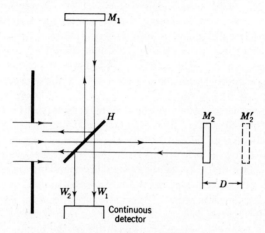

Fig. 13-13. *Schematic diagram of a Michelson interferometer in the arrangement for measuring longitudinal coherence in an approximately unidirectional radiation field. The entrance aperture is to be covered by a region of coherence. Rays with arrowheads indicate the several essentially plane waves traversing the system. The position of mirror M_2 shown in solid lines is that which gives equal optical paths, while M_2' is a displaced position of M_2.*

One can now imagine a similar superposition of the amplitude at P_1 on that at a variable point on a short segment at P_3 (Fig. 13-12). In this way one is led to the concept of a degree of *longitudinal coherence* in a wave field. The instrument for making an experimental observation is the Michelson interferometer,[1] of which the essential parts are shown in Fig. 13-13.

The distant source is assumed to be very far away and have a very small angular diameter, and the entrance aperture is to be small enough to be covered by a region of coherence, yet large enough to be very many wave-

---

[1] This instrument is to be distinguished from Michelson's stellar interferometer. It is interesting to note that lateral and longitudinal coherence are studied with two instruments associated with the name of Michelson.

lengths across. Then the wave entering the instrument can be regarded as part of a plane wave, and diffraction can be neglected. The reason for this restriction on the distance and size of the source is the following: Longitudinal coherence will turn out to be related to the spectrum of the source in the same way that lateral coherence is related to the angular spread. The awkward dependence of the transmission function of two pinholes on frequency and its simple dependence on angular spread made it appropriate to discuss lateral coherence only for quasi-monochromatic sources, or equivalently, for a narrow band of the spectrum isolated by a filter. In contrast, the Michelson interferometer has a difficult dependence on angular spread and a simple dependence on frequency. It is therefore appropriate in discussing this instrument to restrict the size of the source and leave the spectrum arbitrary. (Instead of a distant small source, a pinhole and lens could be used in the arrangement of Fig. 13-11a.)

It should be realized that we are dealing only with limited aspects of the general question of coherence, or correlation, between the instantaneous amplitudes at two arbitrarily chosen points in a wave field when the source is completely arbitrary. Lateral coherence when the source is quasi-monochromatic but only reasonably small in angular size, and longitudinal coherence when the source is essentially a point but only reasonably restricted in width of spectrum, are the most useful concepts.

The interferometer consists of a plane, semitransparent film H set exactly at 45° to the direction of propagation of the incident wave. The nature and properties of the film and the means of supporting it will be taken up in a later chapter. For the moment suppose the film is self-supporting and is of negligible thickness. The incident wave is divided into two waves propagating at right angles to each other, each carrying a certain fraction of the incident irradiance. These waves fall at exactly normal incidence on two plane mirrors M_1 and M_2. The wave reflected by M_1 is partially transmitted by H to give a wave W_1 falling on a continuous detector, while that reflected from M_2 is partially reflected at H to give a second wave W_2 traveling in exactly the same direction as W_1. These two waves will have equal irradiances, since each has undergone one reflection and one transmission at H. The detector responds to the resultant of W_1 and W_2.

Let M_2 be mounted on a slide controlled by a screw such that it can be moved in the direction of its normal. For some position of M_2, say the one shown in solid lines in the figure, the two optical paths from the plane of the entrance aperture to the surface of the detector (both surfaces are assumed coincident with wave fronts) are equal. It is assuming quite a bit to imply that this equality holds simultaneously for all frequencies and polarizations. However, suffice it for the moment to say that there are types of semireflectors H for which this assumption is valid over a substantial range of frequencies, and by various means such a range can be placed anywhere in the visible, the infrared, or the microwave frequencies. Any spectrum to be considered will be supposed confined to such a range. The reflectance and transmittance of H (fraction of the incident irradiance reflected and transmitted, respectively) can be essentially constant over the range of frequencies. However, they are different for the two linear polarizations in and perpendicular to the plane of Fig. 13-13, so that the resultant wave at the detector is strongly polarized even though the incident wave is unpolarized. As will be pointed out more specifically in a moment, taking this dependence on polarization into account would lengthen the argument without affecting the conclusions, and so let us neglect it. We can then think in terms of scalar waves for simplicity.

With these restrictions and assumptions on the semireflector H, we have the situation that when M_2 is positioned for equality of optical paths, the dependences on time of the amplitudes of the two waves W_1 and W_2 at a point of the detecting surface are the same. Moreover, they are the same as the dependence of the amplitude at the plane of the entrance aperture, except for the temporal delay occasioned by transit through the instrument with the velocity of light. If M_2 is shifted through a distance D to the position M_2' in Fig. 13-13, the temporal delay associated with the wave W_2 is increased by $2D/c$, and the geometrical path is increased by $2D$. For an ideal monochromatic wave the optical path is increased by $2D/\lambda$. With this displacement D, the instrument has clearly done the equivalent of superposing the instantaneous amplitudes occurring at the two longitudinally displaced points P_1 and P_3 in Fig. 13-12 if these points are separated by distance $2D$.

Now the irradiance measured by the detector for a given displacement D may not be the sum of the irradiances of the separate waves W_1 and W_2 (which can be isolated by covering M_1 or M_2 with a black surface). This departure from simple additivity and its dependence on the displacement D are indications of longitudinal coherence. To render the idea quantitative, we make a calculation analogous to that of Sec. 13-9.

To find the transmission function of the instrument, choose a reference point P_r anywhere near the entrance aperture, and suppose that a monochromatic plane wave of frequency ω and of unit average irradiance is incident. Let M_2 be displaced a distance D from the position for equal paths. The average irradiance at any point of the detecting surface is then the transmission function, and in terms of the wave number $k = \omega/c$ and the geometric increment of path $\Delta = 2D$, one clearly has

$$\Im(k,\Delta) = C|1 + e^{ik\Delta}|^2 = 2C(1 + \cos k\Delta) \qquad (13\text{-}44)$$

where C is an unimportant constant depending on the reflectance and transmittance of H. [To be more complete, there are two functions of this form, one for each of the linear polarizations in and perpendicular to the plane of Fig. 13-13. They differ only in the value of C, and (13-44) is the over-all function for unpolarized incident radiation if it is obtained by averaging in the manner of (13-15).]

Let $\mathcal{S}(k)$ be the power spectrum of the incident radiation referred to a scale of wave number k, so that the incident irradiance at the reference point P_r is

$$I(P_r) = \int_0^\infty \mathcal{S}(k)\, dk$$

The irradiance at a point P of the surface of the detector is

$$I(P) = \int_0^\infty \Im \mathcal{S}\, dk = 2C[I(P_r) + \phi(\Delta)] \tag{13-45}$$

where $$\phi(\Delta) = \int_0^\infty \mathcal{S}(k) \cos k\Delta\, dk \tag{13-46}$$

The integral on the right of (13-46) is called a *Fourier cosine integral*, and $\phi(\Delta)$ is said to be the *Fourier cosine transform* of $\mathcal{S}(k)$ for $k \geqq 0$. The integral defines ϕ for all Δ, but this function is even; that is, $\phi(-\Delta) = \phi(\Delta)$. Using this symmetry in connection with the Fourier theorem (11-1) and (11-2) gives the inversion formula:

$$\mathcal{S}(k) = \frac{2}{\pi} \int_0^\infty \phi(\Delta) \cos k\Delta\, d\Delta \tag{13-47}$$

We can now draw the following conclusions: The function $\phi(\Delta)$, which indicates longitudinal coherence if it does not vanish, is proportional to the variable part of the observed irradiance $I(P)$. Since ϕ is an even function, it need be measured only for displacements of the mirror M_2 in the one direction indicated in Fig. 13-13. The power spectrum and the function ϕ are related by the Fourier cosine integrals (13-46) and (13-47), so that the interferometer not only reveals the presence of longitudinal coherence, but also serves as a spectrograph.

Any given instrument imposes an upper limit on the range of Δ beyond which ϕ has to be set equal to zero arbitrarily. With this truncated function the spectrum calculated by (13-47) differs from the true one. As a spectrograph, the instrument therefore has limited resolution, but this resolution can be very high, since Δ can be made very large in comparison with the longest wavelength in the spectrum. Note that this interferometric spectrograph has a transmission function quite different from that of a prism or grating, with the result that the observed function ϕ, which has often been called an *interferogram*, bears no resemblance to the spectrum, but contains information from which the latter can be calculated.

As an example, suppose the observed interferogram is

$$\phi(\Delta) = e^{-\Delta^2/a^2} \cos b\Delta \qquad ab \gg 1$$

Using a table of definite integrals and ignoring constant factors gives the spectrum as

$$S(k) = e^{-a^2(k-b)^2/4}$$

These two functions are shown in Fig. 13-14. The spectrum has a gaussian profile centered at $k = b$. The corresponding wavelength is

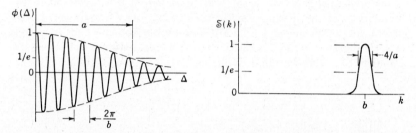

Fig. 13-14. *Interferogram of a single spectrum line having gaussian profile. Scales of ordinates have been chosen for simplest representation. The variable Δ is twice the displacement D shown in Fig. 13-13; k is the wave number $2\pi/\lambda$.*

$\lambda_0 = 2\pi/b$, which is just the period of the oscillations in ϕ as a function of Δ. (Recall that $\Delta = 2D$, so that displacement of M_2 through $\lambda_0/2$ carries ϕ from one maximum to the next.)

As another example, let the interferogram be

$$\phi(\Delta) = e^{-\Delta^2/a^2} \cos f\Delta \cos b\Delta \qquad b \gg f, \; af \gg 1$$

The spectrum is

$$S(k) = e^{-a^2(k-b-f)^2/4} + e^{-a^2(k-b+f)^2/4}$$

and is therefore two lines of equal intensities and equal widths, as shown in Fig. 13-15. More examples are cited in the problems.

Historically, Michelson used this method, beginning in 1891, in the first spectroscopic observations with resolution much higher than could be attained with diffraction gratings. He measured shapes of individual lines and of hyperfine structures in atomic spectra. He also advanced to very high precision the measurement of wavelengths in terms of the standard meter. While Michelson's interferometer has been superseded in both these uses by the interferometer of Fabry and Perot, it still has potentialities as a practical spectrograph for measuring broad and complicated spectra. Qualitatively, this is because a detector of given response time can obtain an interferogram covering a given range of Δ, and therefore leading to a given spectral resolution, in less time than a spectrogram can be recorded by scanning the pattern produced by a grating of the same resolution with the same detector and a narrow slit. Modern computing techniques make Fourier inversion a rapid process. For more detail on these considerations see Jacquinot [49] and Strong [88], appendix F.

The most celebrated application of the Michelson interferometer was in the experiment of Michelson and Morley, which contributed to the foundations of the special theory of relatively. Any text on this theory describes the experiment. The Michelson interferometer and its various adaptations have many applications in technical optics. References are Candler [15], Michelson [64], Williams [101], and Wood [103].

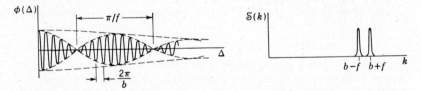

Fig. 13-15. *Interferogram of a spectral doublet of two identical profiles.*

If the source irradiating the instrument in Fig. 13-13 is of large angular size and is uniform in radiance and spectrum, then when an observer substitutes his eye for the detector, he sees circular fringes, provided the path difference Δ is not so large that the interferogram ϕ has settled to a vanishingly small value. (With white light this means that Δ must be within a mean wavelength or so. See Prob. 13-18.) Fringes with a certain similarity of character occur for the same reason in the Fabry-Perot interferometer; they will be discussed later in connection with that instrument. A very good treatment special to the Michelson interferometer is given in Jenkins and White [53], beginning on p. 244.

The function $\phi(\Delta)$ will become and remain essentially zero when Δ reaches and exceeds some sufficiently large value Δ_0, because in (13-46) the cosine ultimately oscillates so rapidly as a function of k that the spectrum, whatever its shape, becomes essentially constant over any given cycle. This critical value Δ_0 is called the *coherence length* of the incident wave and represents the largest separation of longitudinally oriented points in the field between which there is appreciable correlation of instantaneous amplitudes. Corresponding to the coherence length Δ_0 is the *coherence time* $t_0 = \Delta_0/c$, the time in which a point moving with the velocity of light traverses the distance Δ_0.

If a steady source is pictured as emitting wave trains at random times, each train essentially confined to the same length L (for example, the damped waves in Sec. 12-6, or the waves considered in Prob. 13-20), then L is the coherence length. Quanta emitted by atoms have sometimes been thought of as being representable by such wave trains, and the coherence length has been spoken of as the length of a photon. Such a notion may be justifiable in some sense, but on the surface it is certainly misleading and should be avoided. The topic will be taken up again in Chap. 19.

If a source has a spectrum extending over a range of frequencies very small compared with the mean frequency, then the irradiance $I(P)$ given by (13-45) oscillates sinusoidally about the mean value $2CI(P_r)$, except that the amplitude of oscillation varies comparatively slowly and eventually becomes negligibly small. As a partial but easily observed description of this irradiance, Michelson introduced the visibility (13-43), a function of Δ. The minimum in this formula is always to be that one preceding or following a given maximum. Michelson used observed visibilities to deduce profiles of spectrum lines, but the results were sometimes in error, since knowledge of the visibility alone is not equivalent to complete knowledge of the interferogram, except when the spectrum is symmetrical about some frequency Jacquinot [49] gives a detailed discussion of this point.

When the spectrum is broad, and particularly when it is irregular, the observed irradiance as a function of Δ does not yield a clear-cut visibility function (see Prob. 13-18). In such cases the interferogram stands as the one significant measure of longitudinal coherence.

13-12 Polarization of Polychromatic Waves It has been noted repeatedly that a perfectly monochromatic plane wave is always polarized, and this polarization is characterized by the motion of the end point of an arrow representing the electric vector at a point of observation. In the general case the motion describes an ellipse with unequal principal axes, and there is a direction of rotation, that is, a handedness of the polarization. The conventions of terminology were given at the end of Sec. 2-5. In the special case of linear motion there is a preferred axis but no handedness, while with a circular motion there is handedness but no preferred axis.

If a wave from a steady source is polychromatic but has a spectrum covering a range of frequencies very small compared with the mean frequency, there is an additional dimension, so to speak, to the range of possible polarizations. At the one extreme the wave can appear to have the properties of a perfectly monochromatic wave with one of the definite polarizations possible for such waves, and the polychromatic wave is then said to be completely polarized. At the other extreme no experiment involving a detector slow enough to give a steady reading indicates that the wave has a preferred axis or a handedness, and the wave is said to be unpolarized.   Between these extremes is a range of partial polarizations.

It is appropriate to discuss polarization with reference to nearly monochromatic waves only.   The reasons will be shown later and will have to do with the sources that emit polarized waves and with the devices available for studying polarization experimentally.   A source may have a spectrum with a wide range of frequencies, and the wave may show polarization, but if narrow bands of the spectrum are isolated, the polarization may change drastically from one band to another.   An example will be seen in the Zeeman effect, in which a gaseous discharge is polarized through the action of a static magnetic field.   The field splits a spectrum line into a number of components separated by small differences in frequency.   All the components are polarized, but not all in the same way, and each must be examined separately.

When a wave from a steady source is nearly monochromatic, one may discuss its properties entirely in terms of instantaneous amplitudes and irradiances and their long-time averages, and thereby obtain a simpler and more direct picture of these properties than would result from the alternative method of Fourier analysis.   Suppose the source is small enough and far enough away that the wave arriving at a point of observation is essentially a plane wave traveling in the z direction.   If the mean frequency of the spectrum is ω_0, the components of the electric field at a fixed point can be written

$$\mathbf{e}_x = a_x(t) \cos \left[\omega_0 t - \theta_x(t)\right] \qquad \mathbf{e}_y = a_y(t) \cos \left[\omega_0 t - \theta_y(t)\right] \quad (13\text{-}48)$$

The amplitudes a_x and a_y and the phase angles θ_x and θ_y are functions of the time.   Since the wave is nearly monochromatic, these functions vary slowly enough that they are essentially constant over a fairly large number of cycles beginning at any instant.   Over a long time, the amplitudes will fluctuate in some way, perhaps independently, or perhaps with some correlation.   The phase angles will wander about and eventually cover the range zero to 2π with uniform probability.   Again there may or may not be correlation.   It will turn out that the wave shows some degree of polarization only if there is some correlation between the components (13-48).

From (13-48) one can arrive at a mental image of the various types of polarization.   On the basis of Sec. 2-3, particularly the discussion of (2-35), the electric vector describes during any small number of cycles an ellipse quite steady in size, eccentricity, and directions of principal axes; the handedness (if the motion is not along a straight line) remains fixed. As time goes on, one or more of these characteristics of the motion will change slowly.

Complete polarization results when only the size of the ellipse varies or, equivalently, when the amplitudes a_x and a_y have a constant ratio and the difference $\theta_x - \theta_y$ is constant. The x and y components of the electric field are then completely correlated. It will be shown that in any experiment such a wave behaves essentially as would a perfectly monochromatic wave with the same shape of ellipse and the same handedness.

The wave is unpolarized if the characteristics of the ellipse vary in such a way that, over a long time, the moving point describes a path showing no preferred axis or direction of rotation. Many such motions are conceivable. A simple example, which can be produced artificially, is that in which the oscillation is always linear, but the line of the motion changes and covers all directions uniformly in less than the response time of the detector. In a wave from an unpolarized atomic source the amplitudes and phase angles vary independently and at random, and the ellipse passes through all shapes and orientations and is as likely to be right-hand as left-hand. Such different possible motions cannot be distinguished by any observation that averages over a long time, and there must therefore be some unique characterization applicable to all these possibilities as far as observable effects are concerned.

Partial polarization occurs when the motion shows a degree of irregularity intermediate between the extremes just described, so that over a long time there remains some preferred axis or direction of rotation or both. Again, a given set of observational results can arise with waves differing in details, and a common characterization based on experiment is to be sought.

We shall now obtain a general formula for the irradiance observed at the output of an arbitrary optical instrument when (13-48) is the input wave. From this formula we shall determine the minimum information required to calculate such an irradiance and how special experiments can be devised for obtaining this information when it is not known from theory.

Let the optical system be the general one described in Sec. 13-3 up to formulas (13-9). Take (13-48) to be the field in the incident plane wave at the reference point P_r. These components can be regarded as the real parts of the complex representations

$$\mathsf{e}_x^{(c)}(t;P_r) = A_x(t)\, e^{-i\omega_0 t} \qquad \mathsf{e}_y^{(c)}(t;P_r) = A_y(t)\, e^{-i\omega_0 t} \qquad (13\text{-}49)$$

where
$$A_x = a_x e^{i\theta_x} \qquad A_y = a_y e^{i\theta_y} \qquad (13\text{-}50)$$

At the point of observation P the components of the field will have complex representations

$$\mathsf{e}_\xi^{(c)}(t;P) = B_\xi(t)\, e^{-i\omega_0 t} \qquad \mathsf{e}_\eta^{(c)}(t;P) = B_\eta(t)\, e^{-i\omega_0 t} \qquad (13\text{-}51)$$

in which the complex amplitudes B_ξ and B_η remain to be found.

Suppose the system is such that the transfer functions in (13-9) are essentially constant over the small range of frequencies in the spectrum of the input wave. Then, with negligible error,

$$B_\xi(t) = \tau_{\xi x}(\omega_0;P,P_r)A_x(t) + \tau_{\xi y}(\omega_0;P,P_r)A_y(t)$$
$$B_\eta(t) = \tau_{\eta x}(\omega_0;P,P_r)A_x(t) + \tau_{\eta y}(\omega_0;P,P_r)A_y(t) \tag{13-52}$$

That is, (13-9) can be applied as though (13-49) were perfectly monochromatic with frequency ω_0. Actually, we should justify (13-52) by making a Fourier analysis of (13-49) into its monochromatic components with a small range of frequencies about ω_0, applying (13-9) to each component, and finally synthesizing after evaluating the transfer functions at ω_0 and taking them outside the integral.

The instantaneous Poynting vector at P is given by (13-3) with x, y, and z replaced by ξ, η, and ζ, respectively. The components of the field are to be the real parts of (13-51). The result shows a rapid sinusoidal variation at frequency $2\omega_0$ and a much slower variation due to the temporal dependence of B_ξ and B_η. Only the latter is of interest, so let the Poynting vector be averaged over one cycle beginning at time t. Denoting this average by $I_t(t;P)$, it is easily seen that

$$I_t(t;P) = \frac{c}{8\pi}\,[|B_\xi(t)|^2 + |B_\eta(t)|^2]$$

To obtain the steady irradiance $I(P)$ that would be observed with a slow detector, the last expression must be averaged over a long time. Denoting such averaging by brackets $\langle\ \rangle$,

$$I(P) = \frac{c}{8\pi}\,[\langle|B_\xi(t)|^2\rangle + \langle|B_\eta(t)|^2\rangle] \tag{13-53}$$

Substituting from (13-52) and (13-50) gives the final formula:

$$I(P) = \frac{c}{8\pi}\,\{(|\tau_{\xi x}|^2 + |\tau_{\eta x}|^2)\langle a_x{}^2\rangle + (|\tau_{\xi y}|^2 + |\tau_{\eta y}|^2)\langle a_y{}^2\rangle$$
$$+ 2\,\mathrm{Re}\,[(\tau_{\xi x}\tau_{\xi y}^* + \tau_{\eta x}\tau_{\eta y}^*)\langle a_x a_y e^{i(\theta_x-\theta_y)}\rangle]\} \tag{13-54}$$

We now reach the conclusion that in order to calculate the irradiance $I(P)$ when the four transfer functions characterizing the system are known at the mean frequency ω_0, it is sufficient to know the following four real quantities associated with the input wave (13-48):

$$\langle a_x{}^2\rangle \qquad \langle a_y{}^2\rangle \qquad \langle a_x a_y \cos(\theta_x - \theta_y)\rangle \qquad \langle a_x a_y \sin(\theta_x - \theta_y)\rangle \tag{13-55}$$

The common practice is to characterize the incident wave by the four *Stokes parameters* I, Q, U, and V defined in terms of the averages (13-55) in the following way:

$$I = \frac{c}{8\pi}\left(\langle a_x{}^2\rangle + \langle a_y{}^2\rangle\right) \qquad\qquad Q = \frac{c}{8\pi}\left(\langle a_x{}^2\rangle - \langle a_y{}^2\rangle\right)$$

$$U = \frac{c}{8\pi}\langle 2a_x a_y \cos\left(\theta_x - \theta_y\right)\rangle \quad ' \quad V = \frac{c}{8\pi}\langle 2a_x a_y \sin\left(\theta_x - \theta_y\right)\rangle \tag{13-56}$$

The parameter I is just the irradiance of the wave and is always positive. The other three can have either sign; they characterize the polarization in a manner to be brought out in Sec. 13-14.

If the Stokes parameters are known, the averages appearing in (13-54) can be expressed in terms of them to give, as the most convenient formula for $I(P)$,

$$I(P) = \tfrac{1}{2}(|\tau_{\xi x}|^2 + |\tau_{\eta x}|^2)(I + Q) + \tfrac{1}{2}(|\tau_{\xi y}|^2 + |\tau_{\eta y}|^2)(I - Q)$$
$$+ \operatorname{Re}\left[(\tau_{\xi x}\tau_{\xi y}^* + \tau_{\eta x}\tau_{\eta y}^*)(U + iV)\right] \tag{13-57}$$

In connection with this formula, bear in mind that the transfer functions refer to the reference point P_r, to the point of observation P, to the mean frequency ω_0, and to the choice of the x, y, ξ, and η axes. The Stokes parameters refer to the reference point P_r and to the choice of the x and y axes.

13-13 Measurement of the Stokes Parameters

The averages appearing in (13-55) may on occasion be derivable from a knowledge of the manner in which the incident wave originated. For example, waves from the gaseous sources treated in Chap. 12 surely give $Q = U = V = 0$, and such a set of parameters characterizes unpolarized radiation. Suppose now that nothing is known about the incident wave and the problem is to measure the Stokes parameters.

There are many ways to proceed, but the simplest and most common is to use a linear polarizer and a quarter-wave plate. The functions of these two devices will be characterized for the present discussion without reference to practical realization. Realization depends on where in the electromagnetic spectrum the radiation lies, but the principles are always the same. In the visible range both these devices are available in the form of thin slabs of anisotropic material, so for a definite picture let us think of them as thin slabs to be oriented with their plane surfaces perpendicular to the incident beam.

A linear polarizer has the property of being perfectly transparent to a normally incident plane wave linearly polarized with its electric vector along a certain direction associated with the plate, and opaque to a linearly polarized wave whose electric vector is perpendicular to this direction. Let this characteristic direction be indicated by a line drawn on one of the faces of the plate and labeled E. If an arbitrary wave is incident, then the electric vector is to be resolved into linear components parallel and perpendicular to E. The emergent wave is then linearly polarized and consists of just the parallel component. No mention need be made of the magnetic field. It is present in both the incident and emergent waves and always bears its simple relation to the electric field.

Consider now the arrangement of a linear polarizer and cartesian axes shown in Fig. 13-16. The x and ξ axes are parallel, and the angular orientation of the polarizer is specified by the angle ψ between the line E and the plane of these axes. The sense in which this angle is reckoned positive is indicated by the arrow in the figure. The first problem is to find the transfer functions appearing in (13-57). Imagine that the incident wave is monochromatic with frequency ω_0 and is linearly

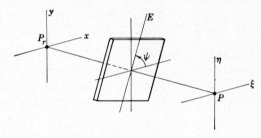

Fig. 13-16. *Linear polarizer referred to cartesian axes. The large faces are parallel to the xy plane.*

polarized with the electric field along the x axis. Let the amplitude of the wave be unity, and let the phase angle of the oscillation at the reference point P_r be zero. Then in complex representation, the x component of the electric field at P_r is just $e^{-i\omega_0 t}$, and the y component is zero. By the definition of the transfer functions [formula (13-9)] the complex amplitude of the ξ component of the wave arriving at P is equal to $\tau_{\xi x}$, and that of the η component is equal to $\tau_{\eta x}$. The component along the axis E of the oscillation at P_r is $e^{-i\omega_0 t} \cos \psi$. This component passes freely through the polarizer and arrives at P after traversing some path whose optical length expressed in radians (2π times the length in wavelengths—Sec. 7-12) is α, so that the oscillation at P is $e^{i(\alpha - \omega_0 t)} \cos \psi$ and is directed along E. Since α cancels out on substitution of the transfer functions in (13-57), its value is unimportant. Finally, this linearly polarized wave at P is to be resolved into ξ and η components, and we have

$$\tau_{\xi x} = e^{i\alpha} \cos^2 \psi \qquad \tau_{\eta x} = e^{i\alpha} \cos \psi \sin \psi \qquad (13\text{-}58)$$

By the same argument, starting with the electric vector along the y axis,

$$\tau_{\xi y} = e^{i\alpha} \cos \psi \sin \psi \qquad \tau_{\eta y} = e^{i\alpha} \sin^2 \psi \qquad (13\text{-}59)$$

Substituting these transfer functions in (13-57) gives

$$I(P;\psi) = \tfrac{1}{2}(I + Q \cos 2\psi + U \sin 2\psi)$$

Giving ψ the three values 0, $\pi/4$, and $\pi/2$, we have

$$I(P;0) = \tfrac{1}{2}(I + Q) \qquad I\left(P;\frac{\pi}{4}\right) = \tfrac{1}{2}(I + U) \qquad I\left(P;\frac{\pi}{2}\right) = \tfrac{1}{2}(I - Q)$$

Measurement of these three irradiances then gives I, Q, and U. To find V requires use of the quarter-wave plate.

A quarter-wave plate transmits a linearly polarized wave without change of polarization or amplitude if the electric vector is along one of two perpendicular directions, but the optical length of path between two points lying on opposite sides of the plate and connected by a ray of the incident beam differs by one-quarter wavelength for the two polarizations.

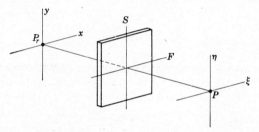

Fig. 13-17. *r-wave plate with slow and fast axes in a special orientation with respect to cartesian axes.*

The direction of the electric vector in the wave associated with the longer path defines the *slow axis* of the plate, indicated by a line labeled S in one of the faces. The axis at right angles is called the *fast axis*, labeled F.

Passage of an arbitrary wave through the plate is treated by resolving the electric vector in the incident wave into components along the slow and fast axes. The emerging wave then differs from what it would be in the absence of the plate in that the component along the fast axis is advanced longitudinally by one-quarter wavelength with respect to the other component.

A quarter-wave plate is a special case of an *r-wave plate*, in which the two optical lengths of path differ by an arbitrary number r of wavelengths. Let us work out some formulas for the general case and then see the usefulness of the case $r = \tfrac{1}{4}$.

Consider the particular orientation of the *r*-wave plate shown in Fig. 13-17. If $\epsilon = 2\pi r$, and β is the optical length of path in radians between P_r and P for the fast polarization, the transfer functions are

$$\begin{aligned} \tau_{\xi x} &= e^{i\beta} & \tau_{\eta x} &= 0 \\ \tau_{\xi y} &= 0 & \tau_{\eta y} &= e^{i(\beta+\epsilon)} \end{aligned} \qquad (13\text{-}60)$$

Substituting in (13-57) gives $I(P) = I$ independently of the value of ϵ. Nothing new is learned with an r-wave plate by itself (see further in Prob. 13-24).

Now let the r-wave plate in Fig. 13-17 be followed by the polarizer in Fig. 13-16. The transfer functions are then

$$\tau_{\xi x} = e^{i\gamma} \cos^2 \psi \qquad \tau_{\eta x} = e^{i\gamma} \cos \psi \sin \psi$$
$$\tau_{\xi y} = e^{i(\gamma+\epsilon)} \cos \psi \sin \psi \qquad \tau_{\eta y} = e^{i(\gamma+\epsilon)} \sin^2 \psi \qquad (13\text{-}61)$$

where γ is the total optical length of path from P_r to P (in radians) when the incident wave is linearly polarized with the electric vector along the fast axis. Formula (13-57) reduces to

$$I(P;\psi,\epsilon) = \tfrac{1}{2}[I + Q \cos 2\psi + (U \cos \epsilon + V \sin \epsilon) \sin 2\psi]$$

The choice $\psi = \pi/4$, $\epsilon = \pi/2$, the latter corresponding to a quarter-wave plate, gives

$$I\left(P;\frac{\pi}{4}, \frac{\pi}{2}\right) = \tfrac{1}{2}(I + V)$$

Thus V is found.

The four measurements yielding the Stokes parameters are summarized graphically in Fig. 13-18. The quarter-wave plate and the linear

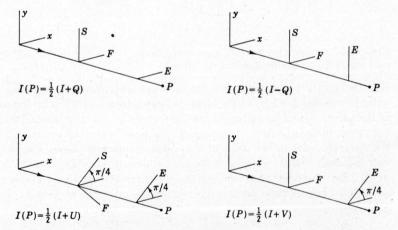

Fig. 13-18. *Four measurements of irradiance at P from which the Stokes parameters of the incident wave can be found. A quarter-wave plate is indicated by its slow and fast axes, S and F. A linear polarizer is indicated by its E axis.*

polarizer are indicated by their axes only. Figure 13-18 shows how measurements can be made with both plates always in the system in order to gain the following experimental advantage: There are always some losses due to reflections and internal absorption that reduce the observed irradiance from the ideal value by some factor; with both plates always in place, all four measurements and all four parameters are affected by the same factor. Usually only relative values of the parameters are of interest.

Many detectors of radiation are sensitive to polarization, some types of photomultipliers being especially so. In measurements of the irradiance at P in the four cases of Fig. 13-18, the detector should rotate with the linear polarizer.

13-14   **Properties and Interpretation of the Stokes Parameters**
An important property of the Stokes parameters is the following: If an essentially plane quasi-monochromatic wave arriving at an optical system consists in a superposition of two waves originating in two independent sources, then any one of the four parameters of the resultant wave is the sum of the corresponding parameters of the two component waves. The proof consists in showing additivity of the four averages (13-55). If (13-50) are the complex amplitudes of the resultant electric field, then each consists of a sum of two parts, for example,

$$A_x = a_x e^{i\theta_x} = a_{1x} e^{i\theta_{1x}} + a_{2x} e^{i\theta_{2x}}$$

We have $a_x{}^2 = |A_x|^2$, whence

$$\langle a_x{}^2 \rangle = \langle a_{1x}{}^2 \rangle + \langle a_{2x}{}^2 \rangle + 2\langle a_{1x} a_{2x} \cos (\theta_{1x} - \theta_{2x}) \rangle$$

The a's and θ's on the right are functions of the time, and since the sources are assumed uncorrelated, all vary independently. The average in the third term on the right can therefore be factored into three separate averages, and the average of the cosine is zero. Additivity of the first of (13-55) is thus demonstrated; proofs for the other three are similar.

Conversely, a given wave can be thought of as an incoherent superposition of two or more waves such that any one of the parameters of the given wave is the sum of the corresponding parameters for the several components. Such a resolution can be made in an infinite number of ways (see Prob. 13-28) and often proves to be a useful possibility in making calculations.

Now one never measures a polarization directly, but rather one measures irradiances after a wave has passed through appropriate optical systems and infers the character of the polarization from these measurements. Formula (13-57) is the most general one governing the performance of optical systems when a plane wave is incident, and it follows that a set of measurements can do no more than yield the Stokes parameters of the incident wave. There is never any indication that this wave may have come about as some superposition of component waves traveling in essentially the same direction ("essentially" in the sense that the optical system is incapable of resolving the sources giving rise to the component waves). On the other hand, the four parameters enter linearly in (13-57); one is therefore free to make an arbitrary resolution of a given incident wave into an incoherent superposition as in the last paragraph above and to calculate the irradiance $I(P)$ resulting from the given wave as the sum of the irradiances for the several components. Use will be made of this freedom in later chapters.

It remains to give relations between the Stokes parameters and the description of the polarization of a wave in terms of elliptical motions described by the electric vector. Consider first the class of completely polarized waves. Recall that a wave of this class is represented by (13-48) if the amplitudes a_x and a_y remain in constant ratio to each other

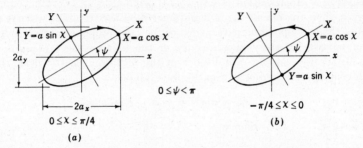

Fig. 13-19. *Specification of a general elliptical polarization by parameters a, χ, and ψ. The waves are propagating toward the reader.* **a.** *Right-hand polarization.* **b.** *Left-hand polarization. Corresponding ranges of χ are indicated. The range specified for ψ applies to both figures. The X axis is always the major axis.*

and the difference $\delta = \theta_x - \theta_y$ is constant. The ellipse then has constant eccentricity and fixed directions of principal axes, but varies slowly in size.

The parameters a_x, a_y, and δ have the rather inconvenient relation to the ellipse brought out at the end of Sec. 2-3. A more direct description of the ellipse results from introducing the alternative parameters a, χ, and ψ defined in Fig. 13-19. Here the x and y axes are those employed heretofore, and the wave is traveling in the z direction (toward the reader). The axes X and Y coincide with the major and minor axes of the ellipse, respectively. The parameter a varies slowly with time and determines the instantaneous size of the ellipse and the irradiance of the wave, while the two angles χ and ψ remain constant and determine the polarization. With χ restricted to the range $-\pi/4 \leq \chi \leq \pi/4$, X is never the minor axis. The ratio of major to minor diameters is $|\tan \chi|$; this ratio can have any value from zero to unity, representing all cases from linear to circular, respectively. By convention, right-hand polarization is identified by positive values of χ, and left-hand by negative. The angular orientation of the major axis is fixed by the angle ψ, which is to be limited to the range $0 \leqq \psi < \pi$. With any given polarization there is now associated a unique pair of values of χ and ψ in their respective ranges (except that ψ is indeterminate for the circular cases), and, conversely, a pair of values of the angles uniquely determines a polarization in an easily visualized way.

The Stokes parameters (13-56) can be reexpressed in terms of a, χ, and ψ, the results being

$$I = \frac{c}{8\pi} \langle a^2 \rangle \qquad\qquad Q = I \cos 2\chi \cos 2\psi$$
$$U = I \cos 2\chi \sin 2\psi \qquad V = I \sin 2\chi \qquad\qquad (13\text{-}62)$$

The proof of this transformation is a lengthy calculation which will not be reproduced here. It can be found in Born and Wolf [9], pp. 24–31.

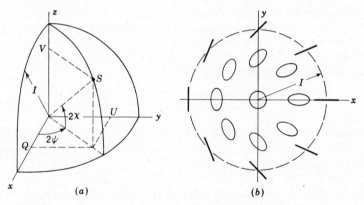

Fig. 13-20.   **a.** *Representation of a completely polarized wave of irradiance I by a point P on the Poincaré sphere of radius I. The ellipse, apart from handedness, is fixed by the coordinates Q and U as illustrated by the ellipses in the xy plane in* (**b**)**.** *The handedness is right or left according as V is positive or negative, respectively.*

From (13-62) it is seen that the Stokes parameters for a completely polarized wave satisfy

$$Q^2 + U^2 + V^2 = I^2 \qquad\qquad (13\text{-}63)$$

an equation suggestive of a sphere. It was Poincaré's idea to let Q, U, and V represent the x, y, and z coordinates, respectively, of a point S. Then S lies on a sphere of radius I, and by (13-62) its position is fixed alternatively by the angles χ and ψ in the manner of Fig. 13-20a. With a position of S is uniquely associated a wave of irradiance I having a definite polarization, and conversely. The parameters Q and U determine the angular orientation and eccentricity of the ellipse; the various cases are illustrated in Fig. 13-20b. The parameter V serves only to fix the handedness of the polarization through its sign—right-hand if positive, left-hand if negative.

Problems 13-25 to 13-27 will strengthen one's feeling for the various sets of parameters that can be used to specify a completely polarized wave.

An unpolarized wave has no preferred axis or handedness. It has some irradiance I, but the other three Stokes parameters satisfy $Q = U = V = 0$. In a partially polarized wave, Q, U, and V are not all zero, but in contrast to (13-63),

$$Q^2 + U^2 + V^2 < I^2 \tag{13-64}$$

If one defines irradiances I_p and I_u by

$$Q^2 + U^2 + V^2 = I_p{}^2 \qquad I_u = I - I_p \tag{13-65}$$

then the partially polarized wave can be regarded as an incoherent superposition of an unpolarized component of irradiance I_u and a completely polarized component of parameters Q, U, and V, the latter being representable on the Poincaré sphere of radius I_p. One can speak of the *fractional polarization*, defined to be

$$\text{F.P.} = \frac{I_p}{I} \tag{13-66}$$

Problem 13-28 describes a type of decomposition of an unpolarized wave that is often useful. This problem also mentions the distinction between coherent and incoherent superposition.

13-15   Techniques for Problems Involving Polarization   If an optical system consists of several parts in tandem, a simple method of calculating the transfer functions $\tau_{\xi x}$, etc., for the whole system when the functions for the individual parts are known is one employing multiplication of matrices.[1] The whole system is characterized by (13-9), which can be written in the matrix form

$$\begin{pmatrix} V_\xi \\ V_\eta \end{pmatrix} = \begin{pmatrix} \tau_{\xi x} & \tau_{\xi y} \\ \tau_{\eta x} & \tau_{\eta y} \end{pmatrix} \begin{pmatrix} V_x \\ V_y \end{pmatrix} \tag{13-67}$$

Suppose the system consists of two parts. In the space between them choose a reference point P', and draw axes ξ' and η' perpendicular to the direction of propagation of the wave at P'. Let the components of the complex amplitude of the electric vector at P' be $V_{\xi'}$ and $V_{\eta'}$. There is a

---

[1] If the reader is unfamiliar with matrices, the definition of a matrix and the operation of multiplication, all that will be needed, can be learned in a few minutes from such a reference as Margenau and Murphy [62].

set of transfer functions connecting the reference point P_r in front of the system and the point P', and there is another set connecting P' and the point of observation P behind the system. In matrix form,

$$\begin{pmatrix} V_{\xi'} \\ V_{\eta'} \end{pmatrix} = \begin{pmatrix} \tau_{\xi'x} & \tau_{\xi'y} \\ \tau_{\eta'x} & \tau_{\eta'y} \end{pmatrix} \begin{pmatrix} V_x \\ V_y \end{pmatrix} \tag{13-68}$$

$$\begin{pmatrix} V_{\xi} \\ V_{\eta} \end{pmatrix} = \begin{pmatrix} \tau_{\xi\xi'} & \tau_{\xi\eta'} \\ \tau_{\eta\xi'} & \tau_{\eta\eta'} \end{pmatrix} \begin{pmatrix} V_{\xi'} \\ V_{\eta'} \end{pmatrix} \tag{13-69}$$

Substituting the right side of (13-68) for the column matrix in the right of (13-69) and comparing the result with (13-67) gives

$$\begin{pmatrix} \tau_{\xi x} & \tau_{\xi y} \\ \tau_{\eta x} & \tau_{\eta y} \end{pmatrix} = \begin{pmatrix} \tau_{\xi\xi'} & \tau_{\xi\eta'} \\ \tau_{\eta\xi'} & \tau_{\eta\eta'} \end{pmatrix} \begin{pmatrix} \tau_{\xi'x} & \tau_{\xi'y} \\ \tau_{\eta'x} & \tau_{\eta'y} \end{pmatrix} \tag{13-70}$$

This result can be written in the symbolic form

$$T = T_2 T_1 \tag{13-70a}$$

where the T's stand for the square matrices in (13-70) and can be called *transfer matrices*. The subscripts 1 and 2 distinguish the first and second parts of the system in the order in which the wave passes through them. It is important to note the arrangement of the τ's in the matrices and the order of the factors in (13-70a). (Multiplication of matrices is not commutative.) If the system consists of three parts, then $T = T_3 T_2 T_1$, and so on for any number of parts.

The only application of the matrix method to be made in this book is to systems consisting of linear polarizers and r-wave plates in tandem. Consider the example of an r-wave plate followed by a polarizer in the arrangement that gave the transfer functions (13-61). The x and ξ axes were chosen parallel. It will now be shown how these functions can be found by multiplication of matrices.

Between the elements choose a point P' and axes ξ' and η', with ξ' parallel to x. Then for the first element the transfer functions (13-60) hold if primes are added to ξ and η, and if β is the optical length of path in radians between P_r and P' for a wave linearly polarized along the fast axis. For the second element, (13-58) and (13-59) hold with x and y replaced by ξ' and η', respectively. The optical length of path α is now that between P' and P. Substituting in the two matrices on the right of (13-70) and using the rule that a factor multiplying all the elements in a matrix can be taken outside and written as a factor multiplying the whole matrix,

$$\begin{pmatrix} \tau_{\xi x} & \tau_{\xi y} \\ \tau_{\eta x} & \tau_{\eta y} \end{pmatrix} = e^{i\alpha} \begin{pmatrix} \cos^2 \psi & \cos \psi \sin \psi \\ \cos \psi \sin \psi & \sin^2 \psi \end{pmatrix} e^{i\beta} \begin{pmatrix} 1 & 0 \\ 0 & e^{i\epsilon} \end{pmatrix}$$

$$= e^{i\gamma} \begin{pmatrix} \cos^2 \psi & e^{i\epsilon} \cos \psi \sin \psi \\ \cos \psi \sin \psi & e^{i\epsilon} \sin^2 \psi \end{pmatrix}$$

where $\gamma = \alpha + \beta$. The multiplication has thus produced the matrix made up of the elements (13-61) in their proper places. It has already been seen that the factor $e^{i\gamma}$ is unimportant, and the unimodular factors multiplying the matrices can therefore be omitted for brevity. Problems 13-29 to 13-31 call for additional applications of the matrix method and bring out some important results.

Many problems call only for the irradiance $I(P)$ at a point of observation following an optical system, the formula being (13-57), but it is often also necessary to find the other three Stokes parameters $Q(P)$, $U(P)$, and $V(P)$ in order to know the polarization of the output wave. The electric field at P is (13-51), and in analogy with (13-56),

$$Q(P) = \frac{c}{8\pi} [\langle |B_\xi(t)|^2 \rangle - \langle |B_\eta(t)|^2 \rangle]$$

$$U(P) + i\,V(P) = \frac{c}{8\pi} \langle 2B_\xi(t)\,B_\eta^*(t) \rangle$$

Using (13-52), (13-50), and (13-56), we obtain the following formulas to be coupled to (13-57):

$$Q(P) = \tfrac{1}{2}(|\tau_{\xi x}|^2 - |\tau_{\eta x}|^2)(I + Q) + \tfrac{1}{2}(|\tau_{\xi y}|^2 - |\tau_{\eta y}|^2)(I - Q) \\ + \mathrm{Re}\,[(\tau_{\xi x}\tau_{\xi y}^* - \tau_{\eta x}\tau_{\eta y}^*)(U + iV)] \tag{13-71}$$

$$U(P) + i\,V(P) = \tau_{\xi x}\tau_{\eta x}^*(I + Q) + \tau_{\xi y}\tau_{\eta y}^*(I - Q) \\ + \tau_{\xi x}\tau_{\eta y}^*(U + iV) + \tau_{\xi y}\tau_{\eta x}^*(U - iV) \tag{13-72}$$

Whereas (13-71) and (13-72) are invaluable in solving complicated problems, such powerful methods are not required in many simple cases. For example, if the plate in Fig. 13-17 is a quarter-wave plate and the incident wave is linearly polarized with the electric vector along a line bisecting the angle between the positive x and y axes, the wave at P obviously has left-hand circular polarization. Problem 13-33 calls for a check of this statement using (13-57), (13-71), and (13-72). Problems 13-34 to 13-37 contain more examples of this simple nature. Problem 13-36 is an especially valuable exercise.

The Stokes parameters and the formulas associated with them have proved to be very convenient for treating polarization of electromagnetic waves in a perfectly general and straightforward way. The parameters have been shown to be applicable in the quantum theory of electromagnetic radiation, and they have been applied to the quantum-mechanical problem of scattering of polarized beams of particles with spin (although for the latter problem it appears that a more convenient method is that of the density matrix, discussed in texts on quantum statistics). Numerous references to literature on the Stokes parameters and the Poincaré sphere are given in Born and Wolf [9], p. 550.

13-16   Measurement of Spectrum and Coherence by Means of Beat Frequencies   Suppose a plane wave of visible or near-visible radiation falls normally on a plane cathode in a vacuum photoelectric cell.   For simplicity let the wave be linearly polarized, so that the instantaneous electric field at the cathode is specified by a single scalar function $e(t)$.   The output of the cell is a current $i(t)$ which is, at least in idealization, proportional to the instantaneous irradiance of the wave, and therefore to the square of $e(t)$.   If C is a constant of proportionality,

$$i(t) = Ce^2(t) \tag{13-73}$$

Before experimental evidence on the range of validity of (13-73) is cited, some consequences of assuming it to be universally true will be worked out.

Let us think of the input to the photocell as being the function $e(t)$ rather than the instantaneous irradiance.   With this point of view the device is called a *square-law detector* because of the quadratic dependence in (13-73).   What we shall deal with in this section is a standard problem in the theory of noise in which the characteristics of the output function of a square-law detector are to be related to those of the input, especially when the input is pure noise and therefore specifiable only by statistical terms such as power spectrum and fluctuations.   Let us first work out a simple idealized example not involving statistics.

Let the incident wave be a superposition of two monochromatic waves of different frequencies, so that the electric field at the detector is

$$e(t) = A \cos \omega_1 t + B \cos \omega_2 t \tag{13-74}$$

Substitution in (13-73) and application of trigonometric identities leads to

$$\begin{aligned}
\frac{i(t)}{C} = {} & \tfrac{1}{2}(A^2 + B^2) + \tfrac{1}{2}A^2 \cos 2\omega_1 t + \tfrac{1}{2}B^2 \cos 2\omega_2 t \\
& + AB \cos (\omega_1 + \omega_2)t + AB \cos (\omega_1 - \omega_2)t
\end{aligned} \tag{13-75}$$

The first term on the right is the long-time-average or d-c component and is the only feature of the detector output that has concerned us up to this point.   The remaining terms represent oscillatory components of the current with frequencies

$$2\omega_1 \qquad 2\omega_2 \qquad \omega_1 + \omega_2 \qquad |\omega_1 - \omega_2| \tag{13-76}$$

If ω_1 and ω_2 are visible frequencies close together, the first three of the frequencies (13-76) are too high to observe, but the last, called the *beat frequency*, can fall in the range of radio frequencies.

The first observation of a beat frequency obtained as a difference of two visible frequencies was made by Forrester, Gudmundsen, and Johnson [30] in 1955.   Their two visible frequencies were two components of the same polarization in a Zeeman pattern (Sec. 18-2), and the magnetic field was adjusted to make the beat frequency 10^{10} cycle sec^{-1} (equivalent wavelength: 3 cm). From such an experiment one concludes that with certain types of cathode surface and proper design of tube the output current responds faithfully to modulation of incident irradiance at frequencies up to at lest 10^{10} cycle sec^{-1}.

A new principle of high-resolution spectroscopy becomes available through observation of beat frequencies. Very narrow spectral profiles (whose total spread, expressed as frequency, falls within the radio range) can be observed with an effective bandwidth of perhaps 1 cycle sec^{-1}. If the profile falls in the visible or near infrared, it can therefore be examined with a resolving power of some 10^{14}, which is orders of magnitude greater than can be realized with optical interferometers and is by no means a fixed upper limit. Such high resolution came to be of great practical importance with the advent of the *laser*, discussed in Sec. 19-8. As background for a part of that section, the theory of the beat-frequency spectrograph will now be worked out and illustrated. The derivation is somewhat involved, but the result (13-81) is very simple.

Suppose a steady source emits a narrow spectrum line or a group of closely spaced lines. Let a shutter in front of the photocell open for a time T. The electric field at the cathode is represented by some scalar function $e(t)$ in this time interval and is zero outside the interval (assuming linear polarization again for simplicity). Let the Fourier transform of this function be $V(\omega)$. Suppose the experiment of opening the shutter for time T is repeated many times. At each value of ω the modulus and angle of this transform will fluctuate from one trial to another, and at the end a statistical average will be taken, but until this average is taken, the calculation deals with one definite example of $e(t)$ and its transform.

The output current is given by (13-73). Let the transform of $i(t)$ be $U(\omega)$. Then by Theorem 5, Sec. 11-3,

$$U(\omega) = C' \int_{-\infty}^{\infty} V(\xi) V(\omega - \xi) d\xi \qquad (13\text{-}77)$$

where C' is a constant.

Now if the current $i(t)$ flows through unit resistance, the energy converted in the resistance is

$$\int_{-\infty}^{\infty} i^2(t) dt = \int_{-\infty}^{\infty} |U(\omega)|^2 d\omega = 2 \int_{0}^{\infty} |U(\omega)|^2 d\omega$$

where the second form is derived by Parseval's theorem, and the third follows from the fact that $i(t)$ is real. These steps are very similar to those in introducing the energy spectrum of radiation in Secs. 12-5 and 13-1, and just as there are spectrographs for measuring the energy spectrum of radiation, there are electronic spectrum analyzers for measuring the energy spectrum of $i(t)$, that is, $2|U(\omega)|^2$, where ω is positive and confined to radio frequencies.

By (13-77),

$$2|U(\omega)|^2 = 2C'^2 \int_{-\infty}^{\infty} V(\xi) \, V(\omega - \xi) \, d\xi \int_{-\infty}^{\infty} V^*(\eta) \, V^*(\omega - \eta) \, d\eta \quad (13\text{-}78)$$

At this point we take a statistical average over fluctuations in the transform V. The left side of (13-78) then becomes an average. Let us divide it by the interval of observation T to obtain the *power spectrum of the photocell current*, to be denoted by $\mathcal{P}(\omega)$. The right side, while it is a product of single integrals, can be regarded as a double integral over an infinite plane referred to cartesian coordinates ξ and η. Thus,

$$\mathcal{P}(\omega) = \frac{2C'^2}{T} \int_{-\infty}^{\infty} \int_{-\infty}^{\infty} G(\xi,\eta;\omega) \, d\xi \, d\eta \quad (13\text{-}79)$$

where

$$G(\xi,\eta;\omega) = [V(\xi) \, V^*(\eta) \, V(\omega - \xi) \, V^*(\omega - \eta)]_{\text{av}} \quad (13\text{-}80)$$

The subscript "av" indicates a statistical average. The value of the integral in (13-79) depends on the nature of the integrand G, which must now be investigated.

The oscillation of the field at the detector is to be regarded as a super-position of a large number of oscillations beginning at random times, each having duration of order τ, the latter being very small compared with the time of observation T. As an example, one can think of the case analyzed in Sec. 12-6. From that analysis it is seen that at any frequency, $V(\omega)$ has statistical average zero (because of its random angle). It is also seen that the fluctuations of V (in magnitude and angle) at two frequencies ω_1 and ω_2 are practically the same if the difference $|\omega_1 - \omega_2|$ is not greater than order T^{-1}, but they become essentially independent at larger difference. Recall that when two or more quantities fluctuate independently the statistical average of a product is the product of the averages. Thus we see that the value of the integral in (13-79) is surely obtained within a factor of order unity if we approximate G in the following way: In the $\xi\eta$ plane consider the narrow strip between the lines $\eta = \xi \pm (2T)^{-1}$. Outside the strip set $G = 0$. Inside, set G equal to its value along the center of the strip; that is,

$$G = [|V(\xi)|^2]_{\text{av}}[|V(\omega - \xi)|^2]_{\text{av}} = \left(\frac{2\pi}{c}\right)^2 T^2 \, \mathcal{S}(\xi)\mathcal{S}(\omega - \xi)$$

where $\mathcal{S}$ stands for the power spectrum of the incident radiation (see the definition near the end of Sec. 13-5).

With this approximation of the integrand G, integration over η merely brings in a factor T^{-1} (the width of the strip measured along a line parallel to the η axis), and the final result is

$$\mathcal{P}(\omega) = K \int_{-\infty}^{\infty} \mathcal{S}(\xi)\mathcal{S}(\omega - \xi)\,d\xi \qquad (13\text{-}81)$$

where K is a constant. Thus the power spectrum $\mathcal{P}$ of the photocurrent is the folding integral of the power spectrum $\mathcal{S}$ of the radiation with itself. Whereas $\mathcal{S}$ has been considered heretofore as defined only for positive frequencies, the way it came into the folding integral requires that it be defined also for negative frequencies by the condition

$$\mathcal{S}(-\omega) = \mathcal{S}(\omega)$$

As an illustration, suppose the spectrum of the radiation consists of two resonance profiles centered at frequencies ω_1 and ω_2, both having the same

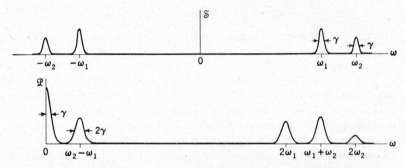

Fig. 13-21. *Upper curve: power spectrum of incident radiation consisting of resonance profiles at two different frequencies. Lower curve: power spectrum of the output of a square-law detector.*

width γ at half-maximum, as shown by the upper curve in Fig. 13-21. Imagine this curve to be traced on tissue paper and the tracing to be gradually translated to the right. Whenever a peak in the tracing sweeps over one in the printed curve, there occurs a peak in the folding integral; the lower curve in the figure is the result. Compare the frequencies of the maxima with (13-76). By the proposition in Prob. 13-7, the profiles in the lower curve are of resonance shape with widths 2γ. (For gaussian profiles, the statement in Prob. 11-10 would be applicable.) One sees that all the characteristics of the radiation spectrum except the absolute frequency ω_1 or ω_2 can be derived from the low-frequency part of the curve of $\mathcal{P}$. It must be remarked, however, that the beat-frequency method is limited in that a function is not uniquely determined by knowledge of the folding integral of the function with itself, except in the case of simple and symmetrical profiles, as in the above example.

The classic experiment of Forrester et al. necessarily involved radiation with a weak power spectrum, and the feeble photocurrent was dominated by shot noise (an effect of the discreteness of the charged particles). Very ingenious methods were required to observe the peak in $\mathcal{P}$ at the beat frequency $\omega_2 - \omega_1$. The observed width of this peak was consistent with a reasonable estimate of the Doppler broadening in the source. The unique properties of the radiation from a laser (Sec. 19-8) make observation of beat-frequency spectra much easier.

As shown in Sec. 13-11, measurement of a spectrum is equivalent to measuring the longitudinal coherence of a radiation field; there is an analogous relation between angular spread of a source and lateral coherence. Brown and Twiss have applied the principle of beat frequencies to measurement of lateral coherence, and the result has been a very significant gain in usable length of base line in a stellar interferometer. The first application [11] was to radio astronomy. Later [12, 13] the technique was extended to the visible range for measurement of angular diameters of visual stars. These experiments employed an extremely clever scheme for overcoming noise. Demonstration of the effect with visible light and the possibility of accounting for it on a classical basis set off much discussion of fundamental physical principles; in this connection see Brown and Twiss [14] and Purcell [73]. A quantum model of the phenomenon has been analyzed by Fano [27].

Problems

13-1. Imagine that the response of a continuous detector to a short pulse has the idealized form shown in Fig. 13-1b. Let radiation falling on the detector deliver unit power during the interval $t = 0$ to $t = 2T$ and no power at other times. Find and plot the deflection of the recorder as a function of time.

13-2. From formulas for Fraunhofer diffraction given in Chap. 9, deduce a general formula for the transfer function $\tau(\omega;P,P_r)$ for a single aperture referred to the coordinate system in Fig. 7-4 when the reference point P_r is taken at the origin O. Make use of the results of Prob. 11-18 to show that with a polychromatic source the oscillation at P is not related to that at P_r merely by a delay in transit and a reduction of amplitude by a constant factor, but that there is some distortion. (If the signal at P_r begins and ends at times separated by an interval T, this distortion always has the effect of making the oscillation at P last longer than T. For simple illustrations of this distortion and lengthening, see Probs. 13-8 and 13-9.)

13-3. Make a rough copy of Fig. 13-2. Denote the value of θ_2 associated with the oscillating curve by $\theta_2^{(1)}$. Add curves for $\sin \theta_2^{(2)} = \frac{1}{2} \sin \theta_2^{(1)}$ and for $\sin \theta_2^{(3)} = \frac{3}{2} \sin \theta_2^{(1)}$.

13-4. In the white-light pattern represented by the solid curve in Fig. 13-5, will the light arriving at points corresponding to values of ξ around $\pi/2$ be reddish or bluish in comparison with light whose spectrum is (13-22)? Justify the answer by reproducing the oscillating curve in Fig. 13-2 and marking off an interval $\omega_1 < \omega < 2\omega_1$, with ω_1 positioned to represent the case in question.

13-5. Draw a curve analogous to Fig. 13-4 for two slits with separation greater than the width of one slit by a large factor, say 100. Draw only the first few orders, so that the dashed envelope for this part of the curve practically coincides with the parabolic curve of 3 at $\theta_2 = 0$ (see Fig. 13-2) and the first zero of the envelope falls far off the right of the figure. Omit the labeling that appears along the frequency axis in Fig. 13-4. Let the energy spectrum of the radiation be (13-22). On the frequency axis of the figure just drawn, mark points ω_1 and $2\omega_1$, with ω_1 in approximately the position to give the first minimum in w [formula (13-14)]. Estimate this minimum value as a fraction of the value of w at $\theta_2 = 0$. (It is not necessary to know the value of θ_2 at which the minimum would occur.) On the basis of this estimate draw a good guess as to what would be the curve of w from the center of the pattern through a few orders until the fringes essentially disappear. [As a very tedious problem, one could find the formula for this curve and plot it. Even with the approximation that for low orders the transmission function is (13-21) times $4 \cos^2 \pi\delta$, the problem is substantially longer than that of the single aperture for which results were given in the text.]

13-6. Suppose a source emits equally in equal intervals of wavelength over one octave of wavelengths. Reexpress this spectrum in terms of ω (see Prob. 12-6 and the footnote in Sec. 13-4). Let radiation with this spectrum fall normally on the double slit of Prob. 13-5. Using the approximate expression for the transmission function valid for low orders, write the integral giving $w(\sin \theta_2)$. [Note that this is simpler than it would be with the spectrum (13-22).] As an optional and tedious continuation of this problem, introduce the variable $\eta = (3\omega_1 d/4c) \sin \theta_2$, where ω_1 is the lowest frequency in the spectrum [compare the ξ in (13-23)], find $w(\eta)/w(0)$, tabulate, and plot. Compare with the monochromatic pattern for frequency $3\omega_1/2$.

13-7. A spectrogram is observed to have the resonance shape

$$C \, \mathfrak{L}(\omega_P - \omega_0; \, \Gamma_1) = \frac{C\Gamma_1/2\pi}{(\omega_P - \omega_0)^2 + \Gamma_1^2/4}$$

where C is a constant, ω_0 is the frequency associated with the point at which the maximum occurs, and Γ_1 is the width at half-maximum. The instrumental profile is the resonance function $D \, \mathfrak{L}(\omega - \omega_P; \, \Gamma_2)$. (This profile sometimes arises in practice.) Show from (13-28) that the spectrum is $\mathcal{S}(\omega) = CD^{-1}\mathfrak{L}(\omega - \omega_0; \, \Gamma_1 - \Gamma_2)$. (This problem is very similar to Prob. 11-10, and the method suggested there can be applied again. The fact that the folding integral of two resonance functions of widths Γ and Γ' is a resonance function of width $\Gamma + \Gamma'$ is of the utmost importance.)

13-8. Imagine that a perfectly monochromatic scalar plane wave of frequency ω_0 falls normally on a grating of N slits covered by a shutter that opens and closes instantaneously and remains open from $t = 0$ to $t = T$. Calculate and draw the theoretical energy spectrum. In the focal plane of a lens located behind the grating, let a spectrogram be taken photographically in order m, and suppose the resolving power mN is large enough to show quite faithfully the zeros and secondary maxima in the spectrum. One now faces the paradox that the part of the input signal in an interval $0 < t < T'$, with $T' < T$, has a spectrum wider than that just calculated and would blacken the plate at places that must in the end be quite clear. Resolve this paradox by considering a point in the vicinity of the order m on the focal plane. Show that the N oscillations at that point due to waves coming from the N slits have the property that the first one ends long before the last one begins, so that before any appreciable exposure builds up, it is ordained what the final exposure will be. To simplify the problem, assume that the oscillation at the output point originating in any one slit is the same as that at the reference point in front of the grating, except for a delay in time and a reduction of amplitude by a constant factor; that is, neglect the distortion brought out in Prob. 13-2. Recall that the order of interference m has the significance of being the difference between the optical lengths of path via two successive slits, measured in wavelengths. This problem involves a range of wavelengths, but it is natural to think primarily of that one associated with the frequency ω_0.

Discussion: Note that the output signal at the point in question lasts much longer than T. This lengthening can be thought of as arising from the instrumental profile being much narrower than the spectrum, for if the width of the instrumental profile is $\Delta\omega$, the oscillation at the output point has a spectrum of width $\Delta\omega$ and lasts a time at least $(\Delta\omega)^{-1}$. At the zeroth order there are only the residual distortion and lengthening introduced by the individual slits, effects avoided in this problem by the simplifying assumption. This problem should be contrasted with that in which the input oscillation at the reference point consists in a superposition of many identical oscillations, each of duration T, beginning at random times in a much longer interval T'. The spectrum, after fluctuations are smoothed out, has the same shape as one of the elementary oscillations. If the width of the instrumental profile is a given fraction of the width of this spectrum, then the resultant signal at the point of observation lasts longer than T' by a factor that approaches unity as T' increases. This phenomenon of distortion and lengthening occurs in any real system and becomes more pronounced as the bandwidth (width of instrumental profile) decreases. It is well known in narrow-band electronic amplifiers, where an input signal of any shape and duration emerges as a roughly sinusoidal function of longer duration. The effect can always be traced to a temporary storage in the system, for example, through transit time in an optical spectrograph, or in resonant combinations of inductance and capacitance in amplifiers.

13-9. To illustrate by specific examples some points brought out in Prob. 13-8, take the instantaneous amplitude of the input oscillation at the reference point to have initial value zero and to be sinusoidal with frequency ω_0 over exactly $\frac{9}{2}$ cycles. Take the grating to have only three slits, and neglect distortion introduced by the individual slits (see Probs. 13-2 and 13-8). Draw, one below another in proper horizontal relationship, the three oscillations contributing to the resultant at the output point at which the order of interference is exactly $m = \frac{1}{2}$ for a monochromatic wave of frequency ω_0. Draw the resultant instantaneous amplitude and the instantaneous irradiance. In the same way draw the instantaneous resultant amplitude of oscillation for $m = 1$ and $m = \frac{3}{2}$. Finally, draw the energy spectrum of the incident wave, and to the same frequency scale draw the transmission function for the first point considered ($m = \frac{1}{2}$). Discuss two ways in which the total flux density of energy w at the point identified by $m = \frac{1}{2}$ could be found from the various curves pertaining to this point.

13-10. Show that formula (13-14) holds for an unpolarized source of very small angular size even when relations (13-9) cannot be reduced to (13-10). A new definition of the over-all transmission function replaces (13-15). Make use of (13-30).

13-11. Write out the proof of the rule for incoherent sources [additivity of the w's as expressed by (13-34)] when the relations (13-9) cannot be reduced to (13-10). Assume that the sources are unpolarized. A review of Prob. 13-10 will be helpful.

13-12. Suppose the quasi-monochromatic source in Fig. 13-10 consists of two parts of equal intensities, each small enough in angular size to be essentially a point. Their angular positions are $\theta_1 = \alpha/2$, $\phi_1 = 0$ and $\theta_2 = -\alpha/2$, $\phi_2 = 0$. The pinholes are identical and are on the x axis at separation s. Write the transmission functions $\Im_1(s,\alpha,\psi)$ and $\Im_2(s,\alpha,\psi)$ associated with the two sources, and apply the rule for incoherent sources to find the irradiance at point P as a function of s, α, and ψ. Extract from the result the degree of coherence $\Gamma(s,\alpha)$. Show that the first vanishing of Γ as a function of s with α fixed gives the formula for the stellar interferometer obtained in Sec. 7-13. See the next problem.

13-13. Show how the Γ found in Prob. 13-12 can be deduced from the general formula (13-41).

13-14. With reference to Fig. 13-10, let the quasi-monochromatic source be a uniform circular disk of angular diameter α centered at O. Write the formula for the degree of coherence Γ between P_r and any other point at distance s. (Use the interpretation of Γ as the positive square root of the irradiance in a certain diffraction pattern.) Draw a curve of this function of s for given angular diameter α and given wavelength λ, and label characteristic dimensions.

13-15. As a variation of Prob. 13-14, take the source in Fig. 13-10 to be a uniform rectangle at distance L bounded by the four lines $X = \pm a/2$, $Y = \pm b/2$. Write the formula for Γ relating to P_r and a point at arbitrary position (x,y). Draw a curve of the result for points on the x axis.

13-16. With reference to Sec. 13-11, let an interferogram be $\phi(\Delta) = e^{-\Delta/a} \cos b\Delta$ for $\Delta > 0$. Suppose that $ab \gg 1$. Draw a curve to represent $\phi(\Delta)$. By means of (13-47) find the formula for the spectrum $\mathcal{S}(k)$, and draw a curve with characteristic dimensions labeled. Describe the shape of the spectrum.

13-17. As the inverse of Prob. 13-16, find the interferogram corresponding to a power spectrum having the resonance shape shown in Fig. 12-4. Make use of a table of definite integrals.

13-18. Use formula (13-46) to find the interferogram $\phi(\Delta)$ for the white power spectrum in which $\mathcal{S}(k)$ is constant over the octave $k_1 < k < 2k_1$ and zero for other wave numbers. Draw a rough curve of the result.

13-19. Let the longest wavelength in the white spectrum of Prob. 13-18 be λ_1. Let radiation with this spectrum pass through the interferometer in Fig. 13-13 when the displacement of mirror M_2 from the position for equal paths is $D = \lambda_1$. Draw the curve of the spectrum of the radiation reaching the detector. Repeat for $D = 10\lambda_1$. (Such output spectra are called *channel spectra*.)

13-20. In Fig. 13-13 let an incident plane scalar wave be a sinusoidal train such that the instantaneous amplitude at a point in the entrance aperture is $\cos \omega_0 t$ for $0 < t < T$, with $\omega_0 T \gg 1$. Two such trains will then arrive at the detector with a relative temporal delay determined by the path difference $\Delta = 2D$. Let the detector be of the integrating type. Apart from an arbitrary constant of proportionality, find directly, from consideration of the instantaneous irradiance of the resultant wave, the total flux density of energy w arriving at a point of the detector. Plot the result as a function of Δ. The result should be consistent with the partial answer that w is constant, say equal to A, for $\Delta > cT$, and $w = 2A$ for $\Delta = 0$. [If a steady source were to emit at random times a series of identical wave trains of the type postulated in this problem, the interferogram ϕ would have the same dependence on Δ as the w just found. To establish this result by finding the power spectrum and substituting in (13-46) leads to a difficult integral. An alternative argument could be based on ideas in Sec. 12-6 applied to the series of identical wave trains arriving at the detector, only the reasoning, but no calculations beyond those in finding w above, being required.]

13-21. A common laboratory exercise with the Michelson interferometer is to observe visually the interferogram for the D lines of sodium at wavelengths 5890 A and 5896 A. The interferogram appears as in Fig. 13-15, and Δ is increased only far enough to find the separation of two successive zeros of the sinusoidal envelope. Show that a general formula applicable here is $\delta\lambda = \lambda_0^2/2D$, where λ_0 is the mean wavelength of the doublet, $\delta\lambda$ is the separation, and D is the distance the mirror M_2 (Fig. 13-13) moves between zeros. This formula involves approximations based on the smallness of $\delta\lambda/\lambda_0$.

13-22. The Michelson interferometer can be adapted for use as a refractometer in much the same manner as the double slit is used in the Rayleigh refractometer described in Prob. 7-10. The two identical cells are placed in the paths between the semireflector H and the two mirrors M_1 and M_2 (Fig. 13-13). There is the obvious advantage that these paths are well separated in space, and broad beams can be used. Let the length of each cell between end windows be L. Let the cells be evacuated initially, and let gas be admitted slowly in one until the final refractive index is n. Find a formula for the number of maxima counted by the detector when the radiation is nearly monochromatic with wavelength λ. Compare with the formula for the Rayleigh refractometer, and give the reason for the difference.

13-23. What is the order of magnitude of the (longitudinal) coherence length in the wave emitted by a source consisting of stationary Lorentz atoms with a single resonant frequency in the visible range? (The spectrum in this case is to be the "natural" one, free of broadening due to thermal motions and collisions.) Give two ways in which the answer can be found.

13-24. Write the four transfer functions $\tau_{\xi x}$, etc., for an r-wave plate arranged as in Fig. 13-17, except that the plate is rotated through θ radians in the counterclockwise direction looking from P to P_r. Substitute the results in (13-57) to show that $I(P) = I$ (the same result as was found in Sec. 13-13 for the special orientation $\theta = 0$).

13-25. In connection with the Poincaré sphere (Fig. 13-20), one might be tempted to think of an arrow from the center of the sphere to S as representing a vector whose components with respect to the x, y, and z axes are Q, U, and V. Show that an arrow defined in this way is not actually a vector according to the criterion that the magnitude and direction of a vector must be independent of the coordinate system used in a representation. The proof can proceed as follows: Rotate the coordinate system in Figs. 13-19 and 13-20 through angle θ about the z axis to obtain new axes x' and y'. Find the new parameters Q' and U' in terms of Q and U. (The parameter V is unchanged.) Define an arrow whose components in the rotated system are Q', U', and V. Show that these components are different from those of the original arrow taken along the new axes.

13-26. Write the parameters Q, U, and V as numerical multiples of I for the four linear polarizations lying on the x and y axes of Fig. 13-20b; repeat for the two circular polarizations.

13-27. If (13-48) represents a completely polarized wave, then $a_y(t) = a_x(t) \tan \alpha$ with α constant and lying in the range $0 \leqq \alpha \leqq \pi/2$. Also, $\delta = \theta_x(t) - \theta_y(t)$ is constant and can be restricted to $0 \leqq \delta < 2\pi$. Reexpress (13-56) in terms of the parameters $\langle a_x{}^2 \rangle$, α, and δ. It is sometimes necessary to pass from this set of parameters to the set $\langle a^2 \rangle$, χ, and ψ appearing in (13-62), or vice versa. Special formulas exist for these transformations, but they have no advantage over the following easily remembered method which gives the Stokes parameters as by-product: Given $\langle a_x{}^2 \rangle$, α, and δ, find the Stokes parameters by the form of (13-56) called for above and solve (13-62) for $\langle a^2 \rangle$, χ, and ψ, where χ and ψ are to fall in the ranges specified in the text (see Fig. 13-19). This method can be reversed. As an example, let $\langle a_x{}^2 \rangle = 8\pi/c$, $\tan \alpha = \frac{2}{3}$, and $\delta = 7\pi/4$. Draw the ellipse, and indicate the handedness by the principles of Sec. 2-3. Find $\langle a^2 \rangle$, χ, and ψ, and draw the ellipse by the principles of Fig. 13-19.

13-28. Use the proposition stated at the beginning of Sec. 13-14 and the geometry of Fig. 13-20 to show that an unpolarized wave of irradiance I can be regarded as an incoherent superposition of two completely polarized waves of equal irradiances $I/2$. Both waves can be elliptical. State completely the relations between the elliptical motions in the two waves. (Note that if an unpolarized wave of irradiance I is incident on a system that gives a completely polarized emergent wave of irradiance I', then $I' \leqq I/2$. Compare this problem with Probs. 2-20 and 4-12, which can be regarded as referring to coherent superpositions of completely polarized quasi-monochromatic waves, the resultant, of course, being a completely polarized wave.)

13-29. An unpolarized plane wave is normally incident on two linear polarizers in tandem. The angle between the E axes is θ. Choosing reference axes in some convenient way, find the transfer functions for the system by the matrix method, and substitute in (13-57) to find $I(P)$ as a function of the irradiance I of the incident wave and the angle θ. [*Answer:* $I(P) = \frac{1}{2}I \cos^2 \theta$; this is known as the *law of Malus*.]

13-30. An unpolarized quasi-monochromatic wave, traveling in the z direction, is normally incident on two linear polarizers with their E axes at right angles, the axis of the first being parallel to the x axis. Between them is the r-wave plate of Prob. 13-24. Use the matrix method to find the transfer functions of the system. Substitute in (13-57). [*Answer:* $I(P) = \frac{1}{2}I \sin^2 \pi r \sin^2 2\theta$.]

13-31. A linearly polarized quasi-monochromatic wave is traveling in the z direction. The electric vector is along a line L making an angle θ with the x axis, where θ is measured positively in the counterclockwise direction looking in the negative z direction. The wave falls on a half-wave plate oriented as in Fig. 13-17. The latter is followed by a linear polarizer in the orientation of Fig. 13-16, with angle ψ variable. Write the Stokes parameters of the incident wave. Find the transfer functions of the system by the matrix method. Evaluate (13-57) as a function of ψ, and infer that the wave emerging from the half-wave plate is linearly polarized with its electric vector along a line L' that can be thought of as the reflection of L in either the slow or fast axis. (This is the most important property of a half-wave plate. It can be seen by more elementary arguments than those called for in this problem. The next problem cites an application.)

13-32. Using the result of the last problem, show that if the incident wave of that problem falls on two half-wave plates with the fast axis of the second rotated through the angle ϕ in the counterclockwise direction (looking toward the source) with respect to that of the first, then the final wave is linearly polarized with the line of oscillation rotated in the counterclockwise direction through angle 2ϕ with respect to that of the incident wave. (Note that the result depends only on the angle ϕ, and not on the absolute orientation of either plate. Such a combination of half-wave plates is called an *optical rotator*.)

13-33. In the next to last paragraph in Sec. 13-15, an example was cited which, it was stated, gives an output wave with left-hand circular polarization. Check this statement in the following way: Write the Stokes parameters of the incident wave [using (13-62)], substitute them, together with the transfer functions (13-60) with $\epsilon = \pi/2$, in formulas (13-57), (13-71), and (13-72) to find the parameters of the output wave, and finally show that these parameters represent the stated polarization by solving (13-62) for χ and ψ and referring to Fig. 13-19.

13-34. Let an unpolarized wave be incident on the linear polarizer shown in Fig. 13-16 with $\psi = 0$. Let the polarizer be followed by a quarter-wave plate in the orientation of Fig. 13-17. Now let the quarter-wave plate be rotated through angle θ in the counterclockwise direction looking from P to P_r. Draw to the same scale a set of ellipses representing the polarization of the wave at P for $\theta = n\pi/8$, $n = 0, 1, \ldots, 7$. Do this problem essentially by inspection, recalling the fundamental property of a quarter-wave plate. See the comments in the next problem.

13-35. Let an unpolarized wave be incident on the linear polarizer of Fig. 13-16 with $\psi = \pi/4$. Let the polarizer be followed by an r-wave plate in the orientation of Fig. 13-17. Draw to the same scale a set of ellipses to represent the polarization at P when $r = n/8$, $n = 0, 1, \ldots, 7$. Solve essentially by inspection as in Prob. 13-34. (It will be seen that if r is given a suitable value and the whole system is appropriately rotated about the axis of propagation, any type of completely polarized wave can be produced. The compensators of Babinet and Soleil, to be described in Sec. 17-6, allow r to be varied continuously. From Prob. 13-34 it is seen that any polarization can be produced with a polarizer and quarter-wave plate if both are independently rotatable.)

13-36. The characteristics of a quasi-monochromatic wave are to be measured with a calibrated detector, a linear polarizer, and a quarter-wave plate. Describe a procedure that will give directly the fractional polarization and, for the completely polarized component, will give the shape, orientation, and handedness of the associated ellipse. The answer should take the form of an outline of observations to be made, with each observation followed by interpretations of possible results and statements as to what to do in the event of each possible result. It may help to work a preliminary problem in which the wave is known to be completely polarized.

13-37. A linear polarizer is followed by a quarter-wave plate and a perfectly reflecting metal mirror, all surfaces of these elements being parallel. The fast and slow axes of the quarter-wave plate are at 45° to the E axis of the polarizer. Show that if an unpolarized wave is normally incident on the polarizer, there is no reflected wave emerging from the polarizer (neglecting reflections from the surfaces of the two plates). The following fact concerning reflection at the metal mirror is needed: If an incident wave has the electric field $e(t)$ at the surface of the mirror, the reflected wave has the vector $-e(t)$ at the same surface.

13-38. The normal irradiance of solar radiation at the outer surface of the earth's atmosphere is 1.36×10^6 erg cm^{-2} sec^{-1} (solar constant). What is the root-mean-square magnitude of the electric vector in volts per centimeter?

chapter 14

Scattering

This chapter will treat scattering of radiation by particles. Because of the great variety of problems connected with this topic (most of which are far from elementary) and the wealth of applications in all branches of science, only a bare introduction through simple examples can be attempted here. Nevertheless, it will be possible to bring out many important concepts and give at least some idea of what the rest of the subject amounts to.

14-1 Introductory Survey and Definitions If a plane electromagnetic wave passes over an obstacle, charges in the obstacle are set into motion and radiate secondary waves in all directions. The phenomenon is called *scattering*. According to this definition any of the processes of diffraction considered heretofore could be called processes of scattering, and in the literature there is no clear-cut convention as to when one term is to be used rather than the other. Generally the term scattering is used when small particles are involved, particularly when they are irregularly arranged in space. This dichotomy is especially evident in the field of X rays. Here it is usual to distinguish scattering by atoms in a gas from scattering by atoms in a crystal lattice or in the partially ordered arrangements in liquids by calling the former scattering and the latter diffraction.

Refraction and specular reflection of visible light by polished glass and diffuse reflection by a sheet of paper are also, from a fundamental point of view, processes of scattering in which the ultimate scatterers are the electrons in the constituent atoms. What gives the resultant scattered wave its special characteristics in any given case are the nature, spatial arrangement, and possible interactions of the atoms involved. Parts of the qualitative discussion in this introductory section will have the purpose of indicating how, by using the word scattering in the broadest possible sense, one comes to a unified view of many phenomena, some of which go under names other than scattering and are treated in practical calculations by methods that contain no explicit reference to scattering. Details bearing out some of this qualitative discussion are given in later sections and in parts of following chapters.

As was the case with diffraction, a problem in scattering is solved first for monochromatic and quasi-monochromatic waves, and the characteristics of the scattering turn out to depend on frequency. Scattering of a beam with a given broad spectrum is then easily found.

Let a nearly unidirectional beam having some small cross section and transporting power P be incident on a region containing matter in any form. If the matter is removed, the beam continues undisturbed and defines a *forward direction*, and a detector located in this direction and of a size just to take in the beam measures power P. When the matter is in place, the same detector measures a power P' which is always less than P, and the beam is said to have suffered some *extinction*. The power $P - P'$ lost from the beam has to be accounted for, and in general it is found divided into two parts. One is the power in a scattered wave radiating in various directions from the irradiated region of the matter, and the other is a generation of heat through some mechanism of conversion in the interior of the matter. This generation of heat is called *absorption*. Thus extinction is accounted for partly as scattering and partly as absorption.[1]

Extinction may be total and consist almost entirely of absorption (for example, in an opaque screen of negligible reflectance) or almost entirely of scattering (for example, from a highly reflecting mirror or a very slightly absorbing prism, if reflected and refracted beams are regarded as scattered waves; an example involving less strain on the word scattered is a very thick cloud in the sky—very little light reaches the earth, and there is little absorption, so that most of the incident sunlight is diffusely scattered back out of the upper surface). When scattering is confined to small angles from the forward direction, it is necessary to be more precise about the definition and measurement of extinction, but let the matter rest until Sec. 14-7.

A qualitative description of scattering phenomena will now be given from a completely atomistic point of view by considering a single atom, then gases of low density, and finally gases of high density, liquids, and solids. The last topic will be scattering from assemblies of particles, each

---

[1] The nomenclature used here has become fairly general, but one occasionally finds extinction called absorption, and that part of it complementary to scattering called "true" absorption.

of which consists of an aggregate of atoms, such as molecules and liquid drops. Let us carry in mind throughout an incident wave that is plane and monochromatic, and therefore completely polarized. Calculations in sections to follow will show how to handle the more general case.

When a wave of frequency ω falls on a single atom (pictured as a Lorentz atom), the electric field in the former acts on the elastically bound electrons in the latter and sets them into sinusoidal oscillation with the same frequency ω. Each of the electrons acquires a certain instantaneous dipole moment with respect to its position of equilibrium, and as far as the scattered wave is concerned, the atom can be regarded as a single dipole whose moment is the vectorial sum of those of the several electrons. This point was brought out in Sec. 5-6. Once the dipole moment is known, all the characteristics of the scattered wave follow and are easily visualized by the principles in Chap. 5. Finding the dipole moment requires solving the equations of motion of the electrons under the external force resulting from the incident field. It will turn out that the amplitude of the moment is proportional to that of the applied electric field, and that there is in general a difference of phase. Thus if the moment and the field are expressed in complex form, the complex amplitude of the latter can be multiplied by a complex scalar, called the *polarizability*, to obtain the complex amplitude of the former. The problem then reduces to finding the polarizability as a function of frequency. An example is worked out in Sec. 14-4.

The scattered wave at a point of observation P is characterized by its irradiance and polarization. These properties depend on the irradiance I and polarization of the incident wave and on the distance r and direction of P from the atom. Instead of speaking of the irradiance at P, it is more usual in dealing with the single atom (more generally, any single particle) to think in terms of cross sections for removing power from the incident beam. These cross sections will be precisely defined in Sec. 14-3; their sole advantage is that they eliminate the need of writing I and r in formulas, or, in other words, they are more specific to the particle in describing its scattering properties.

Consider now a gas of atoms. Each gives rise to a secondary wave, and the amplitude of the secondary wave from one atom is weak compared with the amplitude of the incident wave at the location of any other atom, provided the atoms are far apart. The resultant at a given atom of *all* the secondary waves coming from the other atoms is also weak if there are not too many atoms. On qualitative grounds one therefore concludes that if the density of the gas is low enough and the total volume is not too large, the motions of electrons in any atom, and hence its scattered wave, can be calculated as though this atom were alone in the incident field. In this case one speaks of *single scattering*. It is difficult to be more precise in defining conditions under which single scattering holds, and only isolated points on this topic will come out later.

Assume that single scattering obtains. Let the geometry be as in Fig. 14-1. At a point of observation situated a large distance from the sample of gas, all the secondary waves from the several atoms have essentially the same amplitude and polarization, but they must be superposed with due regard for relative phases. In a direction other than the forward one, the secondary waves are separate from the incident beam, and because of the random arrangement of the atoms of the gas, the phases fall at random; moreover, they change rapidly with time because of thermal motions. By the same arguments as applied to the random array in Sec. 7-16, the long-time average of the irradiance at the point of observation when the gas contains N atoms is just N times that

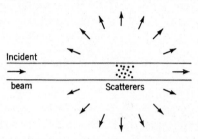

Fig. 14-1. *Qualitative geometry of a scattering arrangement.*

with one atom. In the forward direction special phase relations exist among the secondary waves, and the incident wave is present and cannot be separated from the secondary waves. This special direction will be considered in Sec. 14-7 and, more fully, in the next chapter.

Let us pass now to a case in which single scattering certainly does not hold, namely, a medium in which there are many atoms in any cube whose edge is one wavelength long. Such a medium is said to be *optically dense* at that wavelength, the word dense being used in a sense special to scattering and having to do with the number of atoms in a wavelength cube, not in a unit volume. The normal atmosphere is optically dense at visible wavelengths (some 10^6 molecules in a wavelength cube), and all solids and liquids are optically dense media at all but X-ray wavelengths. Let the discussion here be confined to media that are highly transparent at the frequency in question. There is now the complicating feature that at any given atom the resultant of the secondary electric fields from the other atoms is not negligible. This resultant superposes on the incident electric field to produce at the given atom what is called the *internal field*. It is the internal field that determines the motion of the electrons in the given atom, and hence its secondary wave. The problem is therefore no less than solving simultaneously for the motions of all charges in the body, taking into account the interactions through secondary waves, or the *coupling*, as it is called. A solution has been given by Ewald, Oseen, and others. The details cannot be given here, but the results will now be described.

Suppose the medium is semi-infinite with a plane boundary. Let a plane wave of wavelength λ fall on this surface from vacuum at other than normal incidence. It turns out that, inside the medium, the secondary waves (all being dipole waves with wavelength λ in the wave zone, and all propagating with velocity c) superpose on each other and on the incident wave to give just a plane refracted wave whose wavelength is λ/n and whose velocity of propagation is c/n, where n is the refractive index and is given in terms of the number of atoms per unit volume and the atomic polarizability. The direction of propagation is according to Snell's law. Outside the medium the secondary waves superpose to give a specularly reflected plane wave with wavelength λ. These are just the results already known on empirical grounds. There are no resultant waves, inside or outside the medium, traveling in directions other than those of the refracted and reflected waves. In particular, the incident wave is completely extinguished inside the medium (a result known as the *Oseen extinction theorem*).

Now it is evident from the bluish light scattered by the clear sky and large bodies of pure water and ice when sunlight is incident that dense media give rise to weak scattering in all directions. The theory described above fails to account for this general scattering when it assumes perfectly uniform density in the medium. Thermal motions cause local fluctuation in density, and *it is this fluctuation in density that gives rise to the general scattering from optically dense media*. A theory of this scattering can be built using results on fluctuations from statistical mechanics. The relative fluctuations in liquids are less than in gases; this fact is illustrated by the following measurements by Rayleigh: He found the scattering from a unit volume of liquid ether to be 64 times greater than that from a unit volume of the vapor at 390 mm Hg and 21°C. There were 446 times as many molecules in the liquid, and therefore the scattering *per molecule* was 7 times *less* in the liquid. Scattering per molecule should be still less in the solid, but experiments are difficult because of permanent inhomogeneities, such as bubbles and strains, usually present in solids.

For optically dense gases the theory of scattering by fluctuations gives a surprising result. As long as the ideal gas laws are quite well obeyed, the intensity of scattering is just what would be calculated on the assumption of single scattering regardless of density. (This conclusion hinges in part on the additional condition that the refractive index be very near unity, a condition always satisfied by highly transparent gases.) An experimental check is that measurement of scattering by atmospheric air and other gases, assuming single scattering, has given the Avogadro number with high accuracy.

The Ewald-Oseen theory described above gives as deep an insight into the optics of dense media as is possible on a classical basis, but a more useful approach is through the macroscopic Maxwell equations, to be taken up in the next chapter. These equations make possible the solution of scattering problems in which the scatterers are small bodies of an optically dense medium. An important case is that of spheres, such as drops of water in fog or rain, or metal spheres in colloidal suspension. Single scattering by spheres is called *Mie scattering* after the man who first gave the full solution of this difficult problem, in 1908. Ellipsoids, cylinders, and other shapes have also been treated.

The number of ways in which scattering of electromagnetic waves has been used in the experimental study of particles is enormous. The usual arrangement is to irradiate a sample of scatterers with a collimated, monochromatic beam and to measure the intensity and polarization of the scattered wave as functions of frequency and direction from the scatterers. (In some cases the observation consists in examining the transmitted beam for extinction, polarization, and change of phase. The main discussion of this aspect of scattering is given in the next chapter.) Whenever possible, conditions for single scattering with a random arrangement of the particles are maintained, so that the observations immediately give properties of an individual particle. Now a characteristic of the observational data is that they give only very incomplete information about the particle, but nevertheless information that is useful and easily obtained and may not be obtainable in any other way. The procedure is to seek a fit of the data to theoretical results that have been accumulated for various types of particles, always narrowing the search with any prior knowledge or intuition about the particle being studied.

As an example to illustrate the last remarks, suppose a chemist has produced a molecule of known composition but has predicted the arrangement of the atoms only within a few possibilities. There are standard empirical rules for calculating the intensity of scattering of visible light for each possibility, and a comparison is made with experiment. (In this particular example an observation that is equivalent to measuring the scattering but is easier and more sensitive is to measure the refractive index of the sample.)

As a second example, suppose an industrial process is to produce a colloidal suspension of small dielectric spheres of a certain size (for example, latex spheres). The Mie theory shows that when the wavelength is comparable to the diameter of a sphere, the scattering pattern shows details quite sensitive to size. If the pattern is determined for a standard sample, then scattering can be used as a continuous monitor of the process to show any deviations in size or uniformity.

As a third example, atomic scattering of X rays with a wavelength somewhat less than 10^{-8} cm has given the distribution of electrons in an atom. The results agree with the "new" quantum theory (as distinct from the "old" theory of Bohr).

In the remaining sections of the chapter, the theory of scattering will be worked out for a few of the simplest cases. Some references for further reading are the following: A treatise on single scattering by particles of various sizes and shapes is Van de Hulst [92] (part III, on applications, should not be overlooked). An elementary discussion of scattering by optically dense media can be found in Bhagavantam [4]. Scattering of X rays is treated along classical and semiclassical lines in Compton and Allison [20]. The Ewald-Oseen theory (very advanced reading) is given in part in Born and Wolf [9], p. 97, and more fully in Born [8], pp. 313, 327, and 371. A particularly elegant treatment is in Rosenfeld [78], chap. 6.

14-2 Rayleigh Scattering by a Single Particle

Let a small particle of unspecified nature be at the origin of a cartesian coordinate system, and let a quasi-monochromatic plane wave whose wavelength is much larger than the dimensions of the particle travel in the positive z direction. The scattered wave is to be observed at a point P whose polar coordinates are r, θ, and ϕ, where the polar coordinates are related to the cartesian as in Fig. 14-2.

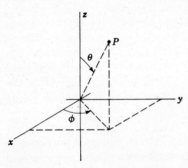

Consider first the case in which the incident wave is perfectly monochromatic and is linearly polarized, with the electric vector along the x axis. Let the amplitude be unity and the phase angle be such that in complex representation the field at the origin is

Fig. 14-2. *Coordinate system to which problems of scattering are referred. The scattering particle is at the origin, and an incident plane wave travels in the positive z direction.*

$$\mathsf{e}_x = e^{-i\omega t} \qquad \mathsf{e}_y = \mathsf{e}_z = 0 \qquad (14\text{-}1)$$

The result of the particle's being subjected to this field is that each of its elastically bound electrons is set into sinusoidal oscillation with frequency ω. Since the particle is small compared with the wavelength, the net scattered wave is just that which would be radiated by a single dipole oscillator with some dipole moment **p** (see Sec. 5-6). It is this property of the scattered wave, guaranteed by the smallness of the particle compared with the wavelength, that characterizes *Rayleigh scattering*.

Two classes of particles must now be distinguished: *isotropic* and *nonisotropic*. Think of the particle as being equivalent, as far as scattering is concerned, to a dipole in which a single point charge is elastically bound to a position of equilibrium. The isotropic case is that in which the stiffness of the binding is the same for a displacement of the charge in any direction with respect to axes fixed in the body. Examples are single atoms and spherical liquid drops. The nonisotropic case, in which the stiffness is not the same in all directions, arises when the particle lacks sufficient symmetry, either in structure (most molecules and crystal lattices), or form (ellipsoids, cylinders, etc.), or both. In discussions of scattering by particles, isotropy will be assumed, except for a few cases to be given passing notice. Anisotropy in large bodies of homogeneous optically dense media gives rise to double refraction and other phenomena to be taken up in later chapters.

The dipole moment of the particle being considered will vary sinusoidally with time and can be written in complex representation as

$$\mathbf{p} = \mathbf{p}_0 e^{-i\omega t} \tag{14-2}$$

When the incident wave is linearly polarized, $\mathbf{p}$ always lies along the same line as $\mathbf{e}$ (in the isotropic case) and is proportional to the latter, so that

$$\mathbf{p} = \alpha \mathbf{e} \tag{14-3}$$

where α is the constant of proportionality called the *polarizability*. The oscillation of $\mathbf{p}$ may not be in phase with that of $\mathbf{e}$, so that α is in general a complex number, and its value depends on the frequency in some way. A specific example will be worked out in Sec. 14-4. The present section will deal with some general consequences of the existence of a polarizability.

From a comparison of (14-1), (14-2), and (14-3) the components of the amplitude of the dipole moment are seen to be

$$p_{0x} = \alpha \qquad p_{0y} = p_{0z} = 0$$

The electric field at a point P in the wave zone of the scattered wave is

$$\mathbf{e} = -\frac{k^2}{r} \mathbf{a} \times (\mathbf{a} \times \mathbf{p}_0) e^{i(kr-\omega t)} \tag{14-4}$$

where $\mathbf{a}$ is a unit vector in the radial direction at P [compare (5-13), in which $-e\mathbf{s}_0$ has the same significance as $\mathbf{p}_0$]. This field is transverse to the radial direction, and its θ and ϕ components can be found most easily by the following method: Let $\mathbf{a}$, $\mathbf{b}$, and $\mathbf{c}$ be the unit vectors at P associated with the polar coordinate system as in Fig. 1-10, and let $\mathbf{i}$, $\mathbf{j}$, and $\mathbf{k}$ be unit vectors along the x, y, and z axes, respectively. By inspection of Fig. 14-2,

$$\mathbf{a} = \mathbf{i} \sin\theta \cos\phi + \mathbf{j} \sin\theta \sin\phi + \mathbf{k} \cos\theta$$
$$\mathbf{b} = \mathbf{i} \cos\theta \cos\phi + \mathbf{j} \cos\theta \sin\phi - \mathbf{k} \sin\theta$$
$$\mathbf{c} = -\mathbf{i} \sin\phi + \mathbf{j} \cos\phi$$

Then
$$\mathbf{p}_0 = \alpha\mathbf{i} = \alpha[(\mathbf{i}\cdot\mathbf{a})\mathbf{a} + (\mathbf{i}\cdot\mathbf{b})\mathbf{b} + (\mathbf{i}\cdot\mathbf{c})\mathbf{c}]$$
$$= \alpha(\mathbf{a} \sin\theta \cos\phi + \mathbf{b} \cos\theta \cos\phi - \mathbf{c} \sin\phi)$$

Evaluation of (14-4) now gives

$$\mathbf{e} = \frac{k^2\alpha}{r}\,(\mathbf{b}\,\cos\theta\,\cos\phi - \mathbf{c}\,\sin\phi)e^{i(kr-\omega t)} \tag{14-5}$$

The importance of (14-5) (which comes from the unrealistic assumption of a perfectly monochromatic wave) is that it gives two of the four transfer functions associated with the scattering problem. The general definition of these functions is expressed by formulas (13-9), which are applied in the present case by taking the reference point P_r to be at the origin of the coordinate system. The V's in those formulas now stand for components of the complex amplitudes of the monochromatic electric fields, and ξ and η are to be replaced by θ and ϕ, respectively. Because of the choice (14-1), we have $V_x = 1$ and $V_y = 0$. Then from (14-5) we read at once,

$$\tau_{\theta x} = \frac{k^2\alpha}{r}\,\cos\theta\,\cos\phi\,e^{ikr} \qquad \tau_{\phi x} = -\frac{k^2\alpha}{r}\,\sin\phi\,e^{ikr} \tag{14-6}$$

To find the other two transfer functions, the incident wave is taken to be the same as before except for being polarized along the y axis instead of the x axis. Then $\mathbf{p}_0 \doteq \alpha\mathbf{j}$, and a calculation analogous to the one above gives

$$\tau_{\theta y} = \frac{k^2\alpha}{r}\,\cos\theta\,\sin\phi\,e^{ikr} \qquad \tau_{\phi y} = \frac{k^2\alpha}{r}\,\cos\phi\,e^{ikr} \tag{14-7}$$

Having the transfer functions, one can find the nature of the scattered wave at any point P when the incident wave is quasi-monochromatic and has any polarization represented by a set of Stokes parameters. Consider the case of an unpolarized incident wave represented by

$$(I,Q,U,V) = (I,0,0,0)$$

From (13-57), (13-71), and (13-72) the parameters of the scattered wave are found to be

$$I(P) = \frac{k^4|\alpha|^2}{2r^2}\,(\cos^2\theta + 1)I \qquad Q(P) = \frac{k^4|\alpha|^2}{2r^2}\,(\cos^2\theta - 1)I$$
$$U(P) = V(P) = 0 \tag{14-8}$$

The interpretation of these results is as follows: We first find the fractional polarization. From (13-65), the irradiance of the completely polarized component is just $|Q(P)|$, and hence (13-66) gives

$$\text{F.P.} = \frac{1 - \cos^2\theta}{1 + \cos^2\theta}$$

The scattered wave is therefore unpolarized in the forward and backward directions, and completely polarized in the directions at right angles to the incident beam. The completely polarized component in any direction is linearly polarized (since $V = 0$). From Fig. 13-20, in which x, y, and z are to be replaced by θ, ϕ, and r, respectively, it is seen that since Q is always negative and $U = 0$, the electric vector in this completely polarized component is along the ϕ direction. The irradiance $I(P)$ for constant r can be represented by a *scattering diagram*, which can take the form of either the polar or the rectangular plot shown in Fig. 14-3.

The calculations just completed illustrate the general and straightforward method of using transfer functions and Stokes parameters to solve a scattering problem. A number of rather complicated formulas

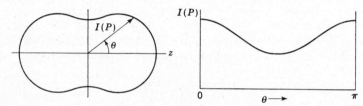

Fig. 14-3. *Polar and rectangular forms of the scattering diagram for Rayleigh scattering from an unpolarized beam.*

from Chap. 13 were required. When a problem has a high degree of symmetry and perhaps other simplifying features, as in Rayleigh scattering by an isotropic particle, one can see simpler methods. Problem 14-2 brings out an example that has doubtless already occurred to the reader. Problem 14-3 gives another example.

14-3 Definitions of Cross Sections Let the wave incident on a scatterer have a given polarization and a given irradiance I. The power P_{sca} carried off by the scattered wave is proportional to I and can be written

$$P_{sca} = \sigma_{sca} I$$

where σ_{sca}, with dimensions of area, is the factor of proportionality called the *total cross section for scattering*. If some mechanism is present whereby heat is generated in the interior of the scatterer, so that the latter shows absorption, the power removed from the incident wave through absorption can be written

$$P_{abs} = \sigma_{abs} I$$

where σ_{abs} is the *cross section for absorption*. (Let us ignore for the present what ultimately happens to the absorbed power, since there are many possibilities.) Adding the last two equations gives the total power removed from the beam:

$$P_{\text{ext}} = \sigma_{\text{ext}} I$$

where $\sigma_{\text{ext}} = \sigma_{\text{sca}} + \sigma_{\text{abs}}$ is the *cross section for extinction*. All these cross sections depend on frequency, and in some cases on the polarization of the incident wave.

The relative intensity of scattering in different directions can be specified by means of an angular factor $f(\theta,\phi)$ so chosen that the power dP defined by

$$dP = I\sigma_{\text{sca}} f(\theta,\phi)\, d\Omega$$

is the power scattered into the solid angle $d\Omega$ in the direction (θ,ϕ). The factor f depends on the polarization of the incident wave and generally on the frequency, and it must be normalized such that its integral over all solid angles is unity. The product $\sigma_{\text{sca}} f(\theta,\phi)$ is called the *differential cross section* for scattering per unit solid angle in the direction (θ,ϕ). The irradiance $I(P)$ at a point of observation can now be written

$$I(P) = \frac{I}{r^2}\,\sigma_{\text{sca}} f(\theta,\phi) \qquad (14\text{-}9)$$

If $I(P)$ is already known, then σ_{sca} is the integral of $I(P)$ over a sphere of radius r when I is unity.

From the $I(P)$ found in the last section for Rayleigh scattering from an unpolarized beam by an isotropic particle,

$$\sigma_{\text{sca}} = \frac{8\pi k^4 |\alpha|^2}{3} \qquad f(\theta,\phi) = \frac{3(\cos^2\theta + 1)}{16\pi} \qquad (14\text{-}10)$$

In this special case f happens to be independent of frequency and the angle ϕ. With an anisotropic particle, or a polarized beam (other than circular), or both, a dependence on ϕ enters (see Prob. 14-5)

14-4 Scattering by a Lorentz Atom and by a Free Electron
Suppose a Lorentz atom has a single elastically bound electron whose resonant frequency is ω_0. Let a monochromatic wave of frequency ω be incident, so that the complex representation of the electric field at the atom is

$$\mathbf{e} = \mathbf{e}_0 e^{-i\omega t} \qquad (14\text{-}11)$$

We are interested in finding the motion of the electron, and from it deducing the polarizability of the atom. The following steps in the calculation are most easily interpreted if the constant vector $\mathbf{e}_0$ is taken to be real, but at the end the reader should return to this point and note that at no step is this assumption essential. Because of the isotropy of the binding of the electron, the same polarizability would be found if $\mathbf{e}_0$

were complex and the field oscillated elliptically instead of linearly (see Prob. 14-6).

The force experienced by the electron (charge $-e$) due to the applied field is $-e\mathbf{e}$. Adding this external force divided by the mass of the electron to the right side of (12-6) gives the equation of motion,

$$\frac{d^2\mathbf{s}}{dt^2} + \omega_0{}^2\mathbf{s} - \frac{2e^2}{3mc^3}\frac{d^3\mathbf{s}}{dt^3} = -\frac{e}{m}\,\mathbf{e}_0 e^{-i\omega t} \tag{14-12}$$

where $\mathbf{s}$ denotes the vectorial displacement of the electron from its equilibrium position. A few comments on this equation are in order.

The significance of the three terms on the left of (14-12) has been discussed in Sec. 12-3. The external force on the right is a physical quantity; the exponential should be replaced by cos ωt. Denote the solution of the equation with this real force by $\mathbf{s}'$, a real function of t. Write a second equation in which the exponential is replaced by sin ωt. This is an arbitrary step, and the equation does not represent the problem at hand, but a real solution can be found and denoted $\mathbf{s}''$. Then if these two real equations are added together after the second is multiplied by i, it follows from the linearity of differentiation together with Euler's formula that $\mathbf{s} = \mathbf{s}' + i\mathbf{s}''$ is the solution of (14-12) as it stands. In other words, the linearity of the equation allows one to substitute the complex representation of the sinusoidal force and find a complex solution, the real part of which is the actual physical motion. This device of using the complex representations shortens the algebra substantially.

Note too that only the force due to the electric field appears in (14-12). There should also be the force $-e\dot{\mathbf{s}} \times \mathbf{b}/c$ due to the magnetic field in the incident wave. This term is neglected because, while $\mathbf{e}$ and $\mathbf{b}$ are equal in magnitude, the velocity of the electron turns out always to be very small compared with c when the field strengths are the weak ones in light waves. If this magnetic term were important, the problem would be much more complicated. (For one thing, the product of $\dot{\mathbf{s}}$ and $\mathbf{b}$ lacks the linearity on which the use of complex representations depends.)

Turning to the solution of (14-12), one feels intuitively that the motion of the electron will be sinusoidal, and one therefore seeks a solution of the form

$$\mathbf{s} = \mathbf{s}_0 e^{-i\omega t}$$

Substitution shows that this is the solution if

$$\mathbf{s}_0 = \frac{e/m}{\omega^2 - \omega_0{}^2 + i\gamma\omega^3/\omega_0{}^2}\,\mathbf{e}_0 \tag{14-13}$$

where the parameter γ is defined by (12-9) (that is, $\gamma = 2e^2\omega_0{}^2/3mc^3$) and has been introduced here partly to simplify the appearance of the formula and partly because it has an important significance in scattering just as it has in emission.

The dipole moment of the atom is $\mathbf{p} = -e\mathbf{s}$, and it follows from the definition (14-3) of the polarizability that $\mathbf{s}_0 = -(\alpha/e)\mathbf{e}_0$. Comparison with (14-13) gives

$$\alpha = \frac{-e^2/m}{\omega^2 - \omega_0^2 + i\gamma\omega^3/\omega_0^2} \tag{14-14}$$

Substituting this polarizability in (14-10) and changing k to ω/c gives the total cross section (omitting the subscript on σ, since only scattering is in question here):

$$\sigma = \frac{8\pi e^4}{3m^2c^4} \frac{\omega^4}{(\omega^2 - \omega_0^2)^2 + (\gamma\omega^3/\omega_0^2)^2} \tag{14-15}$$

The dependence of σ on frequency is complicated, but in the three ranges $\omega \gg \omega_0$, $\omega \approx \omega_0$, and $\omega \ll \omega_0$ simplifying approximations can be made as follows:

1. $\omega \gg \omega_0$. The cross section is essentially

$$\sigma \approx \frac{8\pi e^4}{3m^2c^4} \frac{1}{1 + (\gamma\omega/\omega_0^2)^2} \tag{14-16}$$

Now $\gamma/\omega_0^2 = 2e^2/3mc^3$, which is of order 10^{-23} in cgs units, while even for such a short wavelength as 10^{-8} cm, ω is only of order 10^{19}. The second term in the denominator is therefore negligible compared with the first, and the cross section becomes

$$\sigma \approx \frac{8\pi e^4}{3m^2c^4} = 6.7 \times 10^{-25} \text{ cm}^2 \tag{14-17}$$

The interpretation of these results is the following: The first approximation (14-16) shows no dependence on ω_0; that is, when the frequency becomes sufficiently high, the effect of binding disappears, and we have an essentially free electron. The effect of radiation reaction is still contained in (14-16), but it was found to be negligible at all frequencies of interest to us. The final result (14-17) contains only the effect of the inertial term in the equation of motion of the electron (see Prob. 14-7). The cross section (14-17) for a free electron is called the *Thomson cross section* after J. J. Thomson, who was first to calculate it.

2. $\omega \approx \omega_0$. Since the second term in the denominator of (14-15) keeps σ from becoming infinite at $\omega = \omega_0$, and since this term is very small, there is a very narrow peak in σ. Over the width of this peak it is a good approximation to replace the ω in the numerator and in the second term of the denominator by ω_0 and to write $\omega^2 - \omega_0^2 \approx 2\omega_0(\omega - \omega_0)$. Then

$$\sigma \approx \frac{2\pi^2e^2}{mc} \frac{\gamma/2\pi}{(\omega - \omega_0)^2 + \gamma^2/4} = \frac{2\pi^2e^2}{mc} \mathcal{L}(\omega - \omega_0; \gamma) \tag{14-18}$$

where the normalized resonance function $\mathcal{L}$, illustrated in Fig. 12-6, has been introduced to give the result a form convenient for later reference.

   3. $\omega \ll \omega_0$. The approximate form of the cross section is now

$$\sigma \approx \frac{8\pi e^4}{3m^2 c^4}\left(\frac{\omega}{\omega_0}\right)^4 \tag{14-19}$$

proportional to the fourth power of the frequency. In this range only the force of binding is effective in determining the polarizability (see second part of Prob. 14-7).

The dependence of σ on frequency is illustrated in grossly distorted proportions by Fig. 14-4. The solid curve represents the exact cross section, and the dashed curve is the resonance function (14-18). The

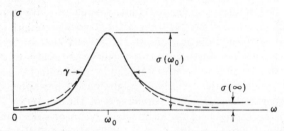

Fig. 14-4. *Total cross section for scattering by a Lorentz atom with a single bound electron. Proportions are greatly distorted for purposes of illustration. The asymptotic value at the right is the Thomson cross section. The dashed curve is the simple resonance function fitting the curve of σ (solid curve) in the vicinity of the maximum.*

Thomson cross section is denoted here by $\sigma(\infty)$. The following ratios give an idea of the actual relative magnitudes occurring in such a plot:

$$\frac{\sigma(\omega_0)}{\sigma(\infty)} = \frac{5.3 \times 10^{55}}{\omega_0^2} \qquad \frac{\sigma(\omega_0)}{h} = \frac{10^{47}}{\omega_0^2} \qquad \frac{\omega_0}{\gamma} = \frac{1.7 \times 10^{23}}{\omega_0}$$

where h is the ordinate of the dashed curve at $\omega = 0$. All these ratios have their smallest values at the highest frequency for which the classical theory is of any interest and are still enormous at $\omega_0 = 2 \times 10^{19}$, corresponding to $\lambda = 1$ A.

14-5 Scattering by Gases In a discussion of scattering by gases, two cases must be distinguished: that in which the frequency of the incident light is far below any resonant frequency, and that in which it is near or coincides with a resonant frequency. Let us consider first the former case and suppose that the pressure is not so high that there is serious departure from the laws of an ideal gas. Then, as remarked in Sec. 14-1, the scattering is the same as though single scattering obtained, even though the actual mechanism has to be understood as local fluctuation in density when the pressure is not very low.   Thus the discussion can be in terms of one particle.

Let the incident beam be white light covering the visible range with a power spectrum $S(\omega)$.   At any point of observation the spectrum of the scattered light is proportional to $\sigma(\omega)S(\omega)$, where $\sigma(\omega)$ is the total cross section for scattering by an atom.   According to (14-19), σ for the case in question is proportional to ω^4, and therefore the scattered light is distinctly blue, as is seen in the sky.   Lord Rayleigh measured, at several frequencies in the visible range, the ratio of the intensity of light from the zenith to that of direct sunlight weakened by reflection from white paper, and found quite good agreement with the fourth-power law.

According to the theory for isotropic particles, the light from the blue sky should be completely polarized when viewed in a direction at right angles to the direction of propagation of the incident sunlight.   Observation through a linear polarizer shows the polarization to be not quite complete.   Suspended dust and water droplets and scattered earthshine complicate the matter, and the most reliable measurements are made in the laboratory (where the technique in eliminating unwanted light must be very elaborate because of the weakness of the scattering, and some correction is necessary because an incident beam of sufficient intensity must be rather far from unidirectional).   Observation of the polarization is made at a scattering angle of 90°, and the results are expressed as a "depolarization" Δ, the ratio of the irradiance following a linear polarizer when its E axis is parallel to the incident beam to that when it is at right angles.   For monatomic gases, $\Delta = 0$, but for ordinary air, $\Delta = 0.031$ and is explained by the anisotropic character of the molecules in air. (In an anisotropic particle the dipole moment is not always in the plane perpendicular to the direction of the incident beam, and when an average is taken over random orientations, a theory of Δ emerges.   A reference is Bhagavantam [4].   The value of Δ in this reference is old.)

Careful measurements show that for air the fourth-power law is only approximately satisfied in the visible range.   The explanation of the departure is that many resonant frequencies are involved with the molecules of the air, some in the ultraviolet and some in the infrared. The polarizability (an average over the different kinds of molecules and their random orientations) then shows a more complicated dependence on frequency than (14-14), and the cross section (14-19) becomes a rather rough approximation in the visible region.   The most sensitive way to investigate the matter is through the refractive index, to be taken up in the next chapter.

When a resonant frequency falls within the spectrum of the incident beam, scattering is very strong at frequencies covered by the high narrow peak in the cross section, and scattering at other frequencies is negligible

in comparison.   This highly selective character of the scattering is so
distinctive that it is given the special name *resonance radiation.*

From a purely classical point of view, resonant scattering differs from
nonresonant only in its strength, but herein lies its first interesting
feature: Unless the pressure of the resonating atoms is very low, all the
power in the incident beam falling in the frequencies covered by the
resonant peak is scattered away in a path less than a wavelength long,
and no scattered light originates in the bulk of the gas.   It was R. W.
Wood who discovered the need for low pressure (in some cases 10^{-7} mm Hg)
in achieving anything approximating single scattering.   In his pioneering
experiment, done in 1904, an evacuated bulb contained some sodium at
the bottom.   Through the bulb was sent a pencil of light with a fairly
narrow spectrum including the frequencies of the resonant D lines of
sodium at 5890 A and 5896 A.   When the bulb was gently warmed,
yellow resonance radiation appeared all along the illuminating beam.
On further warming, the whole gas glowed, indicating that the vapor
pressure had become high enough to cause strong coupling of all the atoms
through secondary waves.   At still higher temperatures, the radiating
volume contracted toward the point of entry of the incident beam, and
ultimately there was only a specular reflection of yellow resonance
radiation from the front surface as though from a mirror with high
reflectance only in narrow bands at the resonant frequencies.   Under
the last condition, the spectrum of the transmitted beam showed complete extinction in the two bands corresponding to the bands reflected
from the front surface.   Further comment on this extinction and reflection
will be deferred to the next two chapters; let us now return to single
scattering.

The classical theory states that at right angles to an unpolarized
incident beam the scattered radiation should be linearly polarized, but
with sodium this is far from the case.   The D_1 line at 5896 A is unpolarized, and the D_2 line at 5890 A is less than half polarized.   Mercury, on
the other hand, has a resonance line in the ultraviolet at 2537 A, and it
shows the classical polarization.   Closely related to these differences is
the fact that the mercury line shows the "normal" or classical Zeeman
effect, whereas both the D lines are anomalous.   The point for the
present is that resonance radiation, like atomic spectra in general, shows
many effects which the classical theory cannot explain.

Suppose the power spectrum of the incident radiation is independent
of frequency over a band many times the width of the resonance line.
According to the theory developed so far, the shape of the line in the
scattered spectrum is just that of the cross section and, therefore, is given
to excellent approximation by the resonance function (14-18).   The
width here is for a stationary unperturbed atom and is determined solely
by radiation reaction.   Resonance lines are also subject to thermal and

pressure broadening, and while the details of the calculation are somewhat different from those of the emission treated in Secs. 12-7 and 12-8, the effects on shape and width come out the same. Again this is purely classical theory, and resonance radiation has the important virtue of making comparison with experiment feasible, whereas in a primary source, such as an arc or a Geissler tube, so many processes are at play, and conditions are so poorly known, that useful quantitative results are hard to obtain.

The theory of thermal broadening is hardly in question. Collisional broadening is studied by introducing various foreign gases up to any pressure. In this way the condition for single scattering by the resonating atoms is not destroyed, since their partial pressure can be kept as low as necessary. Increasing the total pressure is always accompanied by broadening, but the various foreign gases divide into two classes according as they do or do not reduce the intensity of the resonance radiation. If they do, the collisions are said to cause *quenching*. The classical picture of these cases, which bears a certain resemblance to quantum ideas, is that in the nonquenching case the phase of the oscillation of the resonating atom is suddenly changed by a collision, while in the quenching case the amplitude is suddenly reduced to zero. After the collision the oscillation begins a gradual return to what it would have been under the influence of the incident wave in the absence of a collision, the details of the return being governed by one of the transient solutions of the equation of motion. The net effect is to introduce Fourier components that would not be there without collisions; therefore there is a broadening.

When the pressure of the foreign gas is high enough that the broadening is predominantly collisional, it is found that the line becomes somewhat asymmetrical and is shifted to a slightly lower frequency. These departures from the simple theory of Lorentz are explained by the quantum theory of interactions of atoms and molecules in close encounter, and an important experimental datum for checking the latter theory is the cross section for a broadening encounter. It is usually obtained by assuming that the observed width at half-maximum is given by (12-49), except that since the collision is between a resonating atom and a foreign atom or molecule of different mass, the M in (12-49) is to be replaced by the "reduced" mass $M_1 M_2 / (M_1 + M_2)$. This formula then gives a value of D, which represents the mean of the effective diameters of a resonating and a foreign particle, and the cross section is πD^2 (not $\pi D^2 / 4$—see Kennard [54], p. 103). One might now refer back to the remarks on range of interaction in Sec. 12-8.

A quenching collision in which the foreign particle carries energy away from the resonating atom is called a collision of the second kind, of which there are many types. An example is quenching of resonance radiation in mercury by hydrogen gas. The H_2 molecules are dissociated into atoms which then recombine or reduce oxides at the walls. Another type is illustrated by quenching of mercury radiation by sodium atoms. A sodium atom emerges from a quenching collision in a highly excited state and subsequently emits lines in the sodium spectrum, this case being called sensitized fluorescence. The list will not be continued, but the point to note is that the energy taken from the resonating atom may appear as kinetic energy (heat), or it may come off as radiation at other than the frequency of the resonance radiation.

The classical theory of resonance radiation is seriously limited. Further study leads into quantum theory, and an account of the subject as it stood in 1933 has been given by Mitchell and Zemansky [67]. Since then there has been an explosive development, largely through the introduction of new techniques known generally as optical pumping. A wealth of experimental information on atomic processes has been gathered by these sensitive methods, and the whole line of investigation has come to constitute a rather well-defined branch of physics.

This section should not conclude without mentioning the *Raman effect*. If a gas of molecules (not atoms) is irradiated by a beam of very nearly monochromatic visible or ultraviolet radiation with a mean frequency ω_0 far from any resonant frequency, the weak scattered light has a spectrum consisting predominantly of a line at the frequency ω_0, but in addition there are faint neighboring lines. The effect was predicted by Smekal in 1923 and experimentally demonstrated by Raman in 1928. There is a classical explanation corresponding partially with the facts. According to it the nuclei in the molecule are elastically bound together, and vibrations at infrared frequencies are excited by thermal collisions. The vibrations cause a periodic change in the polarizability of the electronic structure, and if one such vibration has frequency ω, then the scattered light should contain frequencies $\omega_0 + \omega$ and $\omega_0 - \omega$. Rotation of the anisotropic molecule introduces additional sum and difference frequencies, and according to the classical theory they form a continuum; this is contrary to the facts—the rotation is quantized. The Raman effect makes possible measurement of vibrational and rotational frequencies by observation in the visible or ultraviolet rather than the infrared, but more important, it gives the vibrational and rotational frequencies of homonuclear molecules—H_2, O_2, etc.—which, because of symmetry, do not acquire dipole moments by virtue of vibration or rotation alone, and therefore emit no infrared spectrum. A treatise on spectra of diatomic molecules is Herzberg [40], in which the classical theory of the Raman effect is given on p. 82.

14-6   Diffraction by Crystals   In briefest outline, the events leading to the discovery of diffraction by crystals are as follows: X rays were discovered by Roentgen in 1895, and accumulated evidence indicated that they are electromagnetic waves. In particular, experiments were performed by Barkla, culminating in 1906, in which a beam of X rays was scattered by a small block of carbon. The secondary radiation was scattered by a second block, and the intensity of the tertiary radiation was measured for various combinations of scattering angles. The results were consistent with the idea that electromagnetic waves were exciting dipole oscillations and giving rise to polarized scattered waves in the manner to be expected (see Prob. 14-8). The first efforts to measure the wavelengths of X rays consisted in looking for diffraction by a narrow slit. After much difficulty a preliminary result appeared in 1912 indicating that ordinarily X-ray tubes produce wavelengths in the range 10^{-9} to 10^{-8} cm. Diffraction effects of large scale require structures with spacings comparable to the wavelength. Von Laue estimated the spacing of atoms in crystal lattices[1] to be 10^{-8} to 10^{-7} cm and conceived these lattices to be ideal for diffracting X rays; the first patterns were obtained at his suggestion by Fiedrich and Knipping in 1912.

A prominent characteristic of X rays is that on passing through small samples of most solids, they show very little extinction and, to a very good approximation, no refraction. In discussing scattering, one is therefore led to begin by assuming single scattering by individual atoms.

No effort will be made here to describe the scattering patterns given by the many different types of crystal lattices or to go into the highly specialized art of deducing a structure from scattering. The only case to be considered is an orthorhombic lattice with one kind of atom. In this lattice the unit cell consists of eight atoms at the corners of a rectangular parallelpiped of dimensions a by b by c. Let the crystal be referred to cartesian axes in such a way that the rows of atoms at spacing a are parallel to the x axis, and those with spacing b are parallel to the y axis. For simplicity let the whole crystal have the same shape as the unit cell, so that there are N layers of atoms counting along the x or the y or the z axis, and the total number of atoms is $M = N^3$.

Let the crystal be at the origin O in the coordinate system of Fig. 7-4, and imagine the incident wave to be ideally plane and monochromatic, and the point of observation P to be very far away. The problem is now essentially the same as that of Fraunhofer diffraction by a regular array of identical apertures in a screen. One atom by itself would produce a scattered wave whose irradiance at P is I_1, the value of which is not important in the following considerations. For the whole crystal, the irradiance at P is $I = I_1|F|^2$, where F has the same significance as in Sec. 7-6 and contains the effect of interference of the waves scattered by the fixed atoms.

[1] It should be mentioned that at that time the existence of lattices was inferred from the regularity of the external forms of crystals, but the external form proved insufficient to establish the internal structure. Von Laue's estimate was based on the density of a crystal, its chemical composition, and the Avogadro number.

For a three-dimensional array the formula for F takes simplest form if the direction from the source to the crystal is specified by the x, y, and z components of a unit vector pointing in this direction. These components are just the direction cosines l_0, m_0, and n_0, and from Fig. 7-4 we have $l_0 = \cos(\pi/2 + \theta_1) = -\sin\theta_1$, $m_0 = -\sin\phi_1$. Also,

$$l_0{}^2 + m_0{}^2 + n_0{}^2 = 1 \qquad (14\text{-}20)$$

Similarly, the direction from the crystal to P is specified by direction cosines l, m, and n, where $l = \cos(\pi/2 - \theta_2) = \sin\theta_2$, $m = \sin\phi_2$, and

$$l^2 + m^2 + n^2 = 1 \qquad (14\text{-}21)$$

One now easily sees that the formula analogous to (7-9) is

$$F = \sum_{j=1}^{M} e^{-ik[x_j(l-l_0)+y_j(m-m_0)+z_j(n-n_0)]}$$

where x_j, y_j, and z_j are the coordinates of the jth atom in the crystal.

The evaluation of $|F|^2$ proceeds in the same way as for the rectangular array in Sec. 7-10; the final result is that the irradiance at P is

$$I = I_1 \frac{\sin^2 N\pi\alpha}{\sin^2 \pi\alpha} \frac{\sin^2 N\pi\beta}{\sin^2 \pi\beta} \frac{\sin^2 N\pi\gamma}{\sin^2 \pi\gamma} \qquad (14\text{-}22)$$

where $\quad \alpha = \dfrac{a(l - l_0)}{\lambda} \qquad \beta = \dfrac{b(m - m_0)}{\lambda} \qquad \gamma = \dfrac{c(n - n_0)}{\lambda}$

Principal maxima, at which the irradiance is $I = N^6 I_1 = M^2 I_1$, occur when α, β, and γ are equal to integers p, q, and r, respectively, or

$$a(l - l_0) = p\lambda \qquad b(m - m_0) = q\lambda \qquad c(n - n_0) = r\lambda \qquad (14\text{-}23)$$

Suppose l_0, m_0, n_0, and λ are given, and p, q, and r are assigned a set of integers. Then (14-21) and (14-23) are four equations for determining only the three unknowns l, m, and n, and in general there is no solution for any integral values of p, q, and r. If, however, the spectrum of the source is a broad continuum, λ becomes a fourth variable, and the equations have a solution. Many principal maxima appear, each identified by integral values of p, q, and r, and each formed in monochromatic radiation, but the spots are in general all different in "color." If the source lies on an axis of symmetry of the crystal, then some symmetry appears in the diffraction pattern, and groups of spots have the same color. Formation of spots with a source having a *continuous spectrum* is the characteristic feature of Laue's arrangement.

Suppose now that the source is monochromatic and is moved about to assume various directions from the crystal. Alternatively, the source may be fixed, and the crystal and its associated x, y, and z axes rotated. With values assigned to p, q, and r, the variables are now the six direction cosines whose values are to be found from the five equations (14-20), (14-21), and (14-23). Thus as the crystal is rotated about some axis fixed in it, there is in general no principal maximum, but for certain positions one (or several if a condition of symmetry happens to prevail) blazes forth in some direction. This technique is called the *rotation method* and was introduced by W. H. Bragg. In both the Laue and rotation methods the spots are usually detected photographically. A method related to the rotation method is described in Prob. 14-10.

The crystal considered above was assumed to have the shape of a rectangular parallelepiped with each of its plane faces perpendicular to the x or y or z axis. Consider the first of the faces perpendicular to z, and let the direction of propagation of a plane monochromatic wave lie in the xz

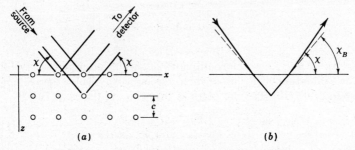

Fig. 14-5. **a.** *Geometry of a crystal spectrometer. The linkage in the instrument is such that the angles χ are variable but always equal.* **b.** *Measured angle χ must be corrected for refraction to obtain accurate Bragg angles. The difference shown is exaggerated but is in the proper direction.*

plane and make an angle χ with the surface of the crystal, as illustrated in Fig. 14-5a. This angle χ is called the *grazing angle* in distinction from the angle of incidence, the latter being the angle made with the normal to the surface. The direction cosines for this incident wave are

$$l_0 = \cos \chi \qquad m_0 = 0 \qquad n_0 = \sin \chi$$

Let a distant detector be located to receive scattered radiation in the direction defined by the law of specular reflection from the surface of the crystal, this direction having direction cosines

$$l = l_0 \qquad m = 0 \qquad n = -n_0$$

From (14-23) the condition that a principal maximum fall on the detector is then

$$2c \sin \chi = r\lambda \tag{14-24}$$

This relation is also evident from inspection of Fig. 14-5a—the path from source to detector via an atom in any layer is greater than that via an atom in the layer next above by $2c \sin \chi$, and all atoms contribute constructively to the signal only if this quantity is an integral number of wavelengths.

The result (14-24) is called the *Bragg condition* and is the basis of the crystal spectrometer. In this instrument the source is fixed, and the crystal is rotated about the y axis. At the same time, the direction to the detector (the latter being commonly an ionization chamber behind a narrow slit) is rotated about the same axis, twice as fast. If a given wavelength is present in the spectrum of the source, it will contribute to the signal at several discrete settings corresponding to the various orders r.

The principles of the crystal spectrometer should be carefully contrasted with those of the ruled grating. For best results, the crystal in a spectrometer is bent to achieve focusing analogous to that of a concave ruled grating (Sec. 7-15).

This section will now conclude with a few more historical points. In 1913 W. H. Bragg established the structure of rock salt by the rotation method. This was the first structure determined, and because the crystal happens to have full cubic symmetry, it was possible to give an unambiguous assignment to the arrangement of the sodium and chlorine atoms (but not the absolute spacing) at a time when no X-ray wavelengths (or even the exact nature of any X-ray spectra) were known. The absolute spacing was calculated from the density of the crystal and the Avogadro number, and rock salt was then available for use in a crystal spectrometer for measuring wavelengths of sharp lines emitted by a tube with a given kind of target and for investigating the continuous background in the spectrum. In the late 1920s a technique for precision measurement of X-ray wavelengths by the use of ruled gratings was perfected, and comparison with data from crystal spectrometers showed that in the latter a small correction must be applied to observed angles χ (Fig. 14-5b) to get the proper Bragg angle χ_B to substitute in (14-24). This correction is interpretable as meaning that the crystal has a refractive index very slightly *less* than unity. From a deeper point of view, it means that single scattering does not hold exactly, and there is a small amount of coupling of atoms through secondary waves. The classical explanation of refractive indices less than unity will come in the next chapter.

14-7 Forward Scattering. Extinction

Suppose a monochromatic plane wave is incident on a particle. The plane wave can be thought of in the following as having infinite lateral extent. If a distant telescope is directed at the particle from any direction but the forward one, the incident and scattered waves give separate images, and the irradiances of the two waves can be measured separately. When the telescope is in the forward direction, there is only one image, and the power falling in it is less with the particle present than with the particle absent; this is the phenomenon of extinction. In the forward direction a telescope is unnecessary, and we can merely place there a detector of a certain diameter. What the detector measures depends on its size, its distance from the particle, and the nature of the scattered wave. The following paragraphs will discuss some important cases.

Suppose first that the amplitude of the scattered wave does not have an extremely sharp maximum in the forward direction. This is the case, for example, in Rayleigh scattering. The amplitude over the surface of the detector is then the superposition of an effectively isotropic spherical wave on the plane incident wave. These two waves have a definite relationship of phase which depends on the nature of the scattering particle (but not on its position along the direction of incidence). The detailed calculation, which will not be given here, leads to the same integrals as occur in Fresnel diffraction, and the results are as follows: Assume the detecting surface to be a plane circular disk centered on and perpendicular to the forward direction. If its diameter is made to increase steadily from zero, the indicated power shows oscillations, but ultimately settles down to a steady value equal to $I_0(A - \sigma_{ext})$, where I_0 is the irradiance of the incident wave, A is the area of the detector, and σ_{ext} is the extinction cross section of the particle, equal to the sum of the cross sections for absorption and scattering. The first term, I_0A, is the power that would be recorded in the absence of the particle. The second term, which is what one would write from simplest reasoning, implies that all the energy in the scattered wave is carried off in directions not intersecting the detector. This can actually be true, for the condition for steady reading turns out to be that the distance from the particle to the edge of the detector exceeds that to its center by many wavelengths. One easily shows from the formula in Sec. 7-1 that this condition can be met with a detector subtending an arbitrarily small angular diameter as seen from the particle if the detector is far enough away. The conclusion is that the extinction can be written simply as $I_0\sigma_{ext}$, but the details of what happens at the surface of the detector involve a complicated interference of scattered and incident waves. The calculation behind the above description can be found in Van de Hulst [92], p. 30.

Consider now the case in which all the scattered wave is confined to a narrow cone about the forward direction. An example, to which the following discussion will be confined, is an opaque body whose dimensions are large compared with the wavelength. The scattered wave is independent of polarization of the incident wave and can be found by the scalar theory of diffraction. As far as distant points of observation are concerned, the body is equivalent to a plane opaque surface having the shape of the body as seen from the forward direction. Let this surface have area S. By Babinet's principle, the scattered wave is the same as the wave issuing from a hole in the complementary screen, and the total power in this wave is $I_0 S$. The total cross section for scattering is therefore $\sigma_{\mathrm{sca}} = S$. The cross section for absorption by the opaque body is $\sigma_{\mathrm{abs}} = S$, and the extinction cross section is $\sigma_{\mathrm{ext}} = 2S$, a result known as the *extinction paradox*. The paradox is resolved by noting that if a detector is far off in the forward direction and is small enough to include only a negligible amount of the scattered wave, it indicates an extinction $2I_0 S$, but if it is large enough to include the whole scattered wave, the extinction is just $I_0 S$. Thus if an object such as a coin is suspended a few inches in front of an illuminated sheet of paper, its effective cross section for reducing the power falling on the paper is just its area, and not twice its area.

14-8 Force and Torque Exerted on a Body by Radiation. Radiation Pressure In Sec. 14-4 it was found that when a monochromatic plane wave is incident on a Lorentz atom with a single elastically bound electron and the electric vector at the atom is (14-11), the electron oscillates sinusoidally with complex amplitude $\mathbf{s}_0 = -(\alpha/e)\mathbf{e}_0$, with α given by (14-14). This result holds when $\mathbf{e}_0$ is an arbitrary complex vector and the incident wave therefore has arbitrary polarization. The solution is an approximation, but an excellent one, in which the effect of the magnetic field on the motion is neglected.

If this approximate motion is taken to be an adequate representation of the true motion, the force acting on the atom due to the magnetic field of the incident wave can be calculated. The instantaneous value of this force is $\mathbf{F} = (-e/c)\dot{\mathbf{s}} \times \mathbf{b}$. Since a product is involved, real values must be substituted, but the item of interest is the time average of $\mathbf{F}$, and it is most easily found as

$$\langle \mathbf{F} \rangle = -\frac{e}{2c} \operatorname{Re} \left(-i\omega \mathbf{s}_0 \times \mathbf{b}_0^* \right) = -\frac{\omega}{2c} \operatorname{Re} \left(i\alpha \mathbf{e}_0 \times \mathbf{b}_0^* \right)$$

where $\mathbf{s}_0$, $\mathbf{e}_0$, and $\mathbf{b}_0$ are the complex amplitudes (compare Probs. 4-10 and 4-11). Now $\mathbf{e}_0 \times \mathbf{b}_0^*$ is real and equals $8\pi\langle \mathbf{S} \rangle/c$, where $\langle \mathbf{S} \rangle$ is the time average of the Poynting vector of the incident wave; if $\alpha = \alpha' + i\alpha''$, we have

$$\langle \mathbf{F} \rangle = \frac{4\pi\omega\alpha''}{c^2} \langle \mathbf{S} \rangle = \frac{3c^2}{2\omega^3} \frac{\alpha''}{|\alpha|^2} \sigma \langle \mathbf{S} \rangle$$

The last form results from multiplying by σ, the total cross section for scattering, and dividing by its value given in (14-10). From (14-14), $\alpha''/|\alpha|^2 = 2\omega^3/3c^3$, and the final result is

$$\langle \mathbf{F} \rangle = \frac{\sigma \langle \mathbf{S} \rangle}{c} \tag{14-25}$$

The other forces acting on the atom are the radiation reaction and the force due to the electric field of the incident wave.   They are sinusoidal and have vanishing time averages.

The force (14-25) can be thought of as arising from a pressure $\langle S \rangle / c$ exerted by the incident wave on the area σ.   Pressure, on the other hand, can be regarded as a rate of transfer of momentum to a unit area of a surface on which it acts, and one is led to say that an electromagnetic wave transports momentum in such a way that momentum $\langle S \rangle / c$ flows in unit time across a unit area oriented perpendicular to the direction of propagation.   In this unit time a cylinder of radiation of length c crosses the unit area, and one concludes that the wave contains momentum with mean density $\langle S \rangle / c^2$.   With these ideas one can solve such problems as the following: A plane wave of irradiance I and cross-sectional area A falls on a perfectly reflecting plane mirror at angle of incidence θ.   Find the force on the mirror without giving any consideration to forces on charges. To find the solution, surround the mirror by a closed surface having two plane facets through which the incident and reflected beams pass normally.   Add vectorially the momenta crossing into the enclosed volume in unit time, and conclude that the force on the mirror acts normally and has magnitude $(2IA/c) \cos \theta$.   A slight generalization appears in Prob. 14-11.

The above discussion has brought out only a limited view of the subject of momentum in radiation.   There is a general theorem analogous to the energy theorem of Poynting.   The energy theorem states that the work done by electrical forces on an assembly of moving charges can be calculated alternatively as a flow of electromagnetic energy into the region enclosed by a surface Σ enclosing the charges.   The momentum theorem states that the change of momentum due to the electrical forces acting on the charges can be calculated alternatively as a flow of electromagnetic momentum across Σ.   The density of energy is a scalar, and the flow of energy is represented by a vector (the Poynting vector); however, the density of momentum is a vector (the Poynting vector divided by c^2), and the flow of momentum is represented by a tensor of second rank, called the stress tensor.   The rate of flow of energy through Σ is the normal surface integral of the Poynting vector, and the result is a scalar.   The rate of flow of momentum through Σ is the normal surface integral of the stress tensor, and the result is a vector.   No details of the general theorem on momentum will be given here, but a result is that at any point of Σ at which a transverse wave crosses at normal incidence, the normal component of the stress tensor is S/c, the same result as was found above.

There is a general theorem on angular momentum of radiation.   It is even more complicated than that on linear momentum, and it is hard to avoid wrong results in using it.   Let us reach a limited view of the matter by considering again the known motion of the electron in scattering by a Lorentz atom.

The moment, taken about the nucleus as center, of the force exerted on the electron by the electric field of the incident wave is $\mathbf{M} = -e\mathbf{s} \times \mathbf{e}$, and the time average is $\langle\mathbf{M}\rangle = \frac{1}{2}\,\mathrm{Re}\,(\alpha\mathbf{e}_0 \times \mathbf{e}_0^*)$. It is left as an exercise to show that if $\mathbf{e}_0 = \mathbf{e}_0' + i\mathbf{e}_0''$, then

$$\langle\mathbf{M}\rangle = \frac{2\sigma I}{\omega}\,\frac{\mathbf{e}_0' \times \mathbf{e}_0''}{|\mathbf{e}_0|^2} \tag{14-26}$$

where I is the irradiance of the incident wave (magnitude of the time average of the Poynting vector), and σ is the cross section for scattering. The presence of the vector product means that $\langle\mathbf{M}\rangle$ is different from zero only if the wave is other than linearly polarized.

The result (14-26) can be interpreted to mean that the incident wave transports angular momentum across a unit area of a surface normal to the direction of propagation at the rate

$$\frac{d\mathbf{J}}{dt} = \frac{2I}{\omega}\,\frac{\mathbf{e}_0' \times \mathbf{e}_0''}{|\mathbf{e}_0|^2} \tag{14-27}$$

In the case of circular polarization, $\mathbf{e}_0'$ and $\mathbf{e}_0''$ are equal and orthogonal, and (14-27) reduces to

$$\frac{d\mathbf{J}}{dt} = \pm\,\frac{\langle\mathbf{S}\rangle}{\omega} \qquad \text{circular polarization} \tag{14-28}$$

where the *positive* sign holds for *left-hand* polarization.

With regard to the other forces acting on the electron, it can be shown that the time average of the moment due to the magnetic field is zero, and that due to the radiation reaction is equal and opposite to (14-26), so that the angular momentum extracted from the incident wave is carried off by the scattered wave. The atom gains no angular momentum in the course of time, as the nature of the motion already indicates.

It is interesting to conclude by introducing a quantum idea into the scattering problem. Radiant energy at frequency ω is detected only in integral multiples of the quantum $\hbar\omega$, where $\hbar$ is Planck's constant h divided by 2π. The linear momentum extracted from the incident wave per quantum of energy is $\hbar\omega/c = \hbar k = h/\lambda$, and the angular momentum in the case of circular polarization is $\hbar$, the natural unit of angular momentum in quantum mechanics.

Problems

14-1. What are the dimensions of the polarizability α defined by (14-3)?

14-2. The properties of the scattered wave represented by (14-8) can be found by the following simple method: Regard the incident unpolarized wave as an incoherent superposition of two linearly polarized waves having electric vectors along the x and y axes, respectively, and having equal irradiances. For each component alone, the scattering pattern has the shape of the toroid illustrated in Fig. 5-12. The total pattern is found by addition as in Fig. 5-13. Because of the symmetry about the z axis, it is sufficient to consider the pattern in the xz plane only. The dependence of $I(P)$ on θ can now be written. The total wave at P is the incoherent superposition of two linearly polarized waves corresponding to the two components in the incident wave, the polarization of each wave being as illustrated in Fig. 5-10a. In one the electric vector has only a ϕ component and an irradiance I_ϕ. In the other there are only a θ component and an irradiance I_θ. The fractional polarization is found as a function of θ by the formula F.P. $= |I_\phi - I_\theta|/(I_\phi + I_\theta)$. Carry out the steps in this outline and compare the results with those in Sec. 14-2.

14-3. In the problem of Rayleigh scattering by an isotropic particle treated in Sec. 14-2, let the incident wave be completely right-hand circularly polarized. Write the Stokes parameters of the incident wave. Find those of the scattered wave at an arbitrary point P by the same method as gave (14-8). Show that the scattered wave is completely polarized, and describe the polarization in the directions $\theta = 0$, $\pi/2$, and π. It is evident (from symmetry if nothing else) that if the incident wave were perfectly monochromatic, **p** would have constant magnitude and would rotate in the xy plane with angular velocity ω in the same sense as the electric vector of the incident wave. The scattered wave would then have the polarization illustrated in Fig. 5-10b. From the geometry of this figure one can find, in terms of the scattering angle θ, the angles χ and ψ to substitute in (13-62). Show that the Stokes parameters Q, U, and V found in this way agree with those found in the first part of the problem. The parameter I can be found as a function of θ from the scattering pattern drawn by the method of Fig. 5-13. (Another method of solving this problem would be to resolve the incident wave into linearly polarized components of equal irradiances as in the last problem. The difference is that the components are now coherent with a definite difference of phase, and the scattered wave is a coherent superposition and is therefore completely polarized.)

14-4. Show that for Rayleigh scattering by an isotropic particle the total cross section is independent of the polarization of the incident wave. Base the first and most satisfying solution on the use of transfer functions and Stokes parameters. Give also a simpler proof suggested by statements in some of the problems in Chaps. 4 and 5.

14-5. Let a problem in Rayleigh scattering by an isotropic particle be referred to the coordinate system in Fig. 14-2. Let an incident wave have a fractional polarization of 0.5, and let the completely polarized component be characterized by an ellipse as in Fig. 13-19, with $\chi = \pi/12$ and $\psi = \pi/4$. Find the differential cross section for an arbitrary polarizability.

14-6. Suppose that in (14-11) the constant $\mathbf{e}_0$ is complex with real and imaginary parts not collinear, so that the oscillation of the field is representable by a point moving on an ellipse. Give the arguments whereby one concludes that the path of the electron in an atom placed in this field is an ellipse having the same shape and the same directions of principal axes, but that there is in general a difference of phase; that is, the instantaneous displacement vector **s** leads or lags the instantaneous electric vector. (This simple relationship together with the ideas in Sec. 5-4 lead to an easy visualization of the wave scattered by an atom or any other isotropic and sufficiently small particle when the incident wave is completely polarized in any way.)

14-7. In the equation of motion (14-12) omit the term representing the binding force (free electron). Omit also the force of radiation reaction. Find the motion and the polarizability (note its sign), and show that the Thomson cross section (14-17) follows.

Make a similar calculation in which only the term for the binding force is retained in the left of (14-12), and show that the cross section is (14-19).

14-8. Let a well-collimated beam of quasi-monochromatic X rays propagate in the z direction and impinge on an atom at the origin of a cartesian coordinate system. At the frequency in question let the cross section for scattering be σ. Let a second atom identical to the first be at $x = r_1$, $y = z = 0$, and let it be outside the primary beam. Consider a point P at $x = r_1$, $y = 0$, $z = r_2$, and a point P' at $x = r_1$, $y = r_2$, $z = 0$. Both these points are shielded from the secondary wave radiated by the first atom, but not from the tertiary wave radiated by the second atom. Let the primary beam be unpolarized and have irradiance I. What are the irradiances at P and at P'? (This problem illustrates the idea of experiments performed by Barkla and mentioned at the beginning of Sec. 14-6.)

14-9. Let a direction with direction cosines l_0, m_0, and n_0 form an angle 2ψ with one whose direction cosines are l, m, and n. Show that $ll_0 + mm_0 + nn_0 = \cos 2\psi$. (*Hint:* Think of unit vectors in the given directions.) Using this result, show that if the crystal considered in Sec. 14-6 has cubic symmetry ($a = b = c$), then $2a \sin \psi = \lambda(p^2 + q^2 + r^2)^{1/2}$.

14-10. A method of observing diffraction by crystals somewhat related to the rotation method is the *powder method*, introduced by Debye, Scherrer, and Hull. A crystal is ground into a fine powder of small crystals, which are then present in all orientations with respect to an incident beam of monochromatic X rays. Maxima in the diffraction pattern occur along all the generators of certain cones whose axes coincide with the incident beam; on a photographic plate lying perpendicular to the incident beam, the pattern consists of circles. (In practice a long strip of film is bent into a circle surrounding the small sample of powder, and two holes are cut at diametrically opposite points to let the incident beam pass. In this way all scattering angles from nearly zero to nearly π can be observed.) For the cubic crystal of the last problem, how many cones are there when $a = \lambda/2$? The *degeneracy* of a cone is defined to be the number of different sets of integral values of p, q, and r giving the same cone. What are the degeneracies of the five cones having the smallest scattering angles 2ψ? Give the argument showing that the intensity of the maximum on a given cone is proportional to the degeneracy.

14-11. A collimated beam transporting power P falls at angle of incidence θ on a plane slab of glass whose reflectance, transmittance, and absorbance are R, T, and A, respectively. $R + T + A = 1$. Find the force on the slab. Consider the case $\theta = 0$, $R = T = 0$ (normal incidence on an opaque black surface). Let the incident light be sunlight at the earth's surface, for which the irradiance is 7.6×10^5 erg cm^{-2} sec^{-1}. Find the radiation pressure in dynes per square centimeter.

14-12. A monochromatic plane wave of frequency ω and arbitrary polarization is incident on a Lorentz atom with a single electron whose resonant frequency is ω_0. Calculate the time average of the rate at which the incident electric field does work on the oscillating electron, and show that the result is $I\sigma$, where I is the irradiance of the incident wave, and σ is the total cross section for scattering. (*Hint:* The instantaneous rate of doing work involves a certain product of oscillating quantities, and the time average can be found by an easy method using complex amplitudes, as in Probs. 4-10 and 4-11 and in Sec. 14-8.)

chapter 15

The Macroscopic Maxwell Theory

The original form of Maxwell's theory of electromagnetism, presented in the 1860s, was inferred from the results of a number of electrical experiments. All these experiments dealt with dense material media, and the observational techniques of the time allowed only coarse spatial and temporal resolution, very coarse indeed as compared with the sizes and spacing of atoms and the rapid temporal changes in and around individual atoms. This theory is therefore *macroscopic* in that it deals with averages over volumes and times large enough to smooth out microscopic fluctuations, but not so large as to lose details that can be observed with a given technique.

Maxwell's theory predicted the existence of electromagnetic waves with a velocity in free space that turned out to equal that of light, and the first major extrapolation of the theory was to account for the phenomena of physical optics. Optical experiments with monochromatic light probe matter with a spatial resolution of the order of the wavelength. A macroscopic theory of the phenomena is possible because in gases at ordinary pressures and in solids and liquids, a volume whose dimensions are small compared with a wavelength in the visible range can still be large enough to contain a very large number of atoms. Thus ordinary optical phenomena do not reveal these media to be other than perfectly continuous, with each medium characterized by a refractive index and a rate of attenuation of a wave propagating through it.

For transparent media (attentuation negligible) the original Maxwell theory applied at optical frequencies related the refractive index n to the dielectric constant ϵ by $\epsilon = n^2$, and then faced the difficulty that there is in general no agreement if ϵ is given the value measured with static electric fields. For example, the refractive index of water for yellow light is 1.33, while the static dielectric constant is 81. This dependence of n, or ϵ, on frequency can be understood only by looking into its origin in the microscopic structure of the medium.

The most correct and satisfying procedure for arriving at the macroscopic theory of Maxwell from the microscopic theory of Lorentz, particularly at high frequencies, follows the lines of the calculation of Ewald and Oseen described in Sec. 14-1. This difficult calculation can be avoided by a few simple and plausible assumptions whereby the more elementary derivation given in this chapter is obtained.

15-1 Derivation of the First Form of the Macroscopic Equations Suppose an essentially monochromatic plane wave with a frequency in the near ultraviolet or lower range is incident from *vacuo* on a plane boundary of a dense medium such as glass, or a metal, or a gas at atmospheric or higher pressure. Experimental observations are interpretable on the assumption that a wave propagates in the medium and has details no finer than those of the wave *in vacuo*. This internal wave has predominantly the character of a plane wave whose amplitude decreases as it propagates, and whose wavelength is different but not far different from the wavelength *in vacuo* associated with the given frequency. There are complicating features in the nature of a weak scattered wave, but altogether this description is far simpler than that given by microscopic considerations, in which the fields are pictured as varying markedly in a complicated manner in the small spaces between the individual charged particles. The problem is to get the simpler description by suitably smoothing out the microscopic details.

Consider the electric field. It is represented in full microscopic detail by the vector $\mathbf{e}(x,y,z,t)$. Let τ be a spherical volume whose center is at an arbitrary point (x_0,y_0,z_0) in the medium, and choose the radius such that it is small compared with the wavelength and yet large enough that many atoms are included in τ. Simple calculation shows that such a choice is possible for the cases supposed at the outset of this section (see Prob. 15-1). A volume τ of this type will sometimes be referred to as a *macroscopically infinitesimal volume*. Let $\mathbf{e}$ be averaged over the volume τ, and take this average to be the value at the point (x_0,y_0,z_0) of a new field $\mathbf{E}$, so that

$$\mathbf{E}(x_0,y_0,z_0,t) = \frac{1}{\tau} \int_\tau \mathbf{e}(x,y,z,t) \, d\tau$$

If the center of τ is shifted to other points, with the radius fixed, $\mathbf{E}$ is eventually defined at all points of space, outside as well as inside the medium.   The field $\mathbf{E}$ is called the *macroscopic electric field,* and the process of obtaining it from the microscopic field $\mathbf{e}$ is called *taking a macroscopic average.*   The microscopic magnetic field $\mathbf{b}$ can be averaged to obtain a macroscopic magnetic field $\mathbf{B}$, and the microscopic densities ρ and $\mathbf{j}$ of charge and current can be averaged to obtain the macroscopic averages ρ_{macro} and $\mathbf{j}_{\text{macro}}$.

Consider next derived fields.   Let g be any cartesian component of $\mathbf{e}$ or $\mathbf{b}$, and consider, for example, the x derivative of g taken with y, z, and t held fixed.   It will now be shown that the macroscopic average of this derivative is equal to the derivative of the macroscopic average of g; that is,

$$\left[\frac{\partial g}{\partial x} \right] = \frac{\partial [g]}{\partial x} \tag{15-1}$$

where brackets indicate a macroscopic average.

Let τ be a spherical volume with center at (x_0, y_0, z_0), and let τ' be a volume of the same radius with center at $(x_0 + dx,\, y_0,\, z_0)$.   Let $d\tau$ be an element of volume in τ at (x, y, z).   In τ' there is a corresponding element $d\tau'$ at $(x + dx,\, y,\, z)$, and a Taylor expansion carried through the linear term gives

$$g(x + dx,\, y,\, z) = g(x, y, z) + \left(\frac{\partial g}{\partial x} \right)_{x, y, z} dx$$

where the parentheses and subscripts indicate the point at which the derivative is to be evaluated.   Both sides of this expression are now to be averaged over τ', but since the terms on the right are to be evaluated at $d\tau$ rather than $d\tau'$, the average of the right side over τ' becomes the sum of two averages over τ.   Thus,

$$[g]_{x_0 + dx, y_0, z_0} = [g]_{x_0, y_0, z_0} + \left[\frac{\partial g}{\partial x} \right]_{x_0, y_0, z_0} dx$$

On the other hand, the macroscopic field $[g]$ is subject to Taylor expansion in the form

$$[g]_{x_0 + dx, y_0, z_0} = [g]_{x_0, y_0, z_0} + \left(\frac{\partial [g]}{\partial x} \right)_{x_0, y_0, z_0} dx$$

Comparison of the last two equations gives (15-1).

It follows from (1-17) and the theorem expressed by (15-1) that the operations of taking the divergence and taking a macroscopic average can be performed in either order.   By (1-18), the same applies to the curl. That this interchangeability applies also to the time derivative is obvious.

The microscopic Maxwell equations (3-1) to (3-4) can now be subjected to macroscopic averaging to obtain

$$\text{div } \mathbf{E} = 4\pi \rho_{macro} \tag{15-2}$$

$$\text{curl } \mathbf{E} = -\frac{1}{c}\frac{\partial \mathbf{B}}{\partial t} \tag{15-3}$$

$$\text{div } \mathbf{B} = 0 \tag{15-4}$$

$$\text{curl } \mathbf{B} = \frac{1}{c}\frac{\partial \mathbf{E}}{\partial t} + \frac{4\pi}{c}\,\mathbf{j}_{macro} \tag{15-5}$$

These equations constitute the *first form of the macroscopic Maxwell equations.* They are of the same form as the microscopic equations, and they are the ones that should have been in mind in treating the examples beginning in Sec. 3-3.

Taking a macroscopic average of the force equation (3-5) can be contemplated, but because products appear on the right with factors that do not fluctuate independently of each other, some care is required. It is not necessary to go into the matter, since the only use of the force equation to be made in the rest of this book will be in relating the optical properties of a medium to its atomic structure. Here the integrated equation (3-8a), supplemented by the force of radiation reaction, will be applied to each elementary charged particle.

15-2 Classification of Charges and Currents. Second Form of the Macroscopic Equations In the most general type of medium there are two classes of charges. Firstly, there are electrons elastically bound to nuclei, and secondly, there are electrons free to migrate about. There may also be mobile ions, but because of their great mass they do not oscillate appreciably as wholes at optical frequencies, and therefore their mobility does not contribute to optical properties.

The macroscopic density of charge appearing in the last section can be written as the sum of the macroscopic densities of the free and bound charges, and similarly for the current density. Let these sums be written in the following notation:[1]

$$\rho_{macro} = \rho_{free} + \rho_{bound} \qquad \mathbf{j}_{macro} = \mathbf{j}_{free} + \mathbf{j}_{bound} \tag{15-6}$$

The next step is to relate the bound densities to the microscopic structure of the medium.

Under excitation by a monochromatic incident wave the bound electrons oscillate about their equilibrium positions. Let us consider the

---

[1] In place of our terms *free* and *bound*, some authors use *true* and *free*, respectively. The latter terms have historical precedence and are perhaps more commonly found, but they are less indicative of the natures of the charges.

situation at a particular instant.   The positions of the atoms can be specified by the positions of their nuclei, and their distribution can be specified in sufficient detail by the macroscopic density N, where N is defined at any point P in the medium as the number of atoms in a macroscopically infinitesimal volume τ, centered at P, divided by the volume τ. The internal state of each atom is specified by the instantaneous positions and velocities of its electrons relative to the nucleus.

To simplify matters, suppose each atom has just one electron, whose displacement from the nucleus is **s**.   Because of interactions between an atom and its neighbors, the vector **s** and its time derivative might conceivably vary radically from atom to atom.   However, we assume that macroscopic densities of bound charge and current can be calculated most

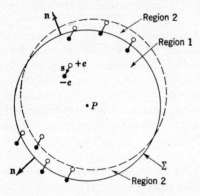

easily and with sufficient accuracy if the medium is replaced by a hypothetical one in which these local variations are smoothed out.   The smoothing operation consists in surrounding a given atom by a sphere enclosing a macroscopically infinitesimal region and replacing the actual **s** and **ṡ** of that atom by the averages taken over all the atoms in the region.   After this smoothing, **s** and **ṡ** change very little from atom to atom and change appreciably only over distances comparable to a wavelength.   The hypothetical medium might be said to be made up of "average atoms," and when

Fig. 15-1. *Geometry for finding macroscopic densities of bound charge and current at point P.*

the dynamical behavior of the medium is related to the exciting fields, the argument will be so framed as to give the behavior of these average atoms.

Consider now a point P in this hypothetical medium at which the macroscopic densities of bound charge and current are to be found. Surround P by a macroscopically infinitesimal volume τ whose surface is the sphere Σ shown in Fig. 15-1.   This figure shows a few typical atoms represented by their nuclei (white dots), electrons (black dots), and connecting vectors **s**.   The atoms entering into consideration divide into two classes: (1) Those whose nuclei and electrons all lie within Σ; their nuclei lie in a volume designated region 1 in the figure.   (2) Those whose vectors **s** are cut by Σ; their nuclei lie in a bipartite volume designated region 2 in the figure.

A contribution to the net charge in Σ can come only from atoms of class 2.   With an element $d\Sigma$ of the surface Σ as base, erect a cylinder extending normally across region 2. All the atoms whose nuclei are in this cylinder have practically the same **s**, and the height of the cylinder is the projection of **s** on the normal at $d\Sigma$. If N is the density of nuclei at $d\Sigma$, and **n** is the outward normal, then it is seen from the figure that the net charge in Σ divided by the volume τ, that is, the macroscopic density of charge, is

$$\rho_{\text{bound}} = \frac{e}{\tau} \int_{\Sigma} N\mathbf{n} \cdot \mathbf{s} \, d\Sigma = e[\text{div} \, (N\mathbf{s})]_P \tag{15-7}$$

The last expression is obtained by applying Gauss' theorem to the surface integral and taking the resulting volume integral to be well approximated as the volume τ multiplied by the value of the divergence at the center P. Writing the divergence implies that **s** is being treated as a continuous field; it is appropriate to do so, since the **s** involved here was defined as a macroscopic average, and such an average can be assigned to each point of space, whether or not a nucleus happens to lie there.

The vector $-N e\mathbf{s}$ is a macroscopic field called the *electric polarization* of the medium and denoted **P**. The final result is then

$$\rho_{\text{bound}} = - \, \text{div} \, \mathbf{P} \tag{15-8}$$

The physical significance of **P** is that it represents at each point of the medium the macroscopic average of the electric dipole moments of the atoms multiplied by the density of atoms at the point; that is, it stands for the *electric dipole moment per unit volume*. The density (15-8) is different from zero only when **P** shows a spatial variation, through variation of the atomic moments $-e\mathbf{s}$, or a variation of density N (particularly at the boundary of a medium), or a combination of both.

The macroscopic density of bound current at point P is the integral of the microscopic density in the volume τ divided by this volume. The integral reduces to the sum of charges of the electrons, each multiplied by its velocity (assuming the nuclei to be at rest). The lowest approximation, which is adequate for treating optical properties, is obtained by neglecting all spatial variation, that is, by taking the density N and velocity $\dot{\mathbf{s}}$ to be constant throughout τ and equal to the macroscopic values pertaining to point P. The result is

$$\mathbf{j}_{\text{bound}} = -N e\dot{\mathbf{s}} = \frac{\partial \mathbf{P}}{\partial t} \tag{15-9}$$

The densities of bound charge and current have now been related to microscopic structure with an accuracy sufficient for optical purposes. The electrical state of the medium has been characterized entirely by the electric polarization **P**. No magnetic properties have been brought out, and some comment should be made on this point.

When a light wave passes through a medium, the electric and magnetic fields acting on an individual atom turn out to have the same order of magnitude. The velocities of the electrons are always very small compared with c. Hence by the argument given in Sec. 14-4 in connection with the equation of motion, the magnetic field has a negligible effect on the motion, but it is only through such effect that a medium shows magnetic properties. The case is different if the atomic model includes amperian currents (see end of Sec. 3-1) and a static or low-frequency magnetic field is applied. If we think of the circulating currents as being circular filaments surrounding area A and carrying current I, it is shown in elementary texts that such a filament has a magnetic moment **m** whose magnitude is IA/c and whose direction is perpendicular to the plane of the filament according to the right-hand rule.[1] A macroscopic *magnetization* **M** can be defined as the magnetic dipole moment per unit volume in analogy with the electric polarization **P**. In the absence of a magnetic field (and in the absence of permanent magnetization of the medium), the elementary moments **m** are oriented at random, and **M** = 0. An applied field acts in combination with thermal agitation to produce a partial alignment of the moments and hence a magnetization of the medium. Thermal agitation not only limits the magnetization achieved, but is essential to any average alignment occurring at all. The theory of the effect will not be gone into here, and we need only note that any process of reorientation depending on thermal agitation has a certain slowness, and the fact is that no magnetization can build up and change at the frequencies of interest to us. It is this fact that justifies omitting current loops from the atomic model when only optical frequencies are in question.

While it follows that we can neglect magnetic effects altogether at very high frequencies, let us at least see how they enter the macroscopic Maxwell equations when they are important. It is shown in texts such as Scott [82], p. 346, that when the magnetization of a medium is **M**, the macroscopic density of bound current receives a contribution c curl **M** from the amperian currents, so that (15-9) is replaced by

$$j_{bound} = \frac{\partial \mathbf{P}}{\partial t} + c \text{ curl } \mathbf{M} \tag{15-10}$$

Note that (15-8) and (15-10) satisfy the equation of conservation of charge (3-9).

If we substitute (15-8) and (15-10) in (15-6) and then substitute the

---

[1] One of the several justifications is that in a constant magnetic field **b** the filament experiences a torque **m** ✕ **b**, just as an electric dipole of moment **p** in a constant electric field **e** experiences a torque **p** ✕ **e**. This statement is a simple consequence of the Lorentz force (3-5).

latter in (15-2) to (15-5), we obtain

$$\operatorname{div} \mathbf{E} = -4\pi \operatorname{div} \mathbf{P} + 4\pi \rho_{\text{free}}$$

$$\operatorname{curl} \mathbf{E} = -\frac{1}{c}\frac{\partial \mathbf{B}}{\partial t}$$

$$\operatorname{div} \mathbf{B} = 0$$

$$\operatorname{curl} \mathbf{B} = \frac{1}{c}\frac{\partial \mathbf{E}}{\partial t} + \frac{4\pi}{c}\frac{\partial \mathbf{P}}{\partial t} + 4\pi \operatorname{curl} \mathbf{M} + \frac{4\pi}{c}\mathbf{j}_{\text{free}}$$

The manner in which $\mathbf{P}$ and $\mathbf{M}$ enter these equations admits a simplification of form. If we define new vectors $\mathbf{D}$ and $\mathbf{H}$ by

$$\mathbf{D} = \mathbf{E} + 4\pi\mathbf{P} \tag{15-11}$$

$$\mathbf{H} = \mathbf{B} - 4\pi\mathbf{M} \tag{15-12}$$

we obtain

$$\operatorname{div} \mathbf{D} = 4\pi \rho_{\text{free}} \tag{15-13}$$

$$\operatorname{curl} \mathbf{E} = -\frac{1}{c}\frac{\partial \mathbf{B}}{\partial t} \tag{15-14}$$

$$\operatorname{div} \mathbf{B} = 0 \tag{15-15}$$

$$\operatorname{curl} \mathbf{H} = \frac{1}{c}\frac{\partial \mathbf{D}}{\partial t} + \frac{4\pi}{c}\mathbf{j}_{\text{free}} \tag{15-16}$$

The four equations (15-13) to (15-16), together with the two definitions (15-11) and (15-12), constitute the second and final form of the macroscopic Maxwell equations. It is usual to call $\mathbf{E}$ the *electric field strength*, $\mathbf{D}$ the *displacement vector*, $\mathbf{H}$ the *magnetic field strength*, and $\mathbf{B}$ the *magnetic induction*. These names have come about through historical evolution, and we need not pause to seek the rationale. The attitude here (as distinct from that in those treatises on electricity that introduce the macroscopic theory at the beginning and treat it on a phenomenological basis) is to accept the microscopic theory and then interpret macroscopic fields on the basis of their derivation from microscopic considerations.

15-3 Susceptibilities, Permeabilities, and Conductivity The equations obtained in the last section do not contain any quantities that distinguish one medium from another, and hence some supplementary relations are needed. In this section parameters appropriate for characterizing a medium will be introduced; later they will be evaluated for specific models of media.

Suppose a medium is excited by monochromatic fields originating in external sources. (Once the response is known for all frequencies, the polychromatic case can be treated by Fourier analysis.) Let the medium contain both free and bound electrons, and let us make the assumption that all the macroscopic vectors $\mathbf{E}$, $\mathbf{P}$, $\mathbf{B}$, $\mathbf{M}$, and $\mathbf{j}_{\text{free}}$ oscillate sinusoidally at each point with the frequency of the incident fields. The vectors $\mathbf{D}$

and **H** then also have this property. This assumption is justified by its leading to results that compare well with observation on any medium when the frequency is high and the exciting fields are weak. It is not justified for strong fields at low frequency, when ferromagnetism and other nonlinear effects can appear.

The sinusoidally varying vectors can be given a complex representation by writing

$$\mathbf{E} = \mathbf{E}_s e^{-i\omega t} \qquad \mathbf{P} = \mathbf{P}_s e^{-i\omega t} \qquad \mathbf{j}_{\text{free}} = \mathbf{j}_s e^{-i\omega t} \qquad \cdots \qquad (15\text{-}17)$$

where the symbols with subscript s are the complex vector amplitudes; they contain the spatial dependence of the fields. It will now be assumed that at each point of the medium

$$\mathbf{P}_s = \chi_e \mathbf{E}_s \qquad \mathbf{M}_s = \chi_m \mathbf{H}_s \qquad \mathbf{j}_s = \sigma \mathbf{E}_s \qquad (15\text{-}18)$$

where χ_e, χ_m, and σ are parameters of the medium called, respectively, the *electric susceptibility*, the *magnetic susceptibility*, and the *conductivity*.

The implication in assuming (15-18) is that the electric polarization and the magnetic polarization depend, respectively, only on the electric field and the magnetic field, and the density of free current depends only on the electric field. The assumption is not always valid. For example, an electric polarization induced by a static electric field can be slightly altered by a very strong static magnetic field. Again, the density of free current brought about by a static electric field can be altered by a magnetic field. In Chap. 18 it will be seen that aspects of these effects enter optics when strong static fields are applied to media in addition to weak high-frequency fields, but in the meantime such static fields will be absent, and (15-18) can be assumed.

Throughout this and the next chapter the parameters χ_e, χ_m, and σ will be taken to be scalars, which is appropriate for isotropic media. Chapter 17 will treat anisotropic media, that is, media showing preferred directions in their structures, and for these media the parameters have the character of tensors.

It will appear on both experimental and theoretical grounds that the parameters are in general complex, so that, for example, **P** and **E** do not oscillate with the same phase in general. Moreover, they depend on frequency. They also depend on density, and therefore on position when the density is not uniform. The next chapter will deal with effects of sudden changes in density and in dependence on frequency that occur on crossing the boundary between two uniform media. No theory will be developed to treat "volume scattering" due to local thermal fluctuations of density about a uniform average, and only some qualitative comments on this effect will be made.

Within the assumptions made, the three parameters introduced in (15-18) completely characterize the medium. In working with the

Maxwell equations it is convenient to define two additional parameters defined by

$$\mathbf{D}_s = \epsilon\mathbf{E}_s \qquad \mathbf{B}_s = \mu\mathbf{H}_s \qquad\qquad (15\text{-}19)$$

From (15-11), (15-12), and the first two of (15-18),

$$\epsilon = 1 + 4\pi\chi_e \qquad \mu = 1 + 4\pi\chi_m \qquad\qquad (15\text{-}20)$$

It is usual to call ϵ the *dielectric constant* in spite of its dependence on frequency, the reason being that the name became established in connection with low-frequency phenomena, where the frequency dependence becomes negligible. The parameter μ is called the *magnetic permeability*.

The only quantity in the Maxwell equations whose behavior has not yet been discussed is the density of free charge. The latter is related to the density of free current by the equation of conservation (3-9), so that

$$\frac{\partial\rho_{\text{free}}}{\partial t} = -\operatorname{div}\mathbf{j}_{\text{free}} = -e^{-i\omega t}\operatorname{div}\mathbf{j}_s$$

This equation can be integrated with respect to time to obtain the sinusoidal dependence

$$\rho_{\text{free}} = \rho_s e^{-i\omega t}$$

where
$$\rho_s = -\frac{i}{\omega}\operatorname{div}\mathbf{j}_s = -\frac{i}{\omega}\operatorname{div}\sigma\mathbf{E}_s \qquad\qquad (15\text{-}21)$$

15-4   Monochromatic Plane Waves in Homogeneous Media

This section will treat the various types of monochromatic plane waves that can exist in a homogeneous medium (medium of ideally uniform density and structure). The question of how such waves are excited by external sources is postponed until the next chapter.

The equations governing the waves are the Maxwell equations (15-13) to (15-16), and since every term now oscillates sinusoidally, a complex representation can be used, and a common factor $e^{-i\omega t}$ eliminated. (Note that the operation $\partial/\partial t$ is equivalent to multiplying by $-i\omega$.) The relations (15-18), (15-19), and (15-21) can be used to reduce the equations to the following form:

$$\operatorname{div}\left(\epsilon + i\,\frac{4\pi\sigma}{\omega}\right)\mathbf{E}_s = 0 \qquad\qquad (15\text{-}22)$$

$$\operatorname{curl}\mathbf{E}_s = i\,\frac{\omega\mu}{c}\,\mathbf{H}_s \qquad\qquad (15\text{-}23)$$

$$\operatorname{div}\mu\mathbf{H}_s = 0 \qquad\qquad (15\text{-}24)$$

$$\operatorname{curl}\mathbf{H}_s = -i\,\frac{\omega}{c}\left(\epsilon + i\,\frac{4\pi\sigma}{\omega}\right)\mathbf{E}_s \qquad\qquad (15\text{-}25)$$

These equations, as they are written, are applicable to inhomogeneous media, in which ϵ, μ, and σ can vary from point to point in a continuous but otherwise arbitrary manner.   This generality is necessary for treating the behavior of waves at boundaries between media (next chapter), but in the interior of a perfectly homogeneous medium there is the simplification that (15-22) and (15-24) reduce to

$$\operatorname{div} \mathbf{E}_s = 0 \qquad \operatorname{div} \mathbf{H}_s = 0 \qquad \text{inside a homogeneous medium} \quad (15\text{-}26)$$

Let us seek solutions of equations (15-23), (15-25), and (15-26) in the form of plane waves; that is, we try writing

$$\mathbf{E}_s = \mathbf{E}_0 e^{i\mathbf{k}_c \cdot \mathbf{r}} \qquad \mathbf{H}_s = \mathbf{H}_0 e^{i\mathbf{k}_c \cdot \mathbf{r}} \qquad\qquad (15\text{-}27)$$

where $\mathbf{E}_0$ and $\mathbf{H}_0$ are constant vectors, in general complex, and $\mathbf{k}_c$ is a wave vector which will turn out to be complex in all but special cases. The significance of a complex wave vector will be discussed later.

The assumption of (15-27) reduces the Maxwell equations to the algebraic equations

$$\mathbf{k}_c \cdot \mathbf{E}_0 = 0 \qquad \mathbf{k}_c \cdot \mathbf{H}_0 = 0 \qquad\qquad (15\text{-}28)$$

$$\mathbf{k}_c \times \mathbf{E}_0 = \frac{\mu\omega}{c} \mathbf{H}_0 \qquad\qquad (15\text{-}29)$$

$$\mathbf{k}_c \times \mathbf{H}_0 = -\left(\epsilon + i \frac{4\pi\sigma}{\omega} \right) \frac{\omega}{c} \mathbf{E}_0 \qquad\qquad (15\text{-}30)$$

(This reduction is easily made with the formulas in Prob. 4-10.   These formulas are valid when $\mathbf{k}$ is complex.)   Substitution of $\mathbf{H}_0$ from (15-29) into (15-30) and use of (1-1) and (15-28) gives

$$(\mathbf{k}_c \cdot \mathbf{k}_c) \mathbf{E}_0 = \mu \left(\epsilon + i \frac{4\pi\sigma}{\omega} \right) \frac{\omega^2}{c^2} \mathbf{E}_0$$

whence

$$\mathbf{k}_c \cdot \mathbf{k}_c = n_c{}^2 k_0{}^2 \qquad\qquad (15\text{-}31)$$

where

$$k_0 = \frac{\omega}{c} \qquad n_c{}^2 = \epsilon\mu + i \frac{4\pi\mu\sigma}{\omega} \qquad\qquad (15\text{-}32)$$

We call k_0 the *vacuum wave number* and n_c the *complex refractive index* of the medium.   Let real and imaginary parts be indicated by the notation

$$n_c = n + i\kappa \qquad \mathbf{k}_c = \mathbf{k} + i\mathbf{a} \qquad\qquad (15\text{-}33)$$

Then the real and imaginary parts of (15-31) are

$$k^2 - a^2 = k_0{}^2(n^2 - \kappa^2) \qquad\qquad (15\text{-}34)$$

$$\mathbf{k} \cdot \mathbf{a} = k_0{}^2 n\kappa \qquad\qquad (15\text{-}35)$$

The four real quantities appearing in (15-33) are given names, although usage in connection with κ and $\mathbf{a}$ varies.   Let us call n the *refractive index*, κ the *extinction index*, $\mathbf{k}$ the *wave vector*, and $\mathbf{a}$ the *attenuation vector*.   The appropriateness will be seen presently.

To summarize, there exist plane-wave solutions (15-27) with the wave vector $\mathbf{k}_c$ in general complex and subject to condition (15-31), or equivalently, (15-34) and (15-35). The amplitudes $\mathbf{E}_0$ and $\mathbf{H}_0$ are subject to the conditions

$$\mathbf{k}_c \cdot \mathbf{E}_0 = 0 \qquad \mathbf{H}_0 = \frac{1}{\mu k_0} \, \mathbf{k}_c \times \mathbf{E}_0 \qquad (15\text{-}36)$$

Thus $\mathbf{E}_0$ can be an arbitrarily chosen complex vector except that it must satisfy the first of (15-36), which is called the *transversality condition;* $\mathbf{H}_0$ is then fixed. The transversality condition and the relation of $\mathbf{H}_0$ to $\mathbf{E}_0$ do not have simple geometric interpretations when $\mathbf{k}_c$ is complex. We have now to examine the natures of the waves.

It is important to have in mind the possible values of n and κ. When the theory of ϵ and σ is given in the next section (μ will be set equal to unity at that time), it will turn out that n_c^2, given by (15-32), never has a negative imaginary part, but the real part can be positive or negative. The angle of the complex number n_c^2 therefore always falls in the range zero to π. The complex index n_c itself has a magnitude equal to the positive square root of the magnitude of n_c^2 and an angle equal to half that of n_c^2. (There is a second value of n_c which is the negative of the first, but we shall never use this value.) It follows that n and κ are always positive, and it will turn out that each can be anything from zero to a very large value, depending on the medium and the frequency.

Consider first the simple case of a medium and a frequency for which $\kappa = 0$. (This is the case of perfect transparency, since it will be seen that a wave propagates with no diminution of amplitude. Included here is free space, for which $n_c = 1$ at all frequencies.) Conditions (15-34) and (15-35) reduce to

$$k^2 - a^2 = k_0^2 n^2 \qquad \mathbf{k} \cdot \mathbf{a} = 0 \qquad (15\text{-}37)$$

One type of wave consistent with these conditions has a real wave vector, so that $\mathbf{a} = 0$, $|\mathbf{k}| = k_0 n$, and the electric field is

$$\mathbf{E} = \mathbf{E}_0 e^{i(\mathbf{k} \cdot \mathbf{r} - \omega t)} \qquad (15\text{-}38)$$

This is just the type of plane wave discussed in Sec. 2-5. The velocity of propagation is $\omega/k = c/n$, and the wavelength is $2\pi/k = \lambda_0/n$, where λ_0 is the wavelength in free space corresponding to frequency ω; n therefore has the properties that are always understood to define the refractive index. The amplitude $\mathbf{E}_0$ can be complex, but according to (15-36) its real and imaginary parts are perpendicular to $\mathbf{k}$, and the wave is therefore transverse. The magnetic field is also transverse to $\mathbf{k}$, and the real $\mathbf{H}$ is perpendicular to the real $\mathbf{E}$ in the manner of Fig. 5-11, except that the magnitude of $\mathbf{H}$ is n/μ times that of $\mathbf{E}$.

Conditions (15-37) admit a second type of wave in which the wave vector is complex but has its real and imaginary parts perpendicular to each other. The magnitude k of the real part can now have any value greater than $k_0 n$, and the magnitude a of the imaginary part is then given by the first of (15-37) and is less than k. The electric field has the form

$$\mathbf{E} = \mathbf{E}_0 e^{-\mathbf{a} \cdot \mathbf{r}} e^{i(\mathbf{k} \cdot \mathbf{r} - \omega t)} \qquad (15\text{-}39)$$

The second exponential shows that there is propagation in the direction of $\mathbf{k}$ with velocity ω/k and wavelength $2\pi/k$. The amplitude of the oscillation at point $\mathbf{r}$ is $\mathbf{E}_0\, e^{-\mathbf{a} \cdot \mathbf{r}}$ and therefore is constant over any plane perpendicular to $\mathbf{a}$, but decreases exponentially in the direction of $\mathbf{a}$ (which is at right angles to $\mathbf{k}$). It is usual to call this second type of wave an *inhomogeneous wave,* and then in contrast, the first type, represented by (15-38), is called *homogeneous.* The next chapter will show how inhomogeneous waves can arise.

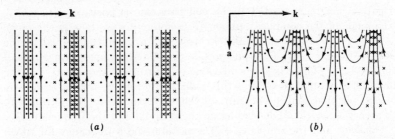

(a)   (b)

Fig. 15-2.   *Streamlines in types of plane waves in a transparent medium.* **a.** *Homogeneous wave linearly polarized with magnetic vector in the plane of the figure.* **b.** *Inhomogeneous wave with TE polarization. In both parts the electric streamlines are straight lines toward the reader (dots) or away (crosses).*

In a homogeneous wave the electric and magnetic fields are very simply related to each other and to $\mathbf{k}$ and are easily visualized, even in the case of elliptical polarization. The situation is more complicated in the inhomogeneous case, and it is appropriate to consider two special polarizations from which an arbitrary one can be constructed by superposition. For the first, take the constant $\mathbf{E}_0$ in (15-39) to have its real and imaginary parts perpendicular to the plane of $\mathbf{k}$ and $\mathbf{a}$. Such a choice is possible because it conforms with the one restriction (15-36). This polarization will be called the *TE mode* (transverse electric), to use a term common in microwave technology. Figure 15-2b shows a set of streamlines of the real electric and magnetic fields over a portion of the space filled by the wave. For comparison, Fig. 15-2a shows a linearly polarized homogeneous wave in the same medium with the same frequency.

The second polarization will be called the *TM mode* (transverse magnetic), and a figure to illustrate it is obtained from Fig. 15-2 by interchanging the electric and magnetic fields and reversing the directions in one of them.　That such a wave is a solution of the Maxwell equations is seen by taking (15-30) and the second of (15-28) as conditions to replace (15-36).　It is then clear that the real and imaginary parts of $\mathbf{H}_0$ can be taken perpendicular to the plane of $\mathbf{k}$ and $\mathbf{a}$.

Consider now a case in which both n and κ are greater than zero.　Then both $\mathbf{k}$ and $\mathbf{a}$ must be different from zero, and the angle between these vectors must be less than 90°.　Among the infinitely many solutions of (15-34) and (15-35), there is a class in which $\mathbf{k}$ and $\mathbf{a}$ point in the same direction; if $\mathbf{k}_0$ is a vector defining this direction and having magnitude ω/c, then the solution becomes unique and is $\mathbf{k} = n\mathbf{k}_0$, $\mathbf{a} = \kappa\mathbf{k}_0$, which can be combined in the complex relation $\mathbf{k}_c = n_c\mathbf{k}_0$.　The electric field is

$$\mathbf{E} = \mathbf{E}_0 e^{i(n_c\mathbf{k}_0\cdot\mathbf{r}-\omega t)} = \mathbf{E}_0 e^{-\kappa\mathbf{k}_0\cdot\mathbf{r}} e^{i(n\mathbf{k}_0\cdot\mathbf{r}-\omega t)} \tag{15-40}$$

and is therefore a wave with wavelength λ_0/n propagating in the direction of $\mathbf{k}_0$ with velocity c/n; unlike (15-38), the amplitude of oscillation decreases exponentially in the direction of propagation.　Both the amplitude and the phase are constant over any plane perpendicular to $\mathbf{k}_0$, and for this reason the wave is said to be of *homogeneous* type. The electric and magnetic vectors are perpendicular to $\mathbf{k}_0$, but the real $\mathbf{H}$ is not perpendicular to the real $\mathbf{E}$ when the polarization is elliptical.　(Elaboration on the last point is called for in Prob. 15-5.) The manner in which n_c enters (15-40) is the justification for calling n_c the complex refractive index of the medium.

The solutions of (15-34) and (15-35) in which $\mathbf{k}$ and $\mathbf{a}$ have

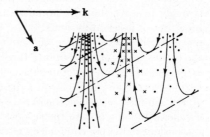

Fig. 15-3.　*Streamlines of an inhomogeneous wave with TE polarization in an absorbing medium.　The pattern propagates to the right in such a way that the magnetic lines maintain tangency with the fixed dashed lines.*

different directions define the class of *inhomogeneous* waves.　The electric field has the form of (15-39).　Surfaces of constant phase are planes perpendicular to $\mathbf{k}$, and surfaces of constant amplitude of oscillation are planes perpendicular to $\mathbf{a}$.　Since $\mathbf{a}$ now always has a positive component in the direction of $\mathbf{k}$, there is always some reduction of amplitude along the direction of $\mathbf{k}$, in contrast to the behavior of inhomogeneous waves in a perfectly transparent medium.　The only polarizations easily visualized are the TE and TM modes; Fig. 15-3 illustrates the former.

All types of plane waves that can occur in a homogeneous medium have now been described.　They are called plane because of the planes over which the amplitude or the phase is constant.　A characteristic feature of waves in a medium whose refractive index is complex is that there is some attenuation of amplitude along a line in the direction of **k**.

15-5 Theory of the Complex Refractive Index The complex refractive index n_c is the function of ϵ, μ, σ, and ω given in (15-32). The permeability μ will be set equal to unity in all cases. While the magnetic field in a wave always affects the motions of charges in a medium, and these alterations of motion in turn affect the propagation of the wave, overwhelming effects come from the influence of the electric field. This is true for all media at very high frequencies, and even at low frequencies for media showing only diamagnetism. We shall want to trace the behavior of the refractive index down to low frequencies, but we can still set $\mu = 1$ if we restrict attention to diamagnetic media.

Only enough of the classical theory will be given to bring out the main features of ϵ and σ for different kinds of media. In solids and liquids the constituent atoms and molecules are in intimate contact and interact strongly in ways that the Lorentz theory can treat only on an empirical basis, and it is certainly remarkable that quite good formulas relating the macroscopic parameters to the microscopic structure were obtained in the earliest days of the Lorentz theory. In later times very penetrating analyses have given new foundations to the formulas and have introduced various corrections and clarified the domains of validity, but the results of the simplest classical theory are amazingly durable and furnish an excellent introduction to the subject.

Consider first a nonconducting medium (each electron elastically bound to a definite nucleus). When a monochromatic wave exists in the medium, an atom located at point P experiences a microscopic electric field $\mathbf{e}_i(P,t)$. This field, which is called the *internal field* at the atom in question, is a superposition of the external field (the field due to the external primary source that would exist at P if the medium were removed) and the secondary fields from all other atoms in the medium. If the internal field were known and expressed in complex representation, the dipole moment of the atom would be $\mathbf{p} = \alpha \mathbf{e}_i$, where α is the polarizability defined in Sec. 14-2 and evaluated for a stationary Lorentz atom in Sec. 14-4. If N is the number of atoms in a unit volume, and if brackets indicate a macroscopic average, the macroscopic polarization of the medium would be

$$\mathbf{P} = N[\mathbf{p}] = N\alpha[\mathbf{e}_i] = N\alpha\mathbf{E}_i \qquad (15\text{-}41)$$

where $\mathbf{E}_i$ stands for the average of the microscopic internal fields existing at the positions of the several atoms in a macroscopically infinitesimal volume.

To obtain the susceptibility χ_e it is necessary to know the relation of $\mathbf{E}_i$ to the ordinary macroscopic field $\mathbf{E}$, and the theory of the dielectric constant is thus concentrated in the difficult problem of finding this relation. Let us deal throughout with the simplest assumption:

$$\mathbf{E}_i = \mathbf{E} \tag{15-42}$$

There are some cases, to be mentioned, in which this relation gives good results. For other cases various corrections have been proposed which lead to formulas for the refractive index that are quantitatively superior, but not qualitatively different from results to be obtained below. A discussion of these refinements and even the barest indication of how they have come to be put on a good theoretical basis would be too lengthy for the purposes of this book, but one example is cited in the problems.

From (15-18), (15-41), and (15-42) we obtain $\chi_e = N\alpha$, and (15-20) gives

$$\epsilon = 1 + 4\pi N\alpha \tag{15-43}$$

This formula is commonly known by the name of Sellmeier, who developed an early theory of the refractive index.

One case in which (15-43) is certainly very good is that of a gas at low pressure; here the classical theory gives especially good results. As a first approximation, assume the atoms to be at rest. The appropriate expression for α is then (14-14) if we assume for the moment that there is just one oscillating electron in an atom. The dielectric constant, which will be written in accordance with (15-32) as $n_c{}^2$, becomes

$$n_c{}^2 = 1 - \frac{4\pi N e^2/m}{\omega^2 - \omega_0{}^2 + i\gamma\omega^3/\omega_0{}^2} \tag{15-44}$$

When N is small enough, the absolute value of the second term on the right is small compared with unity at all frequencies, and a good approximation to n_c itself is the right side of the last equation with the second term divided by two. The real and imaginary parts of n_c are then

$$n \approx 1 - \frac{2\pi N e^2(\omega^2 - \omega_0{}^2)/m}{(\omega^2 - \omega_0{}^2)^2 + (\gamma\omega^3/\omega_0{}^2)^2} \tag{15-45}$$

$$\kappa \approx \frac{2\pi N e^2 \gamma\omega^3/m\omega_0{}^2}{(\omega^2 - \omega_0{}^2)^2 + (\gamma\omega^3/\omega_0{}^2)^2} \tag{15-46}$$

Note that κ is different from zero at all frequencies, but it is exceedingly small, and the gas is almost perfectly transparent, at frequencies well removed from the resonant frequency ω_0.

Both n and κ show their most interesting behaviors in the vicinity of ω_0; here the formulas can be simplified by setting $\omega = \omega_0$ everywhere except in the difference $\omega^2 - \omega_0{}^2$ The latter can be approximated as

$2\omega_0(\omega - \omega_0)$.   Hence for $\omega \approx \omega_0$,

$$n \approx 1 - \frac{\pi N e^2 (\omega - \omega_0)/m\omega_0}{(\omega - \omega_0)^2 + \gamma^2/4} \tag{15-47}$$

$$\kappa \approx \frac{\pi N e^2 \gamma/2m\omega_0}{(\omega - \omega_0)^2 + \gamma^2/4} \tag{15-48}$$

Figure 15-4a shows curves of $n - 1$ and κ plotted to the same vertical scale. A definite scale is indicated only to emphasize that the maximum ordinate must be small compared with unity if the curves are to be good approximations. The geometrical relationships between these curves are stated explicitly in Prob. 15-6. Note that the curve of κ has the same shape as the natural profile in emission found in Sec. 12-5.

The range of frequencies over whch κ is appreciably different from zero is called an *extinction band*. The dependence of n on frequency is called

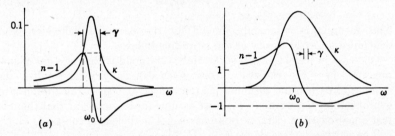

Fig. 15-4.   *Refractive index and extinction index near a resonant frequency for a gas of stationary atoms.* **a.** *Low density.* **b.** *High density.* *Relation of scales of the two parts and the shapes in* (**b**) *are indicative only.*

dispersion; the ranges in which $dn/d\omega$ is positive are called regions of *normal dispersion,* while the range in which $dn/d\omega$ is negative is called the region of *anomalous dispersion.*

Formulas (15-47) and (15-48) refer to a low-density gas in which the atoms are assumed stationary. They must be corrected for the Doppler effect (collisions can be neglected at low densities), and this correction consists in folding the gaussian function defined in (12-37) into the functions (15-47) and (15-48). Now because of its exponential character, a gaussian function falls to zero much more rapidly than the ordinates of the curves in Fig. 15-4, and hence at low temperatures substantial parts of the wings of the corrected curves have the same shape as the uncorrected ones; thus a comparison of (15-47) and (15-48) with observation is possible. It turns out that a fit can be obtained only by making some adjustments in the classical formulas. Firstly, in the numerators of (15-47) and (15-48) the density N of oscillating electrons with the resonant frequency ω_0 must be replaced by fN, where f is some number less than unity, different for different atoms and for different resonant frequencies in a given atom. Secondly, the quantity γ arising from radiation reaction and having the value (12-9) must be replaced by $3f\gamma$. It appears as though an actual atom contains oscillators behaving according to the classical theory of Lorentz, except that each involves only a fraction f of an electron and is subject to radiation damping somewhat different from the classical value. The f's are called *oscillator strengths*, and the way they emerge from the quantum theory will be described in the final chapter. (It will be seen there that the above rule concerning γ is for the special case of transition from ground level to an excited level, with both levels nondegenerate.)

Let us turn now to liquid and solid dielectrics. In these media the density N is of order 10^{22} atoms or molecules per cubic centimeter. This is some 10^3 times greater than the density in a gas at standard conditions, and perhaps 10^9 times greater than the density at which (15-47) and (15-48) are good approximations at a resonant frequency when the latter is in the visible range (see Prob. 15-7). The complication that enters now is that the oscillation of an electron in an atom is strongly perturbed by neighboring atoms with which it is in intimate contact. The classical theory takes these perturbations into account in an empirical way by replacing the polarizability (14-14), which is appropriate for an isolated stationary atom, by

$$\alpha = \frac{-e^2/m}{\omega^2 - \omega_0{}^2 + i\Gamma\omega} \tag{15-49}$$

where Γ becomes an adjustable parameter representing the effects of the perturbations. A common type of argument leading to this form of α is cited in Prob. 15-8.

Let us assume (somewhat incorrectly—see Probs. 15-11 and 15-12) that the simple Sellmeier formula (15-43) continues to hold as N becomes very large. Calculation of ϵ, and from it n and κ, becomes a matter of straight numerical evaluation for given N and Γ. [To represent any real medium, Γ must be much larger than the natural width γ, but still very small compared with ω_0, and so one can simplify by replacing $\Gamma\omega$ in (15-49) by $\Gamma\omega_0$, since this term has an effect only in the immediate vicinity of ω_0.] Figure 15-4b shows qualitatively the behavior of $n-1$ and κ near ω_0 when N is large. The main features in comparison with Fig. 15-4a are much larger ordinates, a broadening, an asymmetry, and a range over which n comes close to zero. The broadening results partly from replacing γ by a larger Γ, but there is additional broadening due just to the forms of Eqs. (15-43) and (15-49). The latter effect can be seen separately by setting Γ equal to zero, as called for in Prob. 15-9.

Our results can now be generalized to represent more completely a liquid or (isotropic) solid. Each atom will involve a number of resonances; with the jth resonance are associated a frequency ω_j, an oscillator strength f_j, and a damping constant Γ_j. The polarizability (15-49) is to be replaced by a sum over j, and (15-43) gives the square of the complex refractive index to be

$$n_c{}^2 = 1 - \sum \frac{4\pi N e^2 f_j/m}{\omega^2 - \omega_j{}^2 + i\Gamma_j\omega} \qquad (15\text{-}50)$$

Figure 15-5 shows the qualitative behavior of n and κ that would be computed from this formula for three resonant frequencies with some set of values of the parameters. Except in the extinction bands, n_c is

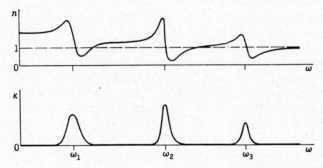

Fig. 15-5. *Qualitative behavior of the refractive index and extinction index for a liquid or solid dielectric with three resonant frequencies.*

essentially real. As ω becomes infinite, n approaches unity from below, and we have the phenomenon of a refractive index slightly below unity at X-ray frequencies, as remarked in Sec. 14-6. When $\omega = 0$, (15-50) gives

$$n^2 = 1 + \sum \frac{4\pi N e^2 f_j}{m\omega_j{}^2} \qquad (15\text{-}51)$$

This n^2 is just the static dielectric constant,[1] and the formula indicates that it has a simple relation to the resonant frequencies and oscillator strengths.

By suitable choice of constants in (15-50), it is possible to fit quite well observational data on n and κ. It is not profitable to pay much attention to what the classical theory says at frequencies in an extinction band, since many quantum effects enter and are represented only in the roughest empirical way by the Γ's. In the ranges of frequencies between extinction

---

[1] The case of a polar liquid is not being described here. Such a medium shows at low frequencies a very high dielectric constant (81 for water) resulting from alignment by an electric field of the permanent dipole moments in their molecules. References are Debye [23], chap. 5, and Böttcher [10], chap. 10.

bands, all the differences $\omega^2 - \omega_j{}^2$ are large enough that the imaginary terms in the denominators in (15-50) can be neglected. Then $n_c{}^2$ becomes equal to n^2, and for the transparent ranges we therefore have

$$n^2 = 1 - \sum \frac{A_j}{\omega^2 - \omega_j{}^2} \qquad (15\text{-}52)$$

where the A_j stand for the numerators in (15-50). This result is called *Sellmeier's equation*. It is usually expressed in terms of wavelength rather than frequency; the form is given in Prob. 15-10.

In a range of transparency between two well-separated extinction bands, observed values of n can be fitted quite well by (15-52) with just two terms in the sum. For example, an optical glass has a range of transparency extending from the near infrared to the near ultraviolet. Beyond this range are extinction bands extending down to radio frequencies and up to the X-ray region, and each involves many resonant frequencies. Yet the values of n in the transparent range can be fitted by assuming just one frequency suitably placed in the infrared and one in the ultraviolet, and choosing values of the two A's.

A prism spectrograph gives good separation of lines only in a range of frequencies in which the prism has a large value of $dn/d\omega$. Figure 15-5 shows that a favorable range occurs just to the left of an extinction band, and to study a given spectral region one therefore seeks a material with an extinction band beginning just off the high-frequency end of the region. In reducing positions of lines on a spectrogram to wavelength by comparison with lines in a known spectrum, it is important to have an interpolation formula taking into account the nonlinear dependence of n on λ. Formula (15-52) or its equivalent in terms of wavelength (see Prob. 15-10) is very awkward for this purpose. In the 1890s Hartmann discovered empirically that, in a range beginning at the low-frequency edge of an extinction band and extending a small fraction of the way to the next band, the curve of n against λ has the appearance of part of a hyperbola with a horizontal asymptote at some index n_0 and a vertical one at some wavelength λ_0, so that over this restricted range a quite accurate formula for n is

$$n = n_0 + \frac{C}{\lambda - \lambda_0} \qquad (15\text{-}53)$$

The three constants are evaluated from observed values of n at three wavelengths chosen at the two ends and the middle of the range in question. For details of the use of Hartmann's formula in an interpolation routine see Sawyer [80], p. 240.

We have now to consider the conductivity σ, for which only a simple classical theory from the era around 1900 will be given. When an electric field $\mathbf{E}$ exists in a metal, the free electrons in a macroscopically infinitesimal region experience an average internal field $\mathbf{E}_i$ which is assumed to be just equal to $\mathbf{E}$. A good justification of this assumption on classical grounds was not forthcoming until 1934.

If no field $\mathbf{E}$ exists, the electrons are moving about at random in the metal. Application of a field superposes a drifting motion. This drift is what concerns us, and it can be described by a vectorial velocity $\mathbf{v}$ which is the average of the velocities of the electrons in a macroscopically infinitesimal region. The macroscopic density of free current, which will be denoted here by $\mathbf{j}$ without subscript, is then

$$\mathbf{j} = -N'e\mathbf{v} \tag{15-54}$$

where N' is the number of free electrons per unit volume.

According to classical ideas, the motion of an electron is impeded by collisions with the positive ions. This impedance is described empirically by saying that on the average the electron moves as though it were in a viscous fluid. The equation of motion governing $\mathbf{v}$ is then

$$m\frac{d\mathbf{v}}{dt} = -e\mathbf{E} - b\mathbf{v} \tag{15-55}$$

where the second term on the right represents the viscous drag, and b is some constant.

If the field $\mathbf{E}$ is sinusoidal in time, we have, at any given point in the medium, $\mathbf{E} = \mathbf{E}_0 e^{-i\omega t}$. Then (15-55) has a solution of the form $\mathbf{v} = \mathbf{v}_0 e^{-i\omega t}$, and $\mathbf{v}_0$ is easily found by substitution. Having $\mathbf{v}$, we know $\mathbf{j}$, and from the definition $\mathbf{j} = \sigma\mathbf{E}$ we finally get

$$\sigma = \frac{N'e^2/m}{b/m - i\omega} \tag{15-56}$$

At $\omega = 0$ this expression must reduce to the static conductivity σ_0, and hence

$$b = \frac{N'e^2}{\sigma_0} \tag{15-57}$$

The complex refractive index is given by (15-32). It will be assumed that $\mu = 1$. For ϵ we substitute the right side of (15-50); and for σ, (15-56) and (15-57). The result is

$$n_c^2 = \epsilon + i\frac{4\pi\sigma}{\omega} = 1 - \frac{4\pi N'e^2/m}{\omega^2 + i\Gamma_0\omega} - \sum \frac{4\pi Ne^2 f_j/m}{\omega^2 - \omega_j^2 + i\Gamma_j\omega} \tag{15-58}$$

where

$$\Gamma_0 = \frac{N'e^2}{m\sigma_0} \tag{15-59}$$

The term in (15-58) involving Γ_0 is the contribution of the free electrons, and the terms in the sum are due to bound electrons in the medium. The term for the free electrons is similar to the others, except that the binding force, and hence the resonant frequency, is zero.

When ω is small, $n_c{}^2$ is dominated by the term for the free electrons, since this term tends to infinity. In fact, when ω is sufficiently small, we have

$$n_c{}^2 \approx \frac{i4\pi\sigma_0}{\omega}$$

Taking the square root and resolving into real and imaginary parts gives

$$n \approx \kappa \approx \left(\frac{2\pi\sigma_0}{\omega}\right)^{\frac{1}{2}} \tag{15-60}$$

In the next chapter experimental evidence will be cited that, for good conductors such as copper or silver, (15-60) is good up to $\omega \approx 10^{14}$ sec^{-1}, corresponding to a wavelength *in vacuo* of about 10^{-3} cm. The significance is that at all frequencies up to the far infrared the optical properties of a good conductor can be predicted with high accuracy from a knowledge of just the static conductivity (see Prob. 15-13).

Through the near infrared, the visible, and the near ultraviolet n and κ show a complicated behavior and vary markedly from metal to metal. The free electrons remain important and cause the characteristic metallic reflection, but for formula (15-58) to reproduce the observations would certainly require a liberal admixture of terms for bound electrons. It is not worthwhile to push the classical theory so far.

It appears from (15-58) that at sufficiently high frequencies the presence of the free electrons should become unimportant, and a metal should be no different from a dielectric. Experimentally it is found that such a transition occurs in the far ultraviolet, with the unfortunate consequence that the reflectance of a metal becomes as poor as that of a dielectric in this region.

15-6 Energy Theorem In the macroscopic theory there exists a formula analogous to the microscopic relation (4-8). Writing the scalar product of $\mathbf{E}$ with Eq. (15-16) and the scalar product of $\mathbf{H}$ with (15-14), we have

$$4\pi\mathbf{E} \cdot \mathbf{j}_{\text{free}} = c\mathbf{E} \cdot \text{curl } \mathbf{H} - \mathbf{E} \cdot \frac{\partial \mathbf{D}}{\partial t}$$

$$0 = -c\mathbf{H} \cdot \text{curl } \mathbf{E} - \mathbf{H} \cdot \frac{\partial \mathbf{B}}{\partial t}$$

Then by (1-21),

$$\mathbf{E} \cdot \mathbf{j}_{\text{free}} = -\frac{c}{4\pi} \text{div } (\mathbf{E} \times \mathbf{H}) - \frac{1}{4\pi}\left(\mathbf{E} \cdot \frac{\partial \mathbf{D}}{\partial t} + \mathbf{H} \cdot \frac{\partial \mathbf{B}}{\partial t}\right)$$

The form of this relation suggests that the left side represents the rate of generation of Joule heat per unit volume of the medium; the second term on the right has to do with storage of energy in fields, and the first term on the right gives, as the appropriate Poynting vector in the macroscopic theory,

$$\mathbf{S} = \frac{c}{4\pi} \, \mathbf{E} \times \mathbf{H} \tag{15-61}$$

The Poynting vector is the only item relating to energy that will be needed in the work to follow. The argument leading up to it is admittedly sketchy and far short of a satisfying discussion of energy in the macroscopic theory. When we use (15-61), it will therefore be appropriate to stop occasionally for a side investigation to be sure that a correct interpretation is being given to $\mathbf{S}$. Let us make two such investigations now.

First, it is to be noted that when a wave travels through a region of free space well removed from matter, there is no difference between microscopic and macroscopic fields, so that $\mathbf{E} = \mathbf{e}$, and $\mathbf{H} = \mathbf{B} = \mathbf{b}$. Then (15-61) reduces properly to (4-7).

Second, consider a monochromatic beam propagating through a gas at low pressure. The gas has a nonvanishing extinction index at any frequency, and the beam therefore suffers attenuation or, in other words, loses energy along its path. We have worked out a theory of the complex refractive index for stationary atoms, and in this case the extinction can originate only in scattering of radiation out of the beam. We have a theory of this scattering and can now make a calculation to check for consistency.

Let the beam have a cross section 1 cm square, and let the wavelength be a very small fraction of a centimeter. Diffraction can then be neglected, and within the beam the wave can be treated as part of a plane wave with electric and magnetic fields represented by (15-40) and with a similar expression for $\mathbf{H}$, with $\mathbf{H}_0$ given by (15-36). (Assume $\mu = 1$.) Let the beam travel in the z direction, and for simplicity let it be linearly polarized with $\mathbf{E}$ along the x axis. Then

$$E_x = E_0 e^{-\kappa k_0 z} e^{i(n k_0 z - \omega t)}$$
$$H_y = (n + i\kappa) E_x$$

where $k_0 = \omega/c$. The Poynting vector in the beam lies in the z direction, and the time average of its magnitude is

$$\langle S \rangle = \frac{c}{8\pi} \, \mathrm{Re} \, (E_x H_y^*) = \frac{nc}{8\pi} \, |E_0|^2 \, e^{-2\kappa k_0 z}$$

The power lost from the beam in traveling from z to $z + \delta z$ is

$$\delta W = \langle S \rangle_z - \langle S \rangle_{z+\delta z} \approx \langle S \rangle_z 2\kappa k_0 \, \delta z$$

For κ we can substitute (15-46), and the result becomes

$$\delta W = \langle S \rangle_z \, \sigma N \, \delta z$$

where σ is the total cross section for scattering given by (14-15). [It is necessary here to make use of the expression for γ given in (12-9) and to use $k_0 = \omega/c$.] Now $N \, \delta z$ is the total number of atoms lying in the beam between z and $z + \delta z$. We have therefore achieved the desired balance of power.

From this calculation we draw the following conclusions: The Poynting vector (15-61) properly represents the flux density of power in a wave as far as it is represented by the macroscopic fields, but it does not include the microscopic details of the power scattered by individual atoms. The macroscopic theory treats nearly (but never perfectly) homogeneous media as being perfectly homogeneous, and the attenuation due to scattering (which originates in the microscopic irregularities) is introduced through the complex refractive index. The theory of this index involves microscopic considerations, but once it is known, all microscopic details can be ignored, and the macroscopic equations, including the Poynting vector (15-61), applied.

Problems

15-1. Consider a cube 1000 A on an edge. Calculate the number of molecules in this cube for an ideal gas at standard conditions and for a liquid or solid (take water or ice as an example for which the relevant constants are known by heart). It will be evident that for a wavelength of 1000 A (fairly far into the ultraviolet), a macroscopically infinitesimal volume τ, as defined in Sec. 15-1, can be chosen in these cases.

15-2. At what pressure in millimeters of Hg at 0°C does a gas have, on the average, one molecule in a cube one wavelength on an edge when $\lambda = 5000$ A?

15-3. Let an inhomogeneous wave in a transparent medium be polarized in the TE mode illustrated in Fig. 15-2b. Describe by a figure the elliptical oscillation of the real vector **H** at an arbitrary point fixed in space. Show the orientation of the ellipse and direction of rotation in relation to the vectors **k** and **a**, and give the ratio of major to minor diameter. What is the range of possible shapes of this ellipse? (Answer the last question on the basis of the contents of Sec. 15-4, ignoring the possibility that a restriction may come in later from the way in which an inhomogeneous wave is actually produced.)

15-4. In an inhomogeneous wave in a transparent medium a characteristic of the attenuation is the distance one must travel in the direction of **a** in order that the amplitude falls in the ratio $1:1/e$. Using (15-37), express this distance in terms of $\lambda_0 (= 2\pi/k_0)$, $\lambda (= 2\pi/k)$, and n. What is the limiting form when λ approaches zero [which is possible according to (15-37) taken independently of physical limitations to arise in the next chapter]?

15-5. Consider a monochromatic homogeneous plane wave in a medium with a complex refractive index. Consider first the case in which the electric field is linearly polarized. The magnetic field is then linearly polarized at right angles to it. Show that at any fixed point the two fields oscillate with a difference of phase, and find a formula giving this difference in terms of n and κ.   (It will be seen that this difference vanishes with κ, so that in a transparent medium the fields at any fixed point attain their maximum values at the same time.)   Consider now the case in which the electric wave is elliptically polarized, so that at a fixed point it is represented by a motion around an ellipse, as in Fig. 5-11.   (Exclude the special case of circular polarization.) With respect to this ellipse describe the size, shape, and orientation of the ellipse described by the magnetic vector.   Find an expression for the angle between the real **E** and the real **H**, and note that, except when $\kappa = 0$, it is not $\pi/2$ and is not constant in time.

15-6. Figure 15-4a shows the maximum and minimum in $n - 1$ falling at frequencies defining the half-maximum points of κ, and the maximum of $n - 1$ as being one-half that of κ.   Prove that these relationships are correct.

15-7. Let a gas consist of atoms with a single resonant frequency ω_0.   Consider a cube whose edge is the resonant wavelength $\lambda_0 = 2\pi c/\omega_0$.   From formula (15-48) derive a formula for the number ν of atoms in this cube such that the maximum value of κ has a prescribed value κ_m.   [The result takes a very simple form when the expression for γ given in (12-9) is used.]   Evaluate ν for $\kappa_m = 0.1$, and give the corresponding density N and the pressure (in atmospheres at $0°C$) when $\lambda_0 = 5000$ A.   Would the value of ν be altered if an oscillator strength f were included?   Would it be changed on consideration of the Doppler effect?   (The required numerical value of ν turns out to be of order unity, so that the arguments of the macroscopic theory come in doubt, and the formulas for the refractive index at such low densities should properly be established by a straight scattering theory.   The results would be the same.)

15-8. When an atom (assumed for simplicity to have a single elastically bound electron) is a constituent of a liquid or a solid, it is sometimes assumed that the effects of neighboring atoms on the motion of the electron are equivalent to a viscous drag, so that a term $\Gamma \, ds/dt$ is to be added to the left of the equation of motion (14-12).   In this case the term representing radiation reaction is neglected.   Show that (15-49) is the consequence.

15-9. Set Γ equal to zero in (15-49).   Then α is always real but has an infinite singularity at ω_0.   Draw a qualitative plot of ϵ as given by (15-43), and directly below draw by inspection curves of n and κ.   Include only the vicinity of ω_0.   Note that there is a range of ω extending from ω_0 to some higher frequency in which $n = 0$ and $\kappa > 0$, while at all other frequencies $\kappa = 0$ and $n > 0$.   There is therefore an extinction band even when $\Gamma = 0$.   Indicate qualitatively how the width of this band increases with N.   Discuss the types of monochromatic plane waves that are possible when $n = 0$ and $\kappa > 0$.   (It has been shown in a number of different ways that the behavior of n and κ brought out in this problem would be exhibited by an ideal crystal with stationary nuclei.   Such a crystal would show no scattering at any wavelength longer than the dimensions of the unit cell, and there would be no conversion of radiant energy into thermal vibrations.   These facts are not inconsistent with the existence of extinction bands because of the peculiar nature of the waves that can exist at frequencies in these bands.   The phenomena arise in connection with the propagation of any kind of waves through perfectly uniform and perfectly dissipationless structures with resonant frequencies.)

15-10. Show that in terms of wavelength Sellmeier's equation (15-52) takes the form

$$n^2 = B_0 + \sum \frac{B_j \lambda^2}{\lambda^2 - \lambda_j{}^2}$$

where the B's stand for expressions involving the A_j and λ_j (or ω_j).

15-11. In a dielectric medium, at frequencies for which it is transparent (refractive index real), a relation superior to (15-42) is $\mathbf{E}_i = \mathbf{E} + 4\pi\mathbf{P}/3$.   Show that the consequence is

$$n^2 = \frac{1 + 8\pi N\alpha/3}{1 - 4\pi N\alpha/3}$$

and find an equivalent expression giving $4\pi N\alpha$ as a function of n^2. (This formula for n^2 was advanced independently and at the same time—1880—by Lorentz and Lorenz, whose names are pronounced the same! It is called the *Lorentz-Lorenz formula*. The original derivation, given in Lorentz [59], pp. 137 and 305, has since been replaced by much more elaborate ones which clarify the question of when the formula is applicable and when corrections are necessary.)

15-12. At $\lambda = 5893$ A (yellow sodium light) the refractive index of nitrogen gas at 0°C and 760 mm Hg is $n_g = 1.000297$, and that of the liquid at -196°C is $n_l = 1.205$. The density of the gas is 1.251×10^{-3} g cm^{-3}, and that of the liquid is 0.808 g cm^{-3}. From (15-43) find $N_g\alpha$ for the gas, and from the result obtain $N_l\alpha$ for the liquid. Compute n_l by (15-43) and again by the Lorentz-Lorenz formula in Prob. 15-11, and compare with the observed value. (The L-L formula is better here, but still not excellent. For many substances a calculation of this type gives no agreement at all, for the reason that there is molecular association or some other difference between the elementary unit in the liquid and the gas.)

15-13. In formula (15-58) for a conductor, drop the sum of terms representing bound electrons. Take the case of copper, and find N' and σ_0 from handbook data. (Assume one free electron per atom, and pay attention to consistency of units.) Calculate n and κ for a number of frequencies differing by factors of 10 to find the approximate upper limit of the frequencies for which (15-60) is good. Compare with the experimental results of Hagen and Rubens stated in Sec. 16-5. (Agreement should be quite good.)

chapter **16**

Reflection and Transmission

When a wave is incident on the interface between two homogeneous media, there is partial reflection and partial transmission. This phenomenon can be treated by the macroscopic theory of Maxwell; under the conditions that the interface and the waves are plane, the problem reduces to one of algebra—but a rather complicated one.

Once the single interface is treated, one can go on to problems in which there are several boundaries with reflection occurring at each. Much attention will be paid to cases of several plane and parallel boundaries and nearly monochromatic radiation, since these cases involve striking effects of interference and include such important instruments as the Fabry-Perot interferometer. The latter problems are quite distinct from those typified by reflection of white light from the nonplanar surfaces of an ordinary windowpane, in which no interference is noticed and the multiple reflections can be treated by addition of irradiances rather than amplitudes.

16-1 Collection of Formulas for a Single Medium For ease of reference let us summarize in the most convenient form the essential results of the last chapter. Consider the case in which all fields are monochromatic with some frequency ω. Results to be obtained under this restriction will be applicable to each Fourier component in the polychromatic case.

The electric and magnetic fields can be given a complex representation. The electric field has the form $\mathbf{E}_s e^{-i\omega t}$, where $\mathbf{E}_s$ is a complex function depending only on spatial position in the medium; similarly for the magnetic field. Formulas can be abbreviated by omitting the exponential temporal factor and omitting the subscript s. *Thus throughout the following, $\mathbf{E}$ and $\mathbf{H}$ will stand for just the spatial factors in the complex representations of the monochromatic fields.*

As usual, we assume $\mu = 1$. The complex refractive index of the medium is

$$n_c = n + i\kappa \tag{16-1}$$

where n is the real refractive index, and κ the extinction index, and

$$n_c^2 = \epsilon + \frac{i4\pi\sigma}{\omega}$$

The Maxwell equations (15-22) to (15-25) become

$$\operatorname{div}(n_c^2\mathbf{E}) = 0 \qquad \operatorname{div}\mathbf{H} = 0 \tag{16-2}$$
$$\operatorname{curl}\mathbf{E} = ik_0\mathbf{H} \qquad \operatorname{curl}\mathbf{H} = -ik_0 n_c^2\mathbf{E}$$

where $k_0 = \omega/c$.

The general plane-wave solution of (16-2) is

$$\mathbf{E} = \mathbf{E}_0 e^{i\mathbf{k}_c \cdot \mathbf{r}} \qquad \mathbf{H} = \mathbf{H}_0 e^{i\mathbf{k}_c \cdot \mathbf{r}} \tag{16-3}$$

under the following conditions: The complex wave vector $\mathbf{k}_c$, which is of the form $\mathbf{k} + i\mathbf{a}$, must satisfy

$$\mathbf{k}_c \cdot \mathbf{k}_c = k_0^2 n_c^2 \tag{16-4}$$
or
$$k^2 - a^2 = k_0^2(n^2 - \kappa^2) \tag{16-5}$$
$$\mathbf{k} \cdot \mathbf{a} = k_0^2 n\kappa \tag{16-6}$$

The constant $\mathbf{E}_0$, which is the value of $\mathbf{E}$ at the origin of the position vector $\mathbf{r}$, is an arbitrary complex vector, except that it must satisfy

$$\mathbf{k}_c \cdot \mathbf{E}_0 = 0 \tag{16-7}$$

This relation is called the *transversality condition*, but its implication is rather complicated when the wave is of inhomogeneous type ($\mathbf{k}$ and $\mathbf{a}$ different from zero and not collinear—see Sec. 15-4). The constant $\mathbf{H}_0$ is related to $\mathbf{E}_0$ by

$$\mathbf{H}_0 = \frac{1}{k_0}\mathbf{k}_c \times \mathbf{E}_0 \tag{16-8}$$

One can show that these several conditions are sufficient for a solution by substituting (16-3) in (16-2), remembering the useful formulas stated in Prob. 4-10.

16-2 Boundary Conditions Let two homogeneous media, designated 1 and 2, be separated by a plane boundary. Draw a unit normal $\mathbf{v}$ in either direction from the boundary, and construct a small disk-shaped surface Σ with its two plane faces parallel to and on opposite sides of the boundary, as shown in Fig. 16-1.   Let the thickness of the volume τ enclosed by Σ be very small compared with its diameter, and let the diameter be small enough that throughout that part of τ lying on either side of the boundary the fields change very little.

Gauss' theorem can be applied to the upper two of Eqs. (16-2)[1] to show that the normal surface integrals over Σ of $n_c{}^2\mathbf{E}$ and of $\mathbf{H}$ must vanish. These integrals are essentially equal to just the contributions from the two plane faces; by letting the dimensions of Σ approach zero, we reach the conclusion that at any point of the boundary,

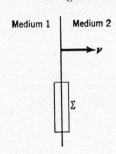

Medium 1   Medium 2

Σ

$$n_{c1}{}^2\mathbf{E}_1 \cdot \mathbf{v} = n_{c2}{}^2\mathbf{E}_2 \cdot \mathbf{v} \qquad \mathbf{H}_1 \cdot \mathbf{v} = \mathbf{H}_2 \cdot \mathbf{v} \quad (16\text{-}9)$$

where subscripts 1 and 2 indicate evaluation of quantities on opposite sides of the boundary.   In words, these relations mean that the component of $n_c{}^2\mathbf{E}$ or of $\mathbf{H}$ in the direction of the normal $\mathbf{v}$ must be continuous across the boundary.

Fig. 16-1.   *Two homogeneous media separated by a plane boundary.   A unit normal and a disk-shaped surface (shown in cross section) are introduced to derive boundary conditions.*

Stokes' theorem in the form (1-12) can be applied to the lower two of (16-2).   The volume integrals of the curls, which are equal to the integrals of the right sides of these equations, must vanish in the limit as τ shrinks to zero, since the fields are everywhere finite.   Hence the tangential surface integrals over Σ of $\mathbf{E}$ and of $\mathbf{H}$ vanish in the limit, and we have

$$\mathbf{E}_1 \times \mathbf{v} = \mathbf{E}_2 \times \mathbf{v} \qquad \mathbf{H}_1 \times \mathbf{v} = \mathbf{H}_2 \times \mathbf{v} \quad (16\text{-}10)$$

These relations are equivalent to the statement that the tangential components of $\mathbf{E}$ and $\mathbf{H}$ (components parallel to the boundary) must be continuous across the boundary.   Relations (16-9) and (16-10) are the *boundary conditions* connecting wave fields in the two media.

16-3   Reflection and Transmission at a Single Interface.   General Formulas

Let medium 1 be so highly transparent that κ_1 can be taken to be zero, and let the incident plane wave be in this medium and be of the homogeneous type (real wave vector).   No restriction will be placed on medium 2, so that its refractive index may be complex.

Given the incident wave, it is possible to find from the formulas in the preceding two sections, without any assumptions, the rest of the fields in the solution, but let us not labor the obvious fact that there will be a

---

[1] The application can be made directly to the equations in complex representation since only linear operations are involved.

reflected wave in medium 1 and a transmitted wave in medium 2. It can also be assumed that these two waves are plane, but their amplitudes and wave vectors can be left to be determined from those of the incident wave and the indices of the media. A consequence of having guessed the solution to this extent is that conditions (16-10) are sufficient to fix the reflected and transmitted waves, and (16-9) are then automatically satisfied, as one can verify in a final check that the solution to be obtained satisfies the Maxwell equations in the interior of each medium and the boundary conditions at the interface.

We therefore take the fields in medium 1 to be

$$\mathbf{E}_1 = \mathbf{E}_i e^{i\mathbf{k}_i \cdot \mathbf{r}} + \mathbf{E}_r e^{i(\mathbf{k}_r + i\mathbf{a}_r) \cdot \mathbf{r}} \tag{16-11}$$

$$\mathbf{H}_1 = \mathbf{H}_i e^{i\mathbf{k}_i \cdot \mathbf{r}} + \mathbf{H}_r e^{i(\mathbf{k}_r + i\mathbf{a}_r) \cdot \mathbf{r}} \tag{16-12}$$

and those in medium 2 to be

$$\mathbf{E}_2 = \mathbf{E}_t e^{i(\mathbf{k}_t + i\mathbf{a}_t) \cdot \mathbf{r}} \tag{16-13}$$

$$\mathbf{H}_2 = \mathbf{H}_t e^{i(\mathbf{k}_t + i\mathbf{a}_t) \cdot \mathbf{r}} \tag{16-14}$$

Here subscripts i, r, and t designate the incident, reflected, and transmitted waves, respectively. The vector $\mathbf{r}$ specifies points in space with respect to an arbitrarily chosen origin. The $\mathbf{k}$'s and $\mathbf{a}$'s are real vectors; $\mathbf{k}_i$ has magnitude $n_1 k_0$ and some given direction, and the rest are to be found. The amplitude $\mathbf{E}_i$ is a given constant vector that must be perpendicular to $\mathbf{k}_i$ but is otherwise arbitrary and in general complex, so that the incident wave can have any irradiance and polarization. The amplitudes $\mathbf{E}_r$ and $\mathbf{E}_t$ and those of the three magnetic waves are to be found.

Throughout the discussion of a single boundary between two media the origin of the position vector $\mathbf{r}$ *will be a point O lying in the boundary.* This choice will simplify the formalism without affecting the usefulness of the results in later extensions to more complicated problems.

Let $\mathbf{r}_P$ be the position vector of an arbitrary point P of the boundary. Either of the boundary conditions (16-10) applied to the above fields at P leads to a relation in which a sum of three terms vanishes, each term consisting of one of the exponentials in (16-11) and (16-13) multiplied by a constant vector. In other words, the three exponentials are linearly dependent, and it follows that the three exponents are equal, or

$$\mathbf{k}_i \cdot \mathbf{r}_P = \mathbf{k}_r \cdot \mathbf{r}_P = \mathbf{k}_t \cdot \mathbf{r}_P \tag{16-15}$$

$$0 = \mathbf{a}_r \cdot \mathbf{r}_P = \mathbf{a}_t \cdot \mathbf{r}_P \tag{16-16}$$

(A proof of this conclusion is given in Courant [22], vol. II, p. 439, Example 2.) If $\mathbf{r}$ is the position vector of an arbitrary point of space, then $\mathbf{v} \times \mathbf{r}$ is that of a point of the boundary and can be substituted for

$\mathbf{r}_P$. Then

$$(\mathbf{k}_i - \mathbf{k}_r) \cdot (\nu \times \mathbf{r}) = (\mathbf{k}_i \times \nu - \mathbf{k}_r \times \nu) \cdot \mathbf{r} = 0$$

and because $\mathbf{r}$ is arbitrary, the difference in parentheses on the right vanishes. By this and the analogous arguments,

$$\mathbf{k}_i \times \nu = \mathbf{k}_r \times \nu = \mathbf{k}_t \times \nu \tag{16-17}$$
$$0 = \mathbf{a}_r \times \nu = \mathbf{a}_t \times \nu \tag{16-18}$$

From (16-17) it is seen that all the $\mathbf{k}$'s and ν lie in one and the same plane, called the *plane of incidence*, and this plane is unambiguously defined if the incident wave does not fall normally on the boundary. From (16-18) it follows that the $\mathbf{a}$'s are collinear with ν. If $\mathbf{a}_r$ were different from zero, it would have to satisfy $\mathbf{a}_r \cdot \mathbf{k}_r = 0$ in accordance with (16-6) and $\kappa_1 = 0$. It is impossible to find a nonvanishing $\mathbf{a}_r$ consistent with this requirement and (16-17), (16-18), and (16-5). The reflected

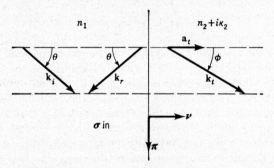

Fig. 16-2. *Relations among the wave vectors when a plane wave in a transparent medium falls on the boundary of a medium with a complex refractive index. Orthogonal unit vectors shown at the bottom are used in finding relations among amplitudes.*

wave is therefore of homogeneous type, and its wave vector has the same magnitude as that of $\mathbf{k}_i$, namely, $n_1 k_0$. The ordinary law of specular reflection is satisfied, since (16-17) now says that $\mathbf{k}_i$ and $\mathbf{k}_r$ must be related as in Fig. 16-2. This figure also shows the type of relation that must be exhibited by $\mathbf{k}_t$ and $\mathbf{a}_t$ when the second medium has a complex refractive index. Convenient formulas for finding the magnitudes of the latter two vectors and the angle between them are

$$k_t \sin \phi = k_0 n_1 \sin \theta \tag{16-19}$$
$$k_t \cos \phi + i a_t = k_0 [(n_2 + i\kappa_2)^2 - n_1{}^2 \sin^2 \theta]^{1/2} \tag{16-20}$$

where θ and ϕ are the angles in Fig. 16-2, and $k_0 = \omega/c$. The first relation comes at once from (16-17), while the derivation of the second is called for in Prob. 16-1. These two relations constitute a generalization of Snell's law. The special case $\kappa_2 = 0$ and the ordinary form of Snell's law will be discussed in the next section.

We have now to find the relations among the amplitudes of the incident, reflected, and transmitted waves. Boundary conditions (16-10) applied at point O (where $\mathbf{r} = 0$) give

$$(\mathbf{E}_i + \mathbf{E}_r) \times \mathbf{v} = \mathbf{E}_t \times \mathbf{v} \qquad (\mathbf{H}_i + \mathbf{H}_r) \times \mathbf{v} = \mathbf{H}_t \times \mathbf{v} \qquad (16\text{-}21)$$

These equations will be dealt with by making a resolution along three orthogonal unit vectors, one of which is the unit normal $\mathbf{v}$; the other two are $\mathbf{ó}$ and $\boldsymbol{\pi}$, defined by

$$\mathbf{ó} = \frac{\mathbf{v} \times \mathbf{k}_i}{|\mathbf{v} \times \mathbf{k}_i|} \qquad \boldsymbol{\pi} = \mathbf{ó} \times \mathbf{v} \qquad (16\text{-}22)$$

These vectors are illustrated in Fig. 16-2. In the problems treated in this chapter, it is very easy to make errors in sign, and one safeguard is to adopt definite and easily remembered conventions at every opportunity. Note therefore that the unit vectors have been chosen to make $\mathbf{v}$, $\boldsymbol{\pi}$, and $\mathbf{ó}$ in that order (the alphabetic order) a right-hand system, and to make $\mathbf{k}_i \cdot \mathbf{v}$ and $\mathbf{k}_i \cdot \boldsymbol{\pi}$ positive. The symbols $\mathbf{ó}$ and $\boldsymbol{\pi}$ originated in the German literature, where they represent the first letters of the words *senkrecht* and *parallel*, meaning perpendicular and parallel (to the plane of incidence), respectively. For normal incidence, no plane of incidence is defined, and $\mathbf{ó}$ can be any unit vector perpendicular to $\mathbf{v}$.

The notation for the resolutions of the $\mathbf{E}$'s, $\mathbf{H}$'s, $\mathbf{k}$'s, and $\mathbf{a}_t$ is illustrated by the examples

$$\mathbf{E}_i = E_{iv}\mathbf{v} + E_{i\pi}\boldsymbol{\pi} + E_{i\sigma}\mathbf{ó} \qquad \mathbf{k}_i = k_{iv}\mathbf{v} + k_{i\pi}\boldsymbol{\pi} \qquad \mathbf{a}_t = a_t\mathbf{v}$$

Equations (16-21) have two components each:

$$E_{i\pi} + E_{r\pi} = E_{t\pi} \qquad E_{i\sigma} + E_{r\sigma} = E_{t\sigma} \qquad (16\text{-}23)$$
$$H_{i\pi} + H_{r\pi} = H_{t\pi} \qquad H_{i\sigma} + H_{r\sigma} = H_{t\sigma} \qquad (16\text{-}24)$$

where $E_{i\pi}$ and $E_{i\sigma}$ are given, and the rest are to be found.

The $\mathbf{H}$'s are related to the $\mathbf{E}$'s as in (16-8). Let us work out the relation for the transmitted wave as the more complicated one:

$$k_0\mathbf{H}_t = (\mathbf{k}_t + i\mathbf{a}_t) \times \mathbf{E}_t = k_{t\pi}E_{t\sigma}\mathbf{v} - (k_{tv} + ia_t)E_{t\sigma}\boldsymbol{\pi}$$
$$+ [(k_{tv} + ia_t)E_{t\pi} - k_{t\pi}E_{tv}]\mathbf{ó}$$

The component E_{tv} appearing here can be expressed in terms of $E_{t\pi}$ by the transversality condition:

$$0 = (\mathbf{k}_t + i\mathbf{a}_t) \cdot \mathbf{E}_t = (k_{tv} + ia_t)E_{tv} + k_{t\pi}E_{t\pi} \qquad (16\text{-}25)$$

The π and σ components of $\mathbf{H}_t$ are then

$$H_{t\pi} = -\frac{k_{t\nu} + ia_t}{k_0} E_{t\sigma}$$

$$H_{t\sigma} = \frac{1}{k_0}\left[(k_{t\nu} + ia_t) + \frac{k_{t\pi}^2}{k_{t\nu} + ia_t}\right] E_{t\pi}$$

$$= \frac{(\mathbf{k}_t + i\mathbf{a}_t)^2}{k_0(k_{t\nu} + ia_t)} E_{t\pi} = \frac{k_0(n_2 + i\kappa_2)^2}{k_{t\nu} + ia_t} E_{t\pi}$$

The last expression comes from (16-4). By merely changing subscripts, one has the analogous formulas for the incident and reflected waves. It is advantageous to express the results in the abbreviated notation

$$
\begin{array}{llll}
H_{i\pi} = -Y_{1\sigma}E_{i\sigma} & H_{r\pi} = Y_{1\sigma}E_{r\sigma} & H_{t\pi} = -Y_{2\sigma}E_{t\sigma} & (16\text{-}26) \\
H_{i\sigma} = Y_{1\pi}E_{i\pi} & H_{r\sigma} = -Y_{1\pi}E_{r\pi} & H_{t\sigma} = Y_{2\pi}E_{t\pi} & (16\text{-}27)
\end{array}
$$

where
$$
\begin{array}{lll}
Y_{1\pi} = \dfrac{k_0 n_1^2}{k_{i\nu}} & Y_{2\pi} = \dfrac{k_0(n_2 + i\kappa_2)^2}{k_{t\nu} + ia_t} & (16\text{-}28)
\end{array}
$$

$$
\begin{array}{lll}
Y_{1\sigma} = \dfrac{k_{i\nu}}{k_0} & Y_{2\sigma} = \dfrac{k_{t\nu} + ia_t}{k_0} & (16\text{-}29)
\end{array}
$$

The reversal of sign in the expressions for $H_{r\pi}$ and $H_{r\sigma}$ is due to $k_{r\nu} = -k_{i\nu}$. Equations (16-24) become

$$Y_{1\pi}(E_{i\pi} - E_{r\pi}) = Y_{2\pi}E_{t\pi} \qquad Y_{1\sigma}(E_{i\sigma} - E_{r\sigma}) = Y_{2\sigma}E_{t\sigma} \quad (16\text{-}30)$$

These equations together with (16-23) yield the following ratios:

$$r_\pi \equiv \frac{E_{r\pi}}{E_{i\pi}} = \frac{Y_{1\pi} - Y_{2\pi}}{Y_{1\pi} + Y_{2\pi}} \qquad r_\sigma \equiv \frac{E_{r\sigma}}{E_{i\sigma}} = \frac{Y_{1\sigma} - Y_{2\sigma}}{Y_{1\sigma} + Y_{2\sigma}} \qquad (16\text{-}31)$$

$$t_\pi \equiv \frac{E_{t\pi}}{E_{i\pi}} = \frac{2Y_{1\pi}}{Y_{1\pi} + Y_{2\pi}} \qquad t_\sigma \equiv \frac{E_{t\sigma}}{E_{i\sigma}} = \frac{2Y_{1\sigma}}{Y_{1\sigma} + Y_{2\sigma}} \qquad (16\text{-}32)$$

The r's and t's are called *reflection coefficients* and *transmission coefficients*, respectively. They refer to the π and σ components. Ratios of the ν components can be written from the transversality conditions of type (16-25):

$$\frac{E_{r\nu}}{E_{i\nu}} = -r_\pi \qquad \frac{E_{t\nu}}{E_{i\nu}} = \frac{k_{i\nu}}{k_{t\nu} + ia_t} t_\pi \qquad (16\text{-}33)$$

Formulas (16-31) to (16-33), together with the definitions (16-28) and (16-29), are the fundamental relations connecting the amplitudes of the three waves at an arbitrary point of the boundary. They have been referred to a type of resolution into components that proves especially convenient when inhomogeneous waves are involved and when extension is made to several media in tandem with plane and parallel boundaries. Another advantage of the resolution is that it brings out an analogy between plane electromagnetic waves in homogeneous media with plane boundaries and waves of voltage and current on long transmission lines connected in series. At a junction of two such lines there is partial reflection, with coefficients given by expressions identical to (16-31) and (16-32) with the Y's standing for the characteristic admittances of the lines. This analogy will not be developed here, but it has resulted in making available to optical problems some elegant theorems and computational methods used in electrical engineering.

The final topic in this section on general principles is the use of the r's and t's to calculate observable quantities in real cases characterized by the incident wave being, not monochromatic, but only quasi-mono-chromatic, and therefore capable of showing the full range of polarizations from completely polarized to unpolarized. The transmitted wave complicates the analysis in that it is sometimes inhomogeneous; this is best deferred to later discussion in special cases. The reflected wave, on the other hand, is in the same transparent medium as the incident wave and is of homogeneous type, and it can be treated in a general and useful way.

When specific problems are taken up, it will be seen that it is very easy to make errors in handling phase angles and thus arrive at the wrong polarizations unless a systematic procedure is employed. A very satisfactory procedure makes use of Stokes parameters. The first question is how these parameters are defined for a wave inside a dense, transparent medium. Consider a single plane, homogeneous, quasi-monochromatic wave in such a medium, and let it be expressed in cartesian representation with the z axis in the direction of propagation. The ideas in Sec. 13-12 now need only a very slight modification. The components of the electric field have the forms (13-48) except that the symbols e_x and e_y are to be replaced by E_x and E_y. Whereas the magnitudes of $\mathbf{e}$ and $\mathbf{b}$ were equal, we now have the magnitude of $\mathbf{H}$ equal to n times that of $\mathbf{E}$, where n is the refractive index of the medium, and in the definitions (13-56) of the Stokes parameters the factor $c/8\pi$ must be replaced by $nc/8\pi$. All the interpretations of the parameters, in particular, Figs. 13-19 and 13-20 and the idea of fractional polarization (13-66), remain the same as before. If a second wave *in the same medium* is referred to cartesian axes ξ, η, ζ, with the ζ axis along the direction of propagation, and if the components of the electric fields of the two waves at the origins of their respective coordinate systems are related by transfer functions as in (13-52), then the Stokes parameters of the second wave are related to those of the first by (13-57), (13-71), and (13-72) without any change. (If the second wave were in a different transparent medium of index n', and if this wave were of homogeneous type so that it could be characterized by Stokes parameters, then the right sides of these three relations would have to be multiplied by n'/n.)

To apply these results to the problem of reflection, let the two sets of cartesian axes have a common origin at a point O of the boundary (this point being also the origin of the position vector $\mathbf{r}$, as before), and let them be oriented as in Fig. 16-3. Note that the axes form right-hand systems, and by convention the y and η axes point in the direction of the unit vector $\mathbf{\sigma}$, the latter being defined by the fixed convention given earlier.

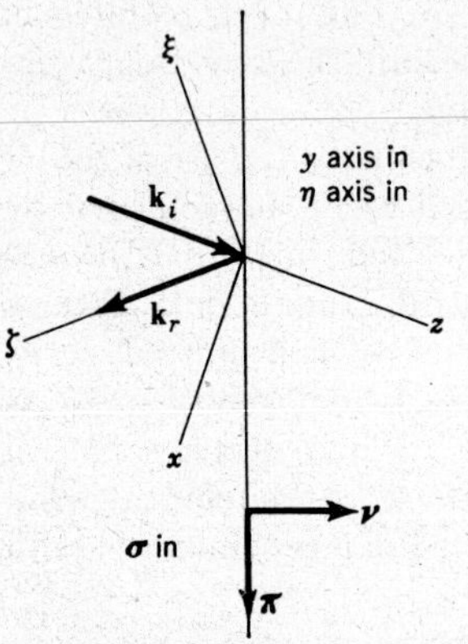

To find the transfer functions $\tau_{\xi x}$ and $\tau_{\eta x}$, we assume a linearly polarized incident wave with $\mathbf{E}_i$ along the x axis and find the ratios $E_{r\xi}/E_{ix}$ and $E_{r\eta}/E_{ix}$; similarly for $\tau_{\xi y}$ and $\tau_{\eta y}$. From (16-31) and (16-33) we obtain at once

$$\tau_{\xi x} = -r_\pi \qquad \tau_{\eta x} = 0$$
$$\tau_{\xi y} = 0 \qquad \tau_{\eta y} = r_\sigma \qquad (16\text{-}34)$$

Let us introduce the quantities

$$R_\pi = |r_\pi|^2 \qquad R_\sigma = |r_\sigma|^2 \qquad (16\text{-}35)$$

and write the complex reflection coefficients in the exponential forms

$$r_\pi = \sqrt{R_\pi}\, e^{i\alpha} \qquad r_\sigma = \sqrt{R_\sigma}\, e^{i\beta} \qquad (16\text{-}36)$$

Fig. 16-3. *Cartesian axes for relating the Stokes parameters of the incident and reflected waves.*

y axis in
η axis in

σ in

Then (13-57), (13-71), and (13-72) reduce to the following relations between the Stokes parameters of the incident and reflected waves:

$$I_r = \tfrac{1}{2}R_\pi(I_i + Q_i) + \tfrac{1}{2}R_\sigma(I_i - Q_i) \qquad (16\text{-}37)$$
$$Q_r = \tfrac{1}{2}R_\pi(I_i + Q_i) - \tfrac{1}{2}R_\sigma(I_i - Q_i) \qquad (16\text{-}38)$$
$$U_r + iV_r = -r_\pi r_\sigma^*(U_i + iV_i) = \sqrt{R_\pi R_\sigma}\, e^{i\delta}(U_i + iV_i) \qquad (16\text{-}39)$$
where
$$\delta = \alpha - \beta + \pi$$

It should be emphasized that a set of Stokes parameters has meaning only in connection with a definite cartesian coordinate system, and the formulas just written refer specifically to the arrangement in Fig. 16-3.

The *reflectance* is defined to be $R \equiv I_r/I_i$. For an unpolarized or circularly polarized incident wave, $Q_i = 0$ and $R = \frac{1}{2}(R_\pi + R_\sigma)$. For π polarization (linear with electric vector parallel to the plane of incidence), $Q_i = I_i$ and $R = R_\pi$, while for σ polarization, $Q_i = -I_i$ and $R = R_\sigma$. Thus R_π and R_σ are interpreted as reflectances for special polarizations.

If the incident wave has π or σ polarization, the three formulas for the Stokes parameters show at a glance that the reflected wave has the same polarization. More interesting applications of these formulas will occur in the problems.

16-4   Case of Two Transparent Media   The consequences of the formulas in the last section will now be investigated for the case in which the refractive index of the second medium is real and has a value n_2.

Assume first that n_2 is greater than n_1, that is, that the *incidence is on the denser medium.* The right side of (16-20), with $\kappa_2 = 0$, is always real. Hence $a_t = 0$, and the transmitted wave is always of homogeneous

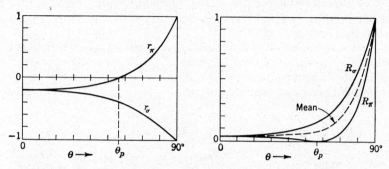

Fig. 16-4. *Reflection coefficients and reflectances for π and σ polarizations with incidence on the denser of two transparent media. Ratio of refractive indices is 1.5.*

type. By squaring and adding (16-19) and (16-20), we get $k_t = n_2 k_0$; substitution in (16-19) gives *Snell's law:*

$$n_1 \sin \theta = n_2 \sin \phi \qquad (16\text{-}40)$$

Another way of getting these results is cited in Prob. 16-3.

The parameters (16-28) and (16-29) become

$$Y_{1\pi} = \frac{n_1}{\cos \theta} \qquad Y_{2\pi} = \frac{n_2}{\cos \phi}$$
$$Y_{1\sigma} = n_1 \cos \theta \qquad Y_{2\sigma} = n_2 \cos \phi \qquad (16\text{-}41)$$

and the reflection coefficients are

$$r_\pi = \frac{n_1 \cos \phi - n_2 \cos \theta}{n_1 \cos \phi + n_2 \cos \theta} \qquad r_\sigma = \frac{n_1 \cos \theta - n_2 \cos \phi}{n_1 \cos \theta + n_2 \cos \phi} \qquad (16\text{-}42)$$

The last two expressions, of which alternative forms are given in Prob. 16-4, are known as the *Fresnel formulas.* It is not necessary to write the transmission coefficients t_π and t_σ, because in this simple problem all information about the transmitted wave will be extracted easily from the r's.

Figure 16-4 shows curves of the functions (16-42) and of the reflectances (16-35) under the assumption $n_2 = 1.5 n_1$ (For visible light the refractive index of glass relative to air ranges from about 1.51 to about 1.8, depending on the type and the wavelength.) At normal incidence the reflectance for any polarization of the incident wave is

$$R = \left(\frac{n_1 - n_2}{n_1 + n_2}\right)^2 \qquad \text{normal incidence} \qquad (16\text{-}43)$$

For an unpolarized incident wave the reflectance remains nearly constant at this value up to $\theta \approx 45°$ (but the reflected wave is partially polarized when the incidence is not normal).

Particularly interesting is the fact that r_π passes through zero at an angle of incidence $\theta = \theta_p$, which is called the *polarizing angle* or *Brewster's angle*. If the numerator of the expression for r_π in (16-42) is set equal to zero, and if Snell's law is applied, we get $\sin 2\theta_p = \sin 2\phi_p$. The pertinent

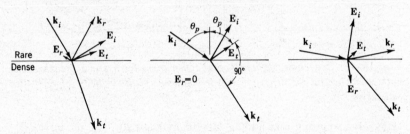

Fig. 16-5. *Relations of the real electric vectors when a wave with π polarization is incident on the denser medium at various angles. At the polarizing angle (center diagram) there is no reflected wave.*

solution is $\theta_p + \phi_p = \pi/2$, so that $\mathbf{k}_r$ and $\mathbf{k}_t$ are at right angles. Substitution of ϕ_p in Snell's law gives *Brewster's law:*

$$\tan \theta_p = \frac{n_2}{n_1} \qquad (16\text{-}44)$$

At the polarizing angle the reflected wave always has σ polarization, and any sheet of glass provides a simple means of obtaining a linearly polarized beam of light in which the direction of the electric vector is known. (The fact that reflection also occurs at the second surface of the sheet does not alter this conclusion about the polarization, as will be seen presently.)

Diagrams to illustrate the relations of the reflected and transmitted waves to the incident wave can be drawn easily with the use of Snell's law, the reflection coefficients, the transversality conditions, and the boundary conditions on the tangential components of the total electric fields on the two sides of the boundary. The great simplification is that the reflection coefficients have turned out to be real. The case of π

polarization is the more interesting, and Fig. 16-5 shows the real instantaneous electric vectors of the three waves at a point of the boundary. As time goes on, these vectors oscillate sinusoidally and are related at each instant in the manner shown. The three diagrams illustrate the cases $\theta < \theta_p$, $\theta = \theta_p$, and $\theta > \theta_p$. The corresponding diagrams for σ polarization are easily imagined. In particular, $\mathbf{E}_i$ and $\mathbf{E}_r$ point in opposite directions for any angle of incidence, and nothing special happens at $\theta = \theta_p$.

An experiment whose interpretation comes from the relations in the third diagram in Fig. 16-5 and the corresponding one for σ polarization is called *Lloyd's mirror*. The arrangement is shown in Fig. 16-6. An observing screen Σ is at the end of a long slab of glass with an optically flat surface. A small monochromatic source is at S, and waves arrive at Σ both directly and by reflection. The reflected wave appears to come

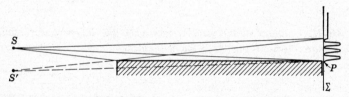

Fig. 16-6. *Arrangement of Lloyd's mirror. At P the direct and reflected waves interfere destructively.*

from the geometric image at S'. This image source is coherent with S and, at nearly grazing incidence, has nearly the same intensity (the reflectance of the glass is nearly unity). Fringes are observed on Σ as indicated by the curve of irradiance to the right of Σ. The *geometric* distances from S and S' to the far end of the mirror (point P) are equal, but the reversal of the electric vector on reflection effectively makes the *optical* path from S' to P differ from the geometric path by one-half wavelength, and the interference at P is destructive.

Let us now turn to the case $n_2 < n_1$ in which the *incidence is on the rarer medium*. The right side of (16-20), with $\kappa_2 = 0$, is real only for $\theta < \theta_c$, where θ_c is the *critical angle* defined by

$$\sin \theta_c = \frac{n_2}{n_1} \qquad (16\text{-}45)$$

For $\theta < \theta_c$, the transmitted wave is of homogeneous type, Snell's law (16-40) applies, and the reflection coefficients are given by (16-42). There is a polarizing angle (see Prob. 16-6).

The new feature that enters is that when $\theta > \theta_c$, the right side of (16-20) is pure imaginary. Then $\phi = \pi/2$, and

$$k_t = k_0 n_1 \sin \theta \qquad a_t = k_0(n_1{}^2 \sin^2 \theta - n_2{}^2)^{1/2} \qquad (16\text{-}46)$$

The wave vector of the transmitted wave has become complex, and the wave is of the inhomogeneous type discussed in Sec. 15-4 and illustrated for one polarization by Fig. 15-2b. (What was called TE polarization there should now be called σ polarization.) Figure 16-7 shows the

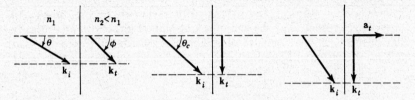

Fig. 16-7. *Changes in the wave vectors when the incident wave falls on the less dense medium and the angle of incidence passes through the critical angle.*

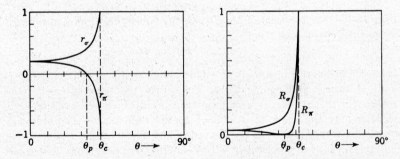

Fig. 16-8. *Reflection coefficients and reflectances for π and σ polarization when incidence is on the less dense of two transparent media. The ratio of refractive indices is 1.5. Above the critical angle, the reflection coefficients are complex with moduli equal to unity.*

changes in the wave vectors on passing through the critical angle. Here $\mathbf{k}_i$ has the fixed length $n_1 k_0$, but $\mathbf{k}_t$ can maintain the fixed length $n_2 k_0$ only up to the critical angle θ_c.

At supercritical angles of incidence, $Y_{1\pi}$ and $Y_{1\sigma}$ are real, and $Y_{2\pi}$ and $Y_{2\sigma}$ are pure imaginary. It follows that the condition $\theta > \theta_c$ implies $R_\pi = R_\sigma = 1$, so that *reflection is total* for any polarization of the incident wave. Figure 16-8 shows the curves analogous to those in Fig. 16-4 for the case $n_1 = 1.5n_2$. The reflection coefficients are real for $\theta < \theta_c$. For $\theta > \theta_c$, the reflection coefficients are complex with unit moduli and varying angles, and the quantity of practical interest is the δ appearing in (16-39). Figure 16-9 shows a curve of δ in the supercritical range. For a ratio of indices of 1.5 this curve has a maximum ordinate of about $45.2°$; the maximum becomes slightly greater for higher ratios. Problem 16-7 and the interesting device described therein are based on this curve.

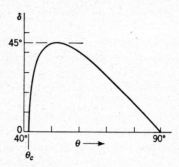

Fig. 16-9. *Angle δ appearing in formula (16-39) for total reflection with a ratio of refractive indices of 1.5. The maximum ordinate is 45.2°.*

16-5 Reflection from Metals The formulas in Sec. 16-3 apply when the second medium has a complex refractive index. Suppose n_2 and κ_2 are given, and the incidence is normal. Then $\mathbf{k}_t$ and $\mathbf{a}_t$ are perpendicular to the boundary and have magnitudes $n_2 k_0$ and $\kappa_2 k_0$, respectively. The incident wave vector has magnitude $n_1 k_0$. Both the reflection coefficients (16-31) are equal to

$$r = \frac{n_1 - n_2 - i\kappa_2}{n_1 + n_2 + i\kappa_2}$$

and for any polarization, the reflectance is therefore

$$R = |r|^2 = \frac{(n_1 - n_2)^2 + \kappa_2{}^2}{(n_1 + n_2)^2 + \kappa_2{}^2} \tag{16-47}$$

Suppose the second medium is a metal. At low frequencies, n_2 and κ_2 should, according to theory, be given in terms of the static conductivity and the frequency by (15-60), so that they are very large compared with unity and nearly equal. Let the first medium be air ($n_1 = 1$), and set κ_2 equal to n_2 in (16-47). Then

$$R = 1 - \frac{4n_2}{1 + 2n_2(1 + n_2)} \approx 1 - \frac{2}{n_2} \approx 1 - \left(\frac{2\omega}{\pi\sigma_0}\right)^{1/2} \tag{16-48}$$

Measurements of R in the far infrared were performed by Hagen and Rubens in 1903, and in the case of a good conductor serious departures from formula (16-48) did not occur until the wavelength of the incident wave became as short as about 10 μ (far infrared).

At frequencies in the near infrared and higher, the classical theory cannot assign values to n and κ for metals, and the theory of reflection is applied in reverse to obtain methods of measuring these parameters. The methods that have been devised involve observations of changes in polarization on reflection at various angles of incidence. Details will not be given here, but it should be remarked that the transmitted wave penetrates only a very small distance into the metal, and measurements of reflection sample only a very thin layer at the surface of the specimen. The results are markedly affected by strains or cracks due to polishing and by any film of oxide or foreign matter. Extreme precautions must be taken if values representative of the bulk material and suitable for comparison with a good theory of the metal are to be obtained.

16-6 Layered Structures. Descriptive Survey The colors exhibited by films of oil on water and by soap bubbles are the longest

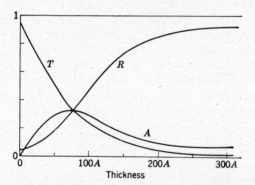

Fig. 16-10. *Typical reflectance, transmittance, and absorbance at visible frequency as a function of thickness for rapidly deposited films of silver or aluminum on glass.*

known of the striking phenomena of interference in thin dielectric films. Apart from the practical application of testing the perfection of optical surfaces, interference in layers with optical thicknesses comparable to a wavelength remained a scientific curiosity until the 1930s, when methods were developed for depositing on a slab of glass or other material one or more layers of solid dielectric of controlled thickness. The technique consists in vaporizing the dielectric in an oven placed in a highly evacuated tank and condensing the vapor (which issues from the oven as a molecular beam) on the cold surface being coated. Layer after layer of different materials of any desired optical thickness can be deposited in this way, and a large segment of the optical industry is based on the many useful properties of these composite structures. The performance of a multiple coating obeys very well a theory to be worked out later in which each layer is treated as a homogeneous medium with sharply defined plane boundaries.

Metal films thin enough to be semitransparent have many optical uses. Evaporation *in vacuo* is the most common method of preparation. The thickness of the film is of the order of 100 A; it is known from studies with the electron microscope that the structure is an agglomeration of metal droplets and that the details of the structure are strongly dependent on the rate of deposition. These observations explain why thin metal films cannot always be treated by the simple theory that assumes a homogeneous medium between plane boundaries. Figure 16-10 shows curves typical of observed reflectance, transmittance, and absorbance for visible light as functions of thickness for rapidly deposited films of good reflectors such as silver or aluminum. Many optical systems call for "beam

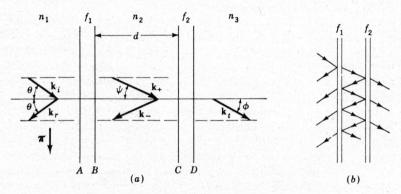

Fig. 16-11. *Geometry of the Fabry-Perot system.*

splitters" that make the intensities of the reflected and transmitted beams equal. If metal films are used for this purpose, the curves show that about one-third of the incident power is lost in absorption. The Fabry-Perot interferometer, to be discussed in the next several sections, calls for films with reflectance of 0.9 or 0.95 and very low absorbance; films of aluminum or silver meet this requirement quite well.

The above survey provides minimum background for the sections to follow. For more details on the preparation and properties of films, reference can be made to Heavens [35], Strong [89], chap. 4, and Tolansky [90], chap. 8.

16-7 Airy Formula The Fabry-Perot interferometer and a number of allied systems involve the arrangement shown in Fig. 16-11a. Three transparent media with refractive indices n_1, n_2, and n_3 are separated by thin films f_1 and f_2. The films may be of any nature, and in a special case might be just simple boundaries between the three media. The thickness

d of the center medium can have any value. The surfaces labeled A, B, C, and D are assumed perfectly plane, parallel, and of unlimited extent. A plane monochromatic wave of frequency ω and irradiance I_i is incident in medium 1 at angle θ, and a transmitted wave of irradiance I_t emerges at angle ϕ in medium 3. The problem is to find the ratio I_t/I_i as a formula involving measurable (or perhaps calculable) properties of the films.

Figure 16-11b shows a narrow incident beam (a ray) traced through the sequence of partial reflections and transmissions at the films. When the incident wave is a plane wave of unlimited extent, these rays represent the normals to the wave fronts of four infinite sequences of plane waves, all the waves in any one sequence being in the same medium and traveling in the same direction. The waves in each sequence superpose to give a resultant plane wave, and the simplest solution of the problem deals directly with these resultant waves.

In Fig. 16-11a the wave vectors of the resultant waves are drawn. The waves traveling to the right and left in medium 2 will be called the *positive* and *negative* waves, respectively, and quantities associated with them will be distinguished by subscripts $+$ and $-$. The following calculations will refer to π polarization, but all arguments and formulas, except one detail to be pointed out in a footnote, apply also to σ polarization.

A horizontal axis and a unit vector π are drawn in Fig. 16-11a. By E_π let us understand the π component of the complex amplitude of the incident wave at the intersection of the axis and the plane A. Let $E_{+\pi}$ and $E_{-\pi}$ be the corresponding quantities for the positive and negative waves at plane B, and, finally, let $E_{t\pi}$ refer to the transmitted wave at the intersection of the axis and plane D. At the intersection of the axis and plane C the π components of the complex amplitudes of the positive and negative waves are, respectively,

$$E_{+\pi}e^{i\beta d} \qquad E_{-\pi}e^{-i\beta d}$$

where
$$\beta = n_2 k_0 \cos \psi \qquad k_0 = \frac{\omega}{c} \tag{16-49}$$

and ψ is the angle shown in Fig. 16-11a.

The amplitude $E_{+\pi}$ can be thought of as a sum of two contributions, one from partial transmission of the incident wave through film 1, and the other from partial reflection of the negative wave at film 1. Thus we can write

$$E_{+\pi} = t_{12}E_{i\pi} + r_{21}E_{-\pi}$$

where t_{12} is the transmission coefficient for a wave incident on the first film from the left, and r_{21} is the reflection coefficient for a wave incident on the first film from the right. The amplitude of the negative wave at plane C is related to that of the positive wave by a reflection coefficient

r_{23}, so that

$$E_{-\pi}e^{-i\beta d} = r_{23}\,E_{+\pi}e^{i\beta d}$$

Finally, the amplitude of the transmitted wave at plane D is related to that of the positive wave at plane C by a transmission coefficient t_{23}, so that

$$E_{t\pi} = t_{23}E_{+\pi}e^{i\beta d}$$

The last three equations can be solved for the over-all transmission coefficient:

$$t_{13} \equiv \frac{E_{t\pi}}{E_{i\pi}} = \frac{t_{12}t_{23}e^{i\beta d}}{1 - r_{21}r_{23}e^{i2\beta d}} \tag{16-50}$$

The over-all transmittance is[1]

$$T_{13} \equiv \frac{I_t}{I_i} = \frac{n_3}{n_1}\,|\tau_{\pi 13}|^2 = \frac{n_3 \cos^2\theta}{n_1 \cos^2\phi}\,|t_{13}|^2 \tag{16-51}$$

Define reflectances and transmittances for the films by

$$T_{12} = \frac{n_2 \cos^2\theta}{n_1 \cos^2\psi}\,|t_{12}|^2 \qquad R_{21} = |r_{21}|^2 \quad \cdots$$

and let ϕ_{21} and ϕ_{23} be the angles of the complex reflection coefficients r_{21} and r_{23}, respectively. The result of substituting (16-50) in (16-51) can then be put in the form

$$T_{13} = T_{\max}\frac{1}{1 + F\sin^2\epsilon} \tag{16-52}$$

where

$$T_{\max} = \frac{T_{12}T_{23}}{(1 - \sqrt{R_{21}R_{23}})^2} \tag{16-53}$$

$$F = \frac{4\sqrt{R_{21}R_{23}}}{(1 - \sqrt{R_{21}R_{23}})^2} \tag{16-54}$$

$$\epsilon = \beta d + \tfrac{1}{2}(\phi_{21} + \phi_{23}) \tag{16-55}$$

Formula (16-52) is called the *Airy formula* after the astronomer who first obtained it in 1833 in connection with interference in a plate of glass with parallel and uncoated surfaces. The formula and its applications will be discussed in the next three sections.

16-8 Fabry-Perot Interferometer Figure 16-12 shows side and end views of a Fabry-Perot interferometer or *etalon*. Two circular plates of the best optical quality of fused silica (less subject to thermal distortion

---

[1] See the discussion of the Stokes parameters in Sec. 16-3. For σ polarization, the ratios of the squares of the cosines are absent in (16-51) and in the definitions of the T's immediately following (16-51). The final formulas (16-52) to (16-55) apply to either π or σ polarization.

than glass) are held parallel by three spacing rods of fused silica or invar. The opposing faces of the two plates are polished flat to within approximately one-hundredth of a wavelength of green light (about the best that can be done) and are coated, except for an outer ring where the spacers rest, with a uniform film of high reflectance and low absorbance. Not shown in the figure is a holder for supporting the plates and spacer which incorporates a means of pressing the plates against the rods with light forces in such a way as not to distort the plates. By adjustment of these forces, exact parallelism is achieved through elasticity of the spacer. In practice the diameter of the plates is commonly 60 mm, the working aperture then being about 50 mm.

The transmission of the etalon when a plane wave is incident is given by the Airy formula. In practice only very small angles of incidence are involved, and the R's, T's, and ϕ's for the films can be given the

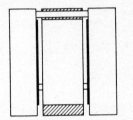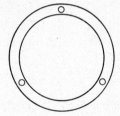

Fig. 16-12.   *Fabry-Perot etalon in side and end view. A metal ring holding the three spacing rods is shown in shaded cross section. The holder for supporting the plates and the spacer is not shown.*

values for normal incidence, where there is no distinction between π and σ polarization. Let us ignore the reflections at the uncoated surfaces of the plates pending a description of how this complication is rendered unimportant by making the plates very slightly wedge shaped. Because of the symmetry of the etalon, the notation in the Airy formula can be simplified to read

$$T = T_{\max} \frac{1}{1 + F \sin^2 \epsilon} \tag{16-56}$$

where
$$T_{\max} = \left(\frac{T_f}{1 - R_f} \right)^2 \qquad F = \frac{4R_f}{(1 - R_f)^2} \tag{16-57}$$

$$\epsilon = \phi + nk_0 d \cos \psi \tag{16-58}$$

Here T_f is the transmittance of the film on one of the plates measured as the ratio of transmitted to incident irradiance at or near normal incidence,[1]

---

[1] The transmittance is the same for either direction of propagation, as can be proved quite generally with the second law of thermodynamics. The transmittance of the film is obtained from that of the whole plate by correcting for the uncoated surface. The reflectances from the two sides of the film may be different.

R_f is the reflectance of the film measured with an incident wave falling on the coated side of the plate, ϕ (not to be confused with that in Fig. 16-11a) is the angle of the complex reflection coefficient of the film for incidence on the coated side of the plate, n is the refractive index of the medium between the plates (usually air, but see below), d and ψ are as defined in Fig. 16-11a, and

$$k_0 = \frac{\omega}{c} = \frac{2\pi}{\lambda_0}$$

where λ_0 is the vacuum wavelength.

The usefulness of the etalon is based on the nature of the function of ϵ multiplying $T_{\max}$ in (16-56) when R_f is near unity and F is therefore a large number. Figure 16-13 shows curves of this function for $R_f = 0.6$ ($F = 15$) and $R_f = 0.8$ ($F = 80$). Sharp maxima occur where ϵ is any integral multiple of π, the integer being called the *order of interference*.

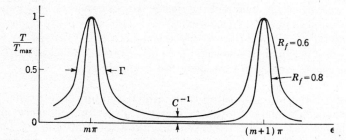

Fig. 16-13. *Transmittance of a Fabry-Perot etalon relative to the maximum transmittance for two values of the reflectance of the films.*

Over most of the range between maxima the transmittance is low, and a useful measure is the *contrast* C, defined as the ratio of maximum to minimum transmittance. From (16-56),

$$C = 1 + F$$

Another useful characteristic is the *width* Γ between half-maximum points, as indicated in Fig. 16-13. Let us find this width by a calculation which shows that when F is large the peaks in the curve are practically of resonance shape. Let ϵ be close to $m\pi$, with m an integer. Then

$$\sin^2 \epsilon = \sin^2 (\epsilon - m\pi) \approx (\epsilon - m\pi)^2$$

and (16-56) gives

$$\frac{T}{T_{\max}} \approx \frac{\Gamma^2/4}{(\epsilon - m\pi)^2 + \Gamma^2/4} \qquad \Gamma = \frac{2}{\sqrt{F}} \tag{16-59}$$

One recognizes the resonance denominator by comparing, for example, with (12-21), and the Γ defined in (16-59) is therefore the desired width.

A third parameter, and the most useful of all, is the *finesse* $\mathfrak{F}$, defined as the ratio of the separation of successive maxima to the width Γ. Thus

$$\mathfrak{F} = \frac{\pi}{\Gamma} = \frac{\pi \sqrt{F}}{2} \tag{16-60}$$

For reflectances R_f equal to 0.8 and 0.95, $\mathfrak{F}$ is equal to 14 and 61, respectively.

Applications of the etalon as a measuring instrument are based on the appearance of the several parameters in the definition (16-58) of ϵ. The presence of n is the basis of the most accurate measurements of the refractive indices of gases. The dependence on wavelength is the basis of its use as a spectrometer of very high resolution. The simultaneous dependence on d and λ is the basis of the most precise comparison of wavelength with mechanical standards of length, such as the standard meter bar. The use of the etalon as a spectrometer for measuring profiles of spectrum lines and the closely spaced groups of lines found in hyperfine structure will now be described. This is one of the applications having the simplifying feature that the angle ϕ in (16-58) and the exact value of d need not be known. As to other types of applications, some of the classic experiments are described in Candler [15].

16-9 Fabry-Perot Etalon as a Spectrometer The original and still common method of using the etalon as a spectrometer makes use of the dependence of ϵ on ψ, the latter being the angle defined in Fig. 16-11a. The same angle ψ is the angle of incidence on the first surface of the first plate and the angle of emergence from the second surface of the second plate. If a source at the left of the etalon in Fig. 16-12 (side view) has an extended area and is monochromatic, the radiation falling on the first plate can be represented through a spatial Fourier analysis as a superposition of plane waves with wave vectors uniformly filling some solid angle. In the focal plane of a lens at the right of the etalon, a set of very fine circular fringes is formed with diameters as stated in Prob. 16-8. If the source is not monochromatic but has a narrow spectrum, each wavelength gives rise to a set of fringes, and the irradiances in the several sets add. A photograph of the pattern is microphotometered, and the spectrum is deduced with a certain limit of resolution. This method will not be elaborated upon here; rather, a scheme called *central-spot scanning*, which is conceptually more ideal and has been widely applied, will be treated.

Figure 16-14 shows the etalon enclosed in an airtight chamber with windows. Initially the chamber is evacuated, and the valve to the pump closed. Air is then allowed to leak in slowly to vary the index n between the plates, and the resulting change in ϵ is the scanning mechanism. On an increase in pressure from zero to atmospheric, the order of interference for a given wavelength in the visible changes by about 10 times the spacing d if the latter is in centimeters.

Radiation from the source passes through a monochromator (a prism or grating spectroscope with exit slit to isolate the spectrum line to be studied) and then falls on the pinhole at the left in the figure. The first lens sends a plane wave normally onto the etalon, and the transmitted wave is brought to focus on a second pinhole behind which is a photoelectric cell connected to an amplifier and strip recorder. A servomechanism maintains the speed of the chart in the recorder proportional to the rate of increase of pressure, and hence of refractive index, of the air in the chamber. The advantage of the photoelectric detector is that it is a linear device (in distinct contrast to the photographic plate), and the deflection of the recorder is directly proportional to the power transmitted by the etalon.

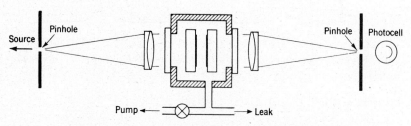

Fig. 16-14.   *Arrangement for central spot scanning.*

At first sight the exit pinhole seems to be unnecessary, but it serves to block ghost images caused by the windows and the uncoated surfaces of the etalon plates. These ghosts are thrown to one side of the hole if the windows are slightly inclined and the etalon plates are made as wedges with an angle of perhaps $0.5°$.

Increasing the size of the entrance pinhole admits more radiation, but a range of angles ψ is introduced, and the resolution eventually suffers. There is an optimum compromise, but the discussion to follow will treat the pinhole as a point; the wave entering the etalon is then a plane wave with $\psi = 0$, and the result is a theoretical resolving power to be compared with what is actually attained.

In Fig. 16-15 the solid curve is a plot of the Airy formula as a function of the index n for a given d and given vacuum wavelength λ_0. The dashed curve shows the shift when the wavelength increases by $\delta\lambda$, and as a criterion, called the *Taylor criterion*, for the minimum detectable shift at order m, one can take the condition that the two curves intersect at half-maximum points, as shown in the figure. (This criterion is in the same spirit as Rayleigh's, since the sum of the solid and dashed curves shows a slight dip, just as in Fig. 7-23b.) The resolving power need not be known precisely, and in (16-58), ϕ can be struck out, since it is always less than 2π, while we are interested in values of ϵ of order $10^3\pi$ at least. To this approximation, the maximum of order m for λ_0 falls at index

$$n = \frac{m\lambda_0}{2d} \qquad (16\text{-}61)$$

as is seen from (16-58) with $\epsilon = m\pi$ and $\phi = \psi = 0$. The maximum of

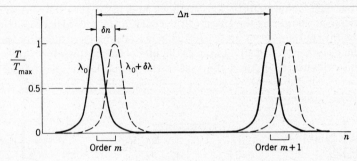

Fig. 16-15. *Criterion for the theoretical resolving power of an etalon in order m.*

order $m + 1$ falls at $n + \Delta n$, and we get

$$\Delta n = \frac{\lambda_0}{2d}$$

The shift δn in Fig. 16-15 is derived by differentiating (16-61):

$$\delta n = \frac{m\,\delta\lambda_0}{2d}$$

The theoretical resolving power is then

$$\Re \equiv \frac{\lambda_0}{\delta\lambda_0} = \frac{m\,\Delta n}{\delta n}$$

Since the Taylor criterion makes $\Delta n/\delta n$ equal to the finesse, we have, as the final result,

$$\Re = m\mathfrak{F} \qquad (16\text{-}62)$$

(The same conclusion would have been reached in connection with the method of circular fringes mentioned at the outset of this section. In that method the scanning variable is $\cos \psi$ rather than n, and these variables enter ϵ in the same way.) Formula (7-19) for a diffraction grating is the same as (16-62) if we take N to be the finesse of the grating; for this instrument N is in fact a good measure of the ratio of separation of orders to width of a principal maximum.

Films are available (Sec. 16-12) which, according to the theoretical formula (16-60), would make $\mathfrak{F}$ equal to 150 or more, but in practice in the visible spectrum the largest observed values of the finesse (always understood to be the ratio of separation of orders to width at half-maximum) are about 30. The limitation comes from the lack of perfect flatness of the plates. An experimental measurement is made by using a short spacer (d equal to 2 or 3 mm), the resolution then being low enough that a narrow line in an atomic spectrum is effectively monochromatic.

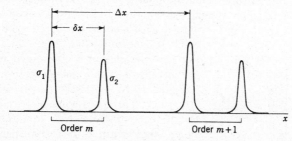

Fig. 16-16. *Typical record obtained with central spot scanning when two sharp spectrum lines are involved.*

An observation gives the finesse and shows that the instrumental profile is not of the resonance shape given by the Airy formula but is usually well fitted by one of the Voigt functions (end of Sec. 12-8), a fact that can sometimes be put to effective use in the methods mentioned in Sec. 13-5.

Suppose the spectrum being studied consists of two sharp lines with slightly different vacuum wavelengths λ_1 and λ_2, and the problem is to measure the difference. In summary, the procedure is as follows: It is convenient here to work with the reciprocals of the wavelengths, that is, the vacuum wave numbers $\sigma_1 = 1/\lambda_1$, $\sigma_2 = 1/\lambda_2$. With a suitable spacer, a record from the strip recorder will appear as in Fig. 16-16, in which x is the linear coordinate along the chart of the recorder. That the orders have been properly related (no overlapping) is established by an auxiliary run with a shorter spacer. The range without overlap (see Prob. 7-13) is

$$\Delta\sigma = (2nd)^{-1}$$

and the desired difference of wave numbers is given in terms of dimensions on the chart by

$$\sigma_2 - \sigma_1 = \Delta\sigma \frac{\delta x}{\Delta x}$$

In these formulas it is sufficiently accurate to substitute a good micrometer measurement of the spacer for nd. It is not necessary to know d to a fraction of a wavelength, or to know ϕ at all. Note that the chart carries its own calibration in the form of the distance Δx between orders.

This section gives a bare introduction to the use of the Fabry-Perot etalon as a spectrometer. Valuable references on points of principle are Jacquinot [48, 49]. A general survey is Meissner [63].

16-10　Interference Filters　If a plane wave of white light falls normally on a Fabry-Perot etalon, the transmitted wave has a spectrum consisting of very narrow bands equally spaced on a scale of frequency or wave number. (The spacing is not exactly uniform because of dispersion in n and ϕ, but let this complication be ignored.) If the separation of the highly reflecting films is small enough, the bands are well enough separated that one of them can be isolated with a suitable colored glass, and the result is a narrow-band filter. This idea was put into practice in a convenient form with the advent of evaporated dielectric films.

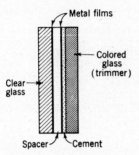

Fig. 16-17. *Construction of the simplest interference filter. Relative thicknesses of films and glass plates are greatly exaggerated.*

Figure 16-17 shows the most common construction, in which a glass plate, which need not be exceedingly flat, is first coated with silver, then with a dielectric spacer (magnesium fluoride or cryolite, very uniform in thickness), and then a second silver film. Finally, a colored glass, opaque to all but the desired band and known in the trade as a "trimmer," is cemented on. Usually the order of interference of the transmitted band is first or second; for the latter, commercially available filters for the visible give a peak transmittance of about 0.3 and a width at half-maximum of about 100 A. Narrower widths (down to about 10 A) and higher peak transmittance (up to about 0.8) are reached by replacing the metal films by multiple dielectric films (Sec. 16-12).

16-11　Single Dielectric Film　Let two semi-infinite transparent media with indices n_1 and n_2 be separated by a dielectric film of index n_f and thickness d. Figure 16-18a shows the wave vectors in the three media in the most important case, namely, that in which there would not be total reflection if the film were of zero thickness or if it were of infinite thickness. All waves are then homogeneous. Part (b) of the figure shows the interesting case in which there would be total reflection if d were infinite but not if d were zero, and (c) shows a realization of this case, easily studied at centimeter wavelengths with prisms of pitch. In (b) the waves in the film are inhomogeneous, and the attenuation is greater the more the angle of incidence exceeds the critical angle. Except very near the critical angle, the transmission through the film is exceedingly small unless the geometrical thickness is a fraction of the vacuum wavelength.

The transmission coefficient of the film in Fig. 16-18a can be derived from the Airy formula, but in some respects this formula is not the most convenient for the present problem. Let us find a fresh solution which will have the advantage of extending with no additional effort to (b) and to multiple films.

In Fig. 16-18a the wave vectors are of the three different lengths $n_1 k_0$, $n_f k_0$, and $n_2 k_0$, where $k_0 = \omega/c$. The construction in the figure shows that Snell's law reads

$$n_1 \sin \theta = n_f \sin \psi = n_2 \sin \phi \qquad (16\text{-}63)$$

Note that the relation of ϕ to θ is independent of the presence of the film. [The same is true in (b).]

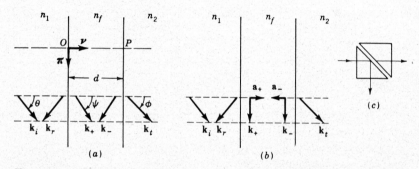

Fig. 16-18. *Wave vectors in two transparent media and a separating dielectric film. At* (**a**) *all waves are homogeneous. At* (**b**) *the waves in the film are inhomogeneous. At* (**c**) *is shown a realization of* (**b**) *with prisms.*

Boundary conditions analogous to (16-23) and (16-30) can be written for points O and P in Fig. 16-18a. A set of Y's is defined as in (16-28) and (16-29):

$$Y_{1\pi} = \frac{n_1}{\cos \theta} \qquad Y_{f\pi} = \frac{n_f}{\cos \psi} \qquad Y_{2\pi} = \frac{n_2}{\cos \phi} \qquad (16\text{-}64)$$

$$Y_{1\sigma} = n_1 \cos \theta \qquad Y_{f\sigma} = n_f \cos \psi \qquad Y_{2\sigma} = n_2 \cos \phi \qquad (16\text{-}65)$$

Each of the equations to follow will be understood to represent two equations: one with subscript π appended to each symbol, and the other with subscript σ. The boundary conditions at O are

$$E_i + E_r = E_+ + E_- \qquad Y_1(E_i - E_r) = Y_f(E_+ - E_-)$$

and at P,

$$E_+ e^{i\beta d} + E_- e^{-i\beta d} = E_t \qquad Y_f(E_+ e^{i\beta d} - E_- e^{-i\beta d}) = Y_2 E_t$$

where
$$\beta = n_f k_0 \cos \psi \qquad (16\text{-}66)$$

The rationale of these equations is obvious with the background of Secs. 16-3 and 16-7. The amplitudes E_+ and E_- can be eliminated to obtain

$$E_i + E_r = \left(\cos \beta d - i \frac{Y_2}{Y_f} \sin \beta d \right) E_t \qquad (16\text{-}67)$$

$$Y_1(E_i - E_r) = (-iY_f \sin \beta d + Y_2 \cos \beta d)E_t \qquad (16\text{-}68)$$

The results have been written in this particular form with extension to multiple films in mind (next section).

The reflection and transmission coefficients can be found from the last two equations just as in (16-31) and (16-32). Consider normal incidence

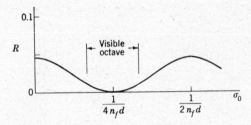

Fig. 16-19. *Reflectance with an ideal antireflection film on glass. The horizontal variable is the wave number (reciprocal of the wavelength) in air.*

and substitute the values of the Y's from (16-64) with $\theta = \psi = \phi = 0$. The reflection coefficient is then

$$r_{12} = \frac{(n_1 - n_2)n_f \cos \beta d - i(n_1 n_2 - n_f{}^2) \sin \beta d}{(n_1 + n_2)n_f \cos \beta d - i(n_1 n_2 + n_f{}^2) \sin \beta d} \qquad (16\text{-}69)$$

From this result can be seen the remarkable fact that $r_{12} = 0$ if $\beta d = \pi/2$ and

$$n_f{}^2 = n_1 n_2 \qquad (16\text{-}70)$$

Thus if the film has an optical thickness of one-quarter wavelength and an index equal to the geometric mean of n_1 and n_2, the reflectance is zero. If $\beta d = 0$ or π, the reflectance is the same as that with no film, regardless of the value of n_f.

Figure 16-19 shows a curve of reflectance for an air-glass surface coated with a film satisfying (16-70). The horizontal variable is the wave number $\sigma_0 = k_0/2\pi = \beta d/2\pi n_f d$, and d has been chosen to place the minimum at the center of the visible octave, where the eye is most sensitive. The result is a very effective *antireflection coating* for white light. The usual material for the film is MgF_2, which makes a wear-resistant film when properly applied. Its index is 1.38, which is too high to satisfy (16-70) for optical glasses, and the consequence is that the minimum in the curve of reflectance is not zero, but is still small. Addition of films, now generally routine, makes a striking improvement in systems with many lenses, not only in brightness of image, but in reduction of haziness caused by scattered light.

16-12 Multiple Dielectric Films

Equations (16-67) and (16-68) can be written in the matrix form

$$\begin{pmatrix} E_i + E_r \\ Y_1(E_i - R_r) \end{pmatrix} = \mathbf{M} \begin{pmatrix} E_t \\ Y_2 E_t \end{pmatrix} \tag{16-71}$$

where

$$\mathbf{M} = \begin{pmatrix} \cos \beta d & -\dfrac{i}{Y_f} \sin \beta d \\ -i Y_f \sin \beta d & \cos \beta d \end{pmatrix} \tag{16-72}$$

The column matrices in (16-71) refer to the incident, reflected, and transmitted waves, while $\mathbf{M}$ refers just to the film and the angle ψ indicated in Fig. 16-18a. The formulas are to be understood as applying to either π or σ polarization, with no distinction at normal incidence.

Suppose now that instead of the one film in Fig. 16-18a, there are N films numbered in order from 1 to N, with the incident wave falling on film 1. The jth film has geometrical thickness d_j and index n_{fj}. Suppose that in no film does the situation in Fig. 16-18b prevail. Then in the jth film there will be positive and negative homogeneous waves with wave vectors forming angle ψ_j with the normal to the boundaries, and

$$n_{fj} \sin \psi_j = n_1 \sin \theta \tag{16-73}$$

One can define parameters $Y_{fj\pi}$, $Y_{fj\sigma}$, and β_j in the manner of (16-64), (16-65), and (16-66), and form matrices $\mathbf{M}_j$ of the form (16-72). The obvious generalization of (16-71) is then

$$\begin{pmatrix} E_i + E_r \\ Y_1(E_i - E_r) \end{pmatrix} = \mathbf{M}_1 \mathbf{M}_2 \cdots \mathbf{M}_N \begin{pmatrix} E_t \\ Y_2 E_t \end{pmatrix} \tag{16-74}$$

The $\mathbf{M}$'s are two-by-two matrices, and their product is a two-by-two of the form

$$\mathbf{M}_1 \mathbf{M}_2 \cdots \mathbf{M}_N = \begin{pmatrix} a & b \\ c & d \end{pmatrix} \tag{16-75}$$

where a, b, c, and d are complex functions of the frequency. Formula (16-74) is equivalent to two ordinary equations from which the reflection and transmission coefficients are found to be

$$r_{12} = \frac{aY_1 + bY_1Y_2 - c - dY_2}{aY_1 + bY_1Y_2 + c + dY_2} \tag{16-76}$$

$$t_{12} = \frac{2Y_1}{aY_1 + bY_1Y_2 + c + dY_2} \tag{16-77}$$

Note that if there is no film between media 1 and 2, we have $a = d = 1$ and $b = c = 0$, and the last two formulas reduce to (16-31) and (16-32).

Exploring the properties of various combinations of films requires the use of high-speed computing machines, but the principle can be illustrated by the following simple and striking example: Let the incident wave be in air ($n = 1$) and fall normally on the first of $2N$ films. Let the medium following the last film also be air. Suppose the indices of the films alternate between two values n' and n'', and, finally, suppose that at the frequency in question all the films have an optical thickness of one-quarter wavelength ($\beta d = \pi/2$). Then

$$\mathbf{M}_1\mathbf{M}_2 = \begin{pmatrix} 0 & \dfrac{-i}{n'} \\ -in' & 0 \end{pmatrix}\begin{pmatrix} 0 & \dfrac{-i}{n''} \\ -in'' & 0 \end{pmatrix} = \begin{pmatrix} \dfrac{-n''}{n'} & 0 \\ 0 & \dfrac{-n'}{n''} \end{pmatrix}$$

and

$$\mathbf{M}_1\mathbf{M}_2 \cdots \mathbf{M}_{2N} = (\mathbf{M}_1\mathbf{M}_2)^N = \begin{pmatrix} \left(\dfrac{-n''}{n'}\right)^N & 0 \\ 0 & \left(\dfrac{-n'}{n''}\right)^N \end{pmatrix}$$

The reflection coefficient is

$$r_{12} = \frac{(-n''/n')^N - (-n'/n'')^N}{(-n''/n')^N + (-n'/n'')^N}$$

It is seen from this result that as long as n' and n'' are different, the reflectance approaches unity as N becomes infinite. The behavior of the reflectance as a function of frequency is not easy to demonstrate, but it turns out that it remains unity over a range of frequencies which increases with the difference between n' and n''; outside this range it becomes low. For the earliest recognition (in 1888) of this phenomenon as occurring naturally in certain crystals, see Lord Rayleigh [75]. For further details, see Raman [74], p. 30.

The idea just brought out can be applied to the problem of high-reflectance films for etalons and filters. Figure 16-20 shows reflectances obtained with the two ways of coating glass ($n = 1.52$) with eight layers alternately of zinc sulphide ($n = 2.3$) and cryolite ($n = 1.35$). All layers are one-quarter wavelength in optical thickness when the wavelength in air is $\lambda_0 = 5000$ A, and the maxima occur at this wavelength. (If the curves were plotted against $\sigma_0 = 1/\lambda_0$, they would be symmetrical about the maximum as long as dispersion in the indices were neglected.) Other values of reflectance are obtained with different numbers of films; for example, nine layers, five being zinc sulphide, gives a maximum of 0.984. If a greater ratio of indices were available, the curve for a given combination would be higher and broader. (Greater ratios can be realized in the infrared, where certain semiconductors are transparent and have large indices.)

For use in etalons, dielectric films have the advantages over metal of having much lower absorbance and showing no deterioration with age. The disadvantages are that they are far more difficult to apply, and a given film is useful over a more limited spectral range. The extremely high reflectance that can be achieved is no advantage, since the limitation in resolution lies in the flatness of the plates, and increasing the reflectance

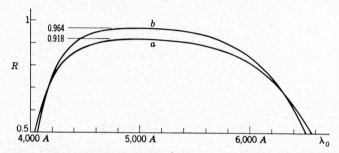

Fig. 16-20. *Reflectance of glass coated with eight films alternately of zinc sulphide and cryolite. All films have optical thickness λ/4 for a vacuum wavelength of 5000 A.* **a.** *Cryolite next the glass.* **b.** *Zinc sulphide next the glass.*

above a certain optimum value decreases the peak transmittance of the etalon without increasing the finesse.

Problems

16-1. Derive formula (16-20). [*Hint:* Start by writing the resolution of k_i and $k_t + ia_t$ along and perpendicular to v, using formula (1-3), and make use of (16-4).]

16-2. A right-hand circularly polarized wave in a transparent medium is normally incident on the boundary of a second medium of any nature. What is the polarization of the·reflected wave? (An argument making use of Stokes parameters is suggested but is not the only one possible.)

16-3. Consider Fig. 16-2 with $\kappa_2 = 0$ and $n_2 > n_1$. Summarize all the restrictions on k_t and a_t, and show that for any value of θ one must have $a_t = 0$ and $n_1 \sin \theta = n_2 \sin \phi$. Do not simply use (16-19) and (16-20); rather model after the remarks just preceding (16-19).

16-4. Show that (16-42) can be put in the equivalent forms

$$r_\pi = -\frac{\tan(\theta - \phi)}{\tan(\theta + \phi)} \qquad r_\sigma = -\frac{\sin(\theta - \phi)}{\sin(\theta + \phi)}$$

16-5. Draw a figure analogous to Fig. 16-5 for the case of incidence on the rarer medium. Take the third of the three angles of incidence to fall between θ_p and θ_c (polarizing and critical angles, respectively).

16-6. Consider a sheet of glass with parallel surfaces. Show that if a wave is incident on the first surface at the polarizing angle, then the refracted wave is incident on the second surface at the polarizing angle.

16-7. Let an incident wave be in glass, and let the second medium be air. There are two angles of incidence, falling in the range giving total reflection, for which the δ in (16-39) is equal to $\pi/4$ (see Fig. 16-9). Let θ_0 be one of these angles, and construct the rhomboidal prism shown in Fig. 16-21. A ray drawn in the figure indicates a

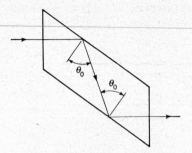

Fig. 16-21. *Fresnel rhomb.*

wave entering the first face of the prism at normal incidence, then suffering two internal reflections, and finally passing normally through the last face. For each internal reflection set up cartesian axes according to the conventions in Fig. 16-3. Let the Stokes parameters of the incident wave at the first reflection be $U_i = I_i$ and $Q_i = V_i = 0$. Illustrate the polarization of this wave in the manner of Fig. 13-19. Find the parameters of the reflected wave after the first reflection, and illustrate the polarization. Write the parameters of the incident wave at the second reflection (that is, switch to the system of axes pertaining to the second reflection). Find the parameters of the reflected wave after the second reflection, and illustrate. (*Answer:* After the second reflection the wave is right-hand circularly polarized. The prism described here is known as a *Fresnel rhomb*, and its invention seems to have been to check the theory of total reflection. Wood [103], p. 354, tells how a rhomb can be made from ordinary plate glass and points out that its performance is fairly independent of wavelength, in contrast to the quarter-wave plates described in the next chapter.)

16-8. With reference to the side view of the etalon in Fig. 16-12, let an extended monochromatic source be at the left, and let a lens of focal length f be at the right. In the focal plane of the lens a set of fine, concentric circular fringes appears. Suppose the center is bright, the order of interference there being an integer m_0. As one passes to rings of increasing radii, does the order of interference increase or decrease? Find a formula for the linear radii of the successive rings. (*Hint:* Since only small angles ψ are of interest, use the approximation $\cos \psi \approx 1 - \psi^2/2$, with ψ in radians. The radii should come out proportional to the square roots of whole numbers.)

16-9. Let the diameter of the windows in the chamber of Fig. 16-14 be some 5 cm. Suppose one makes a hole of 1 cm diam in an opaque card. How could the card be used to test the adjustment for parallelism in the etalon?

16-10. Find an expression for the resolving power $\Re$ of a Fabry-Perot etalon in terms of n, d, λ_0, and $\mathfrak{F}$. (It is not necessary to use an exact expression for the order of interference; hence set $\phi = \psi = 0$.) Substitute $n = 1$, $\lambda_0 = 5000$ A, and $\mathfrak{F} = 30$, and find $\Re$ in terms of d with the latter in centimeters. (It is not uncommon to use a spacer 10 cm long.)

16-11. Comment on the relative magnitudes of the best values of the finesse found in practice at visible wavelengths with a Fabry-Perot etalon, a reflection echelon, and a grating of 1200 grooves per millimeter. Take into account limitations in the fabrication of these instruments as mentioned in the text.

16-12. The performance of an interference filter is governed by the Airy formula, and as simplifying approximations one can take the two glasses and the cement in Fig. 16-17 to have the same refractive index (to make the system symmetric) and can set $\phi = 0$ in (16-58). Suppose one wishes to use the second-order band and have it fall at the vacuum wavelength λ_0. What must be the thickness of the spacer in terms of the wavelength in its medium (index n)? What are the wavelengths of the unwanted bands (to be eliminated by the trimmer) if dispersion in the spacer is neglected and the reflectance of the metal films is assumed to remain high at all wavelengths? (The approximation that ϕ is constant is poor in the case of a filter, where the passband is always wide enough that ϕ changes appreciably over it, and this effect must be taken into account if the calculated width is to be valid.)

16-13. Find equations analogous to (16-67) and (16-68) for Fig. 16-18b. The Y's for the film will be different from those in (16-64) and (16-65), and hyperbolic rather than circular functions of βd will appear. Calculate the reflectance for $n_1 = n_2 = 1.5$, $n_f = 1$, $\theta = 45°$, and $ad = 1$, where a is the length of either attenuation vector in the film; take the case of π polarization.

16-14. Show that the reflectance found from (16-69) is invariant under interchange of subscripts 1 and 2. (Reflectance for any type of nonabsorbing film is the same from either side of the film, but the reflection coefficients have different angles in general.)

16-15. Consider the Airy formula (16-52) applied to Fig. 16-18a (with subscripts changed appropriately). Show that for normal incidence it gives transmittance unity under conditions that make (16-69) vanish.

16-16. Show that condition (16-70) is equivalent to requiring that the normal reflectance at the boundary between two semi-infinite media with indices n_1 and n_f be the same as when the indices are n_f and n_2.

16-17. Let glass ($n = 1.52$) be coated with zinc sulphide ($n = 2.3$). Find the normal reflectance when $\beta d = 0$, $\pi/2$, and π. (The reflectance as a function of βd is at a maximum or a minimum when $\beta d = \pi/2$ according as the index of the film is greater or less than that of the glass. At $\beta d = \pi$, the reflectance is always that of bare glass.)

16-18. Check the maximum values of the reflectance quoted in Fig. 16-20. Use the refractive indices given in the next to last paragraph of Sec. 16-12. (A slide rule is too rough. Use logarithms or a desk calculator.)

16-19. Show that the determinant of the matrix on the right of (16-75) is unity. [Use the theorem on square matrices that the determinant of a product is the product of the determinants, and consider the determinant of (16-72). One use of this result is as a check on numerical calculations.]

16-20. Show that if the order of the factors on the left of (16-75) is reversed, the product is obtained from the right side of this equation by interchanging d and a. [First prove the theorem by direct calculation for two matrices of form (16-72), and then prove it for arbitrary N by induction. If the reflection and transmission coefficients have been found for incidence on the left side of a film, they can quickly be found for incidence on the other side by reversing the whole system left to right, keeping the incident wave on the left, and using the theorem of this problem. The theorem holds true even when extension is made to allow the refractive indices of the layers to be complex, and it can be used to give a general proof that the transmittance in the two directions is the same. One can devise examples in which the two reflectances are different.]

chapter 17

Double Refraction

The last two chapters treated propagation of plane waves in media of a quite special, even though commonly occurring, nature. The opening section of the present chapter will review the respect in which the media considered heretofore are special and will point out the more general cases which exist. The later sections will deal with propagation of waves in the new media and with applications of the results.

17-1 Introductory Survey The homogeneous transparent media considered so far have been characterized optically by a real dielectric constant ϵ (actually a function of frequency) or a refractive index $n = \sqrt{\epsilon}$. Among the solutions of the macroscopic Maxwell equations are the monochromatic plane waves of homogeneous type (wave vector real), and the characteristic of the media is that these waves propagate with a definite velocity c/n and without diminution of amplitude or change of polarization no matter what the polarization and direction of propagation may be. These media are called *singly refracting* for reasons to appear.

Most crystals and many liquids do not have the properties of a singly refracting medium. The new effects observed in various experimental arrangements are at first sight very diverse and complicated, but by the end of this chapter the whole subject will have been reduced to a simple and unified theory in which the central idea is *double refraction*. The present section will describe the fundamental nature of double refraction and the way in which the macroscopic theory accounts for it, and will give some insight into the microscopic origin of the phenomenon. Details of wave propagation and refraction at boundaries will be worked out in following sections. The point to be made at once is that *all transparent media divide into the classes singly refracting and doubly refracting.* Ultimately the media in the latter class will be subdivided according as they are *isotropic* or *anisotropic* and according as they are or are not *optically active.* Finally, the anisotropic media are classed as either *uniaxial* or *biaxial.* When definitions of these terms are given, it will be seen that each medium has a unique description, except that *isotropic, nonactive media are singly refracting, and conversely.*

Experiments with doubly refracting media are interpretable on the assumption that these media can sustain monochromatic plane waves propagating in any direction, but for given frequency and direction there are just two polarizations for which there is a definite refractive index (and therefore a definite wavelength and definite velocity of propagation), and the index is different for the two polarizations. (This statement ignores for the moment a certain degeneracy that occurs for special directions in some crystals.) The two polarizations are in general elliptical, and they are related to each other in that the representative ellipses have the same eccentricity, the major axes are at right angles, and one is right-hand, and the other left-hand. The general plane wave is then a superposition of these two particular ones with appropriate relative amplitudes and phases. It will be seen that because of the different indices the resultant oscillation at a given point is an ellipse whose eccentricity, handedness, and direction of major axis change from point to point along the line of propagation (but not over a plane perpendicular to this line, which is the justification for calling the resultant wave "plane").

The first characterization of doubly refracting media will be according to the natures of the two particular polarizations, the difference of refractive indices, and the way these properties depend on direction of propagation.

A *nonactive medium* is one in which the two polarizations for any given direction of propagation are linear and are at right angles to each other. It is *always anisotropic* (if it is to be doubly refracting), which means, among other things, that the difference of indices is not the same for all directions of propagation. There is always one axis in the medium, and sometimes two, along which, for propagation in either direction, the difference of indices vanishes. Such an axis is called an *optic axis*, and the medium is *uniaxial* or *biaxial* according as there are one or two optic axes. (An optic axis defines a pair of opposite *directions* in the medium and not just one definite line.)

An *optically active medium* is one in which the two polarizations are not linear for all directions. The medium may be *isotropic*, in which case the difference of indices is independent of direction, and the two polarizations are always circular. It may be *anisotropic*, in which case the difference of indices is never zero but shows minima in directions defining one or two optic axes. Along an optic axis the two polarizations are circular, while for all other directions they are noncircular with eccentricity depending on direction.

The ideas in the last two paragraphs will be elaborated upon in due course, and examples of each type of medium will be cited.

In the macroscopic Maxwell theory a dielectric medium is characterized by the relation between **E** and **D** when the excitation is monochromatic with any given frequency. For a transparent singly refracting medium the relation is $D = \epsilon E$, with ϵ a real scalar.[1] To treat doubly refracting media, one naturally tries the most general linear relation, which, with respect to an arbitrary set of cartesian axes fixed in the medium, takes the form

$$\begin{aligned}
D_x &= \epsilon_{xx}E_x + \epsilon_{xy}E_y + \epsilon_{xz}E_z \\
D_y &= \epsilon_{yx}E_x + \epsilon_{yy}E_y + \epsilon_{yz}E_z \\
D_z &= \epsilon_{zx}E_x + \epsilon_{zy}E_y + \epsilon_{zz}E_z
\end{aligned} \tag{17-1}$$

By suitable choice of the nine ϵ's, it is possible to deduce from the Maxwell equations laws of propagation of plane waves in agreement with observation for any of the doubly refracting media. The various choices that have to be made will now be summarized.

For nonactive media all the ϵ's are real, while for active media some are complex. In either case there are six relations that are always satisfied by the ϵ's, and they can be written

$$\epsilon_{ij} = \epsilon_{ji}^* \tag{17-2}$$

where ij stands for any pair of the letters x, y, and z. One can think of a matrix of three rows and three columns made up of the ϵ's in the relative positions they occupy in (17-1), and condition (17-2) is said to make the matrix *hermitian*. It is to be noted that the diagonal elements ϵ_{xx}, ϵ_{yy}, and ϵ_{zz} are always real, and an off-diagonal element is the complex conjugate of the one symmetrically positioned on the other side of the diagonal. If all the ϵ's are real, then the matrix is symmetric (about the diagonal). It can be shown by the argument outlined in Prob. 17-1 that condition (17-2) guarantees that we are always speaking of a transparent medium even though some of the ϵ's may be complex.

Consider first a *nonactive medium*. It is characterized by real ϵ's forming a symmetric matrix. Moreover, the values of the ϵ's depend only on the orientation of the cartesian axes relative to the medium, and not on the direction of propagation of the wave, a remark that is

---

[1] In this chapter, as in the last, the symbols **E**, **D**, and **H** will stand for functions of spatial coordinates only and represent the complex amplitudes of the monochromatic fields after elimination of the exponential time factor (see Sec. 16-1).

not superfluous, since a different situation occurs in active media. If the axes are rotated, the ϵ's change, and there is a theorem on real symmetric matrices according to which the axes can be so oriented with respect to the medium that (17-1) takes the form

$$D_x = \epsilon_x E_x \qquad D_y = \epsilon_y E_y \qquad D_z = \epsilon_z E_z \qquad (17\text{-}3)$$

These particular axes are called the *principal axes* of the medium, and ϵ_x, ϵ_y, and ϵ_z are called the *principal dielectric constants*. The *principal indices of refraction* are defined by

$$n_x = \sqrt{\epsilon_x} \qquad n_y = \sqrt{\epsilon_y} \qquad n_z = \sqrt{\epsilon_z} \qquad (17\text{-}4)$$

Plane-wave solutions of the Maxwell equations are especially easy to find in a principal-axis representation.

Uniaxial crystals are characterized by equality of two of the principal indices, say

$$n_x = n_y = n_o \qquad n_z = n_e \neq n_o \qquad (17\text{-}5)$$

These relations are invariant under rotation of axes about z. The subscripts o and e stand for *ordinary* and *extraordinary* for a reason to be seen later. The z axis (axis of rotational symmetry) will turn out to be the optic axis as defined earlier. When (17-5) holds, it is seen from (17-3) that the real parts of **D** and **E** are collinear when and only when the real part of **E** is either along or perpendicular to the z axis. The same statement holds for the imaginary parts.

In a *biaxial crystal* all three principal indices are different. If

$$n_x > n_y > n_z \qquad (17\text{-}6)$$

then it will turn out that there are two optic axes in the xz plane with the angles between them being bisected by the x and z axes.

In any *optically active medium* referred to suitable cartesian axes, the relation between **D** and **E** in a plane wave takes the form

$$D_x = \epsilon_x E_x + i(\pmb{\delta} \times \mathbf{E})_x \qquad (17\text{-}7)$$

together with two more equations with x replaced by y or z. Here the three ϵ's are real, and $\pmb{\delta}$ is a real vector. The correspondence with the notation of (17-1) is

$$\epsilon_{xx} = \epsilon_x \qquad \epsilon_{xy} = -i\delta_x \qquad \epsilon_{xz} = i\delta_y \qquad \cdots$$

Condition (17-2) is satisfied. The parameters ϵ_x, ϵ_y, and ϵ_z are determined just by the medium and depend weakly on the wavelength, but $\pmb{\delta}$ is complicated in that it depends both on the medium and on the direction of propagation of the plane wave and depends strongly on the wavelength.

The simplest case is an *isotropic active medium*. For it the three ϵ's are equal and define a *mean refractive index* by

$$\epsilon_x = \epsilon_y = \epsilon_z = n^2$$

If **s** is a unit vector in the direction of propagation,

$$\boldsymbol{\delta} = \frac{b}{\lambda_0}\, \mathbf{s}$$

where λ_0 is the vacuum wavelength, and b is a parameter of the medium showing a weak dependence on wavelength analogous to the dispersion of the index n. The value of b may be positive or negative. The relation between **D** and **E** becomes

$$\mathbf{D} = n^2\mathbf{E} + i\frac{b}{\lambda_0}\, \mathbf{s} \times \mathbf{E} \tag{17-8}$$

Optical activity is a small effect; that is, the factor b/λ_0 in (17-8) is small enough that the double refraction to which it gives rise is very slight. The complete theory shows that the difference between **B** and **H**, always small at optical frequencies and ordinarily neglected, contributes to optical activity to the same extent as the second term on the right of (17-8). This point will be left for later consideration.

In *anisotropic active crystals* the behavior of the vector $\boldsymbol{\delta}$ is very complicated, and the basic theory is still in a state of development. Only uniaxial crystals will be discussed, mostly in qualitative terms. These crystals have the simplifying feature that the small contribution to double refraction made by optical activity is noticeable only in directions in which the contribution made by anisotropy is zero or very small, these directions being along or near the optic axis. Along the axis a relation of form (17-8) holds.

Part of the work in the rest of the chapter will be to show for each type of medium that the asserted relation of **D** to **E** leads to the type of double refraction observed in that medium. Let us now give brief attention to the ways in which the various relations of **D** to **E** come from microscopic considerations based on the ideas of the Lorentz electron theory.

In a crystal the constituent atoms are in intimate contact and experience short-range forces bonding the lattice together and affecting internal motions in the atoms. The electrons giving rise to the optical properties are elastically bound to positions of equilibrium, and unless the atoms neighboring a given one are in an especially symmetrical arrangement, the binding in the given atom is anisotropic. A mechanical illustration of anisotropic binding (in two dimensions) is the pendulum bob suspended by string in the arrangement shown in Fig. 17-1. The yoke at the top gives rise to different natural frequencies for oscillations in and perpendicular to the plane of the figure. The various free oscillations of this pendulum (Lissajous figures) are most instructive. In the general three-dimensional case there are three axes, mutually perpendicular, along which linear and sinusoidal free oscillations can occur, and the three natural frequencies are all different.

The strength and anisotropy of elastic binding are generally not the same for all atoms in the lattice, and one has to make (at least in imagination) a long calculation to find the macroscopic polarization $\mathbf{P}$ when a monochromatic field $\mathbf{E}$ is present. If the lattice has cubic symmetry, $\mathbf{P}$ is related to $\mathbf{E}$ by a scalar susceptibility, and the crystal is singly refracting (we ignore for the moment the possibility of optical activity). An example is rock salt (NaCl). Calcite ($CaCO_3$) is an important optical crystal whose lattice can be thought of as being derived from that of rock salt by replacing Na by Ca and Cl by CO_3, but the complex CO_3 distorts the lattice from cubic to rhombohedral. The cartesian components of $\mathbf{P}$ (and hence also of $\mathbf{D}$) are then related to those of $\mathbf{E}$ by a linear relation with coefficients forming a real symmetric matrix, and the crystal can be referred to principal axes to obtain the relations (17-3). Calcite happens to be uniaxial.

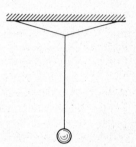

Fig. 17-1. *Pendulum bob suspended by strings to illustrate anisotropic binding to a position of equilibrium.*

It is easily seen in special cases that macroscopic anisotropy gives rise to double refraction. Let x, y, and z be principal axes, and let a plane wave travel in the z direction. If $\mathbf{E}$ oscillates linearly in the x direction, then $\mathbf{P}$ and $\mathbf{D}$ are collinear with $\mathbf{E}$, and the wave propagates with linear polarization and with a velocity determined by the polarizability in the x direction. The same applies to a second wave with $\mathbf{E}$ along y, but the polarizability may be less, so that the medium appears more like free space, and the velocity of the second wave is higher than that of the first.

The microscopic origin of optical activity is seen most easily in the case of an active liquid, of which a water solution of cane sugar is an example. Such a medium does not have the additional complication of macroscopic anisotropy. The essential feature is that the liquid contains molecules whose atoms are so arranged that the molecule cannot be brought into coincidence with its mirror image. Such a molecule is said to be *enantiomorphous*. One can think of a corkscrew arrangement, but there are many others.

In Sec. 14-1 it was pointed out that refraction in a medium is essentially a phenomenon of scattering, so let us consider a single enantiomorphous molecule in the field of a plane monochromatic wave of wave-length λ_0.   Another point made in Sec. 14-1 is that the scattered wave departs appreciably from a simple dipole wave and reveals something of the structure of the scatterer when the wavelength is comparable to the diameter a of the scatterer.   In the case we are considering, λ_0 is very large compared with a, and any effects will be small and propor-tional to a/λ_0.   Without going into details, one can pass from scattering by a single molecule to refraction by a liquid containing such molecules in random orientation and can arrive at the general formula (17-8).   It is apparent that the randomness will not cancel the effect (note that a screw looks the same turned end for end).

In crystals the unit cell of the lattice plays the role of the molecules just considered.   They are all in the same angular orientation, and if the crystal shows double refraction due to optical activity, it usually also shows a much larger double refraction due to macroscopic anisot-ropy.   Quartz, a uniaxial enantiomorphous crystal, is an example. Sodium chlorate is a cubic enantiomorphous crystal and is therefore isotropic but optically active.

A detailed account of the classical molecular theory of optical media as it stood in the early 1930s is given in Born [8], chap. 7.   This work is the standard reference and is the starting point for many subsequent papers.

The discussion so far has dealt with transparent crystals.   Some absorbing crystals show to a marked degree the phenomenon of *dichroism* whereby the attenuation of a wave depends on polarization.   The mineral tourmaline (of complicated and somewhat varying composition) is a uni-axial crystal, and if a plate is cut with surfaces parallel to the optic axis, normally incident linearly polarized light is very strongly absorbed if **E** is perpendicular to the axis, but is only weakly absorbed if **E** is parallel to the axis.   Much more efficient than tourmaline as linear polarizers are artificial dichroic materials produced commercially in the forms of specially treated plastic sheets and lacquers.

The phenomenon of dichroism can be understood qualitatively from the simple theory of the complex refractive index.   An extinction band occurs at and around a resonant frequency, and the resonant frequencies are different for linear vibrations in the two principal directions in the plate.   (The same considerations explain dispersion in the difference of principal indices in transparent crystals.   This idea will be exploited in the next chapter.)

Double refraction can be induced in normally singly refracting media. Methods employing static electric and magnetic fields will be dealt with in the next chapter.   Two other cases will now be mentioned.

Strain birefringence occurs when a material such as glass or transparent plastic contains mechanical strains that distort the arrangement of molecules. The phenomenon is the basis of the method of *photoelasticity* used by engineers and of the common optical test for the quality of annealing of glass. *Flow birefringence* occurs in a liquid flowing through a transparent pipe without turbulence and containing a colloidal suspension of elongated or flattened particles. A fine clay known as bentonite and viruses and polymers show the effect. The cause is a preferential alignment of the particles in the shearing motion of the fluid. Applications are either to a study of fluid flow or to a study of the suspended particles.

17-2 General Laws for Plane Waves The Maxwell equations governing propagation of any monochromatic wave in any dielectric medium in which $\mathbf{B} = \mathbf{H}$ are

$$\text{div } \mathbf{D} = 0 \qquad\qquad \text{div } \mathbf{H} = 0 \qquad\qquad (17\text{-}9)$$
$$\text{curl } \mathbf{E} = ik_0\mathbf{H} \qquad \text{curl } \mathbf{H} = -ik_0\mathbf{D} \qquad (17\text{-}10)$$

where $k_0 = \omega/c$. The vectors $\mathbf{E}$, $\mathbf{D}$, and $\mathbf{H}$ will be understood to represent the complex amplitudes of the fields apart from the time factor $e^{-i\omega t}$. These equations will be applied to homogeneous transparent media.

It has been seen that in a singly refracting medium of refractive index n there exist plane waves with

$$\mathbf{E} = \mathbf{E}_0 e^{i\mathbf{k}\cdot\mathbf{r}} \qquad \mathbf{D} = \mathbf{D}_0 e^{i\mathbf{k}\cdot\mathbf{r}} \qquad \mathbf{H} = \mathbf{H}_0 e^{i\mathbf{k}\cdot\mathbf{r}} \qquad (17\text{-}11)$$

where $\mathbf{k}$ is a real vector with magnitude nk_0 and any direction, and $\mathbf{E}_0$, $\mathbf{D}_0$, and $\mathbf{H}_0$ are constant vectors perpendicular to $\mathbf{k}$ and in general complex. The amplitude $\mathbf{E}_0$ can be given arbitrarily, and the other two are then fixed. The polarization is arbitrary.

In a doubly refracting medium, plane waves of type (17-11) exist for any direction of $\mathbf{k}$ but for two (rather than one) values of the magnitude of $\mathbf{k}$. For each magnitude the polarization is definite. Let us refer to these two solutions as the *two basic types of plane waves for a given direction of propagation* or, in brief, as the *basic waves*. An *arbitrary* monochromatic plane wave traveling in the direction of a unit vector $\mathbf{s}$ is defined by the conditions that it satisfy the Maxwell equations and that the sinusoidal oscillation of any of its three vector fields be the same at all points of any fixed plane perpendicular to $\mathbf{s}$. Any superposition of the two basic waves is a plane wave, but since two values of the magnitude of $\mathbf{k}$ are involved, it is not of form (17-11). Any plane wave can be written as a superposition of basic waves; that is, in technical terminology, the basic waves form a complete set. Let us now turn to the problem of finding the basic waves.

Substitution of (17-11) in (17-9) and (17-10) and use of the formulas cited in Prob. 4-10 gives

$$\mathbf{k} \cdot \mathbf{D}_0 = 0 \qquad \mathbf{k} \cdot \mathbf{H}_0 = 0 \qquad (17\text{-}12)$$
$$\mathbf{k} \times \mathbf{E}_0 = k_0 \mathbf{H}_0 \qquad \mathbf{k} \times \mathbf{H}_0 = -k_0 \mathbf{D}_0 \qquad (17\text{-}13)$$

According to (17-12), $\mathbf{D}_0$ and $\mathbf{H}_0$ are always perpendicular to $\mathbf{k}$. The second of (17-13) then shows that the real parts of $\mathbf{H}_0$ and $\mathbf{D}_0$ are perpendicular to each other, and the same for the imaginary parts. In general $\mathbf{E}_0$ is not perpendicular to $\mathbf{k}$.

Elimination of $\mathbf{H}_0$ from the two equations (17-13) and use of the identity (1-1) gives

$$k^2 \mathbf{E}_0 - (\mathbf{k} \cdot \mathbf{E}_0)\mathbf{k} - k_0^2 \mathbf{D}_0 = 0 \qquad (17\text{-}14)$$

(In a singly refracting medium the second term would vanish.) This is the fundamental equation to be used in conjunction with the relation of $\mathbf{D}$ to $\mathbf{E}$ for the medium in question to find the values of k and the restrictions on $\mathbf{E}_0$ for the two basic waves associated with a given direction of $\mathbf{k}$.

17-3 Nonactive Uniaxial Crystals A uniaxial crystal is characterized optically by (17-5) in conjunction with (17-4) and (17-3). Relation (17-5) is invariant under rotation of the coordinate axes about the z axis through any angle, and it is therefore sufficient to consider only directions of $\mathbf{k}$ lying in some one plane through this axis, say the xz plane. Then

$$k_y = 0 \qquad k^2 = k_x^2 + k_z^2 \qquad (17\text{-}15)$$

and the components of (17-14) are the three scalar equations

$$(k_z^2 - n_o^2 k_0^2) E_{0x} - k_x k_z E_{0z} = 0 \qquad (17\text{-}16)$$
$$(k^2 - n_o^2 k_0^2) E_{0y} = 0 \qquad (17\text{-}17)$$
$$-k_x k_z E_{0x} + (k_x^2 - n_e^2 k_0^2) E_{0z} = 0 \qquad (17\text{-}18)$$

These equations have two solutions. One is

$$E'_{0x} = E'_{0z} = 0 \qquad E'_{0y} \neq 0 \qquad (17\text{-}19)$$
$$k' = n_o k_0 \qquad (17\text{-}20)$$

where the primes distinguish this solution. The corresponding wave vector is denoted $\mathbf{k}'$; note that its magnitude (17-20) is independent of direction. The plane waves associated with this solution therefore have much in common with those in a singly refracting medium, and for this reason they are called *ordinary waves* (a special name for one of the basic waves in a uniaxial crystal), and the principal index n_o is called the *ordinary index*. According to (17-19), the ordinary waves are always linearly polarized with $\mathbf{E}'$ perpendicular to the axis of symmetry. Moreover, $\mathbf{D}'$ is always collinear with $\mathbf{E}'$, and both are perpendicular to $\mathbf{k}'$, which is another way in which the ordinary waves resemble those in singly refracting media.

The second solution, denoted by double primes, has

$$E''_{0y} = 0 \qquad E''_{0x} \neq 0 \qquad E''_{0z} \neq 0$$

The condition for a solution is that the determinant of the coefficients of E_{0x} and E_{0z} in (17-16) and (17-18) vanish. This condition reduces to

$$\frac{k''^2_x}{n_e{}^2} + \frac{k''^2_z}{n_o{}^2} = k_0{}^2 \qquad (17\text{-}21)$$

Either (17-16) or (17-18) then gives

$$\frac{E''_{0z}}{E''_{0x}} = - \frac{n_o{}^2 k''_x}{n_e{}^2 k''_z} \qquad (17\text{-}22)$$

The waves corresponding to this second solution are always linearly polarized with $\mathbf{E}''$ and $\mathbf{D}''$ in the plane defined by $\mathbf{k}''$ and the axis of symmetry, but these waves have peculiarities and are called *extraordinary waves*. The principal index n_e is called the *extraordinary index*.

The results obtained will now be given a graphical illustration. From a fixed point let vectors $\mathbf{k}'$ and $\mathbf{k}''$ radiate out in all directions, the magnitude being always appropriate to the direction. Their end points describe two surfaces of revolution about the symmetry axis of the crystal. They will be called *wave-vector surfaces*. (They are not to be confused with the wave-velocity surfaces and ray-velocity surfaces introduced by most authors in treating double refraction.) By (17-20), the surface for $\mathbf{k}'$ is a sphere of radius $n_o k_0$, and by (17-21), that for $\mathbf{k}''$ is a spheroid whose section through the axis is an ellipse. The principal radius of the ellipse along the axis is $n_o k_0$, and that perpendicular to the axis is $n_e k_0$. We therefore have the sectional curves shown in Fig. 17-2 for $n_e < n_o$. This is said to be the case of a *negative crystal*, of which calcite is an example having indices at λ5893 (Na D) of

$$n_o = 1.6583 \qquad n_e = 1.4864$$

(The condition $n_e > n_o$ defines a *positive crystal*. Quartz is the principal example except that it is optically active—see Sec. 17-8.)

Figure 17-2 indicates the lines of oscillation of the real vectors $\mathbf{E}$ and $\mathbf{D}$ considered as functions of time at a fixed point. The only feature not already covered is the direction of $\mathbf{E}''$. It is not perpendicular to $\mathbf{k}''$ and, in fact, is tangent to the ellipse at the end point of $\mathbf{k}''$. The proof is that differentiation of (17-21) gives dk''_z/dk''_x equal to the right side of (17-22).

The Poynting vector is perpendicular to **E** and **H**; therefore in every case it is normal to the wave-vector surface at the end point of the wave vector. For an extraordinary wave the Poynting vector is in general not in the direction of **k**''.

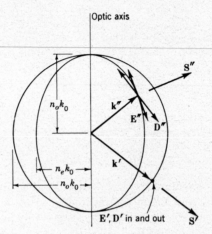

Fig. 17-2. *Wave-vector surfaces for a negative uniaxial crystal (e.g., calcite). Lines of oscillation of the real vectors* **E** *and* **D** *and the direction of the Poynting vector are indicated for an ordinary wave (primes) and an extraordinary wave (double primes). The difference between ellipse and circle is exaggerated.*

The axis of symmetry of the crystal is the optic axis according to the definition in Sec. 17-1, for along this axis k' and k'' are equal. A plane wave of arbitrary polarization propagates along the optic axis exactly as it would in a singly refracting medium of index n_o.

17-4   Nonactive Biaxial Crystals   A crystal in which the principal indices (17-4) are all different is said to be biaxial. There is no axis of symmetry of the type shown by uniaxial crystals, and the components of Eq. (17-14) must be examined in the general form

$$(k_y{}^2 + k_z{}^2 - n_x{}^2 k_0{}^2)E_{0x} - k_x k_y E_{0y} - k_x k_z E_{0z} = 0$$
$$-k_y k_x E_{0x} + (k_z{}^2 + k_x{}^2 - n_y{}^2 k_0{}^2)E_{0y} - k_y k_z E_{0z} = 0$$
$$-k_z k_x E_{0x} - k_z k_y E_{0y} + (k_x{}^2 + k_y{}^2 - n_z{}^2 k_0{}^2)E_{0z} = 0$$

Because of obvious algebraic complication, the solution of these simultaneous equations will not be fully discussed here. Rather, let us be satisfied with gaining some idea of the solution by considering only directions of **k** lying in one or another of the three planes defined by the principal axes. For example, if condition (17-15) is imposed, we have the same problem as in Sec. 17-3 except that n_o and n_e in (17-16) and (17-18) must be replaced by n_x and n_z, respectively, and n_o in (17-17) must be replaced by n_y. Equations for the other two planes are then obtained by cyclicly permuting x, y, and z.

Suppose the principal indices are ordered according to (17-6). Then Fig. 17-3*a*, *b*, and *c* shows loci of end points of possible wave vectors in the three planes. Each figure involves a circle and an ellipse, and the

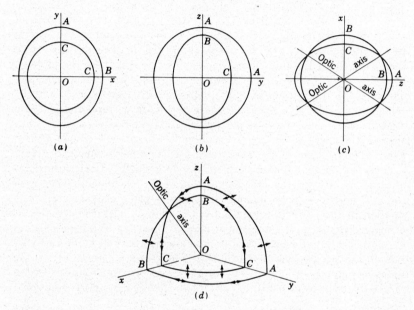

Fig. 17-3. *Wave-vector surfaces for a biaxial crystal. The curves are intersections of the surfaces with planes defined by principal axes. Lengths OA, OB, and OC are as stated in the text. Double arrows indicate oscillation of the electric vector.*

dimensions OA, OB, and OC are equal to $n_x k_0$, $n_y k_0$, and $n_z k_0$, respectively. In the xz plane the crossing points define the two optic axes. Figure 17-3*d* assembles these results in a three-dimensional view of one octant and indicates the directions of oscillation of the electric vectors in the basic waves.

For directions of propagation other than those considered here, there are always two magnitudes of **k** and two linear polarizations orthogonal to each other. A graphical construction for picturing these polarizations is the Fresnel ellipsoid described, for example, in Rossi [79], p. 289, or Sommerfeld [85], p. 137.

Uniaxial crystals can be regarded as limiting cases of biaxial. If n_y becomes equal to n_x, the two optic axes in Fig. 17-3 swing into coincidence with the z axis, and the case becomes negative uniaxial. If n_y becomes equal to n_z, we have a positive uniaxial case with x the optic axis.

17-5 Double Refraction at a Boundary The problem of reflection and transmission of plane waves at a plane boundary between transparent media with one or both media doubly refracting is solved by application of the boundary conditions (16-9) and (16-10). [The first of (16-9) should be rewritten $\mathbf{D}_1 \cdot \mathbf{v} = \mathbf{D}_2 \cdot \mathbf{v}$.] Just as in the case of singly refracting media, one first finds the relations among the several wave vectors, and for this the two relations (16-10) are sufficient. One then finds the reflection and transmission coefficients; here the problem becomes rather complicated and will not be worked out. The principles on which the applications of double refraction discussed in the next section are based involve the relations of the wave vectors, and in those cases in which the reflection and transmission coefficients must be considered, the answers will be obvious because of especially simple geometries. The relations of the wave vectors will now be considered in detail.

Suppose first that the incident wave is in a singly refracting medium of index n. Its wave vector $\mathbf{k}_i$ has magnitude nk_0 and, together with the unit normal $\mathbf{v}$ to the boundary, defines a plane of incidence. The solution to the problem involves a reflected wave with wave vector $\mathbf{k}_r$ of magnitude nk_0 and a transmitted wave consisting of a superposition of two basic waves whose wave vectors are, say, $\mathbf{k}'$ and $\mathbf{k}''$. A restriction on the last two vectors is that their lengths are determined by the wave-vector surfaces of Fig. 17-2 or 17-3. All the wave vectors of the reflected and transmitted waves are then made unique by the additional conditions

$$\mathbf{k}_i \times \mathbf{v} = \mathbf{k}_r \times \mathbf{v} = \mathbf{k}' \times \mathbf{v} = \mathbf{k}'' \times \mathbf{v} \qquad (17\text{-}23)$$

These relations are obtained by the same argument that gave (16-17), and it is being assumed that total reflection is not involved. Clearly, all the wave vectors lie in one and the same plane.

The reflected wave obeys the ordinary law of specular reflection. The construction giving $\mathbf{k}'$ and $\mathbf{k}''$ is illustrated by Fig. 17-4 for a negative uniaxial crystal with the optic axis either in or perpendicular to the plane of incidence, these being important special cases. For other orientations of the optic axis or for biaxial crystals, the geometry is less simple, but the principle is the same.

The conclusion is that the transmitted wave is a superposition of two basic waves whose wave vectors are in general not in the same direction. There are two special polarizations of the incident wave for which one or the other of these basic waves has amplitude zero. These polarizations are π and σ when the optic axis is in or perpendicular to the plane of incidence, as in Fig. 17-4.

Let us confine our attention to uniaxial crystals. The basic waves are called ordinary and extraordinary and will be distinguished by prime and double prime, respectively. 'Since the ordinary wave-vector surface is a sphere, Snell's law always holds for the ordinary wave in the form

$$n \sin \theta = n_o \sin \phi'$$

but the extraordinary surface is a spheroid, and Snell's law with constant indices does not hold.

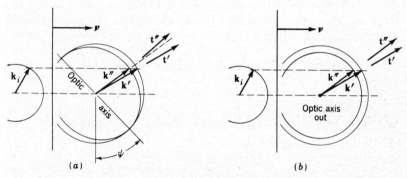

(a)   (b)

Fig. 17-4. *Construction for finding wave vectors and directions of rays in a uniaxial crystal. Proportions are for calcite in air. If the boundary in* (**a**) *is a natural cleavage plane of calcite,* ψ *is 45.5°.*

In Fig. 17-4 unit vectors $\mathbf{t}'$ and $\mathbf{t}''$, called *ray vectors*, are drawn in directions normal to the wave-vector surfaces at the end points of $\mathbf{k}'$ and $\mathbf{k}''$, respectively, and therefore lie in the directions of the Poynting vectors associated with the two waves. The vectors $\mathbf{t}'$ and $\mathbf{k}'$ are always collinear, but $\mathbf{t}''$ is collinear with $\mathbf{k}''$ only in special cases. If the optic axis is neither in nor perpendicular to the plane of incidence, $\mathbf{t}''$ is not in the plane of incidence.

Consider now the problem in which a plane wave in a singly refracting medium is incident on a doubly refracting medium, the latter being followed by a third medium which may be singly or doubly refracting. The wave and ray vectors of the waves in the third medium are found by principles already described; the only new point is that each of the two basic waves in the second medium is treated separately as a wave incident on the third medium. If the latter is singly refracting, it will carry just two linearly polarized waves. If it is doubly refracting, it will in general carry four, although in the most important cases there are only two, for the reason that the polarization of either of the two waves in the second medium is such that it excites only one of the two waves in the third medium to which it may give rise. In specific problems it will be obvious at a glance when this situation exists. The third medium may be followed by a fourth, and so on, and we face a wealth of combinations of crystal plates and prisms to analyze for possible application. In the next section only a few will be discussed.

Some simple experiments will now be described whereby the properties of double refraction can be observed at home. Calcite is a negative uniaxial crystal, insoluble in water, that cleaves readily into rhombohedrons with surfaces good enough for rough observations without polishing, and

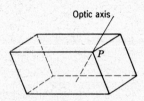

Fig. 17-5. *Rhomb of calcite. All faces are parallelograms. The angle between any pair of edges meeting at P is 102°. The branch of the optic axis extending into the crystal forms an angle of 45.5° with any of the faces meeting at P and an angle of 63.8° with any of the edges meeting at P.*

samples with dimensions of 1 cm or so are available at low cost from suppliers of minerals. Figure 17-5 shows the geometry of a rhomb bounded by natural cleavage planes. The direction of the optic axis is indicated, and some angular relations are given in the caption.

As a first experiment, cover one side of a rhomb with black paper having a pinhole in the center. Cover the opposite side with tissue paper. Let light from the sun fall normally on the hole, and observe two bright spots on the tissue. Hold in front of the pinhole a linear polarizer with the E axis identified (by observing light reflected from a glass plate at the polarizing angle; or use the glass plate or a stack of several plates directly as the polarizer in the experiment), and note that by rotating the crystal one or the other of the spots can be made to vanish.

The interpretation is shown in Fig. 17-6a. The two beams in the crystal are many wavelengths across and can be approximated as parts of plane waves. The wave vectors $\mathbf{k}'$ and $\mathbf{k}''$ are collinear and perpendicular to the boundary, since the incidence is normal, but the ray vectors $\mathbf{t}'$ and $\mathbf{t}''$, which determine the directions of the beams, are different. The ordinary and extraordinary beams are linearly polarized with their electric vectors perpendicular to and in the plane of the figure, respectively.

As a second experiment, lay a rhomb on a printed page, and note that the letters appear in two images displaced with respect to each other, both laterally and vertically. By viewing through a linear polarizer, either image can be extinguished; the letters in the other image are then blacker. To explain this effect, one must regard each point of the page below the crystal as a point source sending out ordinary and extraordinary wave fronts, as indicated in Fig. 17-6b. The theory of these waves will not be worked out, but the following description is reasonable: An ordinary wave front is a sphere. An extraordinary wave front is an oblate ovaloid of revolution approximating very closely a spheroid. (Surfaces of these shapes are obtained by taking the reciprocals of our wave-vector surfaces. These reciprocals are introduced by some authors under the name wave-velocity surfaces, but they refer to plane waves and are not obviously identical to wave fronts from a point source.) As the wave fronts advance into air, they become two sets of approximately spherical surfaces with the different centers labeled o and e in the figure. These are the two images seen by the eye. The ordinary image (which is vertically above the object) is higher than the extraordinary owing to the condition $n_o > n_e$ in calcite.

One can elaborate on either of these experiments by adding a second rhomb in tandem with the first and noting a quadrupling of the beams or

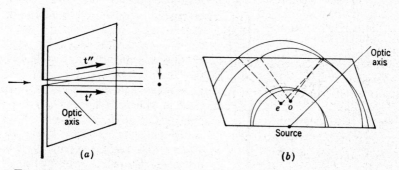

Fig. 17-6. *Two manifestations of double refraction in a calcite rhomb.*

the images and the effects of rotating one rhomb. Consider the experiment with pinhole and tissue paper, since it is easily visualized. While there are generally four bright spots on the tissue, there are four positions of the second rhomb for which the intensity of two of the spots falls to zero. If the rhombs are of equal thickness, one of these positions gives just one spot, which is unaffected by rotating a polarizer in front of the pinhole.

17-6 Applications of Double Refraction in Crystals The simplest application is an r-wave plate (Sec. 13-13) made of a single slab of crystal. One arranges to have two principal axes parallel to the faces. Let these axes be labeled a and b. If the corresponding principal indices satisfy $n_a > n_b$, and the geometrical thickness of the plate is d, then a is the slow axis, and

$$r = (n_a - n_b) \frac{d}{\lambda_0} \tag{17-24}$$

where λ_0 is the vacuum wavelength. To make quarter- and half-wave plates, one uses muscovite, which is an optical grade of mica and a biaxial crystal with the following advantages: It cleaves easily into very thin sheets of large area with two principal axes almost exactly parallel to the cleavage planes; the two indices associated with these axes are close together, being 1.594 and 1.590 for sodium light. (The indices vary from sample to sample, but the difference seems to be always about 0.004. The third index is about 1.561.) Even with this small difference a quarter-wave plate is only about 30 μ thick. (It might be mentioned that selected sheets of cellophane of the ordinary thickness make good half-wave plates.)

The appearance of λ_0 in (17-24) makes r strongly dependent on wavelength. (Dispersion of the difference of indices is a small effect in comparison.) This is a disadvantage of quarter-wave plates made of crystal, since r can equal $\frac{1}{4}$ only at one wavelength. On the other hand, some devices take advantage of this dependence on wavelength (see Prob. 17-13).

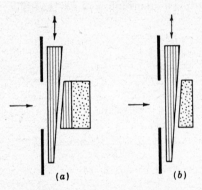

(a)   **(b)**

Fig. 17-7. *Compensators.* **a.** *Soleil.* **b.** *Babinet.*

A device equivalent to an r-wave plate in which r is continuously variable is the *Soleil compensator* illustrated in Fig. 17-7a. The two wedges and the plane-parallel slab are made of quartz with the optic axis in the directions indicated by lines and dots. (For propagation perpendicular to the optic axis, quartz behaves like a nonactive positive uniaxial crystal with indices 1.544 and 1.553 for sodium light.) The angle of the wedges is made very small, and the long wedge is movable by a micrometer screw. The value of r for the equivalent plate increases from zero in proportion to the distance the wedge is displaced (in either direction) from the position making the combined thickness of the two wedges equal to the thickness of the plane-parallel slab. As the wedge passes through this position giving $r = 0$, the fast and slow axes of the equivalent plate interchange.

The *Babinet compensator* is shown in Fig. 17-7b. For given wavelength and position of the movable wedge, this instrument is equivalent to an r-wave plate in which r varies over the aperture. There is no variation in the direction perpendicular to the plane of the figure, but on a line in the plane of the figure r is zero where the two wedges are of equal thickness and increases linearly with distance to either side of this point. The fast and slow axes of the equivalent plate interchange on crossing the point where $r = 0$. If the compensator is placed between crossed polarizers with their E axes at 45° to the optic axes of the wedges, the eye, focused on the wedges, sees parallel fringes (see answer given to Prob. 13-30, or consider the change in polarization on crossing the surface of the second wedge). Along the center of each dark fringe, r has an integral value. The fringe for which $r = 0$ is identified by its being the only one that remains black on broadening of the spectrum (see Prob. 17-8).

The Babinet compensator is a very versatile instrument for analyzing polarized light. Its use will now be illustrated by the problem of measuring r for an unknown wave plate at a given wavelength. First the axes of the unknown plate are located by placing it between crossed polarizers in one of the four orientations that give a dark field with a white source. The E axes of the polarizers are then parallel to the axes of the plate, but it is not determined which is the fast axis. Next the compensator is set up with polarizers in the arrangement described above, and in monochromatic light of the given wavelength the fringes are viewed with a fixed telescope of small aperture having cross hairs in the eyepiece. The compensator is calibrated for the given wavelength by determining the distance the movable wedge must travel (in terms of revolutions of the screw) to produce a shift of one whole fringe at the cross hairs. Next the zero-order dark fringe is identified with white light and is brought to the cross hairs. The unknown plate is added in series with the compensator with its axes parallel to those in the wedges. With white light a dark fringe appears in a new position and is brought to the cross hairs by a *measured* motion of the wedge. If the unknown does not have the same difference of principal indices as quartz, the dark fringe is somewhat diffuse, and a final setting is made with monochromatic light. In the final position the r of the compensator at the cross hairs for the given wavelength (known from the measured motion and the calibration) is just equal to that of the unknown. The fast axis may be identified from the direction the screw had to be turned when the unknown was added, but this requires some knowledge of the construction of the compensator or an observation on a plate whose axes are known (for example, one borrowed from a polarizing microscope).

Another application of double refraction in crystals is in making linear polarizers. Figure 17-8 shows the construction of a *Nicol prism*. It is made of two identical pieces of calcite cemented together with canada balsam. The upper and lower edges are natural cleavage edges, but the parallel entrance and exit faces are slightly different from cleavage planes (compare the angles with those in the caption to Fig. 17-5). The index of the balsam is such that the o wave is totally reflected, but the e wave is not. There is only a small range of direction of incident wave for which this condition holds (about 14° up or down from the one shown).

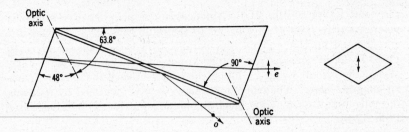

Fig. 17-8.   *Construction of the Nicol prism.   At the left is a cross section, and at the right is a reduced end view.*

There are many other types of prisms that transmit one linearly polarized wave without deviation and throw the wave of complementary polarization to one side.   As one example, Fig. 17-9 shows a *Rochon prism* made of calcite.   The two halves can be stuck together with castor oil or some other medium that does not absorb in the ultraviolet in the way canada balsam does.   The prism works for transmission in either direction.   Often it is made of quartz in order to work far her into the ultraviolet, but then due attention must be paid to optical activity along the optic axis, especially when two prisms are used in tandem.   (A

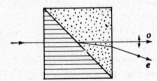

Fig. 17-9.   *Rochon prism of calcite.*

Rochon prism made of quartz does not have the simple properties stated as the definition of a linear polarizer in Sec. 13-13.   This fact will be evident after Sec. 17-8.   See Prob. 17-12.)

17-7   Optical Activity in Isotropic Media   An isotropic medium showing optical activity is characterized by the relation (17-8) between **D** and **E**.   This relation is appropriate only to the fields in a plane wave, and the calculation showing that it implies double refraction is quite analogous to that in Sec. 17-3.

We seek solutions of the Maxwell equations in the form (17-11) with **k** having some given direction.   Relation (17-8) gives

$$\mathbf{D}_0 = n^2\mathbf{E}_0 + \frac{i\beta\mathbf{k} \times \mathbf{E}_0}{k} \qquad (17\text{-}25)$$

where $\beta = b/\lambda_0$.   This value of $\mathbf{D}_0$ is to be substituted in the fundamental equation (17-14) and the result expressed in cartesian representation. There are no special directions in the medium to suggest a choice of axes, so let us take the z axis in the direction of $\mathbf{k}$. We obtain

$$(k^2 - n^2 k_0{}^2)E_{0x} + i\beta k_0{}^2 E_{0y} = 0 \qquad (17\text{-}26)$$

$$-i\beta k_0{}^2 E_{0x} + (k^2 - n^2 k_0{}^2)E_{0y} = 0 \qquad (17\text{-}27)$$

$$n^2 k_0{}^2 E_{0z} = 0 \qquad (17\text{-}28)$$

From (17-28) it is seen that $\mathbf{E}_0$ shares the property of $\mathbf{D}_0$ and $\mathbf{H}_c$ of being perpendicular to $\mathbf{k}$ [see (17-12)].

Equations (17-26) and (17-27) have a solution only if the determinant of the coefficients of E_{0x} and E_{0y} vanishes. This condition can be written in the form

$$[k^2 - (n^2 + \beta)k_0{}^2][k^2 - (n^2 - \beta)k_0{}^2] = 0$$

The roots are

$$k' = k_0(n^2 + \beta)^{\frac{1}{2}} \qquad k'' = k_0(n^2 - \beta)^{\frac{1}{2}} \qquad (17\text{-}29)$$

We are interested only in the positive roots, and since they are different, we have double refraction.

Substituting k' in either (17-26) or (17-27) gives

$$E'_{0y} = iE'_{0x}$$

Let $\mathbf{a}$ and $\mathbf{b}$ be unit vectors in the x and y directions, respectively. Then

$$E'_0 = E'_{0x}\mathbf{a} + E'_{0y}\mathbf{b} = E'_{0x}(\mathbf{a} + i\mathbf{b})$$

where E'_{0x} is an arbitrary complex number. The basic wave associated with the wave number k' is thus left-hand circularly polarized. In the same way the basic wave associated with k'' is right-hand circularly polarized, since it turns out that

$$\mathbf{E}''_0 = E''_{0x}(\mathbf{a} - i\mathbf{b})$$

where E''_{0x} is an arbitrary complex number.

With these left- and right-hand waves are associated refractive indices n_L and n_R defined by

$$k' = n_L k_0 \qquad k'' = n_R k_0$$

Now β is always very small compared with n^2, and we obtain good approximations for n_L and n_R from (17-29) in the form

$$n_L = n + \frac{\beta}{2n} = n + \frac{b}{2n\lambda_0} \qquad (17\text{-}30)$$

$$n_R = n - \frac{\beta}{2n} = n - \frac{b}{2n\lambda_0} \qquad (17\text{-}31)$$

In Sec. 17-1, n was given the name *mean refractive index*, and the reason is now clear. It was also mentioned that optical activity is a small effect and must be corrected to take into account the small difference between **B** and **H**. The correction amounts to removing the factor 2 in the denominators in (17-30) and (17-31). More details are given in Prob. 17-10, but for present purposes the correction can be ignored.

Optical activity is most often studied in the manifestation known as *optical rotation*. Suppose the medium is bounded by two plane parallel surfaces, and let a linearly polarized monochromatic plane wave fall normally on the first. A linearly polarized wave emerges from the second, but the direction of the electric vector has suffered a rotation about the direction of propagation. The laws of this rotation will now be derived.

Let the direction of propagation be the z axis, and let the first boundary be at $z = 0$. Let **a** and **b** be unit vectors along x and y, respectively. Let the incident wave be linearly polarized with **E** along the x axis, and suppose that just inside the boundary the amplitude is

$$\mathbf{E}(0) = A\mathbf{a}$$

with A an arbitrary complex number. The wave in the medium must be a superposition of basic waves, and in order to match the condition on **E** at $z = 0$, it must be

$$\mathbf{E}(z) = \tfrac{1}{2}A[(\mathbf{a} + i\mathbf{b})e^{in_L k_0 z} + (\mathbf{a} - i\mathbf{b})e^{in_R k_0 z}]$$

Define the quantity ρ by

$$\rho = \frac{n_L - n_R}{2}\,k_0 = \frac{\pi(n_L - n_R)}{\lambda_0} = \frac{\pi b}{n\lambda_0^2} \tag{17-32}$$

where λ_0 is the wavelength *in vacuo*, n is the mean index, and the last form is by substitution of (17-30) and (17-31). Then $\mathbf{E}(z)$ can be written

$$\begin{aligned}
\mathbf{E}(z) &= \tfrac{1}{2}A[(\mathbf{a} + i\mathbf{b})e^{i\rho z} + (\mathbf{a} - i\mathbf{b})e^{-i\rho z}]e^{ink_0 z} \\
&= A(\mathbf{a}\cos\rho z - \mathbf{b}\sin\rho z)e^{ink_0 z} \\
&= A\mathbf{d}e^{ink_0 z}
\end{aligned}$$

Thus at any given distance z into the medium the electric field oscillates linearly along the unit vector **d**, and **d** is related to **a** and **b** by the rotation indicated in Fig. 17-10. Depending on the medium, ρ may be positive or negative; the figure, which is drawn looking toward the source of the wave, shows the direction of rotation for positive ρ.

We are led to the following conclusions and nomenclature: The quantity ρ is the *specific rotation* (radians per unit length of path with sign). The medium is *dextrorotatory* if ρ is positive, and *levorotatory* if it is negative. The dependence of ρ on wavelength is primarily as $1/\lambda_0^2$, but there is additional weaker dependence due to dispersion in b/n appearing in (17-32). The total rotation in a given thickness of medium is proportional to the thickness. As an aid to remembering formula (17-32), note that the medium is *dextrorotatory* if the *right-hand* basic wave travels *faster*, and note that the angle of rotation ρz is just *one-half the difference of optical paths* for the two basic waves with each path measured in *radians*. One can easily picture these relations using the idea of Fig. 2-7*b*.

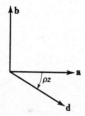

Fig. 17-10. *Rotation of linearly polarized light as seen looking toward the source. The clockwise rotation shown is associated with a positive value of ρ and a dextrorotatory medium.*

The most important examples of the media discussed in this section are solutions of organic compounds, and specific rotation is a measure of concentration, the usual dependence being very nearly linear. For example, if 100 grams of a water solution of cane sugar (sucrose) contains d grams of sugar, $\rho = +0.116d$ radian cm^{-1} at $\lambda5893$ (Na D) to good approximation. The difference of indices is $n_L - n_R = 2.2 \times 10^{-6}d$.

17-8 Optically Active Anisotropic Crystals The theory of optical activity in crystals is very difficult, and this section will be confined to facts about the uniaxial crystal quartz, a material of special importance.

In the lattice of quartz (SiO$_2$) can be seen a kind of corkscrew arrangement, and the mineral occurs in both the mirror-image forms. External evidence is seen in the configuration of the growth planes of the natural crystal. The occurrence of the enantiomorphism guarantees optical activity.

For propagation of waves in directions perpendicular to the optic axis, all uniaxial crystals show the same type of double refraction (basic waves linearly polarized), and quartz behaves like a positive crystal with principal indices at $\lambda5893$ (Na D) of

$$n_o = 1.544 \qquad n_e = 1.553$$

The optical activity shows up most markedly along the optic axis. There the double refraction due to anisotropy is zero, and that due to activity is of the same type as in the last section (basic waves circular). Measurement of specific rotation at $\lambda5893$ gives

$$\rho = \pm 3.79 \text{ radian cm}^{-1}$$

from which $\qquad\qquad n_L - n_R = \pm 7.1 \times 10^{-5}$

(Compare $n_e - n_o = 9 \times 10^{-3}$.) The form of quartz for which ρ is *positive* (dextrorotatory) is called *right-hand*, the other left.

As the direction of propagation swings away from the optic axis, the polarization of the basic waves becomes elliptical with increasing eccentricity. Figure 17-11 shows in gross exaggeration the wave-vector sur-

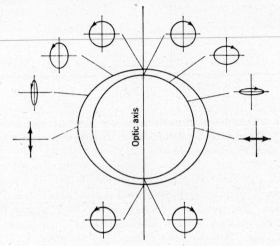

Fig. 17-11. *Wave-vector surfaces (difference exaggerated) and polarizations of basic waves in right-hand quartz. Diagrams of polarization are drawn looking against the wave with the optic axis in the vertical plane. Eccentricities of ellipses are qualitative only.*

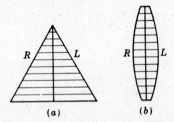

Fig. 17-12. *Quartz prism and lens in the Cornu construction.*

faces for quartz and shows qualitatively the different polarizations of the basic waves.

Quartz is important as a material for prisms in spectrographs for use in the near ultraviolet. Its extinction band begins at about 1850 A. (Dense glass begins to absorb just below 4000 A.) In order to avoid double images of spectrum lines, the prism is made in the Cornu construction shown in Fig. 17-12a, half right-hand and half left-hand. A quartz lens has two focal lengths unless it is made as in Fig. 17-12b.

Problems

17-1. A homogeneous medium is transparent if waves can travel through it without radiant energy being lost from the waves. Analytically, the divergence of the time average of the Poynting vector for a monochromatic wave must be zero. Start with

$$\langle S \rangle = \frac{c}{8\pi} \text{ Re } (\mathbf{E} \times \mathbf{H}^*)$$

Reexpress div $\langle S \rangle$ by means of an identity, use the Maxwell equations (17-10), write the result in cartesian representation, substitute (17-1), and finally show that (17-2) gives div $\langle S \rangle = 0$. Note that the calculation involves no assumption about the ϵ's beyond (17-2).

17-2. Draw the construction giving the wave and ray vectors in the crystal of Fig. 17-6*a*.

17-3. Place on top of the rhomb in Fig. 17-6*a* a second identical rhomb rotated 180° from the position of the first. Trace the rays through the two rhombs and into air.

17-4. If one looks through a calcite rhomb at a *distant* object, the image does not appear doubled. Explain, and contrast with Fig. 17-6*b*.

17-5. A spectroscope contains an equilateral prism made of calcite with the optic axis parallel to the apex edge. From the collimator comes a plane wave of yellow sodium light in such a direction that the ordinary wave in the prism is at minimum deviation (wave vector parallel to the base of the prism). Use drawing instruments to make a good scale drawing of the constructions (of the type shown in Fig. 17-4) for finding all the wave vectors in and on both sides of the prism (neglecting reflected waves). For sodium light the indices of calcite are $n_o = 1.66$ and $n_e = 1.49$. (A prism of this type provides one means of measuring the principal indices. One measures the angle of minimum deviation for the ordinary and for the extraordinary wave and applies a standard formula. Note that for a monochromatic input the spectroscope gives two linearly polarized images.)

17-6. Apply trigonometry to the construction of Prob. 17-5 to find the angle between the two final wave vectors in air.

17-7. Suppose one wanted to use a calcite prism in a spectroscope and avoid the doubling of the image found in Prob. 17-5. Show that this doubling is zero or negligible if the optic axis is parallel to the base and perpendicular to the apex edge and the instrument is used at or near minimum deviation. (This idea is used in connection with quartz prisms, but it is pointed out in Sec. 17-8 that optical activity must be compensated.)

17-8. Suppose the Babinet compensator in Fig. 17-7*b* is preceded and followed by linear polarizers with their E axes crossed and at 45° to the optic axes in the wedges. Let the angle of the wedges be α radian (very small), and let the principal indices differ by δn. Let an unpolarized plane wave be incident and have the ideal white power spectrum $\mathcal{S}(\sigma) = 1$ over the octave $\sigma_1 < \sigma < 2\sigma_1$ and zero outside this range, where σ is the vacuum wave number $1/\lambda_0$. Behind the second polarizer draw an x axis in the plane of the figure, perpendicular to the direction of the incident wave, and take $x = 0$ to be the point at which $r = 0$. Write the function $r(x,\sigma)$, always positive by definition. From the answer given for Prob. 13-30, write the transmission function $\mathcal{3}(x,\sigma)$. Find the irradiance $I(x)$ neglecting any dispersion in δn, and show that $I(0) = 0$ (the black fringe). Make a rough plot of $I(x)$. [The calculations and plotting in this problem have a formal similarity to those in Prob. 13-18. It will be noted that the condition $I(0) = 0$ is independent of the spectrum and of dispersion in δn.]

17-9. Describe how a Soleil compensator can be calibrated so that, for a given wavelength, r is known from the reading of the screw. (There is a simple method in which the only auxiliary equipment required is a pair of linear polarizers.)

17-10. The molecular theory of an optically active isotropic medium gives the following relations between the fields in a monochromatic plane wave with wave vector $\mathbf{k}$:

$$\mathbf{D} = n^2\mathbf{E} + i\,\frac{\beta}{k}\,\mathbf{k} \times \mathbf{E} \qquad \mathbf{B} = \mathbf{H} - i\,\frac{\beta k_0}{k}\,\mathbf{E}$$

Show that the equation determining the basic waves is

$$(k^2 - n^2k_0{}^2)\mathbf{E}_0 - (\mathbf{k} \cdot \mathbf{E}_0)\mathbf{k} - 2i\,\frac{\beta k_0{}^2}{k}\,\mathbf{k} \times \mathbf{E}_0 = 0$$

[One starts with Eqs. (17-13) after revising the first of them. Note that if one assumed $\mathbf{B} = \mathbf{H}$, the factor 2 in the last term of the equation to be proved would be missing. This problem relates to comments following (17-30) and (17-31).]

17-11. Discuss the difference, at a given point of space, between the real rotating vectors $\mathbf{D}$ and $\mathbf{E}$ in one of the circularly polarized basic waves in an isotropic active medium. Why is it not necessary to consider this difference in relating the basic waves to the normally incident and emerging waves in the problem of optical rotation?

17-12. Suppose the Rochon prism in Fig. 17-9 is made of right-hand quartz instead of calcite. (The deviated wave would then go up at a smaller angle.) Let the incident wave be quasi-monochromatic. Discuss the polarization and irradiance of the undeviated wave in the following cases ("parallel" and "perpendicular" mean $\mathbf{E}$ in and perpendicular to the plane of the figure, respectively):

a. Incidence is from the left and the wave is (1) unpolarized, (2) linearly polarized parallel, (3) linearly polarized perpendicular.

b. Incidence is from the right and polarization is as in (1), (2), and (3) above.

For definiteness take the prism to be about 1 cm long and the wavelength in air to be 5893 A, for which constants are given in Sec. 17-8. (When the polarization or irradiance varies over the exit aperture, the variation is to be described, perhaps with drawings.)

17-13. An r-wave plate is between crossed polarizers with their E axes at 45° to the principal axes of the plate. The geometrical thickness of the plate is d, and the two principal indices differ by δn. Write the transmission function of the combination as a function of d and the vacuum wave number $\sigma = 1/\lambda_0$, neglecting dispersion in δn. Plot the result as a function of σ for various d. Explain why the transmitted light is strongly colored when the incident light is white and the plate is thin. (An experiment is easily performed with slips of mica or cellophane. For ultimate simplicity use the polarized light from the blue sky, and observe reflection from a glass plate at the polarizing angle. A serious application of the transmission function found here is the *Lyot filter*, giving a bandwidth of 1 A or less—see Strong [88], appendix O.)

chapter 18

Magneto-optics and Electro-optics

This chapter will deal with a number of effects observable by optical means when a source emitting a wave or a medium transmitting one is subjected to a strong static field, either electric or magnetic. It was through the first discovery of such an effect by Faraday in 1845 that a connection between electromagnetism and light became evident.

The opening section will survey all the effects. Following sections will cover some theoretical points on those effects for which the Lorentz theory has something worthwhile to say. The concluding section will describe an important application.

18-1 Survey of Effects The *Faraday effect* is a rotation of the direction of oscillation of a linearly polarized wave occurring when the wave traverses a thickne...s of transparent medium along the direction of a strong magnetic field. The phenomenon is reminiscent of the rotation occurring in an optically active uniaxial crystal when the propagation is along the axis, but there is the *important difference* that in the Faraday effect the medium is levorotatory for propagation in the direction of the field, and dextrorotatory for propagation in the opposite direction. This rule can be remembered if the magnetic field is thought of as being produced by a solenoid. The optical rotation is then in the same direction as the current in the windings for either direction of propagation of the wave.

The Faraday effect obeys the law

$$\theta = VBl \tag{18-1}$$

where θ is the magnitude of the angle of optical rotation, B is the strength of magnetic field, l is the length of path in the medium, and V is a factor of proportionality called the *Verdet constant*, depending on frequency and, generally, on temperature. If B is in gauss, l in centimeters, and θ in minutes of arc, then V measured with yellow sodium light is typically of order 10^{-5} for gases at standard conditions and of order 10^{-2} for transparent liquids and solids. It becomes much larger for ferromagnetic solids or colloidal suspensions of ferromagnetic particles.

The theory of the Faraday effect will be worked out for a gas of Lorentz atoms in Sec. 18-3. An interesting behavior occurs around a resonant frequency, and in this range the Faraday effect is often given the special name *Macaluso-Corbino effect* after the workers who first observed it in 1898. Its practical importance is that, when translated into quantum terms, it provides one of the means of measuring oscillator strengths for atomic transitions (Secs. 15-5 and 19-6).

If a wave propagates through a transparent medium in a direction at right angles to a static magnetic field, there occurs the kind of double refraction observed in uniaxial crystals at right angles to the optic axis. The basic waves are linearly polarized and have associated with them indices n_σ (for the **E** in the wave perpendicular to the static field **B**) and n_π (**E** parallel to **B**). The difference of optical paths measured in wavelengths for a geometrical length l of medium is

$$\Delta = (n_\sigma - n_\pi) \frac{l}{\lambda_0} \tag{18-2}$$

where λ_0 is the vacuum wavelength. The sign of Δ does not change on reversal of the magnetic field, and the magnitude of Δ is proportional to B^2. The law is

$$\Delta = CB^2l \tag{18-3}$$

The factor C depends on wavelength and temperature; for transparent liquids at $\lambda 5893$ and $20°C$ it is typically of order 10^{-12} gauss^{-2} cm^{-1} and may be of either sign. It becomes much larger for colloidal suspensions of ferromagnetic particles.

The double refraction just described is known generally as the *Cotton-Mouton effect* after the workers who first observed it in liquids in 1907. A special case was observed in 1898 in gases near resonant frequencies, and this manifestation is known as the *Voigt effect*. The theory for a gas of Lorentz atoms will be given in Sec. 18-4.

In liquids containing optically and magnetically anisotropic molecules, the major contribution to the Cotton-Mouton effect, and perhaps also to the Faraday effect, comes from partial alignment of the molecules by the magnetic field. Thermal agitation plays a role both in making alignment possible and in limiting the degree attained, and hence gives the factors V and C a dependence on temperature, the form being $a + b/T$.

Let us turn now to the effect of a magnetic field on a source of radiation. Faraday looked for such an effect, but without success because very strong fields and spectroscopes of good resolution were not available at the time. The first positive results were obtained by Zeeman in 1896 and were described as a broadening of spectrum lines when a field was turned on. In 1897 Lorentz offered an explanation of this *Zeeman effect* according to which a line should be split into three linearly polarized components with a certain separation when the line of observation is perpendicular to the magnetic field, and into two circularly polarized components when the observation is along the field. These predictions were verified, but only for certain spectrum lines showing what is now called the *normal effect*. Other lines split into a greater number of components and are said to be anomalous.

The classical theory of the Zeeman effect (Sec. 18-2) is obtained by considering free oscillations of electrons in the presence of a magnetic field. The same basic idea is then applied to forced oscillation when the driving force comes from the electric field in a light wave, and the result is a theory of the Faraday effect (Sec. 18-3) and the Cotton-Mouton effect (Sec. 18-4).

The first electro-optic effect was discovered in 1875 by Kerr. The *Kerr electro-optic effect*[1] is a double refraction induced in solids and liquids by an electric field. The medium acquires precisely the optical character of a nonactive uniaxial crystal, the optic axis being along the direction of the field, and the double refraction can be specified in terms of an ordinary and an extraordinary refractive index. The difference in optical paths measured in wavelengths for the two basic waves when propagation is at right angles to the field through a geometrical path l is

$$\Delta = (n_e - n_o) \frac{l}{\lambda_0} \qquad (18\text{-}4)$$

The sign of Δ does not change on reversal of the field, and the relation to the strength E of the field is

$$\Delta = K E^2 l \qquad (18\text{-}5)$$

where the factor K is the *Kerr constant* (a function of wavelength and temperature) and is usually positive, but may be negative. Values of K

---

[1] There is also a *Kerr magneto-optic effect* involving a change in polarization of a wave reflected from an iron mirror when the iron is magnetized. It will not be discussed here.

for liquids at $\lambda 5893$ and $20°C$ range from 10^{-7} to 10^{-5} statvolt^{-2} cm.   (E is in statvolts per centimeter.   One statvolt ≈ 300 volt.)

The effect arises from partial alignment of optically anisotropic molecules by the electric field.   The magnitude of K is large for liquids whose molecules combine a large permanent electric moment (polar molecules) with a large optical anisotropy.   The sign of K is positive (the medium becomes similar to a positive uniaxial crystal) if the optical polarizability is greater along the permanent moment than at right angles to it (usually the case).

The *Stark effect* is the analogue of the Zeeman effect when the external field is electric rather than magnetic.   The discovery was made in 1913, and the essential step was to find conditions under which a strong electric field (of order 10^5 volt cm^{-1} or more) can be maintained in a gas.   Spectrum lines split into polarized components according to complicated laws.   Classical theories have been developed, but they are not satisfying, and the Stark effect will not be discussed further.

18-2   Zeeman Effect   Consider a Lorentz atom with a single elastically bound electron of charge $-e$, mass m, and resonant frequency ω_0. The equation of motion governing free oscillations in the absence of a magnetic field is (12-6).   When a static field **B** is present, the Lorentz force must be added, and if we neglect the radiation reaction for the moment, the equation of motion to be solved is

$$\ddot{\mathbf{s}} + \omega_0^2 \mathbf{s} + \frac{e}{mc} \dot{\mathbf{s}} \times \mathbf{B} = 0$$

where **s** is the vectorial displacement of the electron from its position of equilibrium.   Once the solutions are found, it will be evident on the basis of our experience in Sec. 12-3 how the effect of radiation reaction is to be included.   The advantage of this procedure is economy in writing.

We seek sinusoidal solutions of the equation of motion in the form

$$\mathbf{s} = \mathbf{s}_0 e^{-i\omega t} \tag{18-6}$$

and the most straightforward procedure is to use a cartesian representation.   Let **B** point in the positive z direction.   Define the *Larmor frequency*[1]

$$\omega_L = \frac{eB}{2mc} \tag{18-7}$$

---

[1] Larmor's name has been associated with this frequency since the introduction of his theorem concerning the effect of a magnetic field on a system of particles all having the same ratio of charge to mass.   The theorem was given in 1897 and applied to the effects of Zeeman and Faraday in 1899.   Use of Larmor's theorem is a method alternative to the one being given here.

The components of the equation of motion are then

$$(\omega^2 - \omega_0^2)s_{0x} + i2\omega_L\omega s_{0y} = 0 \tag{18-8}$$
$$-i2\omega_L\omega s_{0x} + (\omega^2 - \omega_0^2)s_{0y} = 0 \tag{18-9}$$
$$(\omega^2 - \omega_0^2)s_{0z} = 0 \tag{18-10}$$

There are three solutions. The first is

$$s_{0x} = s_{0y} = 0 \qquad s_{0z} \neq 0 \qquad \omega = \omega_0$$

that is, a linear oscillation along the z axis with frequency ω_0. The other two solutions have

$$s_{0z} = 0 \qquad s_{0x} \neq 0 \qquad s_{0y} \neq 0$$

and the condition for a solution is that the determinant of the coefficients in (18-8) and (18-9) vanish, or

$$(\omega^2 - 2\omega_L\omega - \omega_0^2)(\omega^2 + 2\omega_L\omega - \omega_0^2) = 0 \tag{18-11}$$

Now ω_L is very small in comparison with ω_0 when the latter is of visible or higher frequency and B has any attainable value, and to good approximation the roots of (18-11) are

$$\omega' = \omega_0 + \omega_L \qquad \omega'' = \omega_0 - \omega_L$$

Corresponding to these two frequencies are the ratios

$$s'_{0x} = -is'_{0y} \qquad s''_{0x} = is''_{0y}$$

Let $\mathbf{a}$, $\mathbf{b}$, and $\mathbf{c}$ be unit vectors in the x, y, and z directions, respectively. (Then $\mathbf{B} = B\mathbf{c}$.) Let A_1, A_2, and A_3 be arbitrary complex numbers. The three solutions of form (18-6), called the *normal modes of oscillation*, are then

$$\mathbf{s}_1 = A_1\mathbf{c}e^{-i\omega_0 t} \tag{18-12}$$
$$\mathbf{s}_2 = A_2(\mathbf{a} + i\mathbf{b})e^{-i(\omega_0+\omega_L)t} \tag{18-13}$$
$$\mathbf{s}_3 = A_3(\mathbf{a} - i\mathbf{b})e^{-i(\omega_0-\omega_L)t} \tag{18-14}$$

These motions consist in a linear oscillation along the z axis and opposite circular oscillations in the xy plane, the frequencies all being different. The general solution is the superposition

$$\mathbf{s} = \mathbf{s}_1 + \mathbf{s}_2 + \mathbf{s}_3$$

For purposes of deriving the spectrum it is not necessary to consider the possible paths of motion arising through this superposition.

A point to note is that when B is zero, the three natural frequencies are equal (the three normal modes are then said to be *degenerate*), and the superposition gives the general monochromatic oscillation of frequency ω_0 in accordance with the idea in Prob. 2-19. Adding the static field introduces what is called a *perturbation*, and it removes the degeneracy by making the frequencies of the normal modes unequal. The normal modes themselves are by definition those special motions that remain sinusoidal when the perturbation is added. All these ideas have close analogues in the quantum theory of perturbations.

The effect of radiation reaction is to damp the normal oscillations by the addition of a factor $e^{-\gamma t/2}$, where γ is defined by (12-9). [Strictly speaking, the γ for the circular modes should be obtained from (12-9) by replacing ω_0 by $\omega_0 \pm \omega_L$, but the distinction is unimportant.]

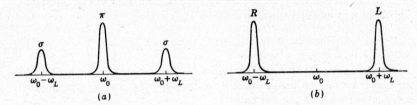

Fig. 18-1. *Spectra predicted by the classical theory of the Zeeman effect.* **a.** *Magnetic field perpendicular to the line of sight.* **b.** *Field toward the observer.*

The spectrum can be drawn at once from the following considerations: The source will consist of many atoms undergoing impulsive excitations in a completely random fashion. An individual excitation of an atom gives rise to a motion consisting in a superposition of damped normal oscillations, and the radiated wave is the superposition of the waves that would be radiated by three electrons, with each undergoing one of the component motions. The source can be regarded as consisting of three independent polarized sources, with the oscillations in each consisting entirely of one of the three normal modes. The polarization of the radiation and the shape of the radiation pattern are then known for each of the three imaginary sources, and the relative sizes of the patterns are determined by the condition that the three sources must radiate the same power (Prob. 18-2). It then turns out that the total radiation, as observed from any direction without spectral resolution, is unpolarized (Prob. 18-3).

Figure 18-1a shows the spectrum as observed in a direction at right angles to the applied field. The three components are linearly polarized as indicated, where π and σ mean electric vector parallel and perpendicular to the applied field, respectively. (In this direction of observation the

two circular normal modes appear in projection as linear motions.)   The
central component is twice as intense as either of the other two in order
that the total radiation be unpolarized.   Figure 18-1b shows the spectrum observed when the applied field points toward the observer.   Two
circularly polarized components of equal intensity appear, one right-hand,
the other left-hand.   All the components in Fig. 18-1 have the same
profile, determined by a combination of natural, thermal, and perhaps
pressure broadening (see Prob. 18-5).

18-3   Faraday Effect   Consider a gas composed of Lorentz atoms of
the type treated in the last section.   Let us first see the origin of the
Faraday effect in such a gas by qualitative reasoning.   If there is no
magnetic field, then the existence of a resonant frequency at ω_0 leads one
to draw the curves of refractive index and extinction index shown in
Fig. 15-4a.   When a field **B** is present, and a wave travels through the gas
in the direction of **B**, there are two resonant frequencies, one at $\omega_0 + \omega_L$

for left-hand circularly polarized
waves, and the other at $\omega_0 - \omega_L$
for right-hand.   One then draws
the curves of the refractive indices
n_L and n_R and their difference
shown in Fig. 18-2.   If the incident wave is linearly polarized and
has frequency ω, the gas is dextrorotatory when ω is between the
resonant frequencies, and levorotatory at other frequencies.   Above
and below the resonant frequencies
the rotation soon becomes too small
to observe.   If the propagation is
in the direction $-\mathbf{B}$, R and L are
to be interchanged.   These considerations hold for liquids and
solids, but here the detailed behavior near a pair of resonant fre-

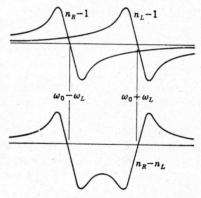

Fig. 18-2. *Explanation of the Faraday effect near a resonant frequency
in a gas for the case of propagation
in the direction of the magnetic field.*

quencies is obscured by a broad and intense extinction band, and in a
band of transparency the two indices and their difference are large enough
to give appreciable rotation throughout.

The Faraday effect in a gas will now be drawn from the Lorentz theory.
The procedure will be to find the general relation between **D** and **E** in a
plane monochromatic wave propagating through the gas in the presence
of a static field **B**.   The methods of Chap. 17 will then be applied to find
the basic waves and the corresponding refractive indices when the wave
propagates in the direction of **B**.

Suppose the atom considered at the outset of the last section is acted upon not only by the static field **B**, but also by a sinusoidal electric field of complex amplitude $\mathbf{E}_0$ and frequency ω. The equation governing the forced oscillation of the electron is

$$\ddot{\mathbf{s}} + \omega_0{}^2 \mathbf{s} + \frac{e}{mc}\dot{\mathbf{s}} \times \mathbf{B} = -\frac{e}{m}\mathbf{E}_0 e^{-i\omega t}$$

Radiation reaction is again omitted; the correction will be made later. The solution of the equation is of the form (18-6). Let $\mathbf{s}_0$ be replaced by $-\mathbf{p}_0/e$, where $\mathbf{p}_0$ is the complex amplitude of the dipole moment of the atom. Then if **c** is a unit vector in the direction of **B**, the equation for $\mathbf{p}_0$ is

$$(\omega^2 - \omega_0{}^2)\mathbf{p}_0 + i2\omega_L\omega\mathbf{p}_0 \times \mathbf{c} = -\frac{e^2}{m}\mathbf{E}_0 \qquad (18\text{-}15)$$

Equation (18-15) will be solved in cartesian representation with the positive z axis in the direction of **c**. The component equations are

$$(\omega^2 - \omega_0{}^2)p_{0x} + i2\omega_L\omega p_{0y} = -\frac{e^2}{m}E_{0x}$$

$$-i2\omega_L\omega p_{0x} + (\omega^2 - \omega_0{}^2)p_{0y} = -\frac{e^2}{m}E_{0y}$$

$$(\omega^2 - \omega_0{}^2)p_{0z} = -\frac{e^2}{m}E_{0z}$$

The solution is

$$p_{0x} = \alpha_{xx}E_{0x} + \alpha_{xy}E_{0y}$$
$$p_{0y} = \alpha_{yx}E_{0x} + \alpha_{yy}E_{0y}$$
$$p_{0z} = \alpha_{zz}E_{0z}$$

where $\quad \alpha_{xx} = \alpha_{yy} = -(\omega^2 - \omega_0{}^2)G \qquad \alpha_{zz} = -\frac{e^2}{m}(\omega^2 - \omega_0{}^2)^{-1}$

$$\alpha_{xy} = -\alpha_{yx} = i2\omega_L\omega G \qquad G = \frac{e^2}{m}[(\omega^2 - \omega_0{}^2)^2 - (2\omega_L\omega)^2]^{-1}$$

When a wave propagates through a gas having N atoms per unit volume, the amplitude of the displacement vector is

$$\mathbf{D}_0 = \mathbf{E}_0 + 4\pi N\mathbf{p}_0$$

or
$$D_{0x} = n_1{}^2 E_{0x} - i\beta E_{0y} \qquad (18\text{-}16)$$
$$D_{0y} = n_1{}^2 E_{0y} + i\beta E_{0x} \qquad (18\text{-}17)$$
$$D_{0z} = n_2{}^2 E_{0z} \qquad (18\text{-}18)$$

where the symbols n_1, n_2, and β have been introduced for ease in referring to Chap. 17 and have the values

$$n_1{}^2 = 1 + 4\pi N\alpha_{xx} = 1 - \frac{4\pi Ne^2(\omega^2 - \omega_0{}^2)/m}{(\omega^2 - \omega_0{}^2)^2 - (2\omega_L\omega)^2} \tag{18-19}$$

$$n_2{}^2 = 1 + 4\pi N\alpha_{zz} = 1 - \frac{4\pi Ne^2/m}{\omega^2 - \omega_0{}^2} \tag{18-20}$$

$$\beta = i4\pi N\alpha_{xy} = -\frac{8\pi Ne^2\omega_L\omega/m}{(\omega^2 - \omega_0{}^2)^2 - (2\omega_L\omega)^2} \tag{18-21}$$

The basic waves and the corresponding refractive indices are found by substituting for $\mathbf{D}_0$ in the fundamental equation (17-14). For the Faraday effect we take the wave vector $\mathbf{k}$ to be parallel or antiparallel to $\mathbf{B}$. Let us take it parallel. The z component of (17-14) reduces to $E_{0z} = 0$, and the x and y components are

$$(k^2 - n_1{}^2k_0{}^2)E_{0x} + i\beta k_0{}^2E_{0y} = 0$$
$$-i\beta k_0{}^2E_{0x} + (k^2 - n_1{}^2k_0{}^2)E_{0y} = 0$$

These equations are of the same form as (17-26) and (17-27), and we draw the conclusions that the basic waves have opposite circular polarizations and that the two refractive indices are given by

$$n_L{}^2 = n_1{}^2 + \beta = 1 - \frac{4\pi Ne^2/m}{\omega^2 - \omega_0{}^2 - 2\omega_L\omega} \tag{18-22}$$

$$n_R{}^2 = n_1{}^2 - \beta = 1 - \frac{4\pi Ne^2/m}{\omega^2 - \omega_0{}^2 + 2\omega_L\omega} \tag{18-23}$$

When the denominators are corrected for radiation reaction in the manner of (15-44), we get the upper curves in Fig. 18-2 in the same way as (15-44) led to Fig. 15-4. Problem 18-6 suggests an alternative way of arriving at these conclusions.

A simple approximation to the lower curve in Fig. 18-2 can be given for frequencies well below or well above the resonant frequencies. We then have

$$\beta \ll n_1 \qquad n_1 \approx 1 - \frac{2\pi Ne^2/m}{\omega^2 - \omega_0{}^2} = n$$

where n is the refractive index in the absence of a magnetic field. Approximations (17-30) and (17-31) are good, and

$$n_R - n_L \approx -\frac{\beta}{n} \approx \frac{8\pi Ne^2\omega_L\omega}{mn(\omega^2 - \omega_0{}^2)^2} \tag{18-24}$$

To a first approximation the Faraday rotation is therefore proportional to B, as stated in (18-1). Since n_R is greater than n_L (left-hand wave faster), the rotation is left-hand for $\mathbf{k}$ parallel to $\mathbf{B}$.

18-4 Cotton-Mouton Effect   To get the Cotton-Mouton effect in a gas, we consider a wave propagating at right angles to the magnetic

field.   A set of curves, drawn to be qualitatively related to Fig. 18-1*a* in
the same way as Fig. 18-2 is related to Fig. 18-1*b*, is shown in Fig. 18-3.
The basic waves are linearly polarized with **D** oscillating either along
or perpendicular to **B**, and the corresponding indices are n_π and n_σ,
respectively.

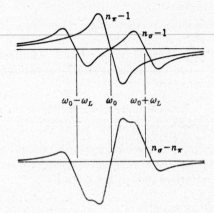

Fig. 18-3.   *Explanation of the Cotton-Mouton effect near a resonant frequency in a gas.*

The Lorentz theory of the effect comes from taking **k** in (17-14) to be
perpendicular to **B**, say along the x axis.   The cartesian components of
this equation, after substituting (18-16) to (18-18), are

$$n_1^2 k_0^2 E_{0x} - i\beta k_0^2 E_{0y} = 0 \tag{18-25}$$
$$(k^2 - n_1^2 k_0^2) E_{0y} - i\beta k_0^2 E_{0x} = 0 \tag{18-26}$$
$$(k^2 - n_2^2 k_0^2) E_{0z} = 0 \tag{18-27}$$

Elimination of E_{0x} from (18-25) and (18-26) gives

$$\left(k^2 - n_1^2 k_0^2 + \frac{\beta^2}{n_1^2} k_0^2\right) E_{0y} = 0 \tag{18-28}$$

One of the basic waves has $E_{0y} = 0$ and $k = n_\pi k_0$, and the other has
$E_{0z} = 0$ and $k = n_\sigma k_0$.   Then (18-27) and (18-28) give

$$n_\pi = n_2 \qquad n_\sigma^2 = n_1^2 - \frac{\beta^2}{n_1^2} \tag{18-29}$$

Problem 18-8 calls attention to a peculiarity of the σ wave.

Let us discuss n_π and n_σ only at frequencies well below or well above
the resonant frequencies, where effects of radiation reaction and thermal
broadening are negligible and expressions (18-19) to (18-21) hold as they

stand. Another simplification at these frequencies is that β^2 is very small compared with n_1^2 and in first approximation can be dropped from (18-29). Finally, n_1^2 and n_2^2 are not far from unity, and we have

$$n_\pi \approx 1 - \frac{2\pi Ne^2/m}{\omega^2 - \omega_0^2}$$

$$n_\sigma \approx 1 - \frac{2\pi Ne^2(\omega^2 - \omega_0^2)/m}{(\omega^2 - \omega_0^2)^2 - (2\omega_L\omega)^2}$$

$$= 1 - \frac{\pi Ne^2/m}{\omega^2 - \omega_0^2 - 2\omega_L\omega} - \frac{\pi Ne^2/m}{\omega^2 - \omega_0^2 + 2\omega_L\omega}$$

It is seen that n_π is the same as the index of the gas without a magnetic field; a single resonance contributes to it. Two resonances with frequencies approximately equal to $\omega_0 \pm \omega_L$ contribute to n_σ, and each has half the strength of that contributing to n_π. The qualitative curves in Fig. 18-3 are in agreement with these results.

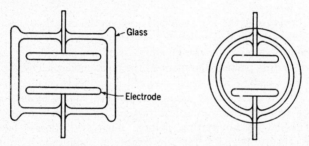

Fig. 18-4. *Side and end views of a Kerr cell.*

A first approximation to the difference of indices is obtained by expanding n_σ in powers of ω_L and keeping only the lowest terms:

$$n_\sigma \approx 1 - \frac{2\pi Ne^2/m}{\omega^2 - \omega_0^2} - \frac{(2\pi Ne^2/m)(2\omega_L\omega)^2}{(\omega^2 - \omega_0^2)^3}$$

Hence

$$n_\sigma - n_\pi \approx - \frac{8\pi Ne^2\omega_L^2\omega^2}{m(\omega^2 - \omega_0^2)^3} \tag{18-30}$$

To this approximation, the difference of indices is proportional to B^2, as in (18-3). Comparison of (18-30) with (18-24) shows that the Cotton-Mouton effect is small compared with the Faraday effect.

18-5 Kerr Electro-optic Shutter   A *Kerr cell* is constructed in the manner shown schematically in Fig. 18-4. A glass envelope with plane windows contains rectangular metal plates serving as electrodes. The envelope is filled (through a side tube not shown) with a polar liquid having a large Kerr constant. The common material is nitrobenzene, for which $K = 2.2 \times 10^{-5}$ statvolt^{-2} cm at $\lambda 5893$.

When a voltage V is applied to the electrodes, the cell becomes similar to an r-wave plate with

$$r = \frac{KV^2 l}{d^2} \tag{18-31}$$

where d is the separation of the electrodes, and l is an effective length slightly different from the length of the electrodes because of fringing of the field. If the cell is placed between crossed linear polarizers with their E axes at 45° to the direction of the electric field, we have a shutter whose transmittance for unpolarized quasi-monochromatic light is

$$\mathfrak{I} = \tfrac{1}{2} \sin^2 \pi r \tag{18-32}$$

The usual operation is between $r = 0$ and $r = \tfrac{1}{2}$. If V is such as to make $r = \tfrac{1}{2}$ in the green, then the transmittance is better than half-maximum at both ends of the visible spectrum (r varies practically as $1/\lambda_0$ for a given V).

The importance of the Kerr cell derives from the fact that (18-31) holds with a fixed value of K even when V varies rapidly with time. An idea of how rapid the variation can be comes from considering that the Kerr effect results from partial alignment of the polar molecules by the electric field and that realignment when the field is suddenly changed is not an instantaneous process. This alignment also determines by far the major part of the dielectric constant at low frequencies, and one can inquire as to what frequency of alternating voltage must be attained before the dielectric constant begins to fall appreciably in magnitude from its static value and to acquire an imaginary component. (An imaginary component means "dielectric loss," or generation of heat in the liquid.) The theory and some experimental results on the dielectric constants of polar liquids at radio frequencies can be found in Böttcher [10], chap. 10. For nitrobenzene the limiting frequency is about 10^{10} radians sec^{-1}. For some other liquids with lower Kerr constants the limiting frequency is still higher.

The Kerr shutter is therefore capable of modulating the intensity of a beam of light at microwave frequencies, and there is considerable interest in pushing this capability to the limit. Complications enter when the transit time nl/c for light passing between the plates of the cell is comparable to the period of the applied voltage; a reference on this point is Holshouser et al. [41]. Problems 18-9 and 18-10 deal with modulation at low frequencies.

In applications to photography the Kerr shutter is placed before the camera lens and "opened" by a square-topped voltage pulse. Commercially available systems have apertures perhaps 50 mm square and can apply pulses of duration 10^{-8} sec or less at any desired time after the onset of a rapidly changing event under study.

The Kerr shutter has been applied to measuring the velocity of light by the time-of-flight method. Galileo and assistants tried such a measurement with hand-operated shutters, but the distance involved made the time of flight far less than the human reaction. Römer made observations in 1675 in which the source was a satellite of Jupiter suffering regular eclipses by the planet. The times between successive eclipses as observed from Earth varies through the year because of variation of the velocity of Earth relative to Jupiter, and the largest and smallest times differ by about 30 sec. From the constants of the solar system a rough value of c was obtained. Fizeau, in 1849, reduced the required path to the order of 10 km by using a shutter consisting in a rotating toothed wheel. With the wheel stationary, a source shining through the gap between two teeth illuminated a distant mirror, and the reflected light was observed through an adjacent gap. When the wheel rotated, the light was chopped into pulses, and at a certain speed the time of flight was equal to the time required for a gap to be replaced by the next tooth, and the observer saw no light. At twice this speed the light rose to a maximum, and at thrice the speed it was zero again. A pair of Kerr shutters driven by the same voltage oscillator serves the same purpose as the toothed wheel. The frequency of chopping can be high enough that the working distance need be only a few meters. The first measurements were made by Karolus and Mittelstaedt, beginning in 1925. More details on measurements of the velocity of light can be found in Jenkins and White [53], chap. 19, and in the article by Bergstrand in the Encyclopedia of Physics [29], vol. 24.

Problems

18-1. A Lorentz atom has a single electron with natural frequency ω_0. A possible motion of the electron is circular with angular velocity ω_0 and any given radius r. Let this motion be in a plane perpendicular to a z axis in the counterclockwise sense as viewed looking in the negative z direction. Suppose now that the atom is in a static magnetic field with **B** directed along the positive z axis. Show that a possible motion is the same as above but with angular velocity $\omega_0 + \omega'$, where ω' is very close to the Larmor frequency when the latter is very small compared with ω_0. The proof is to be drawn from a balance of centrifugal force, elastic binding force, and Lorentz force. (The result of this problem, together with the analogous results for the opposite circular motion and for linear motion along the z axis, forms the basis of a common way of discussing the Zeeman effect. See White [98], p. 149.)

18-2. In deriving the spectrum in Sec. 18-2, the source was pictured as equivalent to three incoherent sources, each involving just one of the normal modes of oscillation in a magnetic field. If the excitation of the actual source is isotropic, then there is a theorem in statistical mechanics according to which the energy of excitation is equally divided among the three hypothetical sources; these sources therefore radiate equal powers. Let the source be at the origin of a spherical polar coordinate system with **B** along the polar axis. Treat the source as being essentially a point. Let I stand for irradiance at any point of a unit sphere centered at the source.   Write I as a function of polar angle θ for each of the three hypothetical sources, and adjust the constants of proportionality to make the radiated power the same for all.   Add the results to obtain a sphere as the radiation pattern for the actual source.   Draw, with proper relative sizes, all the patterns in a plane through the polar axis.

18-3.   As a continuation of Prob. 18-2, let P be a point of observation in a direction from the source making angle θ with the polar axis.   Let ξ and η be rectangular axes pointing in the directions of increasing θ and ϕ, respectively.   With respect to these axes write the Stokes parameters of the three Zeeman components as observed at P. Indicate which frequency belongs to each set.   (The polarizations can be pictured mentally and the parameters written with the aid of Figs. 13-19 and 13-20.)   Add the sets of parameters as for incoherent sources to show that the radiation observed at P without spectral resolution is unpolarized.

18-4.   With respect to the ξ and η axes of Prob. 18-3, draw ellipses representing the polarizations of the Zeeman components for $\theta = 45°$.   Indicate the frequency associated with each figure.   (The solution can be drawn at once without resorting to Stokes parameters.)   Draw the spectrum analogous to Fig. 18-1 with the components having proper relative heights.

18-5.   Let a source consist of Lorentz atoms, each having a mass 100 times that of a proton and a resonant frequency corresponding to a wavelength of 5000 A   Let the atoms have thermal motions corresponding to a temperature of 300°K.   Find the magnetic field B in gauss such that the thermal width Δ given by (12-38) equals the Larmor frequency ω_L.   (Under these conditions the components in Fig. 18-1a would show substantial blending in the wings.   Anomalous Zeeman patterns in atomic spectra sometimes have components separated by less than $0.1\omega_L$—see White [98], p. 161.   A temperature of 300°K—room temperature—is low for an emitting source. Thus one sees the reason for very strong fields in studying the Zeeman effect.)

18-6.   In the calculations in Sec. 18-3 a cartesian representation was used.   The resulting relations between the components of $\mathbf{D}_0$ and $\mathbf{E}_0$ are suitable for use in conjunction with (17-14) in straightforward calculation of the basic waves for any direction of propagation.   In the case of propagation along $\mathbf{B}$ (Faraday effect) one expects a simplification if the wave is treated from the outset as a superposition of opposite circular polarizations, rather than orthogonal linear polarizations.   Analytically this is accomplished by resolving all vectors and vector equations along the vectors

$$\mathbf{e}_1 = \frac{\mathbf{a} + i\mathbf{b}}{\sqrt{2}} \qquad \mathbf{e}_2 = \frac{\mathbf{a} - i\mathbf{b}}{\sqrt{2}} \qquad \mathbf{c}$$

where $\mathbf{a}$, $\mathbf{b}$, and $\mathbf{c}$ are the real unit vectors in the cartesian system, and $\mathbf{B}$ and $\mathbf{k}$ are along $\mathbf{c}$ (z axis).   The vectors $\mathbf{e}_1$ and $\mathbf{e}_2$ are said to be *orthogonal unitary vectors*, since they satisfy

$$\mathbf{e}_1 \cdot \mathbf{e}_1^* = \mathbf{e}_2 \cdot \mathbf{e}_2^* = 1 \qquad \mathbf{e}_1 \cdot \mathbf{e}_2^* = 0$$

(Compare Prob. 2-20.)   These relations are used in writing the resolutions in the same way that the orthogonality of $\mathbf{a}$, $\mathbf{b}$, and $\mathbf{c}$ is used in writing a cartesian resolution.   For notation write, for example,

$$\mathbf{E}_0 = E_{01}\mathbf{e}_1 + E_{02}\mathbf{e}_2 + E_{0z}\mathbf{c}$$

Carry out a complete calculation in the new resolution.   Use (18-15) to find the polarizabilities α_{11}, α_{12}, α_{1z}, α_{21}, etc., and, ultimately, the relations between the components of $\mathbf{D}_0$ and $\mathbf{E}_0$.   Use (17-14) to show that the basic waves have $\mathbf{E}_0$ and $\mathbf{D}_0$ perpendicular to $\mathbf{k}$ and have circular polarizations, and get (18-22) and (18-23).

18-7. Consider three devices for producing a rotation of the line of oscillation of a linearly polarized wave through 45°. One is an optical rotator (Prob. 13-32), the second is a slab of quartz with faces perpendicular to the optic axis (optical activity), and the third is a glass rod in a magnetic field (Faraday effect). Let these devices be placed in succession between a linear polarizer and a plane mirror. Let quasi-mono-chromatic unpolarized light of irradiance I fall normally on the polarizer. What is the irradiance of the wave returning through the polarizer in each case?

18-8. Concerning the π and σ waves found in Sec. 18-4, discuss qualitatively the oscillations of the real fields **D** and **E** at a fixed point of space for a frequency well below the resonant frequencies. If any of these oscillations is elliptical, give the orientation of major and minor axes and the direction of rotation.

18-9. Draw a rough curve of transmittance of a Kerr shutter as a function of applied voltage V. Extend the curve to negative V, corresponding to reversal of polarity. If V_1 is the lowest positive voltage that makes $r = \frac{1}{4}$ and the transmittance half-maximum, note that the curve is fairly straight in the vicinity of V_1. See the next problem.

18-10. Let V_1 be as defined in Prob. 18-9, and let v be an increment of voltage small compared with V_1. Prove the following approximations for the transmittance of a Kerr shutter:

$$\mathfrak{I}(v) \approx \frac{1}{2}\left(\frac{\pi v^2}{4V_1}\right)^2 \qquad \mathfrak{I}(V_1 + v) \approx \frac{1}{4}\left(1 + \frac{\pi v}{V_1}\right)$$

Let $v = v_0 \sin \omega_0 t$, where ω_0 may be a radio frequency, but not so high that the finite transit time through the cell is important. The second formula above shows that, with a static bias V_1 on the cell, the light is modulated sinusoidally at frequency ω_0. From the first formula it follows that without a bias the modulation has a component of frequency $2\omega_0$ and one of frequency $4\omega_0$. Show that an r-wave plate can be placed between one of the polarizers and the Kerr cell and given a suitable orientation and a value of r (call it r_0) suitably related to v_0 such that, in the unbiased case, the modulation is sinusoidal with frequency either $2\omega_0$ or $4\omega_0$, the amplitude of modulation with the second adjustment being comparatively very small. (A Soleil compensator might be used here.)

chapter **19**

Relation of Quantum to Classical Theory

In earlier chapters it was pointed out that the classical theory of radiation leads to good quantitative agreement with observation in such problems as interference and diffraction. It also provides a good working basis for characterizing radiation with regard to spectrum, polarization, and coherence. For treating the problem of atomic radiation and the related problems of scattering and refraction, the Lorentz theory is satisfying in many qualitative and some quantitative details, but the model has the unattractive features that have been lumped under the heading of "nonelectrical forces" in order to point out explicitly the short-comings of the theory. A particularly obvious shortcoming is the failure of the theory to account for the existence of stable atoms with different chemical properties and characteristic spectra. It remains for this final chapter to say something about the prominent role of radiative phenomena in the development of quantum theory and the manner in which this new theory makes up deficiencies of the classical theory and yet agrees with the classical theory when the latter agrees with experience.

The idea of quanta was introduced by Planck in 1900 in obtaining a theory of the spectrum of blackbody radiation. This chapter will begin with a summary of the classical background of the famous problem of this spectrum and will continue with an account of the development of the quantum theory of radiation up to its final form and descriptions of some of the important results.

19-1   Characterization of Radiation Fields   In previous chapters discussion was confined to problems in which a wave traversed a point of space traveling in a unique or nearly unique direction.   For radiometric purposes the notion of irradiance of the wave and its resolution into a power spectrum was sufficient.   We have now to consider the more general case of a field consisting in a superposition of waves traveling in many, perhaps all, directions at once.   An example occurs when an incandescent source subtends a large solid angle as seen from a point of observation or completely surrounds the point.   Only steady, unpolarized sources need be considered.   A useful idea here is the *intensity of the field* and its spectral decomposition.

At a given point of the field consider a small element $d\Sigma$ of an imaginary plane surface.   Let the normal **n** shown in Fig. 19-1 be the polar axis of a coordinate system with angles θ and ϕ.   Let $d\Omega$ be an element of solid angle in a given direction (θ,ϕ).   In unit time all those waves whose directions of propagation fall in $d\Omega$ will transport through $d\Sigma$ an amount of energy

$$dW = \mathcal{I}(\theta,\phi)\,\cos\theta\;d\Sigma\;d\Omega \qquad (19\text{-}1)$$

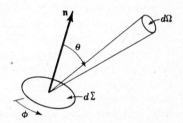

The function $\mathcal{I}(\theta,\phi)$ defined by this relation is the intensity of the field.[1]   It is assumed to be a continuous function of direction.   (A perfectly plane wave with finite irradiance would have infinite intensity in one direction, and zero in all others, but this situation is physically unrealizable.   The connection of the ir-

Fig. 19-1. *Imaginary element of surface and directed element of solid angle for defining intensity in a radiation field.*

radiance I, appearing earlier, with intensity is that an incident wave was supposed to have only a small spread in direction, and the integral of the intensity $\mathcal{I}$ over these directions is what was called irradiance; often the wave could be treated in approximation as a plane wave.)

The intensity can be resolved into a spectral decomposition on a scale of any of the variables ω, ν, λ, $k(= 2\pi/\lambda)$, or $\sigma(= 1/\lambda)$.   Thus

$$\mathcal{I} = \int_0^\infty \mathcal{I}_\omega(\omega)\,d\omega = \int_0^\infty \mathcal{I}_\lambda(\lambda)\,d\lambda = \cdots \qquad (19\text{-}2)$$

[1] According to the best nomenclature for radiometry, the quantity $\mathcal{I}$ defined by (19-1) would be called *radiance* of the field and given the symbol N, as in (13-38) [note that θ and ϕ in the latter formula are not polar angles, and $d\theta\,d\phi$ is an element of solid angle written $d\Omega$ in (19-1)].   In this best nomenclature the term *intensity* is reserved to designate power radiated into a unit solid angle in a given direction from an entire source, such as a lamp bulb or a star (see reference 19, p. 229).   To introduce the letter $\mathcal{I}$ and call it intensity is to follow the almost universal practice in connection with the topics of this chapter.   A point in connection with the quantity $\mathcal{I}$ is brought out in Prob. 19-2.

The subscript indicates the variable with respect to which the decomposition is made, while the symbol in parentheses indicates the value of the argument at which the function is evaluated. Each integrand, called the *spectral intensity*, has the definite physical significance assigned to it by the principles of spectrometry, and the interrelations are of the type brought out in Prob. 12-6, namely, simple change of variable of integration. For the most part the variable ω will be used, in keeping with previous chapters, and $\mathcal{g}_\omega$ has the explicit meaning defined by modifying (19-1) to refer to waves with frequencies between ω and $\omega + d\omega$:

$$dW_\omega = \mathcal{g}_\omega(\omega,\theta,\phi) \cos\theta \, d\omega \, d\Sigma \, d\Omega \tag{19-3}$$

If the spectral intensity is independent of direction, the field is said to be *isotropic*. In this case it is common to introduce as an alternative to spectral intensity $\mathcal{g}_\omega$ the notion of *spectral energy density* u_ω (or u_ν, u_λ, etc.) defined such that the field energy in unit volume contributed by all waves with frequencies between ω and $\omega + d\omega$ is $u_\omega \, d\omega$ (the unit of u_ω is energy per unit volume per unit frequency range).

The relation between u_ω and $\mathcal{g}_\omega$ can be obtained as follows: Consider first those waves with frequencies between ω and $\omega + d\omega$, propagating in a direction $\mathbf{n}$ within solid angle $d\Omega$. Imagine a unit cube with two faces perpendicular to $\mathbf{n}$. All the energy $du_\omega \, d\omega$ of the specified kind in this cube will just leave and be replaced by an equal sample in time c^{-1}. Then according to (19-3), $du_\omega = c^{-1}\mathcal{g}_\omega \, d\Omega$. Integrating over all solid angles (isotropic case),

$$u_\omega = \frac{4\pi\mathcal{g}_\omega}{c} \tag{19-4}$$

The same relation holds for variables of spectral resolution other than ω. Moreover, for the total energy density,

$$u = \int_0^\infty u_\omega \, d\omega = \frac{4\pi\mathcal{g}}{c} \tag{19-5}$$

In the literature the notion of energy density is frequently used, but in the following sections a field will be characterized by its spectral intensity.

In conclusion, intensity and energy density are properties describing the average behavior of steady radiation fields. About these averages there are local and temporal fluctuations which are of considerable interest, since, under circumstances to be mentioned in Sec. 19-7, quantum theory gives different results than does classical theory. Attention in the following will be fixed on the average properties.

19-2 Radiation in Thermal Equilibrium. Cavity and Black-body

Suppose a volume of space is enclosed by opaque walls maintained at some uniform absolute temperature T. If the walls are of real materials (not perfect reflectors for any kind of incident wave), radiation exists in the cavity, and in the equilibrium state there is a certain rate of absorption at the walls in each frequency interval, and an equal rate of emission in that same frequency interval. The principles of thermodynamics can be applied to this equilibrium state, and any conclusions will be of unquestionable validity. Elementary deductions are that a perpetual motion could be constructed (second law of thermodynamics violated) if the radiation does not have the following properties: It is isotropic and unpolarized, and the spectral intensity is independent of position in the cavity, of the material of which the walls are composed, and of the presence of bodies in the cavity (as long as the latter have been allowed to come to equilibrium, and in this state they will be at temperature T). It follows that $\mathcal{I}_\omega$ depends only on ω and T, and $\mathcal{I}$ depends only on T.

A less elementary deduction, obtained from general principles of electromagnetic theory in conjunction with thermodynamics, is *Wien's displacement law*. This law narrows the dependence of $\mathcal{I}_\omega$ on ω and T and states that

$$\mathcal{I}_\omega(\omega, T) = T^3 \, F\left(\frac{\omega}{T}\right) \tag{19-6}$$

or, on a wavelength scale,

$$\mathcal{I}_\lambda(\lambda, T) = T^5 \, G(\lambda T) \tag{19-7}$$

where F and G are universal functions related to each other through the general relation existing between an $\mathcal{I}_\omega$ and the corresponding $\mathcal{I}_\lambda$. (Note that G is a function of the product λT—no comma between the two.) The reader will be interested in the derivation of Wien's law as given, for example, in Born [7], p. 420.

A body is by definition a *blackbody* (in a technical sense, since it may be incandescent) if it absorbs completely any radiation falling on it. It follows, again by elementary thermodynamics, that if such a body is at absolute temperature T, it radiates, and the rate of radiation from an element of surface $d\Sigma$ into frequency interval $d\omega$ and solid angle $d\Omega$ is given by (19-3) if $\mathcal{I}_\omega$ is the intensity in cavity radiation at absolute temperature T.

This relation between a blackbody and a cavity at the same temperature is seen in another way by supposing a small hole cut in the wall of the cavity. Any radiation entering from outside will, with overwhelming probability, be completely absorbed in multiple partial reflections, and a negligible fraction of the original radiation will come back out. The radiation issuing from the hole is essentially that of a blackbody, and this fact is used in practical realization of blackbody radiation for spectroscopic analysis. [Recall the application mentioned under formula (13-26).]

An expression for the total rate of radiation from a unit area of a blackbody is obtained by substituting (19-6) in (19-3), dropping $d\Sigma$, writing $d\Omega = \sin\theta\,d\theta\,d\phi$, and integrating over the ranges $0 < \omega < \infty$, $0 < \theta < \pi/2$, and $0 < \phi < 2\pi$. The result is

$$W = \pi T^4 \int_0^\infty F(x)\,dx = \sigma T^4 \tag{19-8}$$

where $x = \omega/T$, and σ is a constant called the *Stefan-Boltzmann constant*, the experimental measurement of which is discussed in Zemansky [104], p. 105. The value of σ is 5.672×10^{-5} erg cm^{-2} °K^{-4} sec^{-1}. Equation (19-8) is known as the *Stefan-Boltzmann law*. A direct derivation by thermodynamics alone is given in Born [7], p. 420, and Zemansky [104], p. 287.

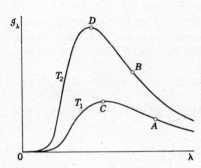

Fig. 19-2. *Spectral intensity of blackbody radiation for two temperatures in the relation $T_2 = 1.2 T_1$.*

The implications of Wien's displacement law are illustrated in Fig. 19-2. Curves of $\mathcal{I}_\lambda$ with the experimentally observed shapes are shown for two absolute temperatures. (It is usual to illustrate the blackbody spectrum by a wavelength resolution.) One curve can be obtained from the other, for if the abscissas of points A and B are related by the left-hand equation below, their ordinates are related by the equation on the right, as read from (19-7):

$$\lambda_B = \frac{T_1}{T_2}\lambda_A \qquad \mathcal{I}_\lambda(\lambda_B, T_2) = \left(\frac{T_2}{T_1}\right)^5 \mathcal{I}_\lambda(\lambda_A, T_1)$$

If C is the maximum of the lower curve, and D is related to it as B to A, then D is the maximum of the upper curve. The condition for a maximum is found from (19-7) to be $G'(\lambda T) = 0$, and because the derivative G' is a universal function, the root of this equation is a universal constant, say b. Hence if $\lambda_{\max}$ is the abscissa of the maximum of $\mathcal{I}_\lambda$ at absolute temperature T,

$$\lambda_{\max} T = b \tag{19-9}$$

This is known as *Wien's displacement law*. The observed value of b is 0.2897 cm °K. Note that the maximum ordinate of $\mathcal{I}_\lambda$ varies as T^5, while the area under the curve varies as T^4. [A curve of $\mathcal{I}_\omega$ against ω shows a maximum as in Fig. 19-2, but the shape is only qualitatively the same.   The area varies as T^4, but the maximum ordinate varies as T^3. The abscissa of the maximum satisfies $2\pi cT/\omega_{max} = b' \neq b$, and ω_{max} for temperature T is *not* related to the λ_{max} in (19-9) as frequency is related to wavelength in a monochromatic wave in free space.   The value of b' is 0.5098 cm °K.]

19-3   Planck's Law and Its Forerunners   The Wien displacement law (19-6) can equally well be written in the form

$$\mathcal{I}_\omega(\omega T\,) \,=\, \omega^3 f\left(\frac{\omega}{T}\right) \tag{19-10}$$

which is more convenient for the following work.   It remains to find the universal function f.   Thermodynamics can contribute no more, and it is necessary to invoke some system capable of absorbing and emitting radiation and to consider the detailed mechanism of this system when it exists at thermal equilibrium in a cavity whose walls are at temperature T.   Since the nature of the radiation in the cavity is unaffected by the presence of any such system, one is free to make any choice, even a hypothetical one, and Planck chose a stationary Lorentz atom with a single electron of natural frequency ω_0.[1]

Waves impinge on this atom from all directions and are scattered. One can think of power being absorbed from incident waves and emitted into scattered waves.   In the process the electron undergoes some complicated motion, but an equilibrium condition prevails at temperature T in which the time average of the mechanical energy of the atom (kinetic plus potential), call it $\langle\epsilon\rangle_T$, must be related in some way to the spectral intensity of the cavity radiation.   Planck showed that the relation given by classical theory is

$$\mathcal{I}_\omega(\omega_0,T) \,=\, \frac{\omega_0{}^2}{12\pi^3c^2} \langle\epsilon\rangle_T \tag{19-11}$$

where ω_0 is the resonant frequency of the atom and can be given any value. In Appendix E this result is drawn from formulas of earlier chapters.

An expression for the time average $\langle\epsilon\rangle_T$ can be obtained by the principles of statistical mechanics developed by Gibbs.[2]   Let us first see what comes on a purely classical basis.

---

[1] Planck's first derivation of the correct blackbody spectrum involved an empirical adjustment of thermodynamic relations and could not be considered as a derivation from established physical principles or as clearly indicating any new ones.   The derivation given here is Planck's second, paraphrased to relate to the Lorentz theory as presented in this book.   This second derivation introduced explicitly the idea of quanta.   The arguments involved some statistical mechanics, and part of Planck's contribution consisted in adapting statistical ideas to a quantized system, but here again the treatment being given departs somewhat from Planck's original writings.

[2] A short account can be found in Kennard [54], chap. 9.

Let the nucleus of the atom be at the origin of a cartesian system of coordinates, and let the coordinates of the electron at any instant be x_1, x_2, and x_3. The instantaneous energy of the atom is then

$$\epsilon = \epsilon_1 + \epsilon_2 + \epsilon_3 \qquad (19\text{-}12)$$

where

$$\epsilon_i = \frac{m}{2}(\dot{x}_i{}^2 + \omega_0{}^2 x_i{}^2) \qquad i = 1, 2, 3 \qquad (19\text{-}13)$$

Thus the atom is equivalent to three separate *linear* oscillators. The time average of ϵ is the sum of the averages of the three terms on the right of (19-12), and because of the isotropic character of the radiation and the atom, these three averages are equal. By this argument the problem is reduced to the especially simple one of finding the behavior of one of the component linear oscillators in thermal equilibrium.

A deduction from classical statistical mechanics is that if one observed the atom at some instant, one would find the energy of the ith component oscillator between ϵ_i and $\epsilon_i + d\epsilon_i$ with probability

$$P(\epsilon_i)d\epsilon_i = Ce^{-\beta\epsilon_i}\,d\epsilon_i \qquad (19\text{-}14)$$

where $\beta = (kT)^{-1}$, k is Boltzmann's constant, and C is a constant normalizing the probability to unity and therefore being

$$C = \left(\int_0^\infty e^{-\beta\epsilon_i}d\epsilon_i\right)^{-1} = \beta$$

The central postulate of classical statistical mechanics is that if the statistical average of ϵ_i is calculated by means of the probability distribution (19-14), then the result is the same as the time average about which we have been speaking. We then have

$$\langle\epsilon\rangle_T = 3\langle\epsilon_i\rangle_T = 3\int_0^\infty \epsilon_i\,P(\epsilon_i)\,d\epsilon_i = 3kT$$

The spectrum (19-11) becomes (allowing ω_0 to assume any value and dropping the subscript)

$$\mathcal{G}_\omega(\omega,T) = \frac{\omega^2 kT}{4\pi^3 c^2} \qquad (19\text{-}15)$$

a result known as the *Rayleigh-Jeans law*. This spectrum is found to agree with observation at low frequencies, but it is wrong at high frequencies, where it tends to infinity. The comparison will be illustrated later.[1]

Planck introduced the hypothesis that a linear oscillator of the sort constituting any one of the component oscillators above does not exhibit the classical property of assuming any energy between zero and infinity.

---

[1] For the history of the Rayleigh-Jeans law, see Whittaker [99], p. 383, and references therein. The chronology relative to the epochal year 1900 is interesting.

Rather it would be found on observation at a given instant to have an energy $n\epsilon_0$, where ϵ_0 is some fixed quantum of energy associated with the oscillator, and n is some positive integer or zero. This idea, presented in 1900, marked the beginning of the quantum theory, and in the following quarter-century the whole subject of physics, including the notion of measurement, was completely overhauled. But in the beginning Planck's hypothesis was merely superposed on an otherwise classical theory, and the result was the correct theoretical spectrum of cavity radiation. From the point of view of the final quantum theory, one can see in several ways why this procedure worked.

With the component oscillators quantized, the principles of statistical mechanics give, as the probability that any one of these oscillators has energy $n\epsilon_0$, the following formula to replace the classical formula (19-14):

$$P(n\epsilon_0) = Ce^{-n\beta\epsilon_0} \tag{19-16}$$

The normalization factor C is now

$$C = \left(\sum_{n=0}^{\infty} e^{-n\beta\epsilon_0} \right)^{-1} = 1 - e^{-\beta\epsilon_0}$$

(The series is a geometric progression.) The statistical average of the energy of the ith component oscillator is

$$[\epsilon_i]_{\text{av}} = \sum_{n=0}^{\infty} n\epsilon_0 P(n\epsilon_0) = -C \frac{d(C^{-1})}{d\beta} \tag{19-17}$$

It is easily seen that the last expression is equivalent to the sum preceding it and provides an easy means of evaluation.

Thrice the statistical average (19-17) replaces the classical time average of ϵ in (19-11); the result is the spectrum

$$\mathcal{I}_\omega(\omega, T) = \frac{\omega^2}{4\pi^3 c^2} \frac{\epsilon_0}{e^{\beta\epsilon_0} - 1} \tag{19-18}$$

This result is consistent with the Wien displacement law (19-10) only if

$$\beta = (kT)^{-1} \qquad \epsilon_0 = \hbar\omega \tag{19-19}$$

where k and $\hbar$ are constants. Plank worked with the ordinary frequency ν and introduced the constant h such that $h\nu = \hbar\omega$ and $\hbar = h/2\pi$; h is called *Planck's constant* and is the universal constant appearing in quantum theory, just as c appears in the electromagnetic theory. The unit of h is erg second, called the unit of *action*.

Formulas (19-18) and (19-19) give the correct blackbody spectrum if k and $\hbar$ are suitably chosen. Planck evaluated these constants by finding from the theoretical spectrum the following expressions for the constants σ and b in (19-8) and (19-9):

$$\sigma = \frac{\pi^2 k^4}{60 c^2 \hbar^3} \qquad b = \frac{2\pi \hbar c}{\alpha k}$$

where α is the root of $5(e^{-x} - 1) + x = 0$ and equals $4.9651 \cdots$. Comparison with the then current measurements of σ and b gave quite good values of k and $\hbar$.[1]   Later improvements have given

$$k \approx 1.38 \times 10^{-16} \text{ erg }°\text{K}^{-1} \qquad \hbar \approx 1.05 \times 10^{-27} \text{ erg sec}$$

The Planck law (19-18) and (19-19) has the following asymptotic

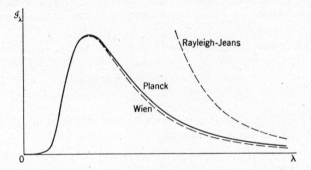

Fig. 19-3.   *Comparison of the Planck law with the classical Rayleigh-Jeans and Wien laws.*

expressions: When $\hbar \omega \ll kT$ (or $\beta \epsilon_0 \ll 1$),

$$\mathcal{J}_\omega(\omega, T) \approx \frac{\omega^2 kT}{4\pi^3 c^2} \tag{19-20}$$

which is the Rayleigh-Jeans law (19-15).   When $\hbar \omega \gg kT$,

$$\mathcal{J}_\omega(\omega, T) \approx \frac{\hbar \omega^3}{4\pi^3 c^2} e^{-\hbar \omega / kT} \tag{19-21}$$

which is known as the *Wien law* and was obtained by Wien in 1896 by a kind of theoretical argument.   He showed that it agreed with observation at high frequencies, but not at low frequencies.

---

[1] At the time Planck evaluated these constants the value of the gas constant R was well known, and the ratio R/k gave the first reliable value of the Avogadro number. Then from the Avogadro number and the known value of the Faraday the charge of the electron was well established for the first time.   Prior to 1900 only the ratio e/m was known with reasonable certainty.

For purposes of illustration, let the spectrum be referred to a wavelength scale. The Planck law becomes

$$\mathcal{I}_\lambda(\lambda, T) = \frac{2hc^2}{\lambda^5} \frac{1}{e^{hc/\lambda kT} - 1}$$

This function and its asymptotic forms (the Rayleigh-Jeans and Wien laws referred to a wavelength scale) are shown in Fig. 19-3. In terms of fractional departure from the Planck law, the Wien law grows worse and the Rayleigh-Jeans law improves as λ increases beyond the limit of the figure.

19-4 Old Quantum Theory of Atoms The spectrum of cavity radiation in thermal equilibrium is only sensitive enough as an indicator of atomic processes to show the need of modifying classical ideas. Once the notion of quanta was introduced, the Planck law was rederived from a number of different models. Far more sensitive an indicator is the characteristic line spectrum emitted by a given species of atom in a source such as an arc or a Geissler tube; these spectra were the chief guide in building up the quantum theory of the electronic structure of atoms and their states of aggregation, and of the interaction with a radiation field.

As early as 1879 it was recognized that the many lines in an atomic spectrum can be grouped into series. In 1885 Balmer gave his famous empirical formula for the frequencies of the series of visible lines of the hydrogen spectrum. In 1908 the regularities and numerical interrelationships observed in the frequencies of atomic spectra were comprehensively summarized in the *Ritz combination principle,* according to which an atom of whatever kind has associated with it an infinite set of numbers called *terms,* with dimensions of frequency; the frequency of any observed spectrum line can be expressed as the difference of two terms. There can thus be many more lines than terms, and the term structure can be discovered without observing all differences. Once the terms are known, one can look for any one of the differences, and one may find it as a relatively strong or relatively weak line or may not find it at all. Certain relationships of relative strengths of lines were noted, but no simple rule emerged.

The first atomic theory to be consistent with the combination principle and to contain stable atoms of distinct kinds was that initiated by Bohr in 1913 and now called the old quantum theory.

Recall that in 1911 Rutherford demonstrated the existence of the nucleus. It was then natural to investigate an atomic model consisting of a nucleus and a number of electrons, all subject just to mutual coulomb forces and forces of radiation reaction, and to apply classical mechanics.

The results for this model are that no matter how the electrons are started, they eventually swirl into the nucleus, giving off energy in the form of radiation, and the spectrum of the radiation consists not of discrete lines, but of some continuous distribution—all contrary to fact.

If one were to omit from the model the dissipative force of radiation reaction and hence the possibility of radiating in a manner consistent with conservation of energy, the electrons, given some initial motion, would continue in motion indefinitely with constant total energy. Bohr's first postulate was that for each kind of atom (defined by the number of electrons) there is a certain discrete set of these classical motions with constant energy, and that the atom can exist only in one or another of them. Moreover, while the atom is executing one of these motions, it gives off no radiation. The motions were called *stationary states*, and rules of quantization were developed for selecting them from the continuous range of classical motions. In the ith state the atom has the classically calculated energy ϵ_i with respect to some arbitrarily chosen zero. The rules give a state of lowest energy in which the electrons are still in motion rather than settled on the nucleus.

The second postulate was that the process of radiation consists in a discontinuous jump of the atom from a state of energy ϵ_i to a state of lower energy ϵ_j, and that the frequency of the radiation is $\omega = (\epsilon_i - \epsilon_j)/\hbar$. The difference of energy $\hbar\omega$ is discontinuously added to the radiation field. No such emission can occur when the atom is initially in the state of lowest energy, called the *ground state*. The inverse process of absorption from an incident field whose spectrum contains the frequency ω occurs when the atom is initially in the state with energy ϵ_j and jumps to ϵ_i with extraction from the field of energy $\hbar\omega$, the field being weakened at frequency ω.

The Bohr theory is consistent with the combination principle, with Einstein's analysis in 1905 of the photoelectric effect (absorption giving rise to ionization rather than excitation to a higher bound state), and with the experiments of Franck and Hertz in 1913 demonstrating directly the existence of discrete energy levels. In its detailed application the theory was highly successful in giving the energy levels of atomic hydrogen, but ran into difficulty with neutral helium, the hydrogen molecule, and more complicated systems. In spite of the preliminary character of the Bohr theory, the ideas in the two postulates persist in the later quantum theory.

An important point to note before proceeding is that the splitting of spectral lines by application of a static magnetic field (Zeeman effect) is to be interpreted as arising from a splitting of each energy level into a certain number of components with certain spacings. (Details can be found in introductory texts on spectra, such as White [98].) If level i is split into g_i components, then when the external field is reduced to zero, the c mponents coalesce, and level i is said to involve g_i *independent states* or to have *degeneracy* or *statistical weight* g_i. In the old quantum theory these states were certain of the classical motions selected by the rules of quantization. (The hypothesis of electron spin and magnetic moment had to be invoked to get the right number and spacing of levels in the Zeeman effect.) When N_i atoms are on level i, these atoms can be regarded as distributed over the degenerate states. In the so-called *natural distribution* all the degenerate states are equally populated, but by various techniques important in experiments on atomic processes, the population of the states can be made selective.

19-5 Einstein's Derivation of Planck's Law. Transition Probabilities

The old quantum theory contained no satisfactory method of predicting strengths of spectrum lines. Approximate results were obtained by clever arguments based on the *correspondence principle*, clearly stated by Bohr in 1923. On this point the reader may refer to Bohm [5], p. 48, and Born [7], p. 105. The final solution of the problem came late in the development of the new quantum theory, but an important preliminary to this solution was a general proposition given in papers by Einstein in 1916 and 1917 and which will now be described.

In spite of the shortcomings of the old quantum theory, the supposition of atomic energy levels and discontinuous transitions between them with accompanying emission and absorption of radiation according to Bohr's postulate could reasonably be accepted as correct in describing real atoms. Einstein considered the equilibrium of a gas of identical stationary atoms in a cavity at absolute temperature T. In spirit the calculation is the same as Planck's, but the atoms are taken to be real ones rather than Lorentz atoms (harmonic oscillators).

Let the levels of one of the atoms have energies $\epsilon_1, \epsilon_2, \ldots$ and statistical weights $g_1, g_2, \ldots$. An observation of the gas at some instant would reveal that the ith level is occupied by some N_i atoms. Statistical mechanics states that when thermal equilibrium prevails, and the total number of atoms is N, the distribution over levels is

$$N_i = \frac{Ng_ie^{-\beta\epsilon_i}}{\Sigma g_ie^{-\beta\epsilon_i}} \qquad \beta = (kT)^{-1} \qquad (19\text{-}22)$$

The sum in the denominator is over all i, and the sum of the N_i equals N. The N_i atoms are equally distributed over the g_i states having energy ϵ_i. The distribution (19-22) is called a *Boltzmann distribution* and is unaffected by adding the same constant to all the energies.

The atoms in the cavity are conceived to be continually making transitions up and down between the various levels, maintaining, apart from fluctuations, the distribution (19-22). This process can be described and general relationships obtained without making any commitments about details of a quantum theory.

Consider the transitions between levels i and j with $\epsilon_i > \epsilon_j$. An atom on level j can jump up to level i by absorbing energy

$$\hbar\omega_{ij} = \epsilon_i - \epsilon_j \tag{19-23}$$

from the waves in the cavity radiation having frequency ω_{ij} defined by (19-23). The number of these transitions occurring in unit time is proportional to the number of atoms on the initial level j and to the spectral intensity of the radiation at frequency ω_{ij}. Introducing a constant of proportionality B_{ij}, the rate of occurrence of the *absorptive transitions* is

$$B_{ij}N_j\, \mathcal{I}_\omega(\omega_{ij},T) \tag{19-24}$$

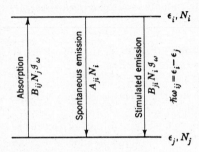

Fig. 19-4. *The three kinds of transition between energy levels i and j, and the rates occurring when atoms are in cavity radiation.*

With regard to radiative transitions from initial level i to lower level j, Einstein pointed out that in order to arrive at the Planck law it is necessary to assume two kinds of transitions. Firstly, there are *spontaneous emissions* occurring at a rate proportional just to the number of atoms in the upper level and therefore equal to

$$A_{ji}N_i \tag{19-25}$$

with A_{ji} some constant. Secondly, there are *stimulated emissions* occurring at a rate proportional to N_i and to the spectral intensity:

$$B_{ji}N_i\, \mathcal{I}_\omega(\omega_{ij},T) \tag{19-26}$$

The total rate of radiative transition is the sum of (19-25) and (19-26) and would reduce to just (19-25) if the atoms were initially brought to natural excitation in some way, but were not immersed in a radiation field.

The three constants of proportionality appearing in the rates of transition are called *Einstein transition probabilities* for transitions between levels i and j. The subscripts have been written according to a convention whereby the second subscript refers to the initial level of the transition. [On the other hand, ω_{ij} will always be defined by (19-23) in such a way as to be a positive number.] Figure 19-4 illustrates graphically the three kinds of transitions. Problem 19-4 points out alternative ways of defining the B's, an important consideration when reading the literature.

Atoms leaving level i may go up or down to many different levels, of which level j is only one. Atoms arriving at i may come from many levels in addition to j. In thermal equilibrium the total rate of departure from i must equal the total rate of arrival, but statistical mechanics now make the stronger statement, contained in the *principle of detailed balancing*, that the rate of transition directly from i to j equals that from j to i. Thus

$$(A_{ji} + B_{ji}\mathcal{G}_\omega)N_i = B_{ij}\mathcal{G}_\omega N_j$$

According to (19-22) and (19-23), if ω stands for ω_{ij},

$$g_i N_j = g_j N_i e^{\beta\hbar\omega}$$

whence
$$\mathcal{G}_\omega(\omega,T) = \frac{g_i A_{ji}}{g_j B_{ij} e^{\beta\hbar\omega} - g_i B_{ji}} \tag{19-27}$$

This result must be consistent with the Planck law for all β, and, in particular, it must reduce to the Rayleigh-Jeans law (19-20) when T is large enough to make $\beta\hbar\omega \ll 1$. In this case (19-27) becomes

$$\mathcal{G}_\omega \approx \frac{g_i A_{ji}}{g_j B_{ij} - g_i B_{ji} + g_j B_{ij}\beta\hbar\omega}$$

Comparison with (19-20) gives

$$g_j B_{ij} = g_i B_{ji} \tag{19-28}$$

$$A_{ji} = \frac{\hbar\omega^3}{4\pi^3 c^2} B_{ji} \tag{19-29}$$

Substitution of these relations in (19-27) gives the Planck law (19-18) and (19-19).

These arguments of Einstein's are of such generality that it becomes a requirement on quantum theory that it account for the three kinds of transition and yield values of the transition probabilities consistent with (19-28) and (19-29).

19-6 Lifetimes and Oscillator Strengths According to the Lorentz model, if an electron, elastically bound in an atom so as to have resonant frequency ω_0, is excited at $t = 0$, and the atom is then left undisturbed, the mechanical energy W converts into radiation and decreases according to the exponential law

$$W = W_0 e^{-t/\tau} \tag{19-30}$$

where τ is defined as the lifetime of the excited state and is given by (12-15) and (12-9) to be

$$\tau = \frac{3mc^3}{2e^2\omega_0{}^2} \qquad (19\text{-}31)$$

Let us now look for the quantum analogue.

Consider an atom with energy levels ϵ_1, ϵ_2, . . . enumerated in ascending order. Suppose a large number of such atoms are on level i at $t = 0$ (equally distributed over degenerate states—"natural" excitation), and all other levels are empty. These atoms will make spontaneous transitions to lower levels, and eventually all atoms will cascade down to the ground level. The law governing the change in the instantaneous population N_i is, according to the meaning of the Einstein A coefficients,

$$\frac{dN_i}{dt} = -N_i \sum_{j<i} A_{ji} \qquad (19\text{-}32)$$

whence $\qquad N_i(t) = N_i(0)\, e^{-t/\tau_i} \qquad \frac{1}{\tau_i} = \sum_{j<i} A_{ji} \qquad (19\text{-}33)$

This exponential decay with lifetime τ_i remains unchanged if the method of excitation happens also to produce an initial population of levels below i, but not above. All spectrum lines arising from transitions with upper level i decrease in strength according to the same exponential law (19-33), and there are techniques using pulsed excitation and fast detectors for measuring τ_i directly (see, for example, the paper by W. R. Bennett, Jr., in Singer [83], p. 28). Often the result is of the same order of magnitude as (19-31).

One can continue and inquire as to the temporal behavior of the population N_j of a level below i when level i, but no higher level, is initially populated. There are now the competing processes of decrease through transitions to states below j and of increase due to arrivals from populated states above, and one has to solve successively for the temporal behaviors of all the populations from N_i down to N_j. Problem 19-5 deals with the beginning of the process.[1] There is not a simple exponential decrease in N_j, and, in fact, if this number is initially zero, it builds up to a maximum and then decreases according to a law not involving just a single lifetime, and transitions down from j give spectrum lines whose intensities show the same time dependence. Hence only the lines originating in level i, the uppermost of the populated ones, show exactly the type of

---

[1] A similar but simpler problem arises in radioactive decay of a parent nucleus through a series, such as the one from Th^{232} to Pb^{208}. The simplification is that each nucleus decays only to the one next lower in the series, possibly with simple branching at a few stages.

exponential decay given by the Lorentz model to be the universal behavior in unperturbed emission.

In spite of this limited similarity between classical and quantum behavior, the above arguments assign to each level i a lifetime τ_i with the significance that it determines under any circumstance of natural excitation the rate at which atoms leave level i due just to the spontaneous transitions downward. In Sec. 19-7 these lifetimes will be related to widths of levels and spectrum lines.

Let us now compare the Lorentz and quantum theories of absorption and refraction occurring when a gas of atoms is steadily irradiated by a beam. Formulas in the two theories are brought to close correspondence by introducing the idea of oscillator strengths.

Consider first the problem of absorption. Let the gas of atoms be irradiated by an unpolarized and approximately unidirectional beam with spectral intensity $\mathcal{I}_\omega(\omega)$, the latter being constant over a small range of directions filling solid angle $d\Omega$, and zero for other directions. Let the spectrum of the beam be independent of frequency over a small range of ω, and zero for other frequencies, and let this range include just one of the frequencies of transition from the ground level of the atom to excited levels, say the one to level i. A steady condition will prevail in which atoms on the ground level become excited at a certain rate, absorbing energy from the beam, and excited atoms cascade back to the ground level by spontaneous emission of radiation in all directions. For the moment let the incident beam be weak enough that a very small fraction of atoms is on level i at a given time and stimulated emissions can be neglected. The radiation from the gas is called *fluorescence*, and that part of it due to transitions directly from level i to the ground level (and therefore having the same frequency as the incident beam) is called *resonance fluorescence*.

For the rate of absorption of energy from the beam by N_1 atoms on the ground level, one is now tempted to write

$$\text{Absorption} = \hbar\omega_{i1}N_1B_{i1}\mathcal{I}_\omega\frac{d\Omega}{4\pi} \qquad (19\text{-}34)$$

that is, just the fraction $d\Omega/4\pi$ of the rate for isotropic irradiation, as in a cavity. If the ground level is degenerate, this formula is correct only if the degenerate states of this level are at all times equally populated; but when atoms are irradiated by a collimated beam, even though unpolarized, it happens in certain cases that the atoms returning to the ground level by spontaneous emission do not fall with equal probability in the several states, and a selective population results. The phenomenon is known as *optical pumping* and involves special considerations that will not be entered into here. Let us therefore *assume* in all the following that degenerate levels are always populated in the "normal" manner. We thereby deal with a special problem having a kind of standard nature in which (19-34) is correct.

For comparison, consider $\mathfrak{N}$ Lorentz atoms with resonant frequency ω_{i1}, and let them be irradiated by the beam described above. If $\sigma(\omega)$ is the classical cross section for scattering, the rate of absorption from the beam is

$$\text{Absorption} = \mathfrak{N}\mathcal{I}_\omega \, d\Omega \int \sigma \, d\omega = \frac{2\pi^2 e^2}{mc} \, \mathfrak{N}\mathcal{I}_\omega \, d\Omega \qquad (19\text{-}35)$$

where the last expression comes from (14-18). Equating (19-34) and (19-35), we can say that the N_1 real atoms absorb at the same rate as a number $\mathfrak{N} = f_{i1}N_1$ of oscillating electrons in Lorentz atoms, where f_{i1} is a fraction called the *oscillator strength of the absorptive transition* and is given by

$$f_{i1} = \frac{mc\hbar\omega_{i1}}{8\pi^3 e^2} \, B_{i1} \qquad (19\text{-}36)$$

Suppose now that the incident beam is so strong that an appreciable fraction of the atoms is on level i at any time, and stimulated transitions to the ground level become important. Now stimulated emission in a gas of uniform density has the special property, to be mentioned again in Sec. 19-8, that the emitted energy does not go off in all directions, but rather reinforces the incident beam and hence amounts to a negative absorption. We are thus led to define an *oscillator strength for stimulated emission:*

$$f_{1i} = - \frac{mc\hbar\omega_{i1}}{8\pi^3 e^2} \, B_{1i} \qquad (19\text{-}37)$$

With the negative sign added (the usual convention), the net rate of absorption from the beam is the classical rate for one Lorentz atom [last expression in (19-35) divided by $\mathfrak{N}$] multiplied by $f_{i1}N_1 + f_{1i}N_i$. Here the first term is positive, the second negative.

The above ideas can be generalized to refer to any pair of levels i and j. If $\epsilon_i > \epsilon_j$,

$$f_{ij} = \frac{mc\hbar\omega_{ij}}{8\pi^3 e^2} \, B_{ij} = - \frac{g_i}{g_j} \, f_{ji} \qquad (19\text{-}38)$$

where ω_{ij} is defined by (19-23) and is positive. Knowledge of oscillator strengths is equivalent to knowledge of transition probabilities. The relation between the f's and the B's depends on the definition of the latter (see Prob. 19-4); but the f's are numbers associated just with the atom, ·and in this respect they are like the A's, in terms of which they can be expressed.

Finally, consider a quasi-monochromatic incident beam whose frequency ω does not coincide with any transition frequency between energy

levels of the atoms.   The gas is then transparent to the beam but has a
refractive index.   In the simplest case all the atoms on which the incident
beam is to fall are in the ground state; it was shown, originally by Ladenburg in 1921, that in this case the atoms have a polarizability

$$\alpha(\omega) = \frac{e^2}{m} \sum_i \frac{f_{i1}}{\omega_{i1}^2 - \omega^2} \tag{19-39}$$

Substitution of this result in the Sellmeier formula (15-43) gives the
refractive index in agreement with the form assumed by (15-50) at a
frequency ω well away from any resonance, when the imaginary parts of
the denominators can be neglected.

19-7   Quantum Theory of Atoms and Radiation   As already
noted, the old quantum theory failed to assign correct values to the
energy levels of atoms more complicated than hydrogen, and it gave
only very limited results on the question of numerical values of transition
probabilities.   In addition, it could say nothing to reconcile observations
that electromagnetic radiation shows the classical properties of waves
under some experimental conditions but appears to be a flight of particles
under others, and that electrons and other material bodies also show this
wave-particle duality.   In a few years beginning in 1925 the "new"
quantum theory, now known simply as *the* quantum theory, was developed, and all the problems just mentioned were solved.

The formalism of the theory is complicated, and one must study it
for some time in connection with simple systems before reaching the
point of incorporating radiation in a thoroughly consistent fashion.   The
present section can only give some results with references (often to
advanced literature); the two following sections describe some spectacular illustrations.   Time and again one sees classical formulas emerge at
the end of a quantum calculation, and ultimately one gains a feeling
for when a problem, even as extreme as some involving gamma radiation
from nuclei, can be analyzed on a classical and therefore very simple
basis after suitable adjustment of some of the constants in the classical
formulas of the Lorentz theory.

The problem of emission, absorption, and scattering of radiation by
atomic systems is treated in the quantum theory by breaking it into
three parts.   Firstly, the mechanical system of charged particles with
coulomb interactions is treated by itself by ignoring the possibility of
radiation.   Secondly, one considers a pure radiation field, that is, a field
that can exist according to the Maxwell theory in the absence of matter.
Finally, the weak interaction between the mechanical system and the
radiation field is included.   A few details of these three parts will now
be given.

When the mechanical problem is set up classically in terms of the Hamiltonian theory of mechanics, one can pass, by a standard procedure, to the quantum formulation. The latter can take various forms, such as the Schrödinger wave theory or the Heisenberg matrix theory, they being the various representations of an over-all abstract theory developed by Dirac [24] and described in concise form in Condon and Shortley [21], chap. 2. For present purposes the following results are relevant: Just as in the classical theory, the problem of the mechanics of the atom splits into that of the motion of the center of mass and that of internal motions relative to the center of mass. The quantum description of these motions is in some respects quite different from the classical, but nevertheless one can contemplate measurement of dynamical quantities such as energy, position, and momentum (without going into the techniques of such measurements). With regard to internal states, the new theory leads to the notions of energy levels, degenerate states of the same energy, and populations of states, just as does the old theory; these bare ideas are all that will be needed in the following discussions. The motion of the center of mass must be considered if one is to account for the Doppler effect and for recoil of the atom in a radiative emission or absorption. For the moment let the nucleus be supposed initially at rest and infinitely heavy, so that it remains permanently at rest. Consequences of recoil of a finite mass will be taken up in the final section.

A pure radiation field in classical description is any solution of the homogeneous Maxwell equations (equations for space completely empty of charge and current). An obvious example is any monochromatic plane wave, and by the principles of Fourier integral analysis an arbitrary pure field can be represented as a superposition of plane waves. By suitably assigning amplitudes, polarizations, and phases to the plane-wave components, one can construct a spherical wave or any other type of radiation field arising in the classical theory. The representation as a superposition of plane waves is commonly used in passing to a quantum theory of the field and making applications.

Once the field is quantized, its coupling to the quantized atomic systems is introduced, and one can consider such problems as an excited atom giving up its energy to the field, and the field in turn giving energy to a neighboring atom in an absorptive transition.

Reduction of all these qualitative ideas to working form is the province of treatises like Fermi [28] and Heitler [37]. In this literature a number of examples are worked out, and the final results will now be described in simple terms by concentrating on the states of the atomic systems and leaving out most of the detailed behavior of the fields in influencing these states. The reason for this omission is that quantization of the fields introduces subtle nonclassical features that cannot be adequately discussed in a short space. In particular, the question of amplitudes and phases is difficult, although in some cases classical results come out, as will be seen.

One of the characteristics of the quantized field that can be profitably considered here is its energy. This energy is to be regarded as carried by the component plane waves. These waves have frequencies filling the continuous range from zero to infinity and all possible directions of propagation. If one imagines a measurement capable of determining the energy in all the waves having frequencies in the small range ω to $\omega + d\omega$ and directions of propagation in the small solid angle $d\Omega$ about a given direction, then the theory states that the result can only be precisely $n\hbar\omega$, where n is some positive integer or zero. One says that these waves contain n quanta or *photons*, each photon representing energy $\hbar\omega$. Note that nothing is said here about localization of the energy in space, a topic that will arise later in specific examples. A different type of measurement would determine the energy between ω and $\omega + d\omega$ without regard for direction, the result always being an integral multiple of $\hbar\omega$. An excited field comes about by some physical process involving material systems. If the process is carried out in many independent repetitions, and at the end of each a measurement on the field of one of the above types is made, the result need not always be the same number of photons. In general one can speak only of the probability of finding any given number of photons in a given small range of frequency and of fluctuations.

Consider now the question of spontaneous emission by an excited atom. A quantum calculation of the mechanics of the atom in the approximation in which coupling to the radiation field is omitted gives the stationary bound states of the atoms and their energies, the latter coming out as discrete and sharply defined numbers relative to some chosen zero. In this approximation the atom can exist permanently in any one of these states. When coupling to the quantized field is included, the mechanics of the atom is somewhat affected (but only slightly—the atom and the field are *almost* independent systems), even when the field initially has no photons in it. The effects are most concisely described as a broadening of the levels and the occurrence of spontaneous transitions.

The broadening is illustrated in Fig. 19-5a. On the vertical energy scale are indicated sharp values ϵ_0, ϵ_i, and ϵ_j representing the ground level and some pair of excited levels in the approximation that ignores radiation. Interaction with the radiation field broadens the excited levels, but not the ground level. With the excited level i is associated a curve extending to the right in the figure and representing a probability $P_i(\epsilon)$ with the significance that when the atom is excited to that level the probability that the energy falls between ϵ and $\epsilon + d\epsilon$ is $P_i(\epsilon)\, d\epsilon$. When the excitation is of what is known as the natural sort (the only case to be considered here), the curve of $P_i(\epsilon)$ has a resonance profile with maximum at ϵ_i (ignoring a very small shift) and some width $\hbar\gamma_i$

between half-maximum points. Thus

$$P_i(\epsilon) = \hbar^{-1} \mathcal{L}\left(\frac{\epsilon - \epsilon_i}{\hbar}; \gamma_i\right) \tag{19-40}$$

where $\mathcal{L}$ is the normalized resonance function defined by (12-33); with the factor $\hbar^{-1}$ included, $P_i(\epsilon)$ is normalized to unity with respect to integration over energy. A similar expression holds for level j, and γ_j is in general different from γ_i, as will be shown presently.

When a spontaneous transition from level i to level j occurs, the energy lost by the atom appears as one quantum of some frequency ω in the

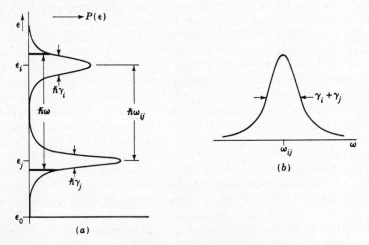

Fig. 19-5. **a.** *Ground level and two excited levels of an atom. The excited levels show broadening due to interaction with the quantized radiation field.* **b.** *Spectrum of spontaneous radiation for the transition i to j.*

radiation field. The frequency ω is not definite, and the spectrum of the radiation (profile of the line) is obtained by finding the probability $P_r(\omega)\,d\omega$ that the frequency falls in the range ω to $\omega + d\omega$. A result of the theory is that if the atom initially has energy given by the probability distribution $P_i(\epsilon)$, then transition to level j leaves the atom with distribution $P_j(\epsilon)$. The probability that the atom has initial energy between ϵ and $\epsilon + d\epsilon$ and emits a quantum of energy $\hbar\omega$ whose frequency falls between ω and $\omega + d\omega$ is then (see Fig. 19-5a)

$$P_i(\epsilon)\,d\epsilon\,P_j(\epsilon - \hbar\omega)\,\hbar d\omega$$

The total probability of emitting a photon in the given frequency range is the integral of this expression over ϵ (from $-\infty$ to $+\infty$ by familiar argument based on the narrowness of the levels), so that by (19-40),

$$
\begin{aligned}
P_r(\omega)\, d\omega &= \frac{d\omega}{\hbar} \int_{-\infty}^{\infty} \mathcal{L}\left(\frac{\epsilon - \epsilon_i}{\hbar}; \gamma_i\right) \mathcal{L}\left(\frac{\epsilon - \epsilon_j - \hbar\omega}{\hbar}; \gamma_j\right) d\epsilon \\
&= \mathcal{L}(\omega - \omega_{ij}; \gamma_i + \gamma_j)\, d\omega
\end{aligned}
$$

Here a folding integral of two resonance functions has arisen and is evaluated by the proposition in Prob. 13-7. The spectrum (as would be observed when many atoms are independently excited to emit and fluctuations are averaged out) has a profile of the shape of $P_r(\omega)$ and is therefore of resonance shape with center frequency ω_{ij} and width $\gamma_i + \gamma_j$, as indicated in Fig. 19-5b. Except for the width, this spectrum is precisely the classical one obtained in Chap. 12.

The quantity γ_i, which fixes the width of level i, turns out to be the reciprocal of the lifetime of level i against spontaneous transitions to all lower levels, so that by (19-33),

$$
\gamma_i = \frac{1}{\tau_i} = \sum_{j < i} A_{ji} \tag{19-41}
$$

Note that this relation implies that strong lines in spectra are comparatively broad, but weak lines need not be comparatively narrow. Another implication is that the ground level has zero width. All this discussion refers to spontaneous emission from a single stationary atom into an empty radiation field. If the atom is subject to collisions or is in an intense radiation field, there are perturbations of its mechanical behavior, with effects that can be described as additional broadening of the levels (including the ground level) and perhaps some changes in shape of profile.

It remains to give a formula for the Einstein A coefficients. Consider first a classical Lorentz atom with natural frequency ω_0, and suppose it oscillates freely with initial complex amplitude $\mathbf{s}_0$. Let the average over one cycle of the instantaneous energy of the atom be W. Then the initial rate of change of W is given by (5-18) to be

$$
-\frac{dW}{dt} = \frac{e^2 \omega_0^4}{3c^3} |\mathbf{s}_0|^2 \tag{19-42}
$$

Consider now a large number of real atoms initially on level i. Suppose for the moment that each level is comprised of a single state (no degeneracy). The initial rate of change of the energy of this system *per atom* due just to spontaneous transitions to level j with emission of photons of frequency ω_{ij} (spread in frequency can be ignored here) is, in the first instance, $\hbar\omega_{ij}A_{ji}$, by definition of A_{ji}. The quantum theory of the process gives

$$
-\frac{dW}{dt} = \hbar\omega_{ij}A_{ji} = \frac{e^2 \omega_{ij}^4}{3c^3}\, 4|\mathbf{s}_{ji}|^2 \tag{19-43}
$$

where s_{ji} is a complex vector (constant) called the *matrix element* of the amplitude vector s; specifically, it is the element connecting initial state i to final state j. Discovery of the notion of matrix elements marked the first formulation of the new quantum theory, of which an account is given in Heisenberg [36], Appendix. The rule for converting the classical formula (19-42) to the quantum form (19-43) was inferred from the correspondence principle some years before it was discovered how to quantize the radiation field and thereby obtain a complete quantum theory.

If levels i and j are degenerate, consisting of g_i and g_j states, respectively, then (19-43) must be modified. Let index a enumerate the states of level i, and index b those of level j. For transition from state a to state b, the transition probability is

$$A_{ba} = \frac{e^2 \omega_{ij}^3}{3\hbar c^3} 4 |s_{ba}|^2$$

The transition probability for transition from state a to any state of level j is the sum of the last expression over b. If a number of atoms are on level i in natural excitation, the fraction $1/g_i$ is in each state. The transition probability for transition from level i to level j in the case of natural excitation is therefore

$$A_{ji} = \frac{1}{g_i} \sum_{a,b} A_{ba}$$

the sum being a double one, over all pairs of states a,b.

The detailed quantum calculation from which the above description of spontaneous emission is drawn can be found, for example, in Fermi [28], p. 98, or Heitler [37], p. 181. For methods of calculating the coefficients A_{ba}, see, for example, Condon and Shortley [21]. The conclusion is that the natural profile of a spectrum line has the shape given by the classical theory, but the width given by the classical theory of radiation damping must be multiplied by a correction factor for each line, although for many of the comparatively intense lines in an atomic spectrum the factor is of order unity.

In speaking of spontaneous emission, we stated merely that a photon is added to the radiation field. The question of how this quantum of energy propagates away from the atom can be investigated in various ways, of which the simplest to describe is the type of calculation given in Fermi [28], p. 100. At a distance r from the emitting atom is a second atom. For simplicity each of the atoms can be supposed to have just two levels with the same difference of energy. The initial conditions at time $t = 0$ are that the emitting atom is excited, no photon is in the field, and the second atom is in the ground state. One calculates the probability that at some later time t the first atom will have emitted a photon and the second will have absorbed it (eventually to reemit). The result is that this probability is zero until $t = r/c$, and thereafter approaches a limiting value in exponential fashion, with a time constant equal to the lifetime of the emitting atom. Moreover, the probability is proportional to $1/r^2$. The probability that the second atom would actually be found excited at time t (allowing for reemission) does not approach a constant value as above, but reaches a maximum and then decays to zero in a manner involving the lifetimes of both atoms. All this is very similar to the classical analogue in which a Lorentz atom emits a damped spherical wave propagating outward with velocity c, and the latter excites a transient oscillation in a neighboring atom having the same resonant frequency. The energy in such a transient (averaged over a cycle) shows the same temporal behavior as the quantum probability (the second one mentioned above) if the damping of the classical oscillators is suitably adjusted. There is the difference, however, that in the classical case the wave spreading from an emitting atom disturbs any and all neighboring atoms, whereas the photon is, with a certain probability, completely absorbed by some one neighboring atom, just one. It is characteristic of classical theory that every neighboring atom behaves in a definite way; in the quantum theory one has only the probabilities, and knowledge that an absorption actually occurred and which neighbor was involved can come only from an observation. Many repetitions of the observation would verify the probability predicted by the theory.

With regard to the dependence of the probability of absorption on direction from emitting to absorbing atom, two cases arise. If no preferred orientation of the emitting atom exists (through some special character of the original exciting process or through the presence of a static field), then the calculation appropriately involves an averaging over all orientations (all directions of the vector matrix element s_{ba}) with the result that the probability is independent of direction. As an example of the opposite case, suppose the emitting atom is in a static magnetic field, and one calculates the probability of absorption of one of the π or σ Zeeman components by a suitably tuned test atom. The probability then depends on direction in the same way as the classical radiation pattern. If the test atom is also in a magnetic field to make it sensitive to polarization of the incident radiation, the polarization is the same as in the classical theory of a π or σ wave.

Let us consider now what the quantum theory says about some aspects of scattering. As a prototype example, let an atom emit a primary photon of frequency ω within the narrow natural spectrum. At a great distance from the primary atom let there be a scattering atom in its ground state, having no absorptive transition near ω. (The phenomenon of scattering involves absorption of the primary photon and a reemission. If the scatterer is left in its initial state, the process is said to be *elastic*, because the two photons have the same frequency and energy, and is also said to be *coherent*, because there are certain phase relations between the incident and scattered fields.   If the scatterer is left in a different state, a process with very small probability, the two photons have different frequencies in accordance with conservation of energy, and one has the *Raman effect*, not to be further discussed here.)   Finally, at a great distance from the scatterer let there be a test atom capable of absorbing a scattered photon of frequency ω and becoming excited.

Let the direction from the primary atom to the scatterer define the polar axis of a spherical polar coordinate system with origin at the scatterer.   The test atom is then in some direction (θ, ϕ), and the probability that it becomes excited by a scattered photon depends on θ and ϕ and the polarization of the primary photon exactly as does the irradiance of the scattered wave in the analogous classical problem of scattering of a plane wave by a Lorentz atom.   This probability is proportional to the probability that a scattering event occurs; the latter can be specified by a total cross section which turns out to be given by the classical formula (14-10) if the polarizability is (19-39).

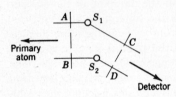

Fig. 19-6. *Geometry of two scattering atoms in relation to a distant primary emitter and a detector of scattered photons.*

One can go on to consider several scatterers at various fixed positions.   The quantum theory gives all the effects of interference and coherence found in the classical theory of secondary waves.   This general statement can be inferred from a study of simple cases.   For example, Heitler [37], p, 193, considers two identical scatterers and a primary photon of definite frequency ω (the quantum analogue of the classical monochromatic wave).   The geometry is shown in Fig. 19-6, in which the scattering atoms are at S_1 and S_2, and the primary atom and detector are off at great distances.   If P_1 is the probability of the detecting atom becoming excited when either scatterer is present alone, then when both are present, the probability is

$$2P_1(1 + \cos k\Delta)$$

where $k = \omega/c$, and Δ is the path difference $AS_1C - BS_2D$.   This is just the classical result and, for the monochromatic case, is good for all path differences.   If the photon frequency is not definite, but is given by a probability distribution defining the spectrum, the question of longitudinal coherence enters.   For example, if the primary atom and the two scatterers are in line, and the detector is set at 90° from the forward direction, then the probability of the detector becoming excited varies with path difference in a way related to the spectrum exactly as in the classical theory of the interferogram in Sec. 13-11. If the spectrum is very narrow, but the primary atom is any one in an extended source so that its direction is uncertain, the phenomenon of lateral coherence enters, and the classical theory of Sec. 13-10 is adequate.

Consider the theory of the refractive index. In a low-density gas the quantum theory merely adds numerical values (resonant frequencies, oscillator strengths, and widths of absorption bands) and leaves the general form of the classical results unaltered. For high densities and the various liquids and solids, the classical theory is less reliable. The internal field, collisions, and various kinds of interaction are difficult questions, and in the literature one finds them attacked by mixtures of classical and quantum theory in all proportions.

Finally, there is the matter of fluctuations. Suppose atoms in a small continuous source emit photons at a steady mean rate and with a certain spectrum. At a distance let there be a detector, such as an ideal photoelectric cell, in which an observable event occurs each time a photon is absorbed. Further, imagine that the detector is multichannel, such that the frequency range of the spectrum is divided into very narrow bands and the photons absorbed in each band are counted. In a time interval of given duration let the count in some one channel be n. On many repetitions n will fluctuate. Let $[n]$ denote the mean value, and let Δn denote the root-mean-square deviation from the mean. Quantum theory gives

$$(\Delta n)^2 = [n]^2 + [n] \tag{19-44}$$

This result is to be compared with the classical (12-28), in which ρ^2, apart from a constant, is the analogue of n. The two become identical when $[n]$ is large enough that the second term on the right of (19-44) can be neglected. The origin of (19-44) in the Bose statistics obeyed by photons is discussed in, for example, Kittel [55], p. 121. Formula (19-44) is a limiting form approached as the width of the channel decreases. With a wide channel the relative fluctuation $\Delta n/[n]$ is less, because of a kind of smoothing action analogous to the classical one discussed in Sec. 12-6. Thus it is explained why, in practical spectroscopy, in which a channel has an appreciable width through which it is arranged to absorb a large number of photons in the integrating time, large relative fluctuations are not observed in repeated observations.

This section has briefly sketched the results of the quantum theory of most of the main topics in preceding chapters. One can hardly fail to be impressed by the Lorentz theory and to regard it, not as outmoded, but as a simple and effective tool when used with insight.

19-8 Amplification by Stimulated Emission. Maser and Laser

Consider a gas whose atoms are on the ground level, and let ω_0 be the transition frequency to an excited level. The gas then has an absorption band at ω_0, and if a monochromatic plane wave whose frequency falls in this band propagates through the gas, its irradiance decreases exponentially along the path. In quantum terms, photons are extracted from the primary wave in absorptive transitions and are reemitted in all directions with phase relations such that there is interference with the primary wave, giving, as a resultant, just a plane refracted wave with behavior describable in terms of a complex refractive index. There is a close parallel with the classical theory.

Suppose that in some way a substantial fraction of the atoms is maintained on the excited level. The primary wave causes stimulated emission, the emitted photons again carrying phase relations. As far as the irradiance of the primary wave is concerned, the effect of the stimulated emission is equivalent to a negative absorption. If there is a population inversion (more atoms on the upper than on the lower level), the net absorption is negative, and the irradiance of the wave increases exponentially. Moreover, if the gas is contained between plane parallel windows, there is a definite phase relation between the incident and emergent waves, and one has a principle for coherent amplification of a wave of arbitrarily high frequency.

Investigation of the various possibilities of producing population inversion in one or another kind of medium and the resulting negative absorption coefficients indicates that a very long path is required for substantial amplification. A way of meeting this requirement, proposed by Townes, is to enclose the active medium in a resonant cavity, with input and output coupling, so that the wave to be amplified is a standing wave or, equivalently, a propagating wave reflecting back and forth between the walls. The first realization was in the microwave region, and the device was called a *maser* (microwave amplification by stimulated emission of radiation). A description and the main part of the theory are given in Gordon, Zeiger, and Townes [32]. A proposal for extension to infrared and visible frequencies was made by Schawlow and Townes [81] and first realized by Maiman [61]. A device operating at these frequencies is commonly called an *optical maser* or a *laser* (light amplification, etc.). Numerous papers and further references can be found in the symposia edited by Townes [91] and by Singer [83]. In the former volume special attention might be called to the paper by Serber and Townes on the fundamental quantum limitation on simultaneous measurement of irradiance and phase of a wave when the latter becomes so weak as to involve a small number of photons. The advent of the maser gave practical importance to this question. A monograph on lasers is Lengyel [56].

There are many aspects to the subject of masers: the frequency, the nature of the amplifying medium, the method of producing the population inversion, the geometry of the resonant structure and input and output coupling, and the type of operation. With regard to the last point, any of the devices can operate as an oscillator as well as an amplifier. With the wave reflecting back and forth in a resonant structure, one has an amplifier with positive feedback; any such amplifier can oscillate spontaneously if the gain for a single pass exceeds a threshhold value. The rest of this section will describe the interesting optical properties of an oscillator at visible or near-infrared frequencies.

The resonant structure in a laser is a Fabry-Perot etalon with the amplifying medium between the highly reflecting, semitransparent films. In Maiman's device the medium was synthetic ruby in the form of a

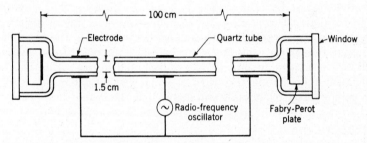

Fig. 19-7. *Schematic diagram of gas laser of Javan et al.*

cylindrical single crystal some centimeter in diameter and a few centimeters long, with the ends polished plane and parallel and coated with silver films. Operation was on a pulsed basis. Later, a laser oscillating continuously and employing a gaseous medium between Fabry-Perot plates was developed by Javan, Bennett, and Herriott. A paper by Herriott [38] deals mainly with the optical aspects. Let us consider this device.

The instrumental arrangement is shown schematically in Fig. 19-7. A long, narrow quartz tube is attached to end chambers sealed by windows and containing Fabry-Perot plates. In the tube a low-pressure mixture of helium and neon is excited by a glow discharge induced by a radio-frequency electric field. The result is to produce a population inversion of two levels of neon with the infrared transition frequency $\omega = 1.63 \times 10^{15}$ rad sec^{-1} ($\lambda = 11{,}530$ A).

Photons are emitted spontaneously by the neon atoms in the upper level, and any one of these photons can be regarded as an excitation of a plane wave in the radiation field with arbitrary direction of propagation and frequency ω falling in the Doppler-broadened spectrum of the spontaneous-emission line. Wherever this wave strikes the wall of the enclosure there is some reflection, transmission, and absorption.   If the wave propagates exactly along the axis of the system, and the frequency satisfies the tuning condition

$$\omega = \omega_m = \frac{m\pi c}{d} \qquad (19\text{-}45)$$

so that a standing wave is set up with m half-wavelengths in the distance d between the Fabry-Perot plates, and if ω_m coincides with the center of the spontaneous-emission spectrum, one has the most favorable conditions for a photon to initiate a wave which grows into a sustained oscillation. In the steady state the power extracted from the gas by stimulated emission comes out through the partially transparent films.

A spontaneously excited wave with slightly different frequency and slightly different direction can also grow into oscillation.   The amplitude of the oscillation decreases rapidly as ω departs from ω_m (the wave between the plates no longer being exactly a standing wave) and as the direction of propagation departs from the axis (the beam walking to one side and striking the narrow tube as it reflects back and forth).   The theory of this falloff of amplitude, the origin of which is only crudely indicated by the parenthetical remarks, is not simple, but the output beam at either end is most remarkable in its degree of collimation and the narrowness of its spectrum.

Let us consider just the spectrum.   Measurements on the 11,530 A line from the gas laser were made by Javan, Ballik, and Bond [52].   The results, limited by available spectral resolution, gave the ratio of the width between half-maximum points to the center frequency to be $\Delta\omega/\omega \sim 10^{-14}$.   An approximate theory indicates that the line may actually have been substantially narrower.   Comparison should be made with the ratio of order 10^{-8} for the natural (unbroadened) profile of a visible line in an atomic spectrum resulting from spontaneous emission.

The relative width $\Delta\omega/\omega$ is a significant measure of the potentialities of an oscillator as a frequency standard or clock.   The laser is very promising, but reproducibility and freedom from drift over long times are problems requiring careful attention.

An interesting point about the gas laser is that with $\Delta\omega \sim 10^{-14}\omega \sim$ 16 radians $\sec^{-1}$ at $\omega \approx 1.6 \times 10^{15}$ radians $\sec^{-1}$, the coherence time and coherence length of the wave (Sec. 13-11) are of order $\frac{1}{16}$ sec and 10^4 km, respectively.   Measurement of the spectral profile by interferometric methods is therefore out of the question, and the method used was the beat-frequency technique of Forrester (Sec. 13-16).   The method works well here because of another unique property of the laser, namely, the enormous peak spectral density of the power compared with conventional light sources.   The total power in the wave from one end of the laser was 0.5 mw.

19-9   Recoil.   Doppler   Shift.   Mössbauer   Effect   Throughout Sec. 19-7 it was assumed that the atomic nucleus was at rest and infinitely heavy.   With a finite mass the phenomenon of recoil and shift of frequency occurs on emission, absorption, or scattering.

Suppose an atom, localized in a fairly small region of space and having a fairly well-known momentum, emits a photon of frequency ω.   If a second atom at a considerable distance is observed to absorb it, then it can be said that the photon was emitted in the direction from the first atom to the second.   The photon carries energy $\hbar\omega$, and it also carries momentum $\hbar\omega\mathbf{a}/c$, where $\mathbf{a}$ is a unit vector in the direction of emission (see end of Sec. 14-8).   Energy and momentum are conserved in the emission process, so that the atom recoils, gaining momentum $-\hbar\omega\mathbf{a}/c$.   A simplified derivation of this result from quantum theory is given in Heisenberg [36], p. 89 (a few minor errors are easily corrected).

The consequences of the conservation laws are brought out by the following calculation after Fermi [28], p. 105.   In addition to the quantities defined above, let $\hbar\omega_0$ be the change in internal energy of the atom (ω_0 would be the frequency of the photon if the atom were held at rest), let M be the mass of the atom, and let $\mathbf{v}$ and $\mathbf{v}'$ be the velocities of the center of mass before and after emission.   Conservation of energy gives

$$\hbar\omega = \hbar\omega_0 + \tfrac{1}{2}M(v^2 - v'^2) \tag{19-46}$$

By conservation of momentum,

$$M\mathbf{v}' = M\mathbf{v} - \frac{\hbar\omega\mathbf{a}}{c} \tag{19-47}$$

From (19-47),

$$\tfrac{1}{2}M(v^2 - v'^2) = \frac{\hbar\omega}{c}\,\mathbf{a}\cdot\mathbf{v} - \frac{1}{2M}\left(\frac{\hbar\omega}{c}\right)^2$$

Before substituting the last result in (19-46), it is permissible to replace ω by ω_0, because the two terms on the right will in all cases be very small compared with $\hbar\omega_0$.   We obtain

$$\omega = \omega_0 + \omega_0\frac{\mathbf{a}\cdot\mathbf{v}}{c} - \frac{1}{2M\hbar}\left(\frac{\hbar\omega_0}{c}\right)^2 \tag{19-48}$$

The second term on the right is the ordinary Doppler shift [see (12-34)]. The third term is the shift due to recoil.

The relative shift due to recoil is

$$\frac{\omega - \omega_0}{\omega_0} = -\frac{\hbar\omega_0}{2Mc^2} \tag{19-49}$$

For a visible frequency ($\hbar\omega \sim 2$ ev) and an atom of unit atomic weight ($Mc^2 \sim 10^9$ ev), this quantity is 10^{-9} and hence is small even in comparison with the natural relative width γ/ω_0 of the spectrum line, the latter being ordinarily of order 10^{-8}. When the inevitable Doppler broadening is considered, it becomes apparent that recoil shift is insignificant at visible frequencies.

The situation is quite different with emission of a gamma ray by a nucleus. Consider the example of Fe^{57}. The first excited level is 14.37 kev above ground and has a lifetime $\tau = 1.4 \times 10^{-7}$ sec. The natural profile of the spectrum line is of resonance shape with width $\gamma = \tau^{-1}$ radians sec^{-1}. Hence[1] $\gamma/\omega_0 \approx 10^{-13}$, whereas the relative shift (19-49) is about 10^{-7}. This result is illustrated with grossly distorted proportions in Fig. 19-8. The emission spectrum for nuclei initially at rest is shown at the left. In the absence of recoil its center would be at ω_0; with freedom to recoil it is shifted to lower frequency by an amount $\Delta\omega$. The cross section for absorption has the same shape and width of profile as the

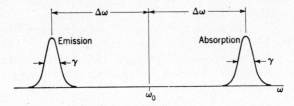

Fig. 19-8. *Shifts of the spectral profiles for emission and absorption of gamma photons by recoiling nuclei initially at rest.*

emission spectrum, and when conservation of energy and momentum are applied to absorption by a nucleus initially at rest, it turns out that the profile is shifted to higher frequency by amount $\Delta\omega$, as shown in Fig. 19-8. Because the two profiles do not overlap, resonance absorption cannot occur when emitting and absorbing nuclei are initially at rest and free to recoil. Doppler shifts due to thermal motion broaden the two profiles, and for heavy nuclei at sufficiently high temperature, the result can be to make the high-frequency tail of the emission profile overlap the low-frequency tail of the absorption profile to the extent that some resonance absorption can be observed.

In 1957, R. L. Mössbauer discovered that if Ir^{191} nuclei are bound in a solid lattice cooled to very low temperature, the 129-kev gamma ray can be emitted or absorbed without recoil shift and without Doppler broadening of the profile. The explanation comes from applying conservation of energy and momentum to the radiative process, taking due account of

---

[1] In connection with calculations of this sort, the following is worth noting: If the energy $\hbar\omega$ is 1 ev, the wavelength corresponding to frequency ω is 12,345 A, a number too low by about 50 A, but easy to remember. Then $\omega = 2\pi c/\lambda \approx 1.5 \times 10^{15}$ radians sec^{-1}.

the quantized nature of lattice vibrations in crystals. It turns out that a certain fraction of events occurs as though the nuclei were rigidly fixed in the heavy crystal; this fraction increases as the temperature is lowered. Other nuclei show the effect, and in 1959 it was discovered that with Fe^{57} the fraction is large even at room temperature and remains appreciable up to the melting point of iron. The latter discovery made the many important experiments that can be based on the Mössbauer effect easy to perform, and activity in the field became very vigorous indeed.

Suppose one has two metal foils, one containing some Fe^{57}, and the other some Co^{57}. The cobalt decays to excited Fe^{57} by electron capture, and the excited nucleus decays to the ground state by successive emission of two photons of energies 123 kev and 14.37 kev. The second photon is involved in the Mössbauer effect.

If the foils are at rest relative to each other and have been suitably treated to eliminate broadening that can occur in the solid state, the profiles for the recoilless emissions and absorptions have the natural shapes indicated in Fig. 19-8, but the two profiles now coincide with each other at ω_0, and resonance absorption is large. If the source moves toward or away from the absorber with velocity v, the emission profile is shifted by Doppler effect, and absorption decreases. The velocity required to shift the profile by its own width γ is given by $v/c = \gamma/\omega_0$, so that for Fe^{57}, $v \approx 10^{-3}$ cm sec^{-1}! By observing the absorption for various velocities, one in effect observes the folding integral of the spectrum with itself. In this way the very narrow profile has been measured with high accuracy.

A brief account of the Mössbauer effect is given in Lustig [60]. For a fuller account of the effect and its applications, with a collection of reprints, see Frauenfelder [31]. In the latter reference special attention might be called to the paper by Lynch, Holland, and Hamermesh reprinted on p. 259 and discussed on p. 66 [original paper in *Phys. Rev.*, **120**:513 (1960)]. Here the reader will see a very interesting experiment explained by a classical calculation using the Lorentz model of emission and anomalous dispersion, together with the principles of Fourier analysis, transfer, and synthesis—a substantial number of the ideas developed in the present volume.

Problems

19-1. Show that if isotropic radiation of intensity $\mathscr{g}$ is contained in a vessel with perfectly reflecting walls, the pressure on the walls is $4\pi\mathscr{g}/3c$ (in terms of energy density: $u/3$). [*Hint:* Use the connection between intensity and irradiance of a nearly unidirectional beam (Sec. 19-1) and the ideas in Sec. 14-8.]

19-2. Consider a radiation field arising from any arrangement of incandescent surfaces. Let L be any straight line in the field, and let **n** be a unit vector in one direction along L.   Consider the intensity $\mathcal{s}$ in the direction $\mathbf{n}$ at a point of L.   Show that this quantity is independent of position on L and is therefore a characteristic of the source at its intersection with the branch of L in the direction $-\mathbf{n}$.   (*Hints:* At two points of L erect normal elements of surface $d\Sigma$ and $d\Sigma'$.   Consider all the radiation that passes through $d\Sigma$ and through $d\Sigma'$ in the sense defined by $\mathbf{n}$.   This is a purely mathematical idea—diffraction is not in question.   Let $d\Omega$ be the solid angle subtended by $d\Sigma'$ from $d\Sigma$, and let $d\Omega'$ be the solid angle subtended by $d\Sigma$ from $d\Sigma'$.   These four differentials satisfy a simple relation.)

19-3. A gas is in thermal equilibrium in a cavity at temperature T.   Consider a pair of atomic levels separated by energy $\hbar\omega$.   Discuss the relative importance of the two kinds of transitions from the upper to the lower level when $\hbar\omega \ll kT$ and when $\hbar\omega \gg kT$.

19-4. The B coefficients of Einstein were defined by (19-24) and (19-26), that is, with reference to specification of the radiation field in the cavity by its spectral intensity $\mathcal{s}_\omega$.   A different set of B's would result if $\mathcal{s}_\omega$ were replaced, say, by the spectral energy density u_ν.   Several of the possible definitions are encountered in the literature.   Find the relation analogous to (19-29) when B_{ij} is defined with reference to u_ν, and again with reference to $\mathcal{s}_\lambda$.

19-5. At time $t = 0$ let one of the excited levels of a given kind of atom be populated with "natural" distribution (see end of Sec. 19-4), and let all other levels be unpopulated.   Number the populated level 1, and the next level below it 2.   Find the formula for the temporal behavior of the population of level 2, assuming it to be above the ground level.   Illustrate the result graphically in a qualitative way.   Write the differential equation governing the population of level 3, the next below 2, assuming it also to be above the ground level.

19-6. If at time $t = 0$ an atom in free space empty of radiation is known to be on level i with equal probability of being in any of the degenerate states of this level, then there is a probability $P(t)$ that at time t the atom would be found still on level i.   A mean lifetime against spontaneous transition can be defined as the integral from $t = 0$ to $t = \infty$ of $tP(t)$.   Show that this lifetime is just τ_i given by (19-33).

appendix *A*

Electrical Units

Controversies over electrical units have furnished much of the comic relief in physics. Many systems have evolved with little besides personal preference or one's major line of work to decide for one system against another, and translation between systems is just tedious enough to have led to spirited advocacy of one or another for universal adoption. Yet there is certainly one unavoidable fact: Important works on physics have been written and will continue to be written using various systems of units. The only course is to gain a thorough understanding of the subject, so that one can easily relate any system to one's own preference.

A-1 General Problem of Setting Up a System of Units; Survey of the Common Systems The unifying element in a general discussion of units is the set of fundamental equations governing the physical phenomena in question. In the case of the classical theory of electromagnetic fields and their interaction with matter, these are Newton's equation of motion and the Maxwell equations. The latter can be expressed either on a microscopic scale or in a macroscopic approximation. If one contemplates the ordinary macroscopic electrical measurements by which two samples of a physical quantity, say two currents in wires, are compared, one should have in mind the macroscopic equations; but since these equations are not discussed until Chap. 15, while this appendix is intended to be read after Chap. 3,[1] let us now regard macroscopic charges and currents as involving no microscopic structure, and apply to them the microscopic

[1] Chapter 15, as a matter of fact, can be read after Chap. 4, although some of its ideas will perhaps be more fully appreciated after reading the intervening chapters.

equations. As remarked in Sec. 3-3, this procedure is valid, and, in fact, it will be seen in Chap. 15 that macroscopic problems can be handled by equations of exactly the same form as the microscopic, except that the microscopic ρ and $\mathbf{j}$ are replaced by smoothed-out distributions which ignore the microscopic structure, and $\mathbf{e}$ and $\mathbf{b}$ are replaced by smoothed-out fields. Newton's equation can also be written in a microscopic and a macroscopic form, the former reading that the microscopic force density at a point, part of which is the Lorentz force density (3-5) and the rest is nonelectromagnetic, is equal to the microscopic mass density times the acceleration at that point. The macroscopic form reads the same, except that all the microscopic quantities are replaced by smoothed-out macroscopic quantities; it is this form that is used in the practical handling of the mechanics of gross bodies.

In the first instance, Newton's law of motion is a statement of proportionality and can be written $\mathbf{F} = km\mathbf{a}$, where k is a constant of proportionality. In every system of units not adapted to very special purposes, k is set equal to unity, and only this choice will be considered. With k fixed, the unit of force is determined in terms of the units of mass and acceleration.

The Maxwell equations are likewise, in the first instance, statements of proportionality and can be written

$$\operatorname{div} \mathbf{e} = \alpha\rho \tag{A-1}$$

$$\operatorname{curl} \mathbf{e} = -\beta \frac{\partial \mathbf{b}}{\partial t} \tag{A-2}$$

$$\operatorname{div} \mathbf{b} = 0 \tag{A-3}$$

$$\operatorname{curl} \mathbf{b} = \gamma \frac{\partial \mathbf{e}}{\partial t} + \delta \mathbf{j} \tag{A-4}$$

$$\mathbf{f} = \eta\rho\mathbf{e} + \zeta \mathbf{j} \times \mathbf{b} \tag{A-5}$$

where α, β, γ, δ, η, and ζ are constants of proportionality. The relation between $\mathbf{j}$, ρ, and the velocity with which the charge moves is in general $\mathbf{j} = \xi\rho\mathbf{v}$. In the most commonly used systems, but not all, $\xi = 1$; only this choice will be considered.

With k and ξ chosen once and for all, the rest of the problem is to obtain a consistent set of units for the physical quantities mass, length, time, charge, etc., and values for the constants α, β, etc., the number of possibilities being a manyfold infinity. Several of the possibilities have been adopted for use, each based on its own particular reasoning. The original systems, and the first to be discussed (in Secs. A-3 and A-4), are the cgs electrostatic and electromagnetic systems. Their drawback is that, in concept and in the general appearance of the Maxwell equations, they are exactly on a par and yet are different and easily confused. The gaussian system (Sec. A-6) mixes the electrostatic and electromagnetic systems in a way that gives greater symmetry to the Maxwell equations and hence provides an aid to memory. All other systems that have come into use have been derived from the gaussian units with one of two objectives in view—either to simplify the appearance of the Maxwell equations, or to incorporate certain units that have come to be used in the practical sciences. These developments are discussed in Secs. A-7 and A-8. The mks system will appear to have achieved both objectives at the same time, but the simplification in the appearance of the Maxwell equations is just sufficiently illusory to prevent its instant adoption in all quarters.

A-2 Some Derived Formulas in Arbitrary Units In the electrostatic and electromagnetic systems the units of charge and current are defined in terms of the forces between point charges and between parallel line currents, definite and simple geometries being involved. Formulas for these forces in terms of arbitrary units can be derived from (A-1) to (A-5) by the same arguments as were used in Chap. 3. The results are as follows: The force F on either of two identical point charges, each of charge q, separated by distance d, is

$$F = \frac{\alpha \eta q^2}{4\pi d^2} \tag{A-6}$$

The force per unit length on either of two parallel wires at separation d, carrying identical currents I, is

$$F = \frac{\delta \zeta I^2}{2\pi d} \tag{A-7}$$

A-3 Electrostatic System The sequence of arguments by which the units and constants are chosen in the electrostatic system will now be given. It will be supposed that the units of mass, length, and time have been chosen as the centimeter, gram, and second (the unit of force then being the dyne); the resulting system is denoted *cgs esu*. However, it will be clear that the following definitions apply with any units for mass, length, and time, so that one could have, for example, a system of fps esu based on the foot, pound, and second (the unit of force being the poundal) Only the cgs esu are in use, and the system is usually denoted simply *esu*.

The unit of charge is defined by the simplest form of Coulomb's law: $F = q^2/d^2$. If one arbitrarily makes the desirable choice $\eta = 1$, it follows from (A-6) that $\alpha = 4\pi$.

In naming the units, one can always speak of "esu of q," "esu of $\mathbf{e}$," etc., but in many cases other names have come about, and the usual name for the unit of charge is the *statcoulomb*. Its definition comes from the defining formula and is that two point charges are 1 statcoulomb each if the force of interaction at 1 cm separation is 1 dyne.   Explicit definitions in words will not be given hereafter.

The unit of ρ is the *statcoulomb per cubic centimeter;* the unit of j is defined by $j = \rho v$ and called the *statampere per square centimeter.*   The unit of e is defined by $f = \rho e$ (with $\eta = 1$) and is called the *statvolt per centimeter* (see Sec. 3-8).   The constant ζ is arbitrarily set equal to unity, whence the unit of b is defined by $f = j \times b$ and has no other name than *esu of b.*

Formula (A-7) becomes

$$F = \frac{\delta I^2}{2\pi d}$$

The constant δ is now determined by an experimental measurement of F with given I and d.   The value, rounded off, is $\delta \approx 4\pi (3 \times 10^{10})^{-2}$. Write this result as $\delta = 4\pi/c^2$, where $c \approx 3 \times 10^{10}$.   Consider now an experimental arrangement involving a region of space in which $j = 0$, but $\partial e/\partial t$ has a known value different from zero, and in which the geometry is simple enough that b can be calculated from (A-4) (see, for example, Prob. 3-13).   A measurement of b then gives the value of γ, and it comes out that $\gamma = 1/c^2$.   From (A-2) one obtains Faraday's law of induction in the form $V = -\beta \, d\Phi/dt$, where V is the difference of potential across a gap in a wire loop through which threads magnetic flux Φ (see Sec. 3-12). The unit of V is obtained from that of e and is called the *statvolt.*   The unit of Φ is defined by that of b and has no special name in the electrostatic system.   An experimental measurement of V for given $d\Phi/dt$ gives $\beta = 1$.

The system is now complete, and the Maxwell equations have the form

$$\text{div } e = 4\pi\rho \qquad\qquad \text{div } b = 0$$
$$\text{curl } e = -\frac{\partial b}{\partial t} \qquad\qquad \text{curl } b = \frac{1}{c^2}\frac{\partial e}{\partial t} + \frac{4\pi}{c^2} j \qquad (A-8)$$
$$f = \rho e + j \times b$$

Now in setting up the electrostatic system, we resorted to three experimental electrical measurements; they gave the values of c, β, and γ. The experimental value of c is always subject to some uncertainty, but it was asserted that $\beta = 1$ and $\gamma = 1/c^2$ without uncertainty, even though actual measurements of the sorts contemplated could not be so exact. This certitude comes from considering two consequences.

The derivational procedure in Sec. 3-11, when applied to (A-4) and (A-1), gives

$$\delta \, \text{div } j = -\alpha\gamma \frac{\partial\rho}{\partial t}$$

If this relation is to represent exact conservation of charge, as it is believed must be the case,

$$\alpha\gamma = \delta \tag{A-9}$$

Hence if $\alpha = 4\pi$ and $\delta = 4\pi/c^2$, $\gamma = 1/c^2$ exactly. [Note that (A-9) and the equation above it represent conservation of charge only if $\mathbf{j} = \rho\mathbf{v}$, which has been assumed all along.] By the procedure in Sec. 3-15 the homogeneous wave equation in $\mathbf{e}$ is found from (A-1), (A-2), and (A-4) to be

$$\nabla^2\mathbf{e} = \beta\gamma \frac{\partial^2\mathbf{e}}{\partial t^2}$$

The velocity of electromagnetic waves implied by this equation is $w = (\beta\gamma)^{-\frac{1}{2}}$. A measurement of the velocity gives $w \approx 3 \times 10^{10}$ cm sec^{-1}, and it is inferred that w and c are the same, whence

$$\beta\gamma = \frac{1}{c^2} \tag{A-10}$$

Having $\gamma = 1/c^2$ requires that $\beta = 1$.

It is clear that the three experimental observations just discussed could be incorporated into the theory once and for all in one of the following equivalent ways:

1. Add to equations (A-1) to (A-5) the statements that charge is conserved and that the velocity of electromagnetic waves is $c \approx 3 \times 10^{10}$ cm sec^{-1} (whence the velocity is known in terms of any units of length and time).

2. Add conditions (A-9) and (A-10) together with the value of c.

3. Reduce by two the number of constants in (A-1) to (A-5) by use of (A-9) and (A-10), and give the value of c.

4. Set up one initial set of units and constants which is consistent with conservation of charge and the observed velocity of electromagnetic waves, and define any new set in terms of this initial one in such a way that the two conditions are automatically satisfied.

The electrostatic system and the electromagnetic, to be obtained in the next section, are here set up in such a way that either one can serve as the initial system in method 4, which method will then be used in the rest of this appendix. General theorems facilitating the use of method 4 appear in footnotes to Sec. A-8.

A-4 Electromagnetic System The abbreviated name of the electromagnetic system is *cgs emu*, or simply *emu*. The sequence of definitions is very similar to that in the electrostatic system. The constants η and ζ are arbitrarily set equal to unity. The unit of current is defined by requiring that (A-7) read $F = 2I^2/d$, so that $\delta = 4\pi$. The unit of I is called an *abampere*, and the unit of j is an *abampere per square centimeter*. The unit of ρ comes from $j = \rho v$ and is called an *abcoulomb per cubic centimeter*. The unit of b comes from $f = j \times b$ and is called a *gauss*. An experiment based on (A-6), which now reads $F = \alpha q^2/4\pi d^2$, gives $\alpha = 4\pi c^2$, where again $c \approx 3 \times 10^{10}$. An experiment based on Faraday's law of induction gives $\beta = 1$. (The unit of Φ is called the *maxwell*.) An experiment based on (A-4) gives $\gamma = 1/c^2$. The system is now complete, and the Maxwell equations take the form

$$\operatorname{div} \mathbf{e} = 4\pi c^2 \rho \qquad\qquad \operatorname{div} \mathbf{b} = 0$$

$$\operatorname{curl} \mathbf{e} = -\frac{\partial \mathbf{b}}{\partial t} \qquad\qquad \operatorname{curl} \mathbf{b} = \frac{1}{c^2}\frac{\partial \mathbf{e}}{\partial t} + 4\pi \mathbf{j} \qquad \text{(A-11)}$$

$$\mathbf{f} = \rho \mathbf{e} + \mathbf{j} \times \mathbf{b}$$

Conditions (A-9) and (A-10) are satisfied.

A-5 Relation of Electrostatic to Electromagnetic Units The esu and emu have been defined independently of each other. The relations between the two systems can be put in the form of a list of conversion factors and may be found in many texts and handbooks. In the definition of the gaussian system the factor relating the units of $\mathbf{b}$ will be needed; it will now be found to illustrate the procedure in setting up a complete list.

Start with the two units of charge; let $q^{(s)}$ be the number representing a given charge in esu, and $q^{(m)}$ the number representing the same charge in emu. For two identical point charges the coulomb force (A-6) can be written in esu and emu, and since the units of force and length are the same in both, $q^{(s)} = cq^{(m)}$, and 1 abcoulomb is c statcoulombs. Then $\rho^{(s)} = c\rho^{(m)}$, and $\mathbf{j}^{(s)} = c\mathbf{j}^{(m)}$. From $\mathbf{f} = \mathbf{j}^{(s)} \times \mathbf{b}^{(s)} = \mathbf{j}^{(m)} \times \mathbf{b}^{(m)}$, one finally obtains $\mathbf{b}^{(s)} = \mathbf{b}^{(m)}/c$. The esu of $\mathbf{b}$ is c gauss.

A-6 Gaussian System The gaussian system measures ρ, $\mathbf{j}$, and $\mathbf{e}$ in esu, and $\mathbf{b}$ in emu. The units of mass, length, time, and force are the cgs units. The form of the Maxwell equations is obtained most directly by starting with those belonging to the esu and merely replacing $\mathbf{b}$ by $\mathbf{b}/c$. The result is

$$\operatorname{div} \mathbf{e} = 4\pi \rho \qquad\qquad \operatorname{div} \mathbf{b} = 0$$

$$\operatorname{curl} \mathbf{e} = -\frac{1}{c}\frac{\partial \mathbf{b}}{\partial t} \qquad\qquad \operatorname{curl} \mathbf{b} = \frac{1}{c}\frac{\partial \mathbf{e}}{\partial t} + \frac{4\pi}{c}\mathbf{j} \qquad \text{(A-12)}$$

$$\mathbf{f} = \rho \mathbf{e} + \frac{1}{c}\mathbf{j} \times \mathbf{b}$$

(There is another form of the gaussian system in which **j** is measured in emu, and the factor $1/c$ multiplying **j** in the above equations disappears. An advantage is that the emu of current is nearer the ampere and is more simply related to it than is the esu, but an overweighing disadvantage is that **j** is no longer equal to ρ**v**.)

A-7 Simplification of the Appearance of the Maxwell Equations; Rationalization and the Vectors d and h   In the microscopic theory introduced in Chap. 3, and in the first form of the macroscopic theory to be obtained in Chap. 15, the electric and magnetic fields are represented by a single vector each, **e** and **b** in the microscopic case, and **E** and **B** in the macroscopic. In the second form of the macroscopic theory the charges and currents arising from polarization in dielectrics and magnetically permeable media are treated in a special way which leads to introducing a new vector **D**, associated with the electric field, and a new vector **H**, associated with the magnetic, so that this form of the theory deals with four vectors instead of two. There is then a physical difference between **E** and **D** and between **B** and **H**. However, in many systems of units the Maxwell equations assume a cleaner and more easily remembered form if four vectors are used even in the microscopic theory, in which case the vectors are denoted **e**, **d**, **b**, and **h**, with **d** differing from **e**, and **h** from **b**, by numerical factors appropriate to each system but having no physical significance. In passing to a macroscopic theory, additional physical distinctions become superimposed on these purely numerical ones. It is the numerical aspect that will be discussed in this section.

If one formally introduces **d** and **h** by writing

$$\mathbf{d} = \epsilon_0 \mathbf{e} \qquad \mathbf{b} = \mu_0 \mathbf{h}$$

where ϵ_0 and μ_0 are numbers denoted by the commonly used symbols, the equations in the electrostatic and electromagnetic systems take the simple form

$$\operatorname{div} \mathbf{d} = 4\pi\rho \qquad\qquad \operatorname{div} \mathbf{b} = 0$$

$$\operatorname{curl} \mathbf{e} = -\frac{\partial \mathbf{b}}{\partial t} \qquad\qquad \operatorname{curl} \mathbf{h} = \frac{\partial \mathbf{d}}{\partial t} + 4\pi\mathbf{j} \qquad\text{(A-13)}$$

$$\mathbf{f} = \rho\mathbf{e} + \mathbf{j} \times \mathbf{b}$$

if

$$\epsilon_0 = 1 \qquad \mu_0 = \frac{1}{c^2} \qquad \text{esu}$$

$$\epsilon_0 = \frac{1}{c^2} \qquad \mu_0 = 1 \qquad \text{emu}$$

The gaussian equations (A-12) cannot be reduced to form (A-13) by suitable choice of ϵ_0 and μ_0. In the gaussian system one does not try to simplify the equations, but rather regards (A-12) as already sufficiently simple and symmetric to be easily remembered. One then enjoys the advantages of working with only two vectors instead of four, and at the same time using units whose definitions are easily remembered and are of long standing and wide use.

Several systems have come into existence which eliminate the 4π's appearing in the Maxwell equations given above. This elimination is called *rationalization*, an idea originally proposed by Heaviside, whose vociferous offense at the sight of these 4π's makes lively reading. Rationalization can be carried out in equations using two vectors or four. Consider first the case of two vectors, and suppose the gaussian equations (A-12) are to be rationalized. Let a prime stand for a quantity measured in rationalized units. Then if a stands for $(4\pi)^{\frac{1}{2}}$, and $\rho' = a\rho$, $j' = aj$, $e' = a^{-1}e$, and $b' = a^{-1}b$, equations (A-12), transformed to primed quantities, are unchanged, except that the 4π's are missing. These rationalized units are called Heaviside-Lorentz units because Heaviside's idea, originally proposed in connection with the phenomenological macroscopic theory of Maxwell, were adopted by Lorentz in his microscopic theory.

Rationalization simplifies not only the Maxwell equations, but also certain derived formulas. For example, the field in the condenser of Sec. 3-9 becomes just σ' in Heaviside-Lorentz units. On the other hand, the field about a point charge (Sec. 3-3) becomes $q'/4\pi r^2$. Thus the 4π's are not completely banished, but show up in problems with spherical geometry. In problems of radiation, spherical and plane geometries are about equally frequent, and the advantages of rationalization are not sufficiently obvious to warrant units of ρ, j, e, and b that differ by the awkward factor $(4\pi)^{\frac{1}{2}}$ from the long-familiar esu and emu.

If one admits four vectors, rationalization can be carried out in the following way: Write the gaussian equations as

$$\text{div } \mathbf{d} = 4\pi\rho \qquad\qquad \text{div } \mathbf{b} = 0$$

$$\text{curl } \mathbf{e} = -\frac{1}{c}\frac{\partial \mathbf{b}}{\partial t} \qquad\qquad \text{curl } \mathbf{h} = \frac{1}{c}\frac{\partial \mathbf{d}}{\partial t} + \frac{4\pi}{c}\mathbf{j}$$

$$\mathbf{f} = \rho\mathbf{e} + \frac{1}{c}\mathbf{j} \times \mathbf{b} \tag{A-14}$$

$$\mathbf{d} = \mathbf{e} \qquad\qquad \mathbf{b} = \mathbf{h}$$

Now change to primed quantities in which $\rho' = \rho$, $j' = j$, $e' = e$, $b' = b$, $d' = d/4\pi$, and $h' = h/4\pi$. Then the 4π's in (A-14) disappear, except that the bottom two become $d' = e'/4\pi$ and $b' = 4\pi h'$. By the use of four vectors one is free to give ρ, j, e, and b any desirable units and to absorb the effects of rationalization in d and h, for which one is not unwilling to let the units be what they will. This manner of rationalizing is employed in the mks units to be obtained in Sec. A-8.

The ultimate in simplification of the Maxwell equations is achieved by those systems derived from the Heaviside-Lorentz by changing the units of mass, length, and time in such a way that equations (A-12) are unchanged, except that all the 4π's and c's are missing. (Elimination of the c's is a great economy in those theoretical discussions in which the sizes of units are of no moment.) Such a change can be made in an infinite number of ways, of which the following is one example: The units of length and force can be left at the centimeter and dyne, and the unit of time can be a *light-second*, defined as the time light takes to travel 1 cm,[1] so that an interval of t sec is $t' = ct$ light-sec. The unit of mass is then $1/c^2$ g, so that $m' = c^2 m$. Let the units resulting from these particular changes be called *light units*, to have a definite name. Their relations to the gaussian units will be investigated in Sec. A-9 as one of the illustrations of the principles set forth in that section.

A-8 Introduction of Practical Units: the mks System For practical applications the statampere is much too small, and the abampere is slightly too large. The *ampere* was adopted and defined to be 0.1 abamp. It is therefore $c/10$ statamp (about 3×10^9 statamp). The statvolt is too large, and the abvolt is too small. The *volt* is defined to be 10^8 abvolts. It is therefore $10^8/c$ statvolt (about $\frac{1}{300}$ statvolt). The practical unit of charge is the *coulomb*, defined to be the charge transported in 1 sec by a current of 1 amp. Hence

$$1 \text{ coulomb} = 0.1 \text{ abcoulomb} \approx 3 \times 10^9 \text{ statcoulombs}$$

The practical unit of time can be none other than the *second*, and Newton's law must read $F = ma$. The erg is too small, and the practical unit of energy is the *joule*, defined to be 10^7 ergs.

With this much of a practical system fixed, one can pose the problem of completing the system, including constants for the Maxwell equations, in such a way as to give it as many desirable features as possible. A solution, first proposed by Giorgi in 1901, is called the *mks system*. This system can be given a rationalized or an unrationalized form, but the latter has been rejected, and only the former, which is being urged for universal adoption, will be discussed. In order to obtain a neat form for the Maxwell equations, it is necessary to use four vectors **e**, **d**, **b**, and **h**.

To obtain the rationalized mks units in a systematic way, one starts with some set of units that are already known and investigates the possible transformations to a new set subject to the conditions of incorporating the above practical units and having the simplest constants in the Maxwell equations. Start with the gaussian units, and, anticipating the necessity of four vectors, start with the gaussian equations in the form (A-14). Let any quantity expressed in the new units be indicated

---

[1] The term "light-second" is most commonly used in a sense defining a unit of length, namely, the distance light travels in 1 sec.

by a primed symbol, while the unprimed symbol indicates the same quantity in gaussian units. For the moment do not think of the m and k in mks as standing for meter and kilogram, so that the new units of length and mass remain to be determined in due course. Thus, to begin with, let the new unit of length be $[l]$ cm (that is, l in brackets stands for the conversion factor for length), and let the new unit of mass be $[m]$ g. Then

$$l' = [l^{-1}]l \qquad m' = [m^{-1}]m \qquad t' = t$$

Now $F' = [l^{-1}m^{-1}]F$, and by the definition of the joule, $F'l' = 10^{-7}Fl$. It follows that

$$[m] = 10^7[l^{-2}]$$

Thus $[m]$ is determined once $[l]$ is fixed. We have

$$\mathbf{v}' = [l^{-1}]\mathbf{v} \qquad\qquad \mathbf{f}' = [l^2m^{-1}]\mathbf{f} = 10^{-7}[l^4]\mathbf{f}$$
$$\operatorname{div}' = [l]\operatorname{div} \qquad \operatorname{curl}' = [l]\operatorname{curl}$$

From the definitions of the coulomb, ampere, and volt,

$$\rho' = 10c^{-1}[l^3]\rho \qquad \mathbf{j}' = 10c^{-1}[l^2]\mathbf{j} \qquad \mathbf{e}' = 10^{-8}c[l]\mathbf{e}$$

(The conversion factors are $[\rho] = 10^{-1}c[l^{-3}]$ gaussian units in the mks unit, etc.) Clearly, $\mathbf{j}'$ will equal $\rho'\mathbf{v}'$ for any choice of $[l]$.

The Maxwell equations in the new units will be obtained by choosing the simplest possible set of constants in the equations

$$\operatorname{div}' \mathbf{d}' = \alpha'\rho' \qquad\qquad\qquad \operatorname{div}'\mathbf{b}' = 0$$

$$\operatorname{curl}' \mathbf{e}' = -\beta' \frac{\partial \mathbf{b}'}{\partial t'} \qquad\qquad \operatorname{curl}' \mathbf{h}' = \gamma'\frac{\partial \mathbf{d}'}{\partial t'} + \delta'\mathbf{j}' \qquad \text{(A-15)}$$

$$\mathbf{f}' = \eta'\rho'\mathbf{e}' + \zeta'\mathbf{j}' \times \mathbf{b}'$$
$$\mathbf{d}' = \epsilon_0'\mathbf{e}' \qquad\qquad\qquad \mathbf{b}' = \mu_0'\mathbf{h}'$$

Introduce the conversion factors $[b]$, $[d]$, and $[h]$, so that

$$\mathbf{b}' = [b^{-1}]\mathbf{b} \qquad \mathbf{d}' = [d^{-1}]\mathbf{d} \qquad \mathbf{h}' = [h^{-1}]\mathbf{h}$$

Then equations (A-15) can be written in terms of unprimed symbols for the physical quantities:

$$\operatorname{div} \mathbf{d} = 10c^{-1}[l^2d]\alpha'\rho$$

$$\operatorname{curl} \mathbf{e} = -10^8c^{-1}[l^{-2}b^{-1}]\beta' \frac{\partial \mathbf{b}}{\partial t}$$

$$\operatorname{div} \mathbf{b} = 0$$

$$\operatorname{curl} \mathbf{h} = [l^{-1}d^{-1}h]\gamma' \frac{\partial \mathbf{d}}{\partial t} + 10c^{-1}[lh]\delta'\mathbf{j}$$

$$\mathbf{f} = \eta'\rho\mathbf{e} + 10^8c^{-1}[l^{-2}b^{-1}]\zeta'\mathbf{j} \times \mathbf{b}$$
$$\mathbf{d} = 10^{-8}c[ld]\epsilon_0'\mathbf{e}$$
$$\mathbf{b} = [bh^{-1}]\mu_0'\mathbf{h}$$

Since equations (A-14) must hold for all possible values of the variables, the coefficient of $\partial \mathbf{b}/\partial t$ in the second of the last set of equations must be equal to c^{-1}, etc. Thus

$$\alpha' = 4\pi \times 10^{-1}c[l^{-2}d^{-1}] \qquad \beta' = 10^{-8}[l^2 b]$$
$$\gamma' = c^{-1}[ldh^{-1}] \qquad\qquad \delta' = 4\pi \times 10^{-1}[l^{-1}h^{-1}]$$
$$\eta' = 1 \qquad\qquad\qquad\qquad \zeta' = 10^{-8}[l^2 b]$$
$$\epsilon_0' = 10^8 c^{-1}[l^{-1}d^{-1}] \qquad \mu_0' = [b^{-1}h]$$

The reason η' has the desirable value unity can be traced back to the fact that the practical units were set up to include the relation that the joule is the volt-ampere-second.

To continue toward a simple set of constants, set $\alpha' = \beta' = \gamma' = 1$. The units of $\mathbf{d}$, $\mathbf{b}$, and $\mathbf{h}$ are thereby made to depend only on the choice of $[l]$, and

$$[d] = 4\pi \times 10^{-1}c[l^{-2}] \qquad [b] = 10^8[l^{-2}] \qquad [h] = 4\pi \times 10^{-1}[l^{-1}]$$

It follows that $\delta' = \zeta' = 1$, very fortunate results.[1] We also have

$$\epsilon_0' = (4\pi)^{-1} \times 10^9 c^{-2}[l] \qquad \mu_0' = 4\pi \times 10^{-9}[l]$$

The choice of $[l]$ is still open and can now be made to best advantage. Clearly, it cannot be chosen to make $\epsilon_0' = \mu_0' = 1$, and hence at least three of the vectors $\mathbf{e}$, $\mathbf{d}$, $\mathbf{b}$, and $\mathbf{h}$ are necessary, and there might as well be four so as to leave freedom to pick an $[l]$ that gives a convenient unit of length. The centimeter, $[l] = 1$, leads to too large a unit of mass, and it is natural to try next the meter, $[l] = 10^2$. Then as a fortunate numerical coincidence, $[m] = 10^3$, giving a reasonable unit of mass: the kilogram.

If we introduce $c' \approx 3 \times 10^8$, the velocity of light in meters per second, the factors for converting from gaussian to mks units and the values of ϵ_0' and μ_0' become

$$[f] = 10^{-1} \qquad\qquad\qquad [F] = 10^5$$
$$[\rho] = 10^{-5}c' \qquad\qquad\qquad [j] = 10^{-3}c'$$
$$[e] = 10^4 c'^{-1} \qquad\qquad\qquad [d] = 4\pi \times 10^{-3}c'$$
$$[b] = 10^4 \qquad\qquad\qquad\qquad [h] = 4\pi \times 10^{-3}$$
$$\epsilon_0' = (4\pi \times 10^{-7}c'^2)^{-1} \qquad \mu_0' = 4\pi \times 10^{-7}$$

---

[1] Note that $\alpha'\gamma' = \delta'$, which, as pointed out earlier, is equivalent to the statement that charge is conserved if the relation $\mathbf{j}' = \rho'\mathbf{v}'$ holds. But conservation of charge in the mks units is already guaranteed, as is seen from the following general and easily proved theorem: If in any initial (unprimed) system $\mathbf{j} = \rho\mathbf{v}$ and div $\mathbf{j} = -\partial\rho/\partial t$, and if in a second (primed) system $\mathbf{j}' = \rho'\mathbf{v}'$, then div' $\mathbf{j}' = -\partial\rho'/\partial t'$. The premises of this theorem are satisfied in the gaussian and mks systems, and hence δ' is bound to be unity if $\alpha'\gamma' = 1$. It can also be shown by a simple general calculation that if in any two systems $\mathbf{j} = \rho\mathbf{v}$ and $\mathbf{j}' = \rho'\mathbf{v}'$, then $\zeta' = \beta'\eta'\beta^{-1}\eta^{-1}\zeta$. In the gaussian system $\beta^{-1}\eta^{-1}\zeta = 1$; hence in the mks, ζ' will be unity if $\eta'\beta' = 1$. The conclusion is that the results $\delta' = 1$ and $\zeta' = 1$ are not numerical accidents hanging on the definitions of the ampere, volt, and joule, except insofar as these definitions lead to $\eta' = 1$.

These conversion factors give the number of gaussian units in the mks unit. A more extensive table, including the names of the mks units, can be found in Stratton [86], p. 602.

The Maxwell equations in mks units are

$$\operatorname{div}' \mathbf{d}' = \rho' \qquad\qquad \operatorname{div}' \mathbf{b}' = 0$$

$$\operatorname{curl}' \mathbf{e}' = -\frac{\partial \mathbf{b}'}{\partial t'} \qquad\qquad \operatorname{curl}' \mathbf{h}' = \frac{\partial \mathbf{d}'}{\partial t'} + \mathbf{j}' \qquad\text{(A-16)}$$

$$\mathbf{f}' = \rho\, \mathbf{e}' + \mathbf{j}' \times \mathbf{b}'$$

$$\mathbf{d}' = \epsilon_0' \mathbf{e}' \qquad\qquad\qquad \mathbf{b}' = \mu_0' \mathbf{h}'$$

The velocity of electromagnetic waves predicted by these equations is found from the form of the wave equation in free space, which is easily shown to be

$$\nabla'^2 \mathbf{g} = \epsilon_0' \mu_0' \frac{\partial^2 \mathbf{g}}{\partial t'^2}$$

where $\mathbf{g}$ stands for any of the four vectors $\mathbf{e}'$, $\mathbf{d}'$, $\mathbf{b}'$, and $\mathbf{h}'$. The velocity[1] is $w' = (\epsilon_0' \mu_0')^{-\frac{1}{2}} = c'$.

The vectors $\mathbf{d}'$ and $\mathbf{h}'$ can be eliminated from (A-16) to give

$$\operatorname{div}' \mathbf{e}' = \epsilon_0'^{-1} \rho' \qquad\qquad \operatorname{div}' \mathbf{b}' = 0$$

$$\operatorname{curl}' \mathbf{e}' = -\frac{\partial \mathbf{b}'}{\partial t'} \qquad\qquad \operatorname{curl}' \mathbf{b}' = \epsilon_0' \mu_0' \frac{\partial \mathbf{e}'}{\partial t'} + \mu_0' \mathbf{j}' \quad\text{(A-17)}$$

$$\mathbf{f}' = \rho' \mathbf{e}' + \mathbf{j}' \times \mathbf{b}'$$

All quantities are still in practical mks units, and the electric and magnetic fields, which are after all single physical ideas, are represented by a single vector each, at the expense of a slightly less pleasing appearance of the Maxwell equations. If the microscopic theory were treated in mks units, there would be an advantage in presenting the microscopic equations in the form (A-17). Then, when in the macroscopic theory it became appropriate on real physical grounds to introduce two additional vectors associated with the electric and magnetic fields, the ideas would not be obscured by the presence of four vectors with purely numerical differences. These numerical differences could be added at the same time that the physical differences appear, and the result would be the usual form of the macroscopic mks equations. The real reason for choosing gaussian rather than mks units in works not dealing with electric circuits or other problems in electrical engineering is that gaussian

---

[1] That this velocity has come out correctly was guaranteed by the following general theorem: Assuming an initial system of units for which the Maxwell equations are (A-15) without primes, the wave equation in free space is $\nabla^2 \mathbf{g} = \beta \gamma \epsilon_0 \mu_0 \partial^2 \mathbf{g}/\partial t^2$. The velocity is $w = (\beta \gamma \epsilon_0 \mu_0)^{-\frac{1}{2}}$. In a primed system, $\nabla'^2 \mathbf{g}' = \beta \gamma \epsilon_0 \mu_0 [l^2 t^{-2}] \partial^2 \mathbf{g}'/\partial t'^2$. Hence $\beta' \gamma' \epsilon_0' \mu_0' = \beta \gamma \epsilon_0 \mu_0 [l^2 t^{-2}]$, and $w' = [l^{-1}t]w$. It follows that w' will have the correct value if w does.

formulas involve the single symbol c, rather than the four symbols ϵ_0 and μ_0 (counting the subscripts). The symbol c has a simple and important physical significance and a very convenient numerical value, while ϵ_0 and μ_0 have awkward numerical values and a complicated relationship to the velocity of light, the fundamental constant in the theory. Moreover, the gaussian units are not as impractical for solving engineering problems as they might seem, since the conversion factors relating them to the practical units are so simple.

A-9 Practical Rules for Converting Formulas A most convenient type of table for converting from one system of units to another is one that states just what to do with each symbol in a formula belonging to one system to get the corresponding formula belonging to the other. Such a table should express conversion factors not as simple numbers, but rather in terms of any symbol or symbols that stand for numerical constants in the desired formulas when they are written in the customary way. This idea will be illustrated by some examples.

Suppose one wishes to translate formulas given in "light units" (end of Sec. A-7) into those appropriate to the gaussian system. The conversion table is constructed in the following way: Let primes indicate quantities expressed in light units. The conversion factors for length, mass, time, velocity, force, and force density are known from the way the light units were set up, and

$$l' = l \qquad m' = c^2 m \qquad t' = ct \qquad \mathbf{v}' = c^{-1}\mathbf{v} \qquad F' = F \qquad \mathbf{f}' = \mathbf{f}$$

These equations mean that if, for example, one finds m' in a given formula, it is to be replaced by $c^2 m$. The conversion formulas for ρ, $\mathbf{j}$, $\mathbf{e}$, and $\mathbf{b}$ are obtained by comparing the Maxwell equations in the two systems. The equations in gaussian units are (A-12), and those in light units are

$$\text{div}' \, \mathbf{e}' = \rho' \qquad\qquad \text{div}' \, \mathbf{b}' = 0$$

$$\text{curl}' \, \mathbf{e}' = -\frac{\partial \mathbf{b}'}{\partial t'} \qquad\qquad \text{curl}' \, \mathbf{b}' = \frac{\partial \mathbf{e}'}{\partial t'} + \mathbf{j}' \qquad (A\text{-}18)$$

$$\mathbf{f}' = \rho' \mathbf{e}' + \mathbf{j}' \times \mathbf{b}'$$

Coulomb's law for equal charges takes the two forms $F = q^2/r^2$ and $F' = q'^2/4\pi r'^2$, and since $F' = F$ and $r' = r$,

$$q' = (4\pi)^{\frac{1}{2}} q \qquad \rho' = (4\pi)^{\frac{1}{2}} \rho$$

The force per unit length between parallel and equal currents is given by $F/L = 2I^2/c^2 r$ and $F'/L' = I'^2/2\pi r'$, whence

$$I' = (4\pi)^{\frac{1}{2}} c^{-1} I \qquad \mathbf{j}' = (4\pi)^{\frac{1}{2}} c^{-1} \mathbf{j}$$

Comparing the two expressions for the Lorentz force density,

$$\mathbf{e}' = (4\pi)^{-\frac{1}{2}} \mathbf{e} \qquad \mathbf{b}' = (4\pi)^{-\frac{1}{2}} \mathbf{b}$$

Note that all the conversion factors have been written with 4π and c appearing explicitly, ready to give gaussian formulas their usual appearance.

To apply all these conversion formulas to a concrete problem, one can transform equations (A-18) into (A-12) and thereby check the list. (Note that $\text{div}' = \text{div}$, $\text{curl}' = \text{curl}$, and $\partial/\partial t' = c^{-1}\partial/\partial t$.) The list can be extended to cover such derived quantities as resistance and capacitance. For example, the potentials (Sec. 3-14) in light units are easily seen to be

$$\phi' = \int \frac{\rho'}{4\pi r'}\,d\tau' \qquad \mathbf{A}' = \int \frac{\mathbf{j}'}{4\pi r'}\,d\tau'$$

(These formulas could stand for either the potentials for static problems or the retarded potentials for dynamic ones.) Then, applying the conversions for ρ', $\mathbf{j}'$, and l',

$$\phi' = (4\pi)^{-\frac{1}{2}}\phi \qquad \mathbf{A}' = (4\pi)^{-\frac{1}{2}}\mathbf{A}$$

If one were dealing with Heaviside-Lorentz units rather than light units, all the above relations for converting to gaussian units would apply if each c were replaced by unity.

Consider now conversion from gaussian to mks units and the reverse. These are the most frequently occurring problems, and to have a set of rules to cover all cases, it is necessary to allow for the use of four vectors in connection with the electric and magnetic fields; by admitting four vectors in the gaussian as well as the mks system, rules can be given that only require reinterpretation of the symbols to be applicable in all forms of the macroscopic theory.

Consider, first, transformation from gaussian to mks units. Let quantities in the latter units be distinguished by primes. The conversion table can be constructed exactly as in the preceding example, except for using equations (A-14) and (A-16), but an easier way is to use the conversion factors appearing just above equations (A-16). One should replace c' by $\epsilon_0'^{-\frac{1}{2}}\mu_0'^{-\frac{1}{2}}$, since mks formulas are rarely written to show c' explicitly. The table is then

$$
\begin{array}{llll}
l = 10^2 l' & m = 10^3 m' & t = t' & \mathbf{v} = 10^2\mathbf{v}' \\
\text{div} = 10^{-2}\,\text{div}' & & \text{curl} = 10^{-2}\text{curl}' & \\
F = 10^5 F' & & f = 10^{-1}f' & \\
q = 10\epsilon_0'^{-\frac{1}{2}}\mu_0'^{-\frac{1}{2}}q' & & \rho = 10^{-5}\epsilon_0'^{-\frac{1}{2}}\mu_0'^{-\frac{1}{2}}\rho' & \\
I = 10\epsilon_0'^{-\frac{1}{2}}\mu_0'^{-\frac{1}{2}}I' & & \mathbf{j} = 10^{-3}\epsilon_0'^{-\frac{1}{2}}\mu_0'^{-\frac{1}{2}}\mathbf{j}' & \\
\mathbf{e} = 10^4\epsilon_0'^{\frac{1}{2}}\mu_0'^{\frac{1}{2}}\mathbf{e}' & & \mathbf{d} = 10^4\epsilon_0'^{-\frac{1}{2}}\mu_0'^{\frac{1}{2}}\mathbf{d}' & \\
\mathbf{b} = 10^4 \mathbf{b}' & & \mathbf{h} = 10^4\mu_0'\mathbf{h}' & \\
c = 10^2\epsilon_0'^{-\frac{1}{2}}\mu_0'^{-\frac{1}{2}} & & 4\pi = 10^7\mu_0' & \\
\end{array}
$$

Note that there are entries even for c and 4π.

As examples of the use of these formulas, one can transform (A-14) into (A-16), and (A-12) into (A-17). As another example, consider the following equation, which occurs in Chap. 4:

$$u = \frac{\mathbf{e} \cdot \mathbf{e} + \mathbf{b} \cdot \mathbf{b}}{8\pi}$$

where u is the energy density associated with an electromagnetic field. Since energy density is essentially force density times length, we clearly have the conversion formula $u = 10u'$, and the transformed equation is

$$u' = \frac{\epsilon_0' \mathbf{e}' \cdot \mathbf{e}' + \mu_0'^{-1} \mathbf{b}' \cdot \mathbf{b}'}{2} = \frac{\mathbf{e}' \cdot \mathbf{d}' + \mathbf{b}' \cdot \mathbf{h}'}{2}$$

where the first form on the right comes directly from the above table and is simplified to the second equivalent form.

The table for transforming from mks to gaussian units should have 4π and c appearing explicitly in the conversion factors. It is

$l' = 10^{-2}l$	$m' = 10^{-3}m$	$t' = t$	$\mathbf{v}' = 10^{-2}\mathbf{v}$
$\text{div}' = 10^2\text{div}$		$\text{curl}' = 10^2\,\text{curl}$	
$F' = 10^{-5}F$		$\mathbf{f}' = 10\mathbf{f}$	
$q' = 10c^{-1}q$		$\rho' = 10^7c^{-1}\rho$	
$I' = 10c^{-1}I$		$\mathbf{j}' = 10^5c^{-1}\mathbf{j}$	
$\mathbf{e}' = 10^{-6}c\mathbf{e}$		$\mathbf{d}' = (4\pi)^{-1} \times 10^5c^{-1}\mathbf{d}$	
$\mathbf{b}' = 10^{-4}\mathbf{b}$		$\mathbf{h}' = (4\pi)^{-1} \times 10^3\mathbf{h}$	
$\epsilon_0' = (4\pi)^{-1} \times 10^{11}c^{-2}$		$\mu_0' = 4\pi \times 10^{-7}$	
$c' = 10^2c$			

The last two tables are easily extended to cover other physical quantities and perhaps some of the more frequently occurring combinations of symbols.

This appendix has not exhausted the list of different systems of units one finds in the literature, but a complete set of principles has been presented whereby one can relate any system to any other in a straightforward manner. Quantum mechanics introduces new fundamental equations and a new constant of nature in addition to the velocity of light, namely, Planck's constant, a quantity of action (work times time) having in the cgs units the value $h \approx 6.6 \times 10^{-27}$ erg sec. This quantity usually enters as $\hbar \equiv h/2\pi \approx 10^{-27}$ erg sec. To avoid the necessity of writing symbols to represent these constants in quantum-mechanical formulas, exotic units are sometimes used. For example, in one system the units are chosen to make $c' = \hbar' = 1$. It can then be shown that no matter what choice is made for the unit of length, the units of mass, time, and electrical quantities can be defined to make all the constants of proportionality in the Maxwell equations equal unity. Such units are usually called "natural," and one can easily apply the principles of this appendix to find the conversion factors relating them to, say, the gaussian units, these factors involving the arbitrary factor for the unit of length.

Radiation Field of a Dipole Oscillator

In this appendix formulas (5-4) and (5-5) for the fields about an atom in which an electron oscillates sinusoidally will be deduced in rigorous fashion from the Maxwell equations. Actually, much more will be accomplished than just obtaining this special solution.

The calculation will consist of three parts. In the first a general solution of the Maxwell equations will be derived to give the fields in terms of retarded potentials when the microscopic densities of charge and current are known as functions of time and position. The result will be the principal theorem of Sec. 3-14, expressed by (3-16) to (3-20). In the second part, the general solution will be specialized to the case of a moving particle when the motion is perfectly general. Finally, the results of the second part will be applied to an electron moving in the immediate vicinity of a nucleus with a motion which is arbitrary except for being slow compared with the velocity of light. Taking the motion to be sinusoidal will then give (5-4) and (5-5), together with conditions (5-7) and (5-8). Much of the calculation has the air of formal mathematics, with many equations not subject to immediate physical interpretation; in this respect the present appendix is of a quite different character from the other parts of the book. However, the most recondite mathematical formula can usually be illuminated by simple comments, and every effort will be made to do so.

B-1 General Solution of the Maxwell Equations by the Method of Retarded Potentials The microscopic Maxwell equations are

$$\text{div } \mathbf{e} = 4\pi\rho \tag{B-1}$$

$$\text{curl } \mathbf{e} = -\frac{1}{c}\frac{\partial \mathbf{b}}{\partial t} \tag{B-2}$$

$$\text{div } \mathbf{b} = 0 \tag{B-3}$$

$$\text{curl } \mathbf{b} = \frac{1}{c}\frac{\partial \mathbf{e}}{\partial t} + \frac{4\pi}{c}\mathbf{j} \tag{B-4}$$

Since div curl $\mathbf{A} = 0$ for any field $\mathbf{A}$, it follows that (B-3) will be satisfied automatically if $\mathbf{b}$ can be found in the form

$$\mathbf{b} = \text{curl } \mathbf{A} \tag{B-5}$$

Substituting (B-5) in (B-2) gives

$$\text{curl}\left(\mathbf{e} + \frac{1}{c}\frac{\partial \mathbf{A}}{\partial t}\right) = 0$$

and since the curl of a gradient vanishes, this equation will be satisfied automatically if $\mathbf{e}$ can be found in the form

$$\mathbf{e} = -\text{grad } \phi - \frac{1}{c}\frac{\partial \mathbf{A}}{\partial t} \tag{B-6}$$

where ϕ is a scalar field. (The negative sign before the gradient is purely a matter of convention.) The problem remains to find a scalar field ϕ and a vector field $\mathbf{A}$ such that $\mathbf{e}$ and $\mathbf{b}$ given by (B-5) and (B-6) will satisfy (B-1) and (B-4) as well as (B-2) and (B-3). Fields ϕ and $\mathbf{A}$ which satisfy this requirement are called *scalar and vector potentials*.

The conditions which the potentials must satisfy are obtained by substituting (B-5) and (B-6) in (B-1) and (B-4). We obtain

$$\text{div}\left(\text{grad } \phi + \frac{1}{c}\frac{\partial \mathbf{A}}{\partial t}\right) = -4\pi\rho \tag{B-7}$$

$$\text{curl curl } \mathbf{A} + \frac{1}{c}\frac{\partial}{\partial t}\left(\text{grad } \phi + \frac{1}{c}\frac{\partial \mathbf{A}}{\partial t}\right) = \frac{4\pi}{c}\mathbf{j} \tag{B-8}$$

Writing div grad ϕ as $\nabla^2\phi$ and using the identity (1-26), the last two equations become, after interchanging the orders of some of the operations,

$$\nabla^2\phi + \frac{1}{c}\frac{\partial}{\partial t}\text{div } \mathbf{A} = -4\pi\rho \tag{B-9}$$

$$\nabla^2\mathbf{A} - \frac{1}{c^2}\frac{\partial^2\mathbf{A}}{\partial t^2} - \text{grad}\left(\text{div } \mathbf{A} + \frac{1}{c}\frac{\partial\phi}{\partial t}\right) = -\frac{4\pi}{c}\mathbf{j} \tag{B-10}$$

Clearly, the steps leading to (B-9) and (B-10) can be reversed to show that if functions ϕ and $\mathbf{A}$ satisfy these equations, then $\mathbf{e}$ and $\mathbf{b}$ given by (B-5) and (B-6) satisfy the Maxwell equations. The problem of solving the four equations (B-1) to (B-4) directly for $\mathbf{e}$ and $\mathbf{b}$ has thus been replaced by that of solving the two equations (B-9) and (B-10) for ϕ and $\mathbf{A}$.

Now if a solution of (B-9) and (B-10) can be found which happens to satisfy at the same time

$$\operatorname{div} \mathbf{A} = -\frac{1}{c} \frac{\partial \phi}{\partial t} \tag{B-11}$$

it follows, after substitution for div $\mathbf{A}$ in (B-9) and (B-10), that ϕ and $\mathbf{A}$ satisfy the following simpler equations, each involving only ϕ or only $\mathbf{A}$, and each of the same type:[1]

$$\nabla^2 \phi - \frac{1}{c^2} \frac{\partial^2 \phi}{\partial t^2} = -4\pi\rho \tag{B-12}$$

$$\nabla^2 \mathbf{A} - \frac{1}{c^2} \frac{\partial^2 \mathbf{A}}{\partial t^2} = -\frac{4\pi}{c} \mathbf{j} \tag{B-13}$$

Conversely, any solution of the three equations (B-11) to (B-13) will obviously satisfy (B-9) and (B-10). While any potentials satisfying (B-9) and (B-10) lead to the same fields $\mathbf{e}$ and $\mathbf{b}$, it is especially convenient to impose the condition (B-11) and work with (B-12) and (B-13), or, to restate the matter, to seek solutions of the three equations (B-11) to (B-13), rather than of the two (B-9) and (B-10).

Condition (B-11) is called the *Lorentz condition*, and it can be shown that if it is possible to find a solution of (B-9) and (B-10), then it is also possible to find solutions of (B-12) and (B-13) which satisfy (B-11). The argument is very simple and can be found in Heitler [37], p. 2. The procedure to be adopted in the present treatment is to write a pair of expressions for ϕ and $\mathbf{A}$ in terms of ρ and $\mathbf{j}$ and show that they satisfy (B-11) to (B-13). These expressions are

$$\phi(P,t) = \int \frac{\rho(P',t')}{r} \, d\tau \tag{B-14}$$

$$\mathbf{A}(P,t) = \int \frac{\mathbf{j}(P',t')}{cr} \, d\tau \tag{B-15}$$

where
$$t' = t - \frac{r}{c} \tag{B-16}$$

They are just the retarded potentials whose interpretation was given in Sec. 3-14. The most important points to keep in mind are that P is an

---

[1] Equations (B-12) and (B-13) are called *inhomogeneous wave equations*. The equations obtained by setting the right sides equal to zero are called *homogeneous wave equations*.

arbitrary field point at which the potentials are being evaluated, P' is the location of the volume element $d\tau$, r is the distance between P and P', and the integrals extend over all space. In the integrands, ρ and $\mathbf{j}$ are evaluated at the location of $d\tau$ and at the retarded time t', the latter being related to the time t, at which the potentials are being evaluated, by (B-16). If in a cartesian system the coordinates of P are x, y, and z, and those of P' are x', y', and z', then

$$r = [(x - x')^2 + (y - y')^2 + (z - z')^2]^{1/2} \qquad \text{(B-17)}$$

It will be shown that (B-14) and (B-15) satisfy (B-11) to (B-13) and hence may be substituted in (B-5) and (B-6) to obtain the fields $\mathbf{e}$ and $\mathbf{b}$ for arbitrary distributions of charge and current. Before we proceed it might be mentioned that it is not necessary to draw the formulas (B-14) and (B-15) out of the air. There are systematic methods for finding them; one based on the principles of Fourier analysis in Chap. 11 is given in Panofsky and Phillips [69], p. 212.

The verification that (B-14) satisfies (B-12) will be carried out in terms of cartesian coordinates, in which ∇^2 is given by (1-22) and (1-27). It is necessary to evaluate the second derivatives of $\phi(x,y,z,t)$ by differentiating the right side of (B-14), in which x, y, z, and t appear as parameters, the first three being involved only where r appears in the denominator and in t', and the last only in t'.

The first thought is to freely interchange the order of differentiation and integration, but it is pointed out in works on advanced calculus that this interchange cannot always be made when the integrand is not finite for all values of the parameters, which is the case in (B-14) whenever $\rho(x,y,z,t) \neq 0$ and $r = 0$.[1] In fact, it will be seen that to make this interchange in the present problem would give a distinctly wrong result. The correct procedure is to use the following artifice: Let the field point P be surrounded by a very small imaginary spherical surface of radius a with center at some fixed point O, not necessarily the same as P. Let all the space outside the surface be denoted by V_1, and the region inside by V_2, and write $\phi(P,t)$ as the sum of two terms:

$$\phi(P,t) = \phi_1(P,t) + \phi_2(P,t) \qquad \text{(B-18)}$$

where ϕ_1 is given by (B-14) with the integral extending only over V_1, and similarly for ϕ_2. As long as $\rho(P',t')$ is always finite, which we assume, the integrand in the expression for ϕ_1 is finite for all values of x, y, and z provided P is inside V_2, and the order of differentiation and integration can be interchanged. On the other hand, the integration giving ϕ_2 can be actually carried out for any position of P in the small volume V_2, and the result can be differentiated, a perfectly legitimate procedure.

---

[1] A discussion of "improper" integrals of this sort, with special reference to electricity, is given in Phillips [71], pp. 122–132.

The differentiation of ϕ_1 goes as follows: For brevity, introduce the notation

$$\rho(P',t') \equiv \rho' \qquad \frac{\partial \rho(P',t')}{\partial t'} \equiv \rho'_t \qquad \frac{\partial^2 \rho(P',t')}{\partial t'^2} \equiv \rho'_{tt}$$

Note that

$$\frac{\partial \rho'}{\partial t} = \frac{\partial \rho'}{\partial t'}\frac{\partial t'}{\partial t} = \rho'_t \qquad \frac{\partial \rho'}{\partial x} = \frac{\partial \rho'}{\partial t'}\frac{\partial t'}{\partial x} = -\frac{\rho'_t}{cr}(x - x') \quad \cdots$$

Then

$$\frac{\partial \phi_1(P,t)}{\partial x} = -\int_{V_1}\left(\frac{\rho'}{r^3} + \frac{\rho'_t}{cr^2}\right)(x - x')\, d\tau$$

$$\frac{\partial^2 \phi_1(P,t)}{\partial x^2} = \int_{V_1}\left\{\left(\frac{\rho'}{r^3} + \frac{\rho'_t}{cr^2}\right)\left[\frac{3(x - x')^2}{r^2} - 1\right] + \frac{\rho'_{tt}}{c^2 r^3}(x - x')^2\right\}d\tau$$

In order to guarantee with minimum mathematical complication that all the above integrals have meaning, it is assumed that ρ'_{tt} is finite; the physical applicability of the calculation remains adequate for our purposes. Adding to the last result the corresponding derivatives with respect to y and z and using (B-17),

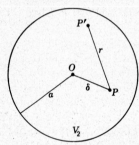

Fig. B-1. *Geometry in the volume V_2.*

$$\nabla^2 \phi_1(P,t) = \int_{V_1}\frac{\rho'_{tt}}{c^2 r}\, d\tau$$

which is equivalent to

$$\left(\nabla^2 - \frac{1}{c^2}\frac{\partial^2}{\partial t^2}\right)\phi_1(P,t) = 0 \qquad \text{(B-19)}$$

Note that if this same procedure were applied (erroneously) to the total potential (B-14), one would not obtain (B-12) when $\rho(P,t) \neq 0$.

With regard to $\phi_2(P,t)$, if the radius a of the sphere is sufficiently small and the first partial derivatives of ρ with respect to the spatial coordinates are finite and continuous, $\rho(P',t')$ is practically equal to $\rho(O,t)$ throughout the volume V_1. Then

$$\phi_2(P,t) \approx \rho(O,t)\int_{V_2}\frac{1}{r}\, d\tau$$

The integral

$$I = \int_{V_2}\frac{1}{r}\, d\tau$$

is recognized as the electrostatic potential at the point P in a sphere of uniform charge density unity. Let O, the center of the sphere, have coordinates x_0, y_0, and z_0, and let the distance between O and P be $\delta = [(x - x_0)^2 + (y - y_0)^2 + (z - z_0)^2]^{1/2}$. The geometry involved is indicated in Fig. B-1. It is easily shown[1] that

---

[1] The easiest way to find I is not to evaluate the integral, but rather to find the static electric field, as in Prob. 3-2, and calculate the line integral from O to P.

$$I = \frac{2\pi}{3}(3a^2 - \delta^2)$$

whence, by simple differentiation, $\nabla^2 I = -4\pi$, and

$$\left(\nabla^2 - \frac{1}{c^2}\frac{\partial^2}{\partial t^2}\right)\phi_2(P,t) = -4\pi\,\rho(O,t) - \frac{2\pi}{3c^2}(3a^2 - \delta^2)\frac{\partial^2\rho(O,t)}{\partial t^2}$$

If we let δ go to zero to bring O into coincidence with the field point P, the latter now being fixed at some particular point of interest, and then let a go to zero, the second term on the right vanishes. Combining the result with (B-19) and (B-18) finally gives (B-12).

By the arguments just employed, but with $\mathbf{j}$ in place of ρ, it follows that (B-15) satisfies (B-13). [This statement is especially obvious if one considers separately the scalar components of (B-13) and (B-15).] To show that (B-11) is satisfied, let space be divided into regions V_1 and V_2 as before, and consider div $\mathbf{A}_1(P,t)$. The operation of taking the divergence is written as a process of differentiation by (1-17), and the differentiation can be carried under the integral sign to give

$$\text{div } \mathbf{A}_1(P,t) = \int_{V_1} \text{div}\frac{\mathbf{j}(P',t')}{cr}\,d\tau$$

The operator div in the integrand involves derivatives with respect to x, y, and z, which appear only in r through (B-17), and r appears in the denominator and in t'. The integrand can be transformed to involve derivatives with respect to x', y', and z', provided one carefully distinguishes between these variables as they appear implicitly in r and as they appear explicitly as coordinates of P' in $\mathbf{j}(P',t')$. Thus, noting the antisymmetric way in which the primed and unprimed variables appear in (B-17),

$$\text{div } \mathbf{A}_1(P,t) = -\int_{V_1} \text{div}'\frac{\mathbf{j}(P',t')}{cr}\,d\tau + \int_{V_1}\frac{1}{cr}\text{div}_{P'}\,\mathbf{j}(P',t')\,d\tau \qquad \text{(B-20)}$$

where div$'$ involves derivatives with respect to x', y', and z' wherever they appear (that is, in P', t', and r), and div$_{P'}$ involves derivatives with respect to the same variables only as they appear explicitly as the coordinates of P'

The first integral in (B-20) can be transformed by Gauss' theorem to the sum of two surface integrals, one over the sphere at infinity, which vanishes when $\mathbf{j}$ is supposed zero there, and one over the small sphere about P, whose value is of the order of the radius a and vanishes with a. Thus, the first integral may be neglected. In the second integral one introduces the equation of conservation of charge,

$$\text{div}_{P'}\,\mathbf{j}(P',t') = -\frac{\partial\rho(P',t')}{\partial t'}$$

and it follows at once that

$$\text{div } \mathbf{A}_1(P,t) + \frac{1}{c}\frac{\partial \phi_1(P,t)}{\partial t} = 0$$

Finally one easily shows that in the limit as a goes to zero,

$$\text{div } \mathbf{A}_2(P,t) = 0 \qquad \frac{\partial \phi_2(P,t)}{\partial t} = 0$$

and (B-11) follows.

The conclusion to be drawn from this section is the following: Let the charge and current densities be given as any functions of coordinates and time which have continuous first spatial derivatives and finite second time derivatives (conditions which can be imposed in all our applications up to a final passage to the limit of a point charge). Then the solution of the microscopic Maxwell equations can be obtained by finding first the retarded potentials as the integrals in (B-14) and (B-15), and then the fields **e** and **b** by (B-5) and (B-6).

B-2 Specialization to a Moving Point Charge. The Liénard-Wiechert Potentials In this section the retarded potentials ϕ and $\mathbf{A}$ will be calculated for a moving charged particle. These special potentials, taken in the limit of a point charge, are known as Liénard-Wiechert potentials after the men who discovered them shortly before 1900.

Ultimately the particle will be regarded as a point charge, but to apply (B-14) and (B-15), it is necessary at first to regard it as having a finite extension with the charge distributed in some continuous and rigid fashion throughout its volume. Let the charge move without rotation, so that at any instant the velocity **v** of every element of charge is the same, and the current density is $\mathbf{j} = \rho\mathbf{v}$. Let a point fixed in the charge describe a path limited only by the requirements that the velocity is always less than c and the acceleration is finite. In order to be able to apply the theory of the preceding section, it is necessary to assume that at any instant the density ρ varies smoothly through space and falls smoothly to zero at the edges of the charge in such a way that, as the charge moves along its path, the second time derivatives of ρ and $\mathbf{j}$ at any point fixed in space are finite. It is possible to construct many suitable functions to represent ρ, and the mere possibility allows us to proceed.

Evaluation of the integrals in (B-14) and (B-15) presents some difficulty. To see the problem, consider a volume element δV which is fixed in the charge distribution, and at some time t' which is earlier than the fixed time t at which the potentials are to be evaluated, let its distance from P be $R(t')$, as indicated in Fig. B-2. Relation (B-16) defines a distance $r(t') = c(t - t')$ such that only elements of charge and current which, at time t', are in a thin spherical shell at this distance from P (that is, in the shell S in Fig. B-2) will contribute to the potentials at P at time t.[1] Thus, under the conditions of the illustration, the charge and current in δV will not contribute to the potentials for the particular choice of t'. Now let t' increase. The shell S will contract with velocity c, and at the same time δV will move along a given path with velocity less than c. Ultimately the shell S will overtake δV and, in a certain short interval, will sweep over it. During this interval there will be a contribution to the potentials from δV, the total amount of which must next be calculated.

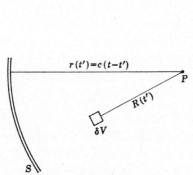

Fig. B-2. *Geometry at time t', before the element δV contributes to the potentials at P and t.*

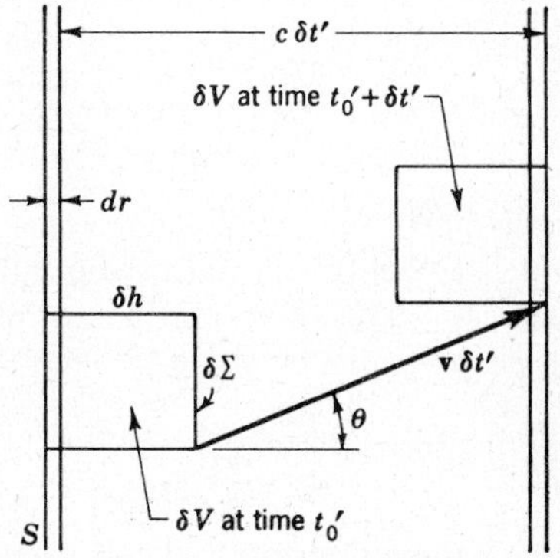

Fig. B-3. *Enlarged view of δV at the beginning and end of the interval during which it contributes to the potentials.*

Figure B-3 shows an enlarged view of the volume δV at the two specially chosen times t'_0 and $t'_0 + \delta t'$. At t'_0 the volume is in the position at the left, and the shell S, of thickness dr, has just overtaken it. At $t'_0 + \delta t'$ the volume has moved with essentially constant velocity $\mathbf{v}$ to the position at the right, and the shell has moved the distance $c\delta t'$ and is about to leave δV. Since the whole of Fig. B-3 is confined to a very small region of space, it can all be regarded as being at essentially the same distance $r(t'_0)$ from P. If the area of the faces of δV which are parallel to the shell S is $\delta\Sigma$, then at any time t' between t'_0 and $t'_0 + \delta t'$ the contributions to the scalar and vector potentials from the shell S are, respectively,

$$\frac{\rho \, dr \, \delta\Sigma}{r(t'_0)} \qquad \frac{\rho\mathbf{v} \, dr \, \delta\Sigma}{c \, r(t'_0)}$$

where ρ is the essentially constant density in δV. To find the total contributions from δV, the last two expressions must be multiplied by

---

[1] A discussion of this idea was given in Sec. 3-14.

the number of shells of thickness dr that can be fitted between the two extreme positions of S shown in Fig. B-3, that is, by $c\ \delta t'/dr$. From the figure it is seen that if $\mathbf{r}$ is the vector from δV to P,

$$c\ \delta t' = \delta h + v\ \delta t'\cos\theta = \delta h + \frac{\mathbf{v}\cdot\mathbf{r}}{r}\ \delta t'$$

or

$$c\ \delta t' = \frac{\delta h}{1 - \mathbf{v}\cdot\mathbf{r}/cr}$$

Both $\mathbf{r}$ and $\mathbf{v}$ must be understood as being evaluated at t_0', the retarded time at which δV contributes. Denoting $\rho\ \delta h\ \delta\Sigma$ by δq, the charge in δV, the contributions to the potentials from δV are

$$\frac{\delta q}{r - \mathbf{v}\cdot\mathbf{r}/c} \qquad \frac{(\mathbf{v}/c)\ \delta q}{r - \mathbf{v}\cdot\mathbf{r}/c}$$

If the particle is small enough, the vectors $\mathbf{r}$ and $\mathbf{v}$ holding at the time at which δq contributes are essentially the same for all elements δq in the particle. Then the total potentials are obtained by replacing δq in the last expressions by the total charge q to give

$$\phi(P,t) = \left[\frac{q}{r - \mathbf{v}\cdot\mathbf{r}/c}\right]_{t-r/c} \qquad \mathbf{A}(P,t) = \left[\frac{q\mathbf{v}/c}{r - \mathbf{v}\cdot\mathbf{r}/c}\right]_{t-r/c} \qquad (B\text{-}21)$$

where the subscripts indicate that $\mathbf{r}$ and $\mathbf{v}$ are to be evaluated at the retarded time $t - r/c$. Recall that $\mathbf{r}$ points from the particle to P.

The potentials (B-21) are the Liénard-Wiechert potentials. They depend only on the total charge and not on the details of the volume distribution because we assumed that the particle is small. The approximation improves as the size of the particle decreases, and there is nothing to hinder its passing to the limit of a point charge.

B-3 Fields of a Dipole Oscillator If a particle of charge q moves with velocity less than c, but otherwise arbitrarily, the fields associated with it are obtained by substituting the potentials (B-21) in (B-5) and (B-6). However, $\mathbf{r}$ and $\mathbf{v}$ in these potentials are to be evaluated at time t' defined by $t' = t - r(t')/c$, and this complicated relation makes difficult the task of taking derivatives with respect to t, x, y, and z in calculating the exact fields. Nevertheless, the process can be carried out to give the fields as closed but rather complicated expressions (see, for example, Heitler [37], p. 20).

Consider an atom in which an electron moves slowly compared with the velocity of light and is always very near a fixed nucleus. The exact fields at points not too near the atom are essentially the same as the first terms in an expansion of the exact fields in powers of the small quantities s/r and v/c, where s is the distance between the nucleus and the electron, and r is the distance from the atom to the field point P. These approximate fields are adequate for applications to atomic radiation, and the problem of finding them can be approached in two ways: (1) Find the exact fields, expand in a series, and keep only the important terms or (2) expand the potentials (B-21) in a series, and find the fields resulting from only the important terms. The second approach is simpler and will now be followed. The calculation will be carried only through the first approximation, although the procedure for carrying the expansion further will be set up. In certain types of problems, not to be taken up in this book, it is important to go to at least the second approximation.

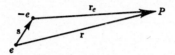

Fig. B-4. *Vectors specifying the positions of an electron* $(-e)$ *and a field point P relative to a fixed nucleus* (e).

The potentials at the field point P at time t consist of sums of contributions of the form (B-21) due to the nucleus and to the electron. Let the vector from the fixed nucleus to P be $\mathbf{r}$, that from the nucleus to the electron be $\mathbf{s}$, and that from the electron to P be $\mathbf{r}_e$. These vectors are illustrated in Fig. B-4. The problem involves the following times:

t The time at which the potentials and fields at P are to be found.

t' Defined by $t' = t - r/c$, the retarded time at the fixed position of the nucleus corresponding to time t at P. The parts of the potentials at P and t due to the nucleus depend on the presence and (fixed) position of the latter at time t'.

t_e' Defined by $t_e' = t - r_e(t_e')/c$, the retarded time of the electron. The parts of the potentials at P and t due to the electron depend on the latter's position and velocity at time t_e'.

In addition to these particular times, it will be convenient to speak of an arbitrary time τ which may be assigned any particular value. The position of the electron is supposed given as some function $\mathbf{s}(\tau)$; the velocity $d\mathbf{s}(\tau)/d\tau$ will be denoted by $\dot{\mathbf{s}}(\tau)$, and the acceleration by $\ddot{\mathbf{s}}(\tau)$. The electron will always be less than some maximum distance $|\mathbf{s}|_{max}$ from the nucleus, and the fields will be found only at points P such that

$$r \gg |\mathbf{s}|_{max} \qquad\qquad (B-22)$$

The velocity of the electron will always be less than some $|\dot{\mathbf{s}}|_{max}$, and it is assumed that

$$|\dot{\mathbf{s}}|_{max} \ll c \qquad\qquad (B-23)$$

The potentials due to the nucleus are

$$\phi_n(P,t) = \frac{e}{r} \qquad \mathbf{A}_n(P,t) = 0 \tag{B-24}$$

Those due to the electron are

$$\phi_e(P,t) = -\frac{e}{r_e}\left(1 - \frac{\dot{\mathbf{s}} \cdot \mathbf{r}_e}{cr_e}\right)^{-1} \qquad \mathbf{A}_e(P,t) = -\frac{e\dot{\mathbf{s}}}{cr_e}\left(1 - \frac{\dot{\mathbf{s}} \cdot \mathbf{r}_e}{cr_e}\right)^{-1} \tag{B-25}$$

In the expressions in parentheses in (B-25) the second term is small because of (B-23), and one can make the expansions

$$\phi_e(P,t) = -\frac{e}{r_e}\left(1 + \frac{\dot{\mathbf{s}} \cdot \mathbf{r}_e}{cr_e} + \cdots\right)$$

$$\mathbf{A}_e(P,t) = -\frac{e\dot{\mathbf{s}}}{cr_e}\left(1 + \frac{\dot{\mathbf{s}} \cdot \mathbf{r}_e}{cr_e} + \cdots\right) \tag{B-26}$$

Now r_e is determined by $\mathbf{s}$ and $\mathbf{r}$, as is seen in Fig. B-4, and it is advantageous to eliminate $\mathbf{r}_e$. We have

$$\mathbf{r}_e = \mathbf{r} - \mathbf{s} \tag{B-27}$$

$$\frac{1}{r_e} = \frac{1}{r}\left(1 - 2\frac{\mathbf{s} \cdot \mathbf{r}}{r^2} + \frac{s^2}{r^2}\right)^{-1/2} = \frac{1}{r} + \frac{\mathbf{s} \cdot \mathbf{r}}{r^3} - \frac{s^2}{2r^3} + \cdots \tag{B-28}$$

Recall that $\mathbf{s}$ and $\dot{\mathbf{s}}$ are to be evaluated at time t'_e, and as a result the time t enters the potentials in a complicated way. It is possible to express these vectors in terms of t', which is simply proportional to t and is only slightly different from t'_e. The relation between t'_e and t' is

$$t'_e = t' + \frac{r - r_e(t'_e)}{c} = t' + \frac{l(t'_e)}{c}$$

where l is an abbreviation for $r - r_e$. If $x(\tau)$ stands for $\mathbf{s}(\tau)$ or $\dot{\mathbf{s}}(\tau)$, one can use a theorem on page 133 of Whittaker and Watson [100][1] which states that

$$x(t'_e) = x(t') + \sum_{n=1}^{\infty} \frac{1}{c^n n!} \frac{d^{n-1}}{dt'^{n-1}}\left\{\dot{x}(t')\,[l(t')]^n\right\}$$

$$= x(t') + \frac{\dot{x}(t')\,l(t')}{c} + \cdots \tag{B-29}$$

For l we have

$$l = r\left[1 - \left(1 - 2\frac{\mathbf{s} \cdot \mathbf{r}}{r^2} + \frac{s^2}{r^2}\right)^{1/2}\right] = \frac{\mathbf{s} \cdot \mathbf{r}}{r} - \frac{s^2}{2r} + \cdots \tag{B-30}$$

---

[1] This theorem is given in terms of functions of a complex variable, since it is most easily proved in these terms, but it is applicable to functions of a real variable. It is not necessary to enter into the proof if it is accepted that the conditions of the theorem are satisfied in the present problem.

The final expansion of the potentials is now obtained by first substituting (B-30) in (B-29), then setting x equal to s or $\dot{s}$, as required, and finally substituting these expansions of $s(t'_e)$ and $\dot{s}(t'_e)$ together with (B-27) and (B-28) in (B-26). The result for either ϕ or $\mathbf{A}$ will be a series of terms involving $\mathbf{r}$, $s(t')$, and the derivatives of $s(t')$ with respect to t'. The terms will fall into groups constituting the successive approximations. In the first group the letter s appears once in each term (either as s or as $\dot{s}$); in the second it appears twice (as products s^2, $s \cdot \dot{s}$, etc.); in the third, three times; and so on. For purposes of the text, only the first approximation will be needed, but it is worthwhile to survey the whole expansion qualitatively. The first group in ϕ and the first in $\mathbf{A}$, taken by themselves and substituted in (B-5) and (B-6), give the first approximation to the fields, called the electric-dipole approximation, since only the electric-dipole moment $-e\mathbf{s}$ and its time derivative enter. The second groups by themselves give the first correction to the fields. This correction breaks into two parts called the electric-quadrupole and the magnetic-dipole fields. The higher groups give further corrections, and the nth groups give rise to fields consisting always of two parts, one called the electric 2^n-pole field and the other called the magnetic 2^{n-1}-pole field. By including higher and higher corrections, one can progressively relax conditions (B-22) and (B-23); that is, the fields are accurately represented at points nearer and nearer the atom and for higher and higher velocities of the electron. When (B-22) and (B-23) are well satisfied, the corrections to the dipole approximation are negligible. Finally, it should be remarked that if several electrons move in the same atom, the fields are the superpositions of those due to the individual electrons. If the motion is such that at all times the resultant electric-dipole moment vanishes, there may still be radiation of the higher-multipole type which gives rise to significant but usually small effects. In this book only the first approximation will be considered.

It is evident that in obtaining higher and higher terms in the expansion of ϕ and $\mathbf{A}$, the labor goes up enormously. However, the lowest approximation is easily written as

$$\phi(P,t) = -e\left(\frac{\mathbf{s} \cdot \hat{\mathbf{r}}}{r^2} + \frac{\dot{\mathbf{s}} \cdot \hat{\mathbf{r}}}{cr}\right)$$

$$\mathbf{A}(P,t) = -e\frac{\dot{\mathbf{s}}}{cr} \tag{B-31}$$

where $\hat{\mathbf{r}}$ is the unit vector $\mathbf{r}/r$, and s and $\dot{s}$ are evaluated at $t' = t - r/c$. These expressions are to be substituted in (B-5) and (B-6), and the gradient and curl are most conveniently found with the use of a cartesian representation. A derivative with respect to t is the same as one with respect to t'. In taking a derivative with respect to x, it must be noted that x appears in the r in the denominators in (B-31) and in the r in t'.

One has, for example,

$$\frac{\partial \mathbf{s}(t')}{\partial x} = \dot{\mathbf{s}}(t') \frac{\partial t'}{\partial x} = -\dot{\mathbf{s}}(t') \frac{x - x'}{cr}$$

where x and x' are the x coordinates of P and the nucleus, respectively. It is convenient to use the resolution (1-3) to express the fields $\mathbf{e}$ and $\mathbf{b}$ in components along and perpendicular to the vector $\mathbf{r}$. The final expressions for the electric-dipole fields are now easily shown to be

$$\mathbf{e}(P,t) = -e \left\{ \left[\left(\frac{2\mathbf{s}}{r^3} + \frac{2\dot{\mathbf{s}}}{cr^2} \right) \cdot \hat{\mathbf{r}} \right] \hat{\mathbf{r}} + \hat{\mathbf{r}} \times \left[\hat{\mathbf{r}} \times \left(\frac{\mathbf{s}}{r^3} + \frac{\dot{\mathbf{s}}}{cr^2} + \frac{\ddot{\mathbf{s}}}{c^2 r} \right) \right] \right\}_{t-r/c}$$

$$\mathbf{b}(P,t) = e\hat{\mathbf{r}} \times \left(\frac{\dot{\mathbf{s}}}{cr^2} + \frac{\ddot{\mathbf{s}}}{c^2 r} \right)_{t-r/c} \tag{B-32}$$

If the electron moves in a sinusoidal motion whose complex representation is

$$\mathbf{s}(\tau) = \mathbf{s}_0 e^{-i\omega\tau} \tag{B-33}$$

and if $k = \omega/c$, then the fields (B-32) become (5-4) and (5-5). In this sinusoidal case, condition (B-23) is equivalent to (5-8), as brought out in the discussion of the latter in Chap. 5.

[Note that while the correct first approximations to the fields are certainly obtained by substituting the real part of (B-33) in (B-32), they are also given as the real parts of (B-32) when the complex representation (B-33) is substituted, since $\mathbf{s}$ and its derivatives enter linearly. The formulas for the complex fields are much simpler than those for their real parts. In the higher-multipole corrections, on the other hand, $\mathbf{s}$ and its derivatives appear in products, and the real parts must be substituted. These corrections can be written as sums of monochromatic terms involving frequencies ω, 2ω, 3ω, etc., so that the exact fields for a perfectly sinusoidal oscillation of the electron are not exactly monochromatic. In all cases to be considered, the higher corrections, and hence this departure from monochromaticity, are negligible.]

Problems

B-1. Show that the approximate potentials (B-31) satisfy the Lorentz condition (B-11) *exactly* when $r > 0$.   (See the next problem for comments.)

B-2. Show that the approximate fields (B-32) are *exact* solutions of the Maxwell equations at all pionts with $r > 0$ (at these points $\rho = \mathbf{j} = 0$).   This would be a long problem if one substituted directly into the Maxwell equations.   A short method is to show that the potentials (B-31) satisfy (B-12) and (B-13) with $\rho = \mathbf{j} = 0$ when $r > 0$. This fact is then coupled with the result of Prob. B-1 and the propositions developed in Sec. B-1 to establish the solution of the problem.   To interpret this result, consider just what problem has (B-32) as its exact solution.   In the dipole problem of Sec. B-3, suppose e is multiplied by a positive number p, and s is divided by p. If p becomes infinite, the dipole moment remains constant, and in the limit we speak of a *point dipole*. There is then no need for approximations, since the position and retarded time of the electron are exactly the same as for the nucleus. Formulas (B-32) are the exact fields for a point dipole.

B-3. Consider an idealized antenna consisting of a length l of straight, fine wire carrying uniform current $\mathbf{i} = \mathbf{i}_0 \cos \omega t$. A charge with alternating magnitude accumulates at either end of the wire; it may be assumed to accumulate at a point. The magnitude of this charge at each instant is given by $dq/dt = |\mathbf{i}|$. There is no net charge on the wire. Assume that $l \ll c/\omega = \lambda/2\pi$ and $r \gg l$, r being the distance from the center of the wire to a field point P. (These assumptions allow one to take the retarded time to be the same at all points of the antenna and to use the dipole approximation.) Evaluate the potentials (B-14) and (B-15) at P and t, using appropriate approximations, and find $\mathbf{e}$ and $\mathbf{b}$. The answer is the pair of formulas (B-32) with $-e\mathbf{s}$ replaced by $(\mathbf{i}_0 l/\omega) \sin \omega t$, the dipole moment of the antenna. From this result and the one for the oscillating point electron, one easily conceives the generalization that if equal positive and negative charges are distributed in any manner in a volume and move such that the vector from the centroid of one charge to that of the other varies sinusoidally with frequency ω, then the radiated fields are given by the dipole formulas as long as the charges are confined to a volume with linear dimensions small compared with c/ω. On the basis of this generalization, which can be proved, some authors on the classical theory have been quite general in specifying the distribution of charge in an atom.

Table of Fresnel Integrals[1]

v	$C(v)$	$S(v)$	v	$C(v)$	$S(v)$
0.00	0.0000	0.0000	2.40	0.5550	0.6197
0.10	0.1000	0.0005	2.50	0.4574	0.6192
0.20	0.1999	0.0042	2.60	0.3890	0.5500
0.30	0.2994	0.0141	2.70	0.3925	0.4529
0.40	0.3975	0.0334	2.80	0.4675	0.3915
0.50	0.4923	0.0647	2.90	0.5624	0.4101
0.60	0.5811	0.1105	3.00	0.6058	0.4963
0.70	0.6597	0.1721	3.10	0.5616	0.5818
0.80	0.7230	0.2493	3.20	0.4664	0.5933
0.90	0.7648	0.3398	3.30	0.4058	0.5192
1.00	0.7799	0.4383	3.40	0.4385	0.4296
1.10	0.7638	0.5365	3.50	0.5326	0.4152
1.20	0.7154	0.6234	3.60	0.5880	0.4923
1.30	0.6386	0.6863	3.70	0.5420	0.5750
1.40	0.5431	0.7135	3.80	0.4481	0.5656
1.50	0.4453	0.6975	3.90	0.4223	0.4752
1.60	0.3655	0.6389	4.00	0.4984	0.4204
1.70	0.3238	0.5492	4.10	0.5738	0.4758
1.80	0.3336	0.4508	4.20	0.5418	0.5633
1.90	0.3944	0.3734	4.30	0.4494	0.5540
2.00	0.4882	0.3434	4.40	0.4383	0.4622
2.10	0.5815	0.3743	4.50	0.5261	0.4342
2.20	0.6363	0.4557	4.60	0.5673	0.5162
2.30	0.6266	0.5531	4.70	0.4914	0.5672

[1] From Jenkins and White [53], by permission of McGraw-Hill Book Company, Inc. For a more extensive table, see Jahnke-Emde-Lösch [51].

v	$C(v)$	$S(v)$	v	$C(v)$	$S(v)$
4.80	0.4338	0.4968	5.95	0.4566	0.4688
4.90	0.5002	0.4350	6.00	0.4995	0.4470
5.00	0.5637	0.4992	6.05	0.5424	0.4689
5.05	0.5450	0.5442	6.10	0.5495	0.5165
5.10	0.4998	0.5624	6.15	0.5146	0.5496
5.15	0.4553	0.5427	6.20	0.4676	0.5398
5.20	0.4389	0.4969	6.25	0.4493	0.4954
5.25	0.4610	0.4536	6.30	0.4760	0.4555
5.30	0.5078	0.4405	6.35	0.5240	0.4560
5.35	0.5490	0.4662	6.40	0.5496	0.4965
5.40	0.5573	0.5140	6.45	0.5292	0.5398
5.45	0.5269	0.5519	6.50	0.4816	0.5454
5.50	0.4784	0.5537	6.55	0.4520	0.5078
5.55	0.4456	0.5181	6.60	0.4690	0.4631
5.60	0.4517	0.4700	6.65	0.5161	0.4549
5.65	0.4926	0.4441	6.70	0.5467	0.4915
5.70	0.5385	0.4595	6.75	0.5302	0.5362
5.75	0.5551	0.5049	6.80	0.4831	0.5436
5.80	0.5298	0.5461	6.85	0.4539	0.5060
5.85	0.4819	0.5513	6.90	0.4732	0.4624
5.90	0.4486	0.5163	6.95	0.5207	0.4591

Calculation of the Spectral Profile of a Line Broadened by Thermal Motions and Collisions

This appendix contains the calculation, omitted in Sec. 12-8, whose object is to obtain the averaged energy spectrum (12-47). As stated in that section, the components of the electric field at a point of observation are the superpositions of a very large number, say N, of truncated damped oscillations of the forms

$$e_{jx} = C_j e^{-\gamma(t-t_j)/2} \cos\left[\omega'_{0j}(t - t_j) - \theta_j\right]$$
$$e_{jy} = D_j e^{-\gamma(t-t_j)/2} \cos\left[\omega'_{0j}(t - t_j) - \phi_j\right] \tag{D-1}$$

for $t_j < t < t_j + \tau_{cj}$, $j = 1, \ldots, N$. The times t_j fall at random in an interval T that is very long compared with $1/\gamma$, and the τ_{cj} represent intervals between pairs of successive collisions suffered by a given atom. The probability distribution for τ_c is given by (12-45) and (12-46):

$$P(\tau_c)\, d\tau_c = \frac{1}{a} e^{-\tau_c/a} \qquad a = [\tau_c]_{\mathrm{av}} \tag{D-2}$$

The frequency ω'_{0j} differs from the natural frequency ω_0 in accordance with the Doppler formula and the velocity of thermal motion during the

time between two collisions when the atom gives rise to the contribution
(D-1). The probability distribution for ω_0' is given by (12-37):

$$P(\omega_0') \, d\omega_0' = \mathcal{G}(\omega_0' - \omega_0; \Delta) \, d\omega_0' \tag{D-3}$$

The θ_j and ϕ_j fall at random in the range zero to 2π. The amplitude
constants C_j and D_j fluctuate from one contribution to another, but, just
as in Secs. 12-6 and 12-7, only the sum of their squares (or N times the
statistical average) appears in the final result and fixes the absolute flux
density of energy; the probability distribution need not be known.

The final averaging of the spectrum over the several fluctuating
quantities, all of which fluctuate independently, can be done with respect
to one quantity at a time in any order. Let the averaging over ω_0' be
left until last. Then a formal simplification results from taking, for the
moment, all the ω_{0j}' to be equal to ω_0. This step amounts to neglecting
Doppler broadening until the end.

The Fourier transform of e_{jx}, with ω_{0j}' set equal to ω_0, is easily found to
be

$$V_{jx} = \frac{C_j e^{i(\omega t_j + \theta_j)}}{2\sqrt{2\pi}\,[\gamma/2 - i(\omega - \omega_0)]} \left(1 - e^{[i(\omega - \omega_0) - \gamma/2]\tau_{cj}}\right)$$

The factor in parentheses can be reexpressed in the form $A_j e^{i\psi_j}$, where the
value of ψ_j is unimportant, and

$$A_j{}^2 = 1 - 2e^{-\gamma\tau_{cj}/2} \cos(\omega - \dot{\omega}_0)\tau_{cj} + e^{-\gamma\tau_{cj}} \tag{D-4}$$

The square of the modulus of the transform V_x of the resultant of all
the N contributions (D-1) is

$$|V_x|^2 = \frac{1/8\pi}{(\omega - \omega_0)^2 + \gamma^2/4} \left| \sum_{j=1}^{N} C_j A_j e^{i(\omega t_j + \theta_j + \psi_j)} \right|^2$$

The averaging with respect to the random angles θ_j and fluctuating
constants C_j and A_j is performed by use of the random walk, as in Sec.
12-6, the result being

$$[|V_x|^2]_{\mathrm{av}} = \frac{1/8\pi}{(\omega - \omega_0)^2 + \gamma^2/4} \, N[C^2]_{\mathrm{av}}[A^2]_{\mathrm{av}} \tag{D-5}$$

Equation (D-5) should contain $[C^2A^2]_{\mathrm{av}}$, but this average factors in the
manner shown because of the independence of the fluctuations of C and
A. The theory of the random walk gives (D-5) as the statistical average;
it also shows that there will be large fluctuations, just as found in Secs.
12-6 and 12-7, and the theoretical energy spectrum for a *single* observation of duration T will again have the ragged appearance of Fig. 12-5.

Now

$$[A^2]_{av} = \int_0^\infty A^2\, P(\tau_c)\, d\tau_c$$

After substituting (D-3) and (D-4), straightforward integration and algebraic reduction give

$$[A^2]_{av} = \frac{(\gamma + 2/a)[(\omega - \omega_0)^2 + \gamma^2/4]}{(\gamma + 1/a)[(\omega - \omega_0)^2 + (\gamma/2 + 1/a)^2]}$$

Substituting this result in (D-5),

$$[|V_x|^2]_{av} = \frac{N[C^2]_{av}/4}{\gamma + 1/a}\, \mathscr{L}(\omega - \omega_0;\, \Gamma) \tag{D-6}$$

where $\mathscr{L}(\omega - \omega_0;\, \Gamma) = \dfrac{\Gamma/2\pi}{(\omega - \omega_0)^2 + \Gamma^2/4}$ $\Gamma = \gamma + \dfrac{2}{[\tau_c]_{av}}$

Doppler broadening is now taken into account in the same way as in Sec. 12-7. The frequency ω_0 in (D-6) is changed to ω_0', and an average is taken using (D-3) as weighting function. The result is multiplied by $c/2\pi$ and added to the corresponding term for the y component. The final result is the smoothed spectrum

$$[\mathsf{S}(\omega)]_{av} = w \int_{-\infty}^\infty \mathsf{G}(\omega_0' - \omega_0;\, \Delta)\, \mathscr{L}(\omega - \omega_0';\, \Gamma)\, d\omega_0' \tag{D-7}$$

where $w = \dfrac{c/8\pi}{\gamma + 1/a}\, N[C^2 + D^2]_{av}$ (D-8)

Formula (D-7) is the same as (12-47). Since G and $\mathscr{L}$ are normalized, the integral with respect to ω of the folding integral has the value unity, and w therefore represents the total flux density of energy arriving at the observing point. This interpretation of w can be verified in a different way by writing the instantaneous Poynting vector associated with the contribution (D-1), integrating with respect to t between the limits t_j and $t_j + \tau_{cj}$ to obtain the flux density w_j due to this contribution alone, taking a statistical average of w_j, and finally multiplying by N to obtain (D-8).

Mean Energy of an Oscillator in Cavity Radiation

Formula (19-11), of prime importance in Planck's treatment of cavity radiation, will be derived in this appendix.

The cavity contains equilibrium radiation at temperature T, and in this field is supposed a stationary Lorentz atom with one electron of resonant frequency ω_0. Under the influence of the electric field the instantaneous displacement of the electron is some complicated vector function $\mathbf{s}(t)$. Related to this is the total instantaneous mechanical energy of the atom:

$$\epsilon(t) = \tfrac{1}{2}m\,\dot{\mathbf{s}}(t)^2 + \tfrac{1}{2}m\omega_0{}^2\,\mathbf{s}(t)^2$$

Under equilibrium conditions at temperature T the average of this energy over a sufficiently long time τ has a definite value independent of the instant at which the interval began. Choose a particular interval from t_0 to $t_0 + \tau$, and consider the function equaling $\mathbf{s}(t)$ inside the interval, and zero outside. Let the Fourier transform of this function be $\mathbf{s}_0(\omega)$. Then by the differentiation rule and Parseval's theorem, the average of ϵ over τ for the temperature T can be written

$$\langle\epsilon\rangle_T = \frac{1}{\tau}\int_{t_0}^{t_0+\tau} \epsilon(t)\,dt = \frac{m}{2\tau}\int_{-\infty}^{\infty} (\omega^2 + \omega_0{}^2)\,|\mathbf{s}_0(\omega)|^2\,d\omega \qquad \text{(E-1)}$$

Now it is known that the radiation field has a broad continuous spectrum covering all frequencies. Because of the sharp resonance in the atom, the latter responds in such a way that $s_0(\omega)$ is appreciably different from zero only at and very near $\pm\omega_0$. The last integral in (E-1) is then essentially unaffected if ω^2 is replaced by ω_0^2, and we have

$$\langle\epsilon\rangle_T = \frac{m\omega_0^2}{\tau} \int_{-\infty}^{\infty} |s_0(\omega)|^2 \, d\omega \tag{E-2}$$

[One could go a step farther by applying Parseval's theorem again and reducing the last result to $m\omega_0^2 \langle s(t)^2\rangle$.]

Consider now the average rate of radiation by the atom. Let $e(t)$ and $b(t)$ be the radiated fields at a point at distance r from the atom in the direction of the unit vector $\hat{r}$, and let $e_0(\omega)$ and $b_0(\omega)$ be the transforms of these functions considered only in the interval τ. The time average of the Poynting vector at the point in question can be written by Parseval's theorem as

$$\langle S\rangle = \frac{c}{4\pi\tau} \int_{t_0}^{t_0+\tau} e \times b \, dt = \frac{c}{4\pi\tau} \int_{-\infty}^{\infty} e_0 \times b_0^* \, d\omega$$

Apply the transfer functions in Sec. 11-11 to obtain

$$\langle S\rangle = -\frac{e^2}{4\pi c^3 r^2 \tau} \int_{-\infty}^{\infty} \omega^4 \{\hat{r} \times [\hat{r} \times s_0]\} \times [\hat{r} \times s_0^*] \, d\omega \tag{E-3}$$

where s_0 is the same as appears in (E-2). (The question of retardation is treated lightly here; this is permissible when τ is long and the motion of the electron has a steady character.) The factor ω^4 in (E-3) can be evaluated at ω_0 and taken out of the integral. The average rate of radiation (call it P) is the normal surface integral of (E-3) over a sphere of radius r about the atom. This integration can be carried out under the integral over ω, the steps being the same as in Sec. 5-5. The result is

$$P = \frac{2e^2\omega_0^4}{3c^3\tau} \int_{-\infty}^{\infty} |s_0|^2 \, d\omega = \frac{2e^2\omega_0^2}{3mc^3} \langle\epsilon\rangle_T \tag{E-4}$$

Consider next the rate A at which the atom extracts energy from the isotropic radiation field of spectral intensity $\mathscr{I}_\omega(\omega,T)$. The waves falling on the atom with directions of propagation in a solid angle $d\Omega$ and frequencies in a range $d\omega$ have an irradiance $\mathscr{I}_\omega \, d\Omega \, d\omega$, and by the ideas in Sec. 14-3,

$$dA = \sigma(\omega) \, \mathscr{I}_\omega(\omega,T) \, d\Omega \, d\omega$$

where σ is the cross section for scattering by the atom. Integration over solid angles gives a factor 4π, and in integrating over ω, we note that $\mathscr{I}_\omega$

is a slowly varying function of ω, whereas σ is very sharply peaked at ω_0. Hence

$$A = 4\pi\, \mathcal{I}_\omega(\omega_0, T) \int_0^\infty \sigma(\omega)\, d\omega = \frac{8\pi^3 e^2}{mc}\, \mathcal{I}_\omega(\omega_0, T) \tag{E-5}$$

The last result comes from (14-18). (Note that a time average over some sufficiently long interval is already implied in the definition of $\mathcal{I}_\omega$.)

Finally, we apply the condition for equilibrium by writing $P = A$ and obtain (19-11). Note that the charge and mass of the oscillator have canceled out.

Literature Cited

For the location of a reference in the text, see the author's name in the Index.

1. Baez, Albert V.: Fresnel Zone Plate for Optical Image Formation Using Extreme Ultraviolet and Soft X Radiation, *J. Opt. Soc. Am.*, **51**:405 (1961).
2. Baker, Robert H.: "Astronomy," 7th ed., D. Van Nostrand Company, Inc., Princeton, N.J., 1959.
3. Bennett, Alva H., Harold Osterberg, Helen Jupnik, and Oscar W. Richards: "Phase Microscopy," John Wiley & Sons, Inc., New York, 1951.
4. Bhagavantam, S.: "Scattering of Light and the Raman Effect," Chemical Publishing Company, Inc., New York, 1942.
5. Bohm, David: "Quantum Theory," Prentice-Hall, Inc., Englewood Cliffs, N.J., 1951.
6. Boivin, A.: On the Theory of Diffraction by Concentric Arrays of Ring-shaped Apertures, *J. Opt. Soc. Am.*, **42**:60 (1952).
7. Born, Max: "Atomic Physics," 7th ed., Hafner Publishing Company, Inc., New York, 1962.
8. ———: "Optik," Springer-Verlag OHG, Berlin, 1933.
9. ——— and Emil Wolf: "Principles of Optics," Pergamon Press, New York, 1959.
10. Böttcher, C. J. F.: "Theory of Electric Polarization," Elsevier Publishing Company, Amsterdam, 1952.
11. Brown, R. Hanbury, and R. Q. Twiss: A New Type of Interferometer for Use in Radio Astronomy, *Phil. Mag.*, **45**:663 (1954).
12. ——— and ———: Correlation between Photons in Two Coherent Beams of Light, *Nature*, **177**:27 (1956).
13. ——— and ———: A Test of a New Type of Stellar Interferometer on Sirius, *Nature*, **178**:1046 (1956).
14. ——— and ———: The Question of Correlation between Photons in Coherent Light Rays, *Nature*, **178**:1447 (1956).
15. Candler, C.: "Modern Interferometers," Hilger and Watts, Ltd., London, 1951.
16. Carslaw, H. S.: "Introduction to the Theory of Fourier's Series and Integrals," Dover Publications, Inc., New York, 1930.

17. Chandrasekhar, S.: Stochastic Problems in Physics and Astronomy, *Revs. Mod. Phys.*, **15**:1 (1943). Reprinted in N. Wax (ed.): "Selected Papers on Noise and Stochastic Processes," Dover Publications, Inc., New York, 1954.

18. Churchill, Ruel V.: "Fourier Series and Boundary Value Problems," McGraw-Hill Book Company, Inc., New York, 1941.

19. Committee on Colorimetry, Optical Society of America: "The Science of Color," Thomas Y. Crowell Company, New York, 1953.

20. Compton, Arthur H., and Samuel K. Allison: "X-rays in Theory and Experiment," 2d ed., D. Van Nostrand Company, Inc., Princeton, N.J., 1935.

21. Condon, E. U., and G. H. Shortley: "The Theory of Atomic Spectra," Cambridge University Press, New York, 1951.

22. Courant, R.: "Differential and Integral Calculus," 2d ed., Interscience Publishers, Inc., New York, 1937.

23. Debye, P.: "Polar Molecules," Dover Publications, Inc., New York, 1945.

24. Dirac, P. A. M.: "The Principles of Quantum Mechanics," 3d ed., Oxford University Press, Fair Lawn, N.J., 1947.

25. Ditchburn, R. W.: "Light," Interscience Publishers, Inc., New York, 1953.

26. Dwight, Herbert Bristol: "Tables of Integrals and Other Mathematical Data," 3d ed., The Macmillan Company, New York, 1957.

27. Fano, U.: Quantum Theory of Interference Effects in the Mixing of Light from Phase-independent Sources, *Am. J. Phys.*, **29**:539 (1961).

28. Fermi, Enrico: Quantum Theory of Radiation, *Revs. Mod. Phys.*, **4**:87 (1932).

29. Flügge, S. (ed.): "Encyclopedia of Physics," vol. 24, "Fundamentals of Optics," Springer-Verlag OHG, Berlin, 1956.

30. Forrester, A. Theodore, Richard A. Gudmundsen, and Philip O. Johnson: Photoelectric Mixing of Incoherent Light, *Phys. Rev.*, **99**:1691 (1955).

31. Frauenfelder, Hans: "The Mössbauer Effect," W. A. Benjamin, Inc., New York, 1962.

32. Gordon, J. P., H. J. Zeiger, and C. H. Townes: The Maser—New Type of Microwave Amplifier, Frequency Standard, and Spectrometer, *Phys. Rev.*, **99**:1264 (1955).

33. Hardy, Arthur C., and Fred H. Perrin: "The Principles of Optics," McGraw-Hill Book Company, Inc., New York, 1932.

34. Harrison, George R., Richard C. Lord, and John R. Loofbourow: "Practical Spectroscopy," Prentice-Hall, Inc., Englewood Cliffs, N.J., 1948.

35. Heavens, O. S.: "Optical Properties of Thin Solid Films," Butterworth Scientific Publications, London, 1955.

36. Heisenberg, Werner: "The Physical Principles of the Quantum Theory," Dover Publications, Inc., New York, 1930.

37. Heitler, W.: "The Quantum Theory of Radiation," 3d ed., Oxford University Press, Fair Lawn, N.J., 1954.

38. Herriott, Donald R.: Optical Properties of a Continuous Helium-Neon Optical Maser, *J. Opt. Soc. Am.*, **52**:31 (1962).

39. Hertz, H.: "Electric Waves," Dover Publications, Inc., New York, in preparation.

40. Herzberg, Gerhard: "Molecular Spectra and Molecular Structure I. Spectra of Diatomic Molecules," 2d ed., D. Van Nostrand Company, Inc., Princeton, N.J., 1950.

41. Holshouser, D. F., H. von Foerster, and G. L. Clark: Microwave Modulation of Light Using the Kerr Effect, *J. Opt. Soc. Am.*, **51**:1360 (1961).

42. Hopkins, H. H.: The Concept of Partial Coherence in Optics, *Proc. Roy. Soc. London*, **A208**:263 (1951).

43. ———: On the Diffraction Theory of Optical Images, *Proc. Roy. Soc. London*, **A217**:408 (1953).

44. ———: Applications of Coherence Theory in Microscopy and Interferometry, *J. Opt. Soc. Am.*, **47**:508 (1957).

45. Hufford, Mason E.: Some New Diffraction Photographs, *Phys. Rev.*, **3**:241 (1914).

46. ———: The Diffraction Ring Pattern in the Shadow of a Circular Object, *Phys. Rev.*, **7**:545 (1916).

47. ——— and Harold T. Davis: The Diffraction of Light by a Circular Opening and the Lommel Wave Theory, *Phys. Rev.*, **33**:589 (1929).

48. Jacquinot, Pierre: The Luminosity of Spectrometers with Prisms, Gratings, or Fabry-Perot Etalons, *J. Opt. Soc. Am.*, **44**:761 (1954).

49. ———: New Developments in Interference Spectroscopy, *Repts. Progr. in Phys.*, **23**:267 (1960).

50. Jahnke, Eugen, and Fritz Emde: "Tables of Functions," 4th ed., Dover Publications, Inc., New York, 1945.

51. Jahnke-Emde-Lösch: "Tables of Higher Functions," 6th ed., McGraw-Hill Book Company, Inc., New York, 1960.

52. Javan, A., E. A. Ballik, and W. L. Bond: Frequency Characteristic of a Continuous-wave He-Ne Optical Maser, *J. Opt. Soc. Am.*, **52**:96 (1962).

53. Jenkins, Francis A., and Harvey E. White: "Fundamentals of Optics," 3d ed., McGraw-Hill Book Company, Inc., New York, 1957.

54. Kennard, Earle H.: "Kinetic Theory of Gases," McGraw-Hill Book Company, Inc., New York, 1938.

55. Kittel, C.: "Elementary Statistical Physics," John Wiley & Sons, Inc., New York, 1958.

56. Lengyel, Bela A.: "Lasers," John Wiley & Sons, Inc., New York, 1962.

57. Lighthill, M. J.: "Introduction to Fourier Analysis and Generalized Functions," Cambridge University Press, New York, 1958.

58. Linfoot, E. H.: "Recent Advances in Optics," Oxford University Press, Fair Lawn, N.J., 1955.

59. Lorentz, H. A.: "Theory of Electrons," 2d ed., Dover Publications, Inc., New York, 1952.

60. Lustig, Harry: The Mössbauer Effect, *Am. J. Phys.*, **29**:1 (1961).

61. Maiman, T. H.: Stimulated Optical Emission in Fluorescent Solids I. Theoretical Considerations, *Phys. Rev.*, **123**:1145 (1961). See also part II immediately following.

62. Margenau, Henry, and George Moseley Murphy: "The Mathematics of Physics and Chemistry," 2d ed., D. Van Nostrand Company, Inc., Princeton, N.J., 1956.

63. Meissner, Karl Wilh.: Interference Spectroscopy (in two parts), *J. Opt. Soc. Am.*, **31**:405 (1941); **32**:185 (1942).

64. Michelson, Albert A.: "Light Waves and Their Uses," The University of Chicago Press, Chicago, 1907.

65. ――― and F. G. Pease: Measurement of the Diameter of α Orionis with the Interferometer, *Astrophys. J.*, **53**:249 (1921).

66. Mills, B. Y., and A. G. Little: A High Resolution Aerial System of a New Type, *Australian J. Phys.*, **6**:272 (1953).

67. Mitchell, Allan C. G., and Mark W. Zemansky: "Resonance Radiation and Excited Atoms," Cambridge University Press, New York, 1961.

68. O'Neill, Edward L.: "Selected Topics in Optics and Communication Theory," ITEK Corporation, Boston, 1958.

69. Panofsky, Wolfgang K. H., and Melba Phillips: "Classical Electricity and Magnetism," Addison-Wesley Publishing Company, Inc., Reading, Mass., 1955.

70. Pawsey, J. L., and R. N. Bracewell: "Radio Astronomy," Oxford University Press, Fair Lawn, N.J., 1955.

71. Phillips, H. B.: "Vector Analysis," John Wiley & Sons, Inc., New York, 1933.

72. Plass, Gilbert N.: Classical Electrodynamic Equations of Motion with Radiative Reaction, *Revs. Mod. Phys.*, **33**:37 (1961).

73. Purcell, E. M.: The Question of Correlation between Photons in Coherent Light Rays, *Nature*, **178**:1449 (1956).

74. Raman, Sir C. V.: "Lectures on Physical Optics," Part I, Indian Academy of Sciences, Bangalore, 1959.

75. Rayleigh, Lord: On the Remarkable Phenomenon of Crystalline Reflexion Described by Prof. Stokes, *Phil. Mag.*, **26**:256 (1888).

76. ――――: "Scientific Papers," 6 vols., Cambridge University Press, London, 1899–1920.

77. Rohrlich, F.: The Classical Description of Charged Particles, *Phys. Today*, **15**(3):19 (1962).

78. Rosenfeld, L.: "Theory of Electrons," North Holland Publishing Company, Amsterdam, 1951.

79. Rossi, Bruno: "Optics," Addison-Wesley Publishing ·Company, Inc., Reading, Mass., 1957.

80. Sawyer, Ralph A.: "Experimental Spectroscopy," 2d ed., Prentice-Hall, Inc., Englewood Cliffs, N.J., 1951.

81. Schawlow, A. L., and C. H. Townes: Infrared and Optical Masers, *Phys. Rev.*, **112**:1940 (1958).

82. Scott, William Taussig: "The Physics of Electricity and Magnetism," John Wiley & Sons, Inc., New York, 1959.

83. Singer, Jay R. (ed.): "Advances in Quantum Electronics," Columbia University Press, New York, 1961.

84. Smith, R. A., F. E. Jones, and R. P. Chasmar: "The Detection and Measurement of Infra-red Radiation," Oxford University Press, Fair Lawn, N.J., 1957.

85. Sommerfeld, Arnold: "Optics," Academic Press, Inc., New York, 1954.

86. Stratton, Julius Adams: "Electromagnetic Theory," McGraw-Hill Book Company, Inc., New York, 1941.

87. Stroke, George W.: Attainment of High-resolution Gratings by Ruling under Interferometric Control, *J. Opt. Soc. Am.*, **51**:1321 (1961).

88. Strong, John: "Concepts of Classical Optics," W. H. Freeman and Company, San Francisco, 1958.
89. ———: "Procedures in Experimental Physics," Prentice-Hall, Inc., Englewood Cliffs, N.J., 1942.
90. Tolansky, S.: "High Resolution Spectroscopy," Pitman Publishing Corporation, New York, 1947.
91. Townes, Charles H. (ed.): "Quantum Electronics," Columbia University Press, New York, 1960.
92. Van de Hulst, H. C.: "Light Scattering by Small Particles," John Wiley & Sons, Inc., New York, 1957.
93. ——— and J. J. M. Reesinck: Line Breadths and Voigt Profiles, *Astrophys. J.*, **106**:121 (1947).
94. Van der Ziel, Albert: "Noise," Prentice-Hall, Inc., Englewood Cliffs, N.J., 1954.
95. Weatherburn, C. E.: "Elementary Vector Analysis," G. Bell & Sons, Ltd., London, 1942.
96. ———: "Advanced Vector Analysis," G. Bell & Sons, Ltd., London, 1937.
97. Wheeler, John Archibald, and Richard Phillips Feynman: Interaction with the Absorber as the Mechanism of Radiation, *Revs. Mod. Phys.*, **17**:157 (1945).
98. White, Harvey Elliott: "Introduction to Atomic Spectra," McGraw-Hill Book Company, Inc., New York, 1934.
99. Whittaker, E. T.: "A History of the Theories of Aether and Electricity. The Classical Theories," Thomas Nelson & Sons, New York, 1951.
100. ——— and G. N. Watson: "Modern Analysis," 4th ed., Cambridge University Press, New York, 1935.
101. Williams, W. Ewart: "Applications of Interferometry," 4th ed., John Wiley & Sons, Inc., New York, 1950.
102. Wills, A. P.: "Vector Analysis with an Introduction to Tensor Analysis," Dover Publications, Inc., New York, 1958.
103. Wood, Robert W.: "Physical Optics," 3d ed., The Macmillan Company, New York, 1934.
104. Zemansky, Mark W.: "Heat and Thermodynamics," 4th ed., McGraw-Hill Book Company, Inc., New York, 1957.
105. Zernike, F.: The Concept of Degree of Coherence and Its Application to Optical Problems, *Physica*, **5**:785 (1938).
106. Zworykin, V. K., and E. G. Ramberg: "Photoelectricity," John Wiley & Sons, Inc., New York, 1949.

Index

Abbe, E., 224
Abbe theory of microscope, 224–232
Absolute value (*see* Magnitude)
Absorption, 335, 472, 475, 476
  negative, 486
  resonant, by nuclei, 490–491
  (*See also* Extinction; Oscillator
    strength; Transition probability)
Airy disk, 176
Airy formula, 405–408
Airy pattern, 176, 207
Allison, S. K., 340, 531
Ampère, A. M., 4
Amperian currents, 56, 368
Amplification by stimulated emission, 486
Amplitude of oscillation, complex, 35, 37
  graphical representation, 36–38
  instantaneous, 35, 37
Angstrom unit, 96n.
Angular frequency, 35
Angular momentum of radiation, 358,
  359
Anisotropic binding, 340, 341, 424, 425
Anisotropic medium, 370, 421, 424
Anomalous dispersion, 378
Antenna, effective area, 139–141
  Mills cross, 141, 155
  polarization, 138, 139
  in radio astronomy, 137–141
  reciprocity law for, 138, 139
Antireflection film, 414
Atom structure, 5
  (*See also* Lorentz theory; Quantum
    theory)
Attenuation vector, 372

Babinet compensator, 436, 437, 443
Babinet's principle, 166, 167, 171, 172
Baez, A. V., 207, 530
Baker, R. H., 186, 287n., 530
Ballik, E. A., 488, 532
Barkla, C. G., 352
Basic waves, 427, 428
Beat frequency, 323
Beat-frequency spectrograph, 324–327
Bennett, A. H., 236, 530
Bennett, W. R., Jr., 474, 487
Bergstrand, E., 457
Bhagavantam, S., 340, 348, 530
Biaxial crystal, 421, 423, 430–432

Binding, isotropic and anisotropic, 245,
  340, 341, 424, 425
  (*See also* Lorentz theory)
Blackbody, 460, 463
  spectrum, 467–469
  (*See also* Cavity radiation; Planck law)
Blazed grating, 178
Blue sky, 338, 348
Bohm, D., 471, 530
Bohr, N., 469, 471
Boivin, A., 207, 530
Boltzmann constant, 466–468
Boltzmann distribution, 471
Bond, W. L., 487, 532
Born, M., 156, 186, 208, 224, 229, 319,
  322, 340, 426, 464, 471, 530
Böttcher, C. J. F., 380n., 456, 530
Bound charge, 365–368
Boundary conditions for reflection, 389,
  390
Bracewell, R. N., 142, 533
Bragg, W. H., 354, 355
Bragg condition, 355
Brewster, D., 3
Brewster's angle, 398
Brewster's law, 398
Broadening in spectra, pressure, 264–267
  thermal, 260–264
Brown, R. H., 327, 530

c (in Maxwell equations), 58
  numerical value, 64, 65
  relation, to electromagnetic waves, 65,
    72, 98
    to velocity of light, 65
Calcite, 425, 429, 434, 435
Candler, C., 308, 408, 530
Carslaw, H. S., 211, 241, 530
Cavity radiation, 288, 462–469
  (*See also* Displacement law; Planck
    law; Rayleigh-Jeans law; Stefan-
    Boltzmann law; Wien law)
Cellophane, 436
Central-spot scanning, 408–411
cgs units (*see* Electrical units; Gaussian
  units)
Chandrasekhar, S., 148, 531
Channel spectrum, 330
Charge, 51, 52
  conservation, 3, 68, 69

Charge, density, 52, 364
  free and bound, 365–368
  magnetic, nonexistence, 70, 71
Chasmar, R. P., 275, 533
Churchill, R. V., 211, 531
Circular aperture, diffraction by, Fraunhofer, 175, 176
  Fresnel, 201–205
Clark, G. L., 532
Classical theory, characteristics, 52, 65, 67
Coherence, 274, 299, 300
  degree, 300
  lateral, 302, 327, 485
  longitudinal, 302–309, 327
  region, 274
Coherence length, 308
Coherence time, 308
Coherent illumination, 224, 301
Coherent sources, 300, 399
Collision frequency, 265
Collisions, 55, 264–267, 350, 351
Combination principle, 469
Committee on Colorimetry, Optical
  Society of America, 285n., 461n., 531
Compensator, Babinet, 436, 437
  Soleil, 436
Complementary polarizations, 86
  [See also Orthogonal polarizations
    (equivalent term)]
Complex amplitude, 35, 37
Complex number, 30–34
  absolute value, 32, 33
  conjugate, 31
  exponential form, 33
  graphical representation, 31
  magnitude or modulus, 32, 33
  unimodular, 33
Complex refractive index, 372, 376–383
Complex representation, hazards in use, 46, 47
  of oscillation, in one dimension, 35
    in three dimensions, 37
  (See also Sinusoidal scalar wave;
    Sinusoidal vector wave)
Complex vector, 36
  magnitude, 220
Component of vector, 10, 458
Compton, A. H., 340, 531
Concave grating, 145, 146
Condenser (see Electric field)
Condon, E. U., 478, 482, 531
Conductivity, 370, 381, 382
Conjugate, complex, 31
Conjugate radii of ellipse, 38
Conjugate variables, 212
Conservation, of charge, 3, 68, 69
  of energy, 248, 252, 384, 385
Coordinate system, 11
  cartesian, spherical polar, cylindrical
    polar, 19
  for Fraunhofer diffraction, 117, 168
  right-hand, 20
Cornu prism and lens, 442
Cornu spiral, 191
Correlation, 151, 274, 310

Correspondence principle, 471
Cosine, Euler formula for, 34
Cotton-Mouton effect, 446, 453–455
Coulomb's law, 61, 62
Coupling, 337, 349, 355
Courant, R., 391, 531
Critical angle, 399
Critical illumination, 302
Cross section, 336, 343, 344
  for collision, 350
  differential, 344
  of free electron, 346
  of Lorentz atom, 346, 347
  Thomson, 346
Crossed array, Fraunhofer diffraction
  by, 130
Crystal spectrometer, 355
Curl, 14, 16
  calculation in coordinate representa-
    tion, 21–24
  components, 17
Curl curl, 27
Curl gradient, 26
Current, density of, 52, 364
  displacement, 69

Damped oscillation, 250
Dark-field illumination, 232, 235
Davis, H. T., 532
Debye, P., 361, 380n., 531
Decomposition of oscillation, 45, 49
Degeneracy, 450, 471
∇^2 (divergence gradient), 26, 27
Dense medium, optically, 337
Detailed balancing, 473
Detection of radiation, 274–277, 317, 323, 324
Dextrorotatory medium, 440
Dichroism, 426
Dielectric constant, 363, 371
Dielectric film, 412–417
  high-reflection, 416, 417
  low-reflection, 414
Differentiation rule, 217
Diffraction, assumption of point mono-
    chromatic source, 110
  definition, 107
  discovery, 2, 107
  edge effects, 113, 206
  fringes, 107
  luminous edge, 109, 166, 205
  physical origin, 109–114
  by plane mirrors, 167
  with polychromatic light, 280, 284–286
  with quasi-monochromatic light, 294, 295
  of X rays, 352–355, 361
  (See also Fraunhofer diffraction;
    Fresnel diffraction)
Diffraction fringes, 107
Diffraction grating, 142
  blazed, 178
  concave, 145, 146
  in history of physics, 145, 146
  missing orders, 177
  overlapping of orders, 143, 154

Diffraction grating, reflection, 145, 177–180
  reflection echelon, 179, 180
  resolving power, 144, 178, 180
  (*See also* Spectroscope)
Dipole field, conditions on, 88–90, 96
  for elliptical oscillator, 89, 96–98
  fourth-power law for, 99
  general, 238, 239, 516–520
  intermediate zone, 93
  inverse-square law for, 99
  for linear oscillator, 90–96
  Poynting vector, 98–105
  radial and transverse components, 88, 90
  radiation pattern, 99, 100, 103
  rate of radiation, 100–105
  with several oscillators, 101–105
  static, 88
  static zone, 92, 95
  wave zone, 93, 95–98
  (*See also* Lorentz theory; Rayleigh scattering; Scattering, by Lorentz atom)
Dipole moment, 88, 367, 368
Dirac, P. A. M., 478, 531
Directional derivative, 13
Disk, Fresnel diffraction by, 205, 206
Dispersion, 142, 378
  anomalous, 378
Displacement current, 69
Displacement law, 463, 464
Displacement vector, 369
Distributive laws for vectors, 9
Ditchburn, R. W., 224, 531
Divergence, 14, 15
  calculation in coordinate representation, 21–24
Divergence curl, 26
Divergence gradient, 26, 27
Divergence theorem (Gauss' theorem), 16
Doppler effect, 260, 261, 489
Double aperture, Fraunhofer diffraction by, 121–124, 133–137, 286, 295–299
Double refraction, 2, 420–427
  basic waves in, 427, 428
  at boundary, 432–435
  induced, 426, 427
  polarization by, 2, 434, 435, 437, 438
  (*See also* Biaxial crystal; Cotton-Mouton effect; Faraday effect; Kerr electro-optic effect; Optical activity; Refractive index; Uniaxial crystal; Wave-vector surface)
Dwight, H. B., 213, 531

Echelon grating, 179, 180
Effective area of antenna, 139–141
Einstein, A., 470, 471
Electric field, 4, 57, 58
  energy density, 78, 81
  macroscopic, 363, 364
  measurement, 66, 67
  in plane-parallel condenser, 67, 68

Electric field, relation to charge and current, 57, 58, 71–73
  of spherical charge, 60, 61
  (*See also* Dipole field)
Electrical forces, 54–56, 58, 59
Electrical length of cable, 138
Electrical units, 58, 59, 493
  conversion of formulas, 505–507
  electromagnetic system, 497, 498
  electrostatic system, 495–498
  rationalized, 500, 501
  (*See also* Gaussian units; mks units)
Electromagnetic field, energy density, 81, 82
  flux density of energy, 82
  propagation, 5, 72, 73, 94, 98
Electromagnetic units (*see* Electrical units)
Electromagnetic wave, Hertz's discovery, 5
  homogeneous, 374, 375
  inhomogeneous, 374, 375
  Maxwell's prediction, 5
  plane monochromatic, 75, 85, 98, 371–376
  propagation, 5, 72, 73, 94, 98
  velocity, 5, 65, 72
  wave equation for, 73, 74, 510
  (*See also* Dipole field; Light)
Electromagnetism and optics, 4, 5
Electron, discovery, 6
  (*See also* Lorentz theory)
Electrostatic units (*see* Electrical units; Gaussian units)
Ellipse, conjugate radii, 38
  principal radii, 39
  representative, in sinusoidal vector wave, 43, 44
Elliptical oscillation, decomposition, 45, 49
  phase, 97
  representation, complex vector, 37, 38
  real cartesian, 39
Emde, F., 175, 532
Emission, spontaneous, 472, 479–483
  stimulated, 472
  amplification by, 486
  (*See also* Oscillator strength; Transition probability)
Enantiomorphism, 425, 426
Energy, conservation, 248, 252, 384, 385
  density, in electric and magnetic fields, 78–82, 462
  flux, in electromagnetic field, 82, 384, 385
  spectral, 462
  general theorem on (Poynting), 80–84, 383–385
  (*See also* Intensity; Irradiance; Radiance)
Energy levels, 470, 471
  broadening, 479–481
  degeneracy and statistical weight, 471
Energy spectrum, 253, 273
Ensemble, representative, 148

Equation of motion, 247, 248, 345, 448, 452
Ether, 3–5, 69
Euler's formula, 33, 34
  for sine and cosine, 34
Ewald-Oseen theory, 337, 338, 340, 425, 426
Excitation, atomic, 54, 245, 246
  natural (or distribution), 471
Exponential, complex, 33
Extended source, 131, 132, 295–299
Extinction, 335, 356
Extinction band, 378–380
Extinction index, 372
  (*See also* Complex refractive index)
Extinction paradox, 357
Extraordinary refractive index, 423, 429
Extraordinary wave, 429

Fabry-Perot interferometer, 291, 405–412
  circular fringes, 408
  free range for, 411
  instrumental profile, 407, 411
  as refractometer, 408
  resolving power, 410, 411
  as spectrometer, 408–412
Fano, U., 327, 531
Faraday, M., 4
Faraday effect, 4, 445, 451–453
Faraday's law of induction, 69, 70
Fermi, E., 478, 482, 489, 531
Feynman, R. P., 248, 534
Field (*see* Dipole field; Electric field; Internal field; Magnetic field; Scalar field; Vector field; Wave)
Films by evaporation, 402, 403
  (*See also* Dielectric film)
Filter, interference, 412
  Lyot, 444
Finesse, 408, 410
Fizeau, A. H. L., 133
Fluctuations, 150, 257, 273, 275, 485
  role in scattering, 338
  in spectra, 257–265, 485
Flügge, S., 531
  (*See also* Bergstrand)
Fluorescence, 351, 475
Flux, magnetic, 70
Foerster, H von, 532
Folding integral, 217, 218
  of gaussian functions, 240
  of resonance functions, 328
  of resonance and gaussian functions, 267
Folding rule, 217, 218
Force, lines, 4
  between parallel currents, 64
  between point charges, 61, 62
  (*See also* Lorentz force; Lorentz theory)
Force density, Lorentz, 58, 59
Forrester, A. T., 323, 531
Forward direction, 128, 335
Fourier analysis, 212, 213
  of linear systems, 236–240
Fourier cosine transform, 306

Fourier synthesis, 212
Fourier theorem, 210–213
  for several variables, 219
  for vector functions, 220
Fourier transform, 212
  examples, 213–216
  theorems on, 216–220
Fourth-power law, 99, 347, 348
Fractional polarization, 320
  in Rayleigh scattering, 342
Franck and Hertz experiment, 470
Franklin, B., 3
Frauenfelder, H., 491, 531
  (*See also* Lynch)
Fraunhofer, J. von, 145
Fraunhofer diffraction, by circular aperture, 175, 176
  coordinate system for, 117, 168
  by crossed array, 130
  definition, 115, 116
  by double aperture, 121–124, 133–137, 286, 295–299
  forward direction, 128
  Fourier integrals, 220, 221
  irradiance by scalar theory, 170
  Kirchhoff integral, form for, 169, 170
  lenses, use in, 132
  by linear array, 124–128
  by N identical apertures, general principles, 115–121
  by random array, 146–152
  by rectangular aperture, 172–175, 284–286
  by rectangular array, 128, 129
  transmission coefficient, 171
  with white light, 174, 284–286
Free charge, 365
Free range, for diffraction grating, 154
  for Fabry-Perot interferometer, 411
Frequency, 35
Fresnel, A. J., 3, 157
Fresnel diffraction, by circular aperture, 201–205
  definition, 116, 188
  by disk, 205, 206
  by rectangular aperture, 189–195, 204, 205
  relation to geometrical optics, 195
  by slit, 196, 197
  by straight edge, 197, 198
  by strip, 198, 199
  transition to Fraunhofer diffraction, 195, 199–201
Fresnel ellipsoid, 431
Fresnel formulas, 397
Fresnel integrals, 190
  table, 522
Fresnel rhomb, 418
Friedrich, W., 352
Fringes, 107, 108
  visibility, 298
  (*See also* Fabry-Perot interferometer; Fraunhofer diffraction; Fresnel diffraction; Michelson interferometer)

Gauss' theorem, 16
Gaussian function, normalized, 262
Gaussian unit, charge, 62
  current, 62
  electric field, 66
  magnetic field, 66
Gaussian units, 59, 498, 499
  advantages, 59, 94, 504, 505
  conversion to mks units, 506, 507
Geissler tube, 243–245
  classical model, 245, 246
Geometrical optics, 2, 107, 108, 195
  (*See also* Sine condition)
Geometrical shadow, 107, 194
Geometrically perfect optical system,
  180, 181
Gibbs, J. W., 148, 260, 465
Gordon, J. P., 486, 531
Gradient, 13
  calculation in coordinate representa-
    tion, 24
Gradient divergence, 27
Grazing angle, 354
Green's theorem, 28
Grimaldi, F. M., 107
Gudmundsen, R. A., 323, 531

Hagen, E., 387, 401
Half-period zones, Fresnel, 206
Half-wave plate, 332, 436
Hamermesh, M., 491
Hardy, A. C., 184, 531
Harrison, G. R., 146, 275, 302, 531
Hartmann formula, 381
Heavens, O. S., 403, 531
Heisenberg, W., 482, 489, 531
Heitler, W., 248, 478, 482, 484, 531
Herriott, D. R., 487, 531
Hertz, H., 5, 90, 531
Herzberg, G., 351, 532
High-reflection film, 403, 416, 417
Holland, R. E., 491
Holshouser, D. F., 456, 532
Homogeneous wave, 374, 375
Hopkins, H. H., 299, 532
Hufford, M. E., 203, 206, 532
Hull, A. W., 361
Huygens, C., 2, 157
Huygens' principle, 2, 41, 42

Identities, vector, 10, 25–27
Illumination in optical instruments, 184
Incoherent sources, 291–293, 299
  rule for, 131, 293, 294
Incoherent superposition, 317
Induction, Faraday's law, 69, 70
Inhomogeneous wave, 374, 375
Instrumental profile, 288–291, 302, 407,
  411
Integration rule, 217
Intensity, 121n., 461
  spectral, 461, 462
Interference, 3, 103, 123
  order of, 123, 126, 141, 407
Interference filter, 412
Interference telescope, 131

Interferogram, 306–309, 485
Interferometer, Fabry-Perot, 291, 405–
  412
  Michelson, 303–309
  role in spectroscopy, 145, 146
  stellar, 133–137, 298, 299, 327
Intermediate zone, 93
Internal field, 337, 376
Inverse-square law, 99, 483
Irradiance, effect of interference on, 121
  normal, 121, 184
    omission of term, 121n.
  spatial averaging by coarse observa-
    tion, 103, 147, 151
  (*See also* Poynting vector)
Isotropic binding, 245, 340
Isotropic medium, 370, 421, 422
Isotropic radiation, 462

Jacquinot, P., 241, 308, 309, 412, 532
Jahnke, E., 175, 532
Jahnke-Emde-Lösch, 175, 190, 522n.,
  532
Jansky, K. G., 137
Javan, A., 487, 488, 532
Jenkins, F. A., 224, 308, 457, 522n., 532
Johnson, P. O., 323, 531
Jones, F. E., 275, 533
Jupnik, H., 236, 530

Kennard, E. H., 148, 257, 261, 465n.,
  532
Kerr constant, 447
Kerr electro-optic effect, 447
Kerr electro-optic shutter, 455–457
Kerr magneto-optic effect, 447n.
Kirchhoff, G. R., 113, 157
Kirchhoff integral, 114, 161
  application to diffraction, 161–166
Kittel, C., 150, 485, 532
Knipping, P., 352
Kohlrausch, F. W. G., 5

Ladenburg, R., 477
Larmor frequency, 448
Laser, 324, 327, 486–488
Lateral coherence, 302, 327, 485
Laue, M. von, 352
Laue method in X-ray diffraction, 353
Lengyel, B. A., 486, 532
Level surfaces, 12
Levorotatory medium, 440
Liénard-Wiechert potentials, 514–516
Lifetime, 252, 474, 475, 481
Light, modulation, 324, 456
  scalar model, 114, 157–159
  theory, corpuscular, 2
    electromagnetic, 5
    wave, 2, 108, 188
  velocity, 2, 5, 457
  visible, 96
  (*See also* c; Coherence; Polarized
    light; Spectrum; Stokes param-
    eters; White light)
Lighthill, M. J., 217n., 532
Line integral, 14

Linear array, Fraunhofer diffraction by, 124–128
Linear polarizer, 313, 314, 426, 437, 438
Linear system, 236, 237
Lines of force, 4
  (*See also* Streamlines)
Linfoot, E. H., 208, 532
Little, A. G., 155, 533
Lloyd's mirror, 399
Longitudinal coherence, 302–309, 327
Loofbourow, J. R., 146, 531
Lord, R. C., 146, 531
Lorentz, H. A., 1, 532
Lorentz force, 65, 66
  density, 58, 59
Lorentz profile (*see* Resonance profile)
Lorenz theory, 1, 6, 51–57
  atomic collisions, 55, 264–267, 350, 351
  atomic excitation, 54, 245, 246
  elastic binding force, 54, 55, 245, 424, 425
  electrical forces, 54–56, 58, 59
  electrons, 6, 53
    equilibrium positions, 54, 56
  equation of motion, 247, 248, 345, 448, 452
  of fields for damped oscillation, 251
  freedom in choice of model, 6, 53, 56, 521
  interatomic binding, 55
  limitations, 6, 57, 109, 376, 379, 380, 460
  and magnetism, 56, 367, 368
  nonelectrical forces, 54–56
  radiation reaction, 55, 247–250, 346
  role of nucleus, 6, 53–55
  of spectrum for damped oscillation, 252–267
  (*See also* Cotton-Mouton effect;
      Faraday effect; Refractive index;
      Zeeman effect)
Lorentz-Lorentz formula, 387
Low-reflection film, 414
Luminous edge, 109, 166, 205
Lustig, H., 491, 532
Lynch, F. J., 491
Lyot filter, 444

Macaluso-Corbino effect, 446
Macroscopic average, 364
Macroscopic field (*see* Maxwell equations; Maxwell theory)
Macroscopic theory (*see* Maxwell theory)
Magnetic field, 4, 57, 58
  in cylindrical solenoid, 68
  energy density, 79, 81
  macroscopic, 364
  measurement, 66, 67
  relation to charge and current, 57, 58, 71–73
  around straight wire, 62–64
  (*See also* Dipole field)
Magnetic flux, 70
Magnetic induction, 69, 70, 369
Magnetic moment, 368
Magnetization, 368

Magnitude, of complex number, 32, 33
  of complex vector, 220
  of real vector, 9
Maiman, T. H., 486, 532
Malus, E. L., 3
  law of, 332
Margenau, H., 320n., 532
Maser, 486
Matrix element, 482
Matrix methods, 320–322, 415, 416, 419
Maximum, principal, 126, 129
  secondary, 126, 127, 129
Maxwell, J. C., 5, 69
Maxwell equations, 57, 58
  macroscopic, 365, 369
  microscopic, 58
  separation in static case, 71
  solution, by retarded potentials, 72, 73, 509–514
    in static case, 71, 72
Maxwell theory, 5, 57–59
  macroscopic, 5, 362, 363
  microscopic, 7
  (*See also* Maxwell equations)
Maxwellian distribution, 261
Meissner, K. W., 412, 532
Metals, reflection from, 401, 402
Mica, 436
Michelson, A. A., 133, 137, 145, 308, 533
Michelson interferometer, 303–309
  circular fringes, 308
  as refractometer, 330, 331
  as spectrograph, 306–309
  transmission function, 305
  (*See also* Stellar interferometer)
Micron, 96n.
Microscope, Abbe theory, 224–232
  resolving power, 181–183, 229, 231
Microscope illumination, coherent, 224, 302
  critical, 302
  dark-field, 232, 235
Microscopic theory (*see* Lorentz theory;
      Maxwell theory)
Mie scattering, 339
Millimicron, 96n.
Mills, B. Y., 155, 533
Mills cross, 141, 155
Missing orders, 177
Mitchell, A. C. G., 351, 533
mks units, 60, 501–505
  conversion to gaussian units, 507
Modulation of light, 324, 456
Modulus (*see* Magnitude)
Momentum of radiation, 358, 359
Monochromatic wave, 40
  nonexistence, 110, 210, 271, 272
Mössbauer effect, 490, 491
Multiplication table, for orthogonal complex unitary vectors, 49, 458
  for orthogonal real unit vectors, 11
Multipole fields, 519
Murphy, G. M., 320n., 532
Muscovite, 436

Natural excitation (or distribution), 471
Newton, I., 2
Nicol prism, 437
Nitrobenzene, 455
Nodal lines, 172
Nodal planes, 46
Noise, 275, 323
Nonelectrical forces, 54–56
Normal modes, 449
Nucleus, 6, 53–55
Numerical aperture, 182

Obliquity factor, 165
Oersted, H. C., 4
O'Neill, E. L., 240, 533
Optical activity, 421, 423–426, 438–442
Optical length of path, 132
Optical maser, 486–488
Optical pumping, 351, 475
Optical rotation, 440
Optically dense medium, 337
Optics and electromagnetism, 4, 5
Order of interference or of fringe, 123,
    126, 141, 407
Ordinary refractive index, 423, 428
Ordinary wave, 428
Orthogonal polarizations, 138, 139
    [*See also* Complementary polarizations
        (equivalent term)]
Oscillation, damped, 250
    decomposition, 45, 49
    (*See also* Amplitude of oscillation;
        Complex representation; Elliptical
        oscillation; Sinusoidal scalar
        wave; Sinusoidal vector wave)
Oscillator strength, 379, 446, 476, 477
Osterberg, H., 236, 530
Overlapping of orders (*see* Diffraction
    grating; Fabry-Perot inter-
    ferometer)

Panofsky, W. K. H., 511, 533
Parseval's theorem, 218–221
Partial coherence, 300
Partially coherent sources, 300
Partially polarized light, 310, 311, 320
Path, geometric difference, 119, 120
    geometrical length, 132
    optical length, 132
Pawsey, J. L., 142, 533
Pease, F. G., 137, 533
Period, 35
Permeability, 371
Perrin, F. H., 184, 531
Perturbation, 450
Phase angle, 35
Phase-contrast microscope, 232–236
Phase difference, 119
    (*See also* Elliptical oscillation; Phase
        angle)
Phase object, 232
Phase velocity (wave velocity), 42, 44
Phillips, H. B., 8, 511n., 533
Phillips, M., 511, 533
Photoelectric effect, 324, 470
Photon, 309, 479–485

Photon, momentum, 359, 489
π and σ components, 393
Pinhole camera, 204
Planck, M., 460
Planck constant, 467, 468, 507
Planck law, 467–469
    Einstein's derivation, 471–473
Plane of incidence, 392
Plane wave (*see* Electromagnetic wave;
        Sinusoidal scalar wave; Sinusoidal
        vector wave)
Plass, G. N., 248, 533
Poincaré sphere, 319, 320, 322
Polarizability, 336, 341
    of Lorentz atom, 346
Polarization, by dichroism, 426
    by double refraction, 2, 434, 435, 437,
        438
    electric, 367
    orthogonal, 138, 139
    by reflection, 3, 396, 398
    by scattering, 348, 349
    in Zeeman effect, 450
    (*See also* Complementary polariza-
        tions; Fractional polarization;
        Sinusoidal vector wave; Stokes
        parameters)
Polarized light, 309–311
    partially, 310, 311, 320
    (*See also* Fractional polarization;
        Stokes parameters; Unpolarized
        light)
Polarizer (*see* Compensator; Linear
        polarizer; Quarter-wave plate;
        r-wave plate)
Polarizing angle, 398
Potential, Liénard-Wiechert, 514–516
    retarded, 72, 73, 510
    scalar, 71, 72, 509
    vector, 72, 509
Powder method in X-ray diffraction, 361
Power spectrum, 291, 325
Poynting, J. H., 82
Poynting theorem, 82, 383–385
Poynting vector, 81, 82, 384, 385
    additivity and nonadditivity in super-
        posed waves, 86, 103–105
    caution on use, 83, 84
    in crystal, 430
    in dipole field, 98–105
    general rule for calculating, 105
    spatial averaging by coarse observa-
        tion, 103, 147, 151
    time average in monochromatic wave,
        86, 98
Principal axes, 423
Principal maximum, 126, 129
Principal radii of ellipse, 39
Principal refractive index, 423
Prism, Cornu, 442
    Nicol, 437
    resolving power, 223, 224
    Rochon, 438
Prism spectrograph, 287, 381
Propagation, 5, 72, 73, 94, 98
Purcell, E. M., 327, 533

Quantum theory, 6, 52, 57, 466, 467
  new, 477–485
  old (Bohr), 469–471
  units used, 507
Quarter-wave plate, 315, 436
  (*See also* Compensator)
Quartz, 426, 429, 441, 442
Quasi-monochromatic radiation, 286,
  294, 295
Quenching of radiation, 264, 350, 351

r-wave plate, 315, 435, 436
  (*See also* Compensator; Half-wave
    plate; Quarter-wave plate)
Radiance, 296, 461n.
Radiation, detection, 274–277, 317, 323,
  324
  momentum, 358, 359
  quasi-monochromatic, 286, 294, 295
  quenching, 264, 350, 351
  rate, by dipole, 100–105
  resonance, 349–351, 475
  (*See also* Poynting vector)
Radiation pattern of dipole field, 99,
  100, 103
Radiation pressure, 358
Radiation reaction, 55, 247–250, 346
Radio astronomy, 133, 137
  (*See also* Antenna)
Raman, C. V., 206, 351, 416, 533
Raman effect, 351, 484
Ramberg, E. G., 272, 534
Random array, Fraunhofer diffraction
  by, 146–152
Random phases, superposition of waves
  with, 151
Random walk, 148–150
Ray (*see* Path)
Ray vector, 433
Rayleigh, Lord, 143, 148, 204, 338, 348,
  416, 533
Rayleigh criterion, 144, 181, 223
Rayleigh refractometer, 153, 154
Rayleigh scattering, 340–344
Rayleigh-Jeans law, 466, 468, 469
Reciprocity theorem, 128, 166
  for antennas, 138, 139
Recoil, 489–491
Rectangular aperture, diffraction by,
  Fraunhofer, 172–175, 284, 286
  Fresnel, 189–195, 204, 205
Rectangular array, Fraunhofer diffrac-
  tion by, 128, 129
Reesinck, J. J. M., 267, 534
Reflectance, 305, 396–398
Reflection, boundary conditions for,
  389, 390
  from metals, 401, 402
  plane of incidence, 392
  polarization by, 3, 396, 398
  at simple interface, 390–402
  total, 400
  (*See also* Dielectric film)
Reflection coefficient, 394, 397, 400
Refractive index, 363, 372, 477, 485
  complex, 372, 376–383

Refractive index, ordinary and extra-
  ordinary, 423, 428, 429
  principal, 423
Refractometer, Fabry-Perot, 408
  Michelson, 330, 331
  Rayleigh, 153, 154
Representative ellipse, 43, 44
Resolution, of oscillation, 45, 49
  of transverse wave, 86, 138, 139
  of vector, 10, 11, 20, 458
Resolving power (*see* Diffraction grating;
  Fabry-Perot interferometer;
  Michelson interferometer; Micro-
  scope; Prism; Telescope)
Resonance denominator, 254
Resonance function, normalized, 259
Resonance profile, 254, 266, 407, 479–481
Resonance radiation, 349–351, 475
Resultant (*see* Superposition)
Retardation. 72
Retarded potentials, 72, 73, 510
Retarded time, 73, 510, 511
Richards, O. W., 236, 530
Right-hand rule, 9, 18
Rochon prism, 438
Rock salt, 355, 425
Roentgen, W. K., 351
Rohrlich, F., 248, 533
Römer, O., 2
Rosenfeld, L., 56, 533
Rossi, B., 224, 431, 533
Rotation, optical, 440
Rotation method in X-ray diffraction,
  354
Rotator, optical, 332
Rowland, H. A., 145
Rowland circle, 145, 146
Rubens, H., 387, 401
Rubinowicz, A., 166
Rutherford, E., 6, 469

Sawyer, R. A., 146, 223n., 241, 275, 302,
  381, 533
Scalar field, definition, 11
  level surfaces, 12
  relation to gradient, 14
Scalar potential, 71, 72, 509
Scalar product, 9
  in coordinate representation, 20
Scalar triple product, 10
Scalar wave (*see* Light; Sinusoidal scalar
  wave)
Scattering, definition, 334
  Ewald-Oseen theory, 337, 338, 340,
    425, 426
  fourth-power law, 347, 348
  by free electron, 346
  by Lorentz atom, 336, 344–347
  Mie, 339
  by optically dense medium, 337–339
  quantum theory, 483–485
  Rayleigh, 340–344
  resonant, 349–351, 475
  single, 336
  of X rays, 339, 352
Scattering diagram, 343

Schawlow, A. L., 486, 533
Scherrer, P., 361
Scott, W. T., 368, 533
Secondary maximum, 126, 127, 129
Sellmeier formula, 377, 381
Sensitivity pattern, 128
Serber, R., 486
Series in atomic spectra, 469
Shift rule, 216, 217
Shortley, G. H., 478, 482, 531
σ and π components, 393
Sign conventions, 20, 35, 52, 213, 318, 319, 393, 396, 476
Similarity rule, 216
Sine, Euler formula for, 34
Sine condition, 182–184
Singer, J. R., 474, 486, 533
Single-aperture pattern in Fraunhofer diffraction, 120–123
Sinusoidal scalar wave, 40
  complex representation, 42
  graphical representation, 41, 42
  plane, 40–42
Sinusoidal vector wave, 42
  complex representation, 43
  plane, 43, 44
  representative ellipse, 43, 44
  transverse, 44
Slit, diffraction by, Fraunhofer, 174
  Fresnel, 196, 197
  in spectrograph, 302
  (*See also* Rectangular aperture)
Slow optical system, 277
Smekal, A., 351
Smith, R. A., 275, 533
Smoothed spectrum, 258–260
Snell, W., 2
Snell's law, 223, 393, 397, 433
Sodium chlorate, 426
Solar constant, 333
Soleil compensator, 436
Solenoid (*see* Magnetic field)
Sommerfeld, A., 156, 166, 281, 431, 533
Source, partially coherent, 300
  polarized, 310
  unpolarized, 246, 255, 280, 313
Spatial filtering, 239
Spectra in Abbe theory, 230
Spectral intensity, 461, 462
Spectrogram, 290
Spectroscope (spectrograph), 131, 146
  beat-frequency, 324–327
  general theory, 286–291
  instrumental profile, 288, 302, 411
  X-ray, 355
  (*See also* Diffraction grating; Fabry-Perot interferometer; Michelson interferometer; Prism)
Spectrum, channel, 330
  energy, 253, 273
  power, 291, 325
  smoothed, 258–260
  (*See also* Broadening in spectra; Faraday effect; Fluctuations; Lorentz theory; Quantum theory; Zeeman effect)

Square-law detector, 323
Standard deviation, 150
Standing wave, 46
Stark effect, 267, 448
Static zone, 92, 95
Stationary states, 470, 471
Statistical weight, 471
Steady source, 255, 273
Stefan-Boltzmann law, 464
Stellar interferometer, 133–137, 298, 299, 327
  Michelson's, 135–137
Stigmatic image, 180
Stokes parameters, 312–320, 322, 395
Stokes' theorem, 18
Straight edge, Fresnel diffraction by, 197, 198
Stratton, J. A., 504, 533
Streamlines, 12, 15
Strip, Fresnel diffraction by, 198, 199
Stroke, G. W., 178*n.*, 533
Strong, J., 224, 275, 308, 403, 444, 534
Superposition, incoherent, 317
  oscillations, 44, 45
  principle, 44, 61, 159
  scalar waves, 46
  vector waves, 46
  waves with random phases, 151
Surface integral, normal, 14
  tangential, 16
Susceptibility, 370

Taylor criterion, 409
Telescope, interference, 131
  radio-frequency, 137–142
  resolving power, 181, 182
Term structure of atom, 469
Test particle, 65
Thomson, J. J., 6
Thomson cross section, 346
Time average, definition, 48
  of product of oscillating quantities, 86
  (*See also* Detection of radiation; Irradiance; Poynting vector)
Time derivative, in second-order operations, 26
  of vector, 19
Tolansky, S., 403, 534
Total reflection, 400
Tourmaline, 426
Townes, C. H., 486, 531, 533, 534
Transfer functions, 237
  dipole oscillator, 239
  general optical system, 278, 279
  linear polarizer, 314
  r-wave plate, 315
  for Rayleigh scattering, 342
  for reflection, 396
Transfer matrix, 320, 321
Transition probability, 472, 481, 482
Transitions, 472
Transmission (*see* Dielectric film; Fabry-Perot interferometer; Films by evaporation; Interference filter)
Transmission coefficient, 171, 394

Transmission function, Babinet compen-
    sator, 437, 443
  diffraction grating, 283, 284
  general optical system, 279
  Kerr shutter, 456
  Michelson interferometer, 305
  rectangular aperture, 281–283
  spectrograph, 289
  stellar interferometer, 296, 297
  (*See also* Airy formula)
Transmittance, 305, 402, 405, 406, 419
Transversality condition, 373, 389
Transverse wave, 3, 5, 44, 92, 373
Triple product, scalar, 10
  vector, 10
Twiss, R. Q., 327, 530

Uniaxial crystal, 421, 423, 428–430, 441,
    442
  positive and negative, 429
Unimodular number, 33
Uniqueness theorem, 29
Units for wavelength, 96n.
  (*See also* Electrical units)
Unpolarized light, 310, 311, 313,
Unpolarized source, 246, 255, 280, 313

Van Cittert, P. H., 302
Van de Hulst, H. C., 267, 340, 356, 534
Van der Ziel, A., 275, 534
Vector field, definition 11
  graphical representations, 12
  relation to divergence and curl, 14
  streamlines, 12
  uniqueness theorem, 29
Vector potential, 72, 509
Vector product, 9
  in coordinate representation, 20
Vector triple product, 10
Vector wave (*see* Sinusoidal vector wave)
Velocity, of electromagnetic waves, 5
  of light, 2, 5, 457
  wave, 42, 44
Verdet constant, 446
Visibility of fringes, 298
  (*See also* Interferogram)
Voigt effect, 446
Voigt functions, 267

Watson, G. N., 518, 534
Wave, longitudinal, 3
  transverse, 3, 5, 44, 92
  (*See also* Electromagnetic wave; Light
    Monochromatic wave; Sinusoidal
    scalar wave; Sinusoidal vector
    wave)
Wave equation, 73, 74, 108, 157, 510
  homogeneous, solution, 74, 158
Wave number, 41
Wave vector, 41, 43, 372
Wave-vector surface, 429, 431, 442
Wave velocity, 42, 44
Wave zone, 93, 95–98
Wavelength, 41
Weatherburn, C. E., 8, 534
Weber, W. E., 5
Wheeler, J. A., 248, 534
White, H. E., 224, 308, 457, 458, 470,
    522n., 532, 534
White light, 285n.
  diffraction and interference with, 123,
    137, 174, 284–286, 308
Whittaker, E. T., 7, 466n., 518, 534
Wien law, 468
  (*See also* Displacement law)
Williams, W. E., 308, 534
Wills, A. P., 8, 15, 16, 534
Wolf, E., 156, 186, 208, 224, 229, 319,
    322, 340, 530
Wood, R. W., 308, 349, 418, 534

X rays, 351, 352
  scattering and diffraction, 352–355,
    361
X unit, 96n.

Yates, H. W., 275
Young, T., 3, 123, 157, 166
Young's experiment, 123

Zeeman, P., 6
Zeeman effect, 6, 349, 447–451, 470
Zeiger, H. J., 486, 531
Zemansky, M. W., 351, 464, 533, 534
Zernicke, F., 224, 232, 299, 534
Zone plate, 206, 207
Zworykin, V. K., 275, 534